COMPUTATIONAL PHYSICS

Nicholas J. Giordano

Department of Physics
Purdue University

PRENTICE HALL

Upper Saddle River, New Jersey   07458

Library of Congress Cataloging-in-Publication Data

Giordano, Nicholas J.
  Computational physics / Nicholas J. Giordano.
      p. cm.
  Includes index.
  ISBN 0-13-367723-0
  1. Physics—Data processing.   I. Title.
QC20.7.E4G56 1997   96-20963
530.1'594—dc20   CIP

Executive Editor: Alison Reeves
Editorial assistant: Pam Holland-Moritz
Editorial/production supervision and interior design: ETP/Harrison
Copy editor: Jane Loftus
Cover designer: Bruce Kenselaar
Manufacturing manager: Trudy Pisciotti

 © 1997 by Prentice-Hall, Inc.
Simon & Schuster/A Viacom Company
Upper Saddle River, NJ 07458

Printed in the United States of America

10 9 8 7 6 5 4 3 2 1

ISBN 0-13-367723-0

Prentice-Hall International (UK) Limited, *London*
Prentice-Hall of Australia Pty. Limited, *Sydney*
Prentice-Hall Canada Inc., *Toronto*
Prentice-Hall Hispanoamericana, S.A., *Mexico*
Prentice-Hall of India Private Limited, *New Delhi*
Prentice-Hall of Japan, Inc., *Tokyo*
Simon & Schuster Asia Pte. Ltd., *Singapore*
Editora Prentice-Hall do Brasil, Ltda., *Rio de Janeiro*

To my parents.

Contents

Preface

During the past several years I have worked to develop an undergraduate course on computational physics. The goal of this course has been to introduce students to some basic numerical techniques and then apply these techniques to a number of *modern* topics, that is, problems of current interest to physicists. I have long felt that the traditional introductory physics courses place too much emphasis on topics that have remained unchanged for a century or more. Very little effort is made to introduce the types of problems that *today's* physicists find interesting or to convey the excitement we feel in our work. A standard and perhaps somewhat justifiable excuse given for this shortcoming is that to treat such topics would require a level of mathematical expertise far beyond that of a typical student. It is here that computers can make a qualitative difference. Students with some experience in differential and integral calculus can readily grasp rather sophisticated computational techniques. These students can use computers as tools with which to attack and solve problems that they would not ordinarily encounter in the undergraduate curriculum. I have used this approach to try to convey the excitement of physics, with a variety of problems of current interest.

After I had formulated tentative plans for my course, I was faced with actually putting it together, and an early step in this process was to find a textbook. While there are many new books with the terms "computers" and "physics" in their titles, I was not able to find a text that was suitable for my needs. Most of the books in this area tend to focus heavily on numerical methods rather than physics. Since my goal was to teach a course on *physics*, rather than numerical methods, these books were not a good match. While there are a few books that emphasize the physics that can be done with numerical methods, they are either too advanced for use by undergraduates, or (more commonly) they fail to deal with the types of problems that can profit most from a numerical approach. In too many cases they tend to simply treat the standard problems, which are already dealt with in many traditional texts using analytic methods.

I was, therefore, forced to gather the material for my course from a wide variety of "primary" sources, as will become clear from the references at the end of each chapter. In many cases I started with papers from the recent physics literature and then distilled them to produce problems suitable for an undergraduate class. This book contains the results of my efforts. While it is necessary for this book to introduce a variety of numerical methods of interest to physicists, the overriding emphasis is on the physics that can be done with these methods. The majority of the problems described in this book cannot be solved with purely analytic techniques. A computational approach is required in most cases, and I have tried to use the computer to make the *physics* as clear and as interesting as possible.

How to Use This Book

When my course was in the design stages, one constraint imposed by local realities (i.e., space in our sequence of courses) was that it must fit into the early part of the undergraduate curriculum. My course is taken mainly by sophomores whose only previous physics course is introductory mechanics. Their mathematics backgrounds vary widely. It usually includes a total of two semesters of calculus, so I can assume only that they have been exposed to the basics of differentiation and integration. This background is easily sufficient for a wide variety of topics. My course currently includes projectile motion without and with realistic air resistance, planetary motion and the three-body problem, chaotic motion of the pendulum, waves on a string, and some topics relating to fractal growth and stochastic systems. This material is covered in Chapters 1 through 4, 6 and 7, although these chapters contain many extra topics and examples, which time does not allow me to discuss in the course. In fact, this book contains *far* more material than could possibly be covered in a one-semester course. This extra material is included to give the student (and instructor) some flexibility in the choice of topics and depth of coverage. I have used many of these extra problems for midterm or final projects. This book could also be used as a supplement to other courses. For example, a course in electricity and magnetism could make extensive use of the material in Chapter 5, while an advanced mechanics course might find the examples on chaotic dynamics and waves on a realistic string useful. While a course aimed at advanced undergraduates could certainly make use of the material in the first few chapters, the emphasis would probably be on the examples from statistical physics and quantum mechanics in Chapters 8 through 10. Chapter 11 brings together ideas developed earlier in the book to deal with three interdisciplinary topics and could be of interest to students at virtually any level.

It is obvious that numerical methods play a major role in this book, but given my desire to place the primary emphasis on physics, there is simply not enough space to describe all of the subtleties associated with all of the numerical methods in full detail. Fortunately, there are several excellent books in this area (as mentioned in the references), so the student or instructor who desires an in-depth discussion can readily find one. However, this does *not* mean that I have cut corners with my treatment of numerical methods. I am perhaps a bit old fashioned, as I firmly believe that students should write their own, original programs. This requires a careful treatment of the numerical methods, and this book contains ample explanation of the necessary algorithms. I believe that this book contains *all* the information that a student would need to write programs that perform all of the calculations described here.

While I am, perhaps, as just admitted, old fashioned in my belief that students should write their own programs, I have relented to the requests of those who have reviewed this book (and my publisher!), and provided many example programs. Some of these program listings are sprinkled throughout the book, in connection with discussions of the various problems and algorithms. In addition, Appendix 4 contains full listings of a number of representative programs; these listings can also be obtained through the World Wide Web Page associated with this book. The address is `http://www.physics.purdue.edu/~ng/comp-phys.html`. This page can also be accessed through Prentice Hall's World Wide Web page. However, this book contains many example calculations, and most of these programs are not included. After all, some work must be left for the student.

The inclusion of source code leads naturally to the question of language. My course currently uses the *True Basic* language system, and all of the program listings are in this dialect of Basic. I fully realize that many readers will prefer some other language. My course has, at various times, used Pascal, C, and Fortran. However, if forced to choose one "common denominator" language, I feel that Basic is a good choice. Moreover, *True Basic* has available an excellent library of graphics routines and can be used with a variety of machines. I have used it on IBM compatibles, Macintoshes, Amigas, and Suns, and it is available for other machines, as well. It is a well-structured language (you will not find a single `go to` statement in this book), and in nearly all cases it can easily be translated, usually line-for-line, into the other languages mentioned above. In addition, it is quite readable as a pseudocode, so even students who prefer to work with another language should be able to take full advantage of the examples. In any event, I certainly understand that the choice of computer language can be a highly personal one, and I do not want to imply that any particular language is better than any other for the numerical work encountered in physics. My intent with this book has been to make the ideas underlying the numerical methods as clear as possible, so that students can use the language of their choice, be it C or Fortran or Mathematica or Maple.

This book contains a rather large number of example calculations. The pattern of my presentation is to show the results of specific computations as I introduce and discuss the physics. *All* of the example calculations in this book have been tested by me using *True Basic*. The vast majority can be carried out in a reasonable amount of time (a few minutes or, usually, much less) with a Macintosh containing no more than a 68020 CPU. By the time this book reaches print, such machines will be hard to find, and most microcomputers will be faster by an order of magnitude or more. Hence, computational resources should not be a limitation in working out the problems in this book.

I owe many thanks to many people. The support of Arnold Tubis and the Department of Physics at Purdue, along with that of the National Science Foundation, made my course, and hence this book, possible. Many graduate students have helped me teach and develop the course; Miguel Castro, Chris Parks, Jan Spitz, Stuart Burnett, Todd Jacobs, and Dan Lawrence have taught (and corrected) me a great deal. Of course, the undergraduate students who have willingly submitted to the course have provided much useful feedback; there are too many to mention them all here, although Mike Pennington deserves a special thanks. Many colleagues have provided essential advice and encouragement, including Mark Haugen and Paul Muzikar. I am especially indebted to Paul and Todd for their detailed comments on the manuscript. The suggestions of the reviewers, Wolfgang Christian (Davidson College), Alejandro Garcia (San Jose State University), Jan Tobochnik (Kalamazoo College), and Rodney L. Varley (Hunter College), who were very polite and constructive, have helped me a lot, as have the comments and advice of my editors, Ray Henderson and Alison Reeves. The final impetus to actually write this book was provided by the well-timed encouragement of Earl Prohofsky and Betsy Beasley. And finally, I thank my wife and children for helping in many ways, including numerous dinnertime discussions of the physics of everyday phenomena and the travels of Lucky Star.

Nicholas J. Giordano

1

A First Numerical Problem

Many problems encountered in physics involve ordinary differential equations. Examples include projectile motion, harmonic motion, and celestial mechanics, topics we will be discussing extensively in the next few chapters. We therefore begin with a problem involving a first-order differential equation and use it to introduce some computational techniques that will be employed extensively in later chapters. We will also proceed step by step through the construction of a program to deal with this problem, so as to illustrate in detail how a numerical approach is translated into a (working) computer program.

In this chapter it is not possible to provide a complete introduction to programming for students who have no previous exposure to the subject. Rather, our goal is to enable students with some (even limited) experience in programming to begin writing programs to treat the physics that will be encountered in this book. However, those students with no prior experience should not give up hope! With some extra effort and access to a good instructor or book on computer programming (or both), such students should be able to handle the material in this and later chapters.

1.1   Radioactive Decay

It is well known that many nuclei are unstable. A typical example is the nuclear isotope ^{235}U (the uranium nucleus that contains 143 neutrons and 92 protons, for a total of 235 nucleons), which has a small, but not insignificant, probability for decaying into two nuclei of approximately half its size, along with an assortment of protons, neutrons, electrons, and alpha particles. This process of radioactive decay is random in the following sense. If you were given a single ^{235}U nucleus, you would not be able to predict precisely when its decay would take place. The best you could do would be to give the *probability* for decay. An equivalent way to describe such a process would be to give the average time for decay; for ^{235}U the mean lifetime is approximately 1×10^9 years.

It is useful to imagine that we have a sample containing a large number of ^{235}U nuclei, which would usually be the case if we were actually doing an experiment to study radioactive decay. If $N_U(t)$ is the number of uranium nuclei that are present in the sample at time t, the behavior is governed by the differential equation

$$\frac{dN_U}{dt} = -\frac{N_U}{\tau} \, , \tag{1.1}$$

where τ is the "time constant" for the decay. You can show by direct substitution that the solution to this differential equation is

$$N_U = N_U(0) \, e^{-t/\tau} \, , \tag{1.2}$$

where $N_U(0)$ is the number of nuclei present at $t = 0$. This solution may be familiar to you; similar equations and similar solutions are found in many other contexts.[1] We note that at time $t = \tau$ a fraction e^{-1} of the nuclei has not yet decayed. It turns out that τ is also the mean lifetime of a nucleus.

1.2   A Numerical Approach

While the differential equation (1.1) can be solved without resorting to a numerical approach, this problem is useful for introducing several computational methods that will be used extensively in later chapters. With that in mind we now consider a simple method for solving this problem numerically. Our goal is to obtain N_U as a function of t. Given the value of N_U at one particular value of t (usually at $t = 0$), we want to estimate its value at later times. One line of attack can be seen by examining the Taylor expansion for N_U,

$$N_U(\Delta t) = N_U(0) + \frac{dN_U}{dt} \Delta t + \frac{1}{2} \frac{d^2 N_U}{dt^2} (\Delta t)^2 + \cdots , \tag{1.3}$$

where $N_U(0)$ is the value of our function at time $t = 0$, $N_U(\Delta t)$ is its value at $t = \Delta t$, and the derivatives are evaluated at $t = 0$. If we take Δt to be small, then it is usually a good approximation to simply ignore the terms that involve second and higher powers of Δt, leaving us with

$$N_U(\Delta t) \approx N_U(0) + \frac{dN_U}{dt} \Delta t \, . \tag{1.4}$$

The same result can be obtained from the definition of a derivative. The derivative of N_U evaluated at time t can be written as

$$\frac{dN_U}{dt} \equiv \lim_{\Delta t \to 0} \frac{N_U(t + \Delta t) - N_U(t)}{\Delta t} \approx \frac{N_U(t + \Delta t) - N_U(t)}{\Delta t} \, , \tag{1.5}$$

where in the last approximation we have assumed that Δt is small but nonzero. We can rearrange this to obtain

$$N_U(t + \Delta t) \approx N_U(t) + \frac{dN_U}{dt} \Delta t \, , \tag{1.6}$$

which is equivalent to (1.4). It is important to recognize that this is an *approximation*, which is why it contains the $\approx$ symbol, not the $=$ symbol. The error terms that were dropped in deriving this result are of order $(\Delta t)^2$, which makes them at least one factor of Δt smaller than any of the terms in (1.6). Hence, by making Δt small, we would expect that the error terms can be made negligible. This is, in fact, the case in many problems, but there are situations in which the error terms can still make life complicated.

---

[1] For example, an equation of this kind describes the time dependence of the voltage across a capacitor in an *RC* circuit.

Therefore, it is important to be careful when discussing the errors involved in this numerical approach; we will return to this point later.

From the physics of the problem we know the functional form of the derivative (1.1), and if we insert it into (1.6) we obtain

$$N_U(t + \Delta t) \approx N_U(t) - \frac{N_U(t)}{\tau} \Delta t , \tag{1.7}$$

which forms the basis for a numerical solution of our radioactive decay problem. Given that we know the value of N_U at some value of t, we can use (1.7) to *estimate* its value a time Δt later. Usually we are given, or can manage to discover, the initial value of the function, that is, the value at time $t = 0$. We can then employ (1.7) to estimate its value at $t = \Delta t$. This result can be used in turn to estimate the value at $t = 2\Delta t$, $3\Delta t$, etc., and thereby lead to an approximate solution at times $n \Delta t$ where n is an integer. We cannot emphasize too strongly that the numerical "solution" obtained in this way is only an *approximation* to the "true," or exact, solution. Of course, one of our goals is to make the difference between the two negligible.

The approach to calculating $N_U(t)$ embodied in (1.6) and (1.7) is known as the Euler method and is a powerful, general algorithm for solving ordinary differential equations. We will use this approach, and closely related methods, extensively in this book. Other methods for solving equations of this kind will be discussed in later chapters, and are the subject of Appendix 1. For now, the reader should realize that while the Euler method arises in a very natural way, it is certainly not the only algorithm for dealing with problems of this sort. We will see that the different approaches have their own strengths and weaknesses, which make them more or less suitable for different types of problems.

1.3   Construction of a Working Program

In the previous section we introduced the Euler method as the basis for obtaining a numerical solution to our radioactive decay problem. We now consider precisely how to translate that algorithm into a working computer program. Here, and throughout this book, we will give our examples in the *True Basic* language. This is *not* intended to imply that students using this book must use *True Basic*. We have to use some language for our examples, and we find *True Basic* to be a convenient choice for several reasons. One of these reasons is that this language is very readable as a pseudocode, thus it is possible for someone with little or no experience with *True Basic* to understand the logic and flow of the programs. Hence, our programs can easily be translated into other languages, if the reader is so inclined. Our experience has been that these translations are usually direct, with each *True Basic* statement corresponding to a single statement in Fortran, C, or Pascal. In addition, the overall control structures, that is, loops, decision tests, and subroutines, are essentially identical. You will not find any "go to" statements in this book!

While programming, like handwriting, is a highly individualized process, there are certain recommended practices. After all, as in handwriting, it is important that we be able to understand programs written by others, as well as those we ourselves have written! With that in mind, this book will try to promote proper programming habits. The (admittedly very loose) analogy between handwriting and programming can be carried one step further. The first thing you should do in writing any program is to *think*. Before writing any detailed code, construct an outline of how the problem is to be solved and what variables or parameters will be needed. For our decay problem we have already laid the foundation for numerical solution in our derivation of (1.7). This equation also contains all of the variables we will need, N_U, t, τ, and Δt. Our stated goal was to calculate $N_U(t)$, but since the numerical approximation (1.7) involves the values of N_U only at times $t = 0$, $t = \Delta t$, $t = 2\Delta t$, etc., we will actually calculate N_U at just these values of t. We will use an array to store the values of N_U for later use. An array is simply a table of numbers (which will be described in more detail shortly). The first element in our array, that is, the first entry in the table, will contain N_U at $t = 0$, the second element will be the value at $t = \Delta t$, and so on. For convenience, we will also use an array to store the corresponding values of t. Our general plan is then to apply (1.7) repetitively to calculate the values of $N_U(t)$.

The overall structure of the program consists of three basic tasks: (1) initialize all variables and parameters, (2) do the calculation, and (3) display the result. This structure can be seen from the listing of the main program given here.

```
! Simulation of radioactive decay
! N. Giordano   10-1-94
program decay
   option nolet                   ! can omit the "let" keyword
   library "sgfunc*", "sglib*"    ! the graphics routines are found here
   dim n_uranium(100), t(100)     ! declare the arrays we will need
   call initialize(n_uranium,t,tau,dt)    ! use subroutines to do the work
   call calculate(n_uranium,t,tau,dt)
   call display(n_uranium,t,tau,dt)
end
```

Our program begins with a few comment statements that identify the program and tell a little about what it is supposed to do. In *True Basic* comments are indicated by exclamation marks. Note that the ! symbol and everything following it on a line are ignored by *True Basic*. Hence a comment need not start at the beginning of a line, but can be placed after another statement, as shown on the fourth and later lines. Also, *True Basic* ignores blank lines, so they can be included to enhance readability.

The line

```
program decay
```

gives the name of the main program, but isn't absolutely required. The next line

```
   option nolet
```

tells *True Basic* that we do not want to use `let` to start each assignment statement (more on this later). Note that we have indented this line to show how the code is organized.

```
   library "sgfunc*", "sglib*"   ! the graphics routines are found here
```

announces that this program will be using subroutines contained in the libraries `sgfunc*` and `sglib*`. These libraries are simply files that contain some general purpose graphics routines that will be employed to display our results. Here we use the names for these libraries in the Macintosh version of *True Basic*; the names for other systems are similar and can be found in the *True Basic* documentation.[2]

---

[2]On Unix systems the library path names are usually `"/usr/lib/truebasic/sgfunc.trc"`, etc. These libraries contain some graphics routines, which are very useful for displaying the results of a calculation. In fact, the availability of these routines makes *True Basic* a handy choice for this book. Other language packages generally have similar specialized graphics routines (but they will have different names, of course). Finally, note that these graphics routines are not necessarily part of the "core" of *True Basic*. For example, while they come standard with the Unix version, they must be purchased separately for the Macintosh version.

Our next step is to declare the two arrays that will be used to store N_U and t. This is accomplished with the

```
dim n_uranium(100), t(100)
```

statement. The first array, n_uranium(), will contain the calculated values of the number of uranium nuclei, while t() will contain the corresponding values of the time. As mentioned above, arrays are tables of values; here we have arranged for our tables n_uranium() and t() to each hold 100 values.[3] The different values are accessed via the array *index*. Here n_uranium(1) (i.e., using the index value 1) is the first element in the array holding the values of N_U. Likewise, n_uranium(2) is the second value in the array, and n_uranium(100) is the final value. As we'll see shortly, separating the name of the array, n_uranium, from the value of the index permits convenient access to any desired element in the array.

Note also that we have used the descriptive name n_uranium to make the program easier to read and understand. It is tempting to use the name time for the other array (instead of t), but *True Basic* already uses time as the name of the time-of-day function, so we cannot use it for an ordinary variable. In any case, the name t is certainly not a bad choice. Note that in *True Basic* we need only explicitly declare variables that are arrays. Variables that contain single numeric values, either integers or real numbers, need not be declared. String variables also need not be declared (unless they are arrays), but they must end with a $ symbol to distinguish them from numeric variables.

The rest of the work is done in three subroutines, which are called in succession.

```
call initialize(n_uranium,t,tau,dt)
call calculate(n_uranium,t,tau,dt)
call display(n_uranium,t,tau,dt)
```

The subroutine names describe the function of each routine; these tasks correspond directly to the general program outline mentioned above. The call statements also include the names of the variables that each routine needs to do its job. The subroutine initialize sets the initial values of the variables, calculate uses the Euler method to do the computation, and display plots the results. We next consider these three routines.

```
! initialize variables
sub initialize(nuclei(),t(),time_constant,dt)
   input prompt "initial number of nuclei -> ": nuclei(1)
   t(1) = 0
   input prompt "time constant -> ": time_constant
   input prompt "time step -> ": dt
end sub
```

This subroutine begins officially with the sub initialize statement. The variables listed in parenthesis after the word initialize are passed into the subroutine from the calling routine (here it is the main program, but it could also be another subroutine).[4] This variable list must be in correspondence with the list used when the subroutine is called from the main program (or anywhere else). Here the

---

[3]It is sometimes convenient to allow for the length of an array to be determined or adjusted while the program is running. For simplicity, we will defer discussion of such cases for later.

[4]*True Basic* allows recursion, so a subroutine can call itself.

calling line and the first line of the subroutine are

```
call initialize(n_uranium,t,tau,dt)
sub initialize(nuclei(),t(),time_constant,dt)
```

so the variable list in the "calling" part of the program is `n_uranium,t,tau,dt`, while the list in the "receiving" part of the program is `nuclei(),t(),time_constant,dt`. These two lists appear to be quite different, so we might worry that this will confuse *True Basic*. However, this worry is unfounded. In dealing with this situation *True Basic* compares the two lists, one variable at a time. It begins at the start of each list, where it encounters the variables `n_uranium` and `nuclei()`. It already knows that `n_uranium` is an array, since the corresponding `dim` statement is part of the main program. *True Basic* then notices that `nuclei()` is also an array, since it ends with two parentheses `()`. Since the variables "match," *True Basic* treats them, in effect, as the same variable. That is, the values in `n_uranium` in the main program will appear in the array `nuclei` in the subroutine. Likewise, when the subroutine is finished and control is returned to the main program (when the `end sub` statement is encountered), the values in `nuclei` will be inserted back into `n_uranium`. The key lessons here are: (1) the corresponding variables in the calling and receiving routines need not have the same names, although it doesn't hurt if they do; and (2) corresponding variables must be of the same *type*. Here they were both arrays. It would be an error if one were an array, and the other were not.

After dealing with the first variables in the two lists, *True Basic* moves on to the second variables. Here it encounters two arrays, both named `t()` and proceeds as just described. The next variables are `tau` (in the calling routine) and `time_constant` (in the receiving routine). We again have a match, since both are regular variables (not arrays). The variable `tau` in the main program will then correspond in value with `time_constant` in the subroutine. Likewise with the variable(s) `dt`.[5]

After getting the calling variables organized, the `initialize` subroutine sets the initial values of the number of nuclei and the time. These are just the first values in the arrays `nuclei(1)` and `t(1)`. Array numbering in *True Basic* begins with 1, unless otherwise requested in the `dim` statement. The statement

```
   input prompt "initial number of nuclei -> ": nuclei(1)
```

asks the programmer to enter a number via the keyboard, and `nuclei(1)` is then set to that value. The value of `t(1)` is set by a conventional assignment statement (without the `let`, as noted above). The only other tasks for `initialize` are to set the values of `time_constant` and the time step, `dt`, and this is accomplished with two more `input prompt` statements.

The real work is done in the subroutine `calculate`

```
sub calculate(n_uranium(),t(),tau,dt)
   for i = 1 to size(t)-1              ! now use the Euler method
      n_uranium(i+1) = n_uranium(i)  - (n_uranium(i) / tau) * dt
      t(i+1) = t(i) + dt
   next i
end sub
```

---

[5]This way of dealing with subroutine parameters is known as *passing by reference*, which means that if the value of a parameter is changed in the subroutine, the value of the corresponding variable in the calling routine is also changed. *True Basic* does not allow you to pass by value, although this is permitted in some other versions of Basic.

The key statement is the one in which n_uranium(i+1) is calculated. This statement contains all of the physics of the program and is closely analogous to (1.7). As mentioned above, the array n_uranium corresponds to the variable $N_U(t)$, and the value stored in the ith element of n_uranium is the number of uranium nuclei present at time t(i). A for loop is used to compute the value of n_uranium(i+1) for values of i starting from 1 and running to size(t)-1. The function size(t) is just a number that is the length of the array t(). When i=1, the value of n_uranium(2) is calculated in terms of n_uranium(1), that is, the value at the previous time step. This is a direct translation of the Euler equation (1.7). The for loop also calculates the time at each step t(i+1). The loop stops at i=size(t)-1, which here has the value 99, so that n_uranium(100) is the last value calculated. Using the size function in this way means that the program will not break if we change the lengths of the arrays in the main program (we will not have to hunt through the program to change the limits on all of the loops, etc.).

The final subroutine graphs the result

```
sub display(n_uranium(),t(),tau,dt)
            ! first set up title and label axes for graph
   call settitle("Radioactive Decay    Number of nuclei versus time")
   call sethlabel("Time(s)")
   call setvlabel("Number of Nuclei")
   call datagraph(t,n_uranium,4,0,"black")   ! the graph is produced here
   set cursor 5,30                           ! reposition cursor
   print "time constant = ";tau
   set cursor 6,30
   print "time step = ";dt
end sub
```

This is the only part of our program that is really language specific, as we use several graphics routines that are part of the *True Basic* Scientific Graphics package (the libraries sglib* and sgfunc* discussed earlier). If you are using a different language, you will probably have a similar set of similar routines available, so it is likely that only the names of the graphics routines will be different.

In our *True Basic* program the graph is produced by the subroutine datagraph that is contained in the libraries mentioned at the beginning of the main program. The first two arguments to datagraph are the arrays containing the coordinates of the points to be plotted (the array with the values for the horizontal axis comes first).[6] The third and fourth arguments refer to the point and line styles, respectively. Point style number 1 produces simple dots, while other values give different symbols (0 gives no point at all). Line style number 1 yields a solid line connecting the points, and other values produce broken lines of various styles (0 suppresses the line altogether). The final argument to datagraph is the color of the graph. The statements in subroutine display prior to datagraph take care of labeling the axes and title of the graph. Note that datagraph scales the axes automatically, as well as plots the points and writes out the labels and title. The set cursor statements position the cursor in a convenient location on the screen, so that the values of the time constant and time step can be printed directly on the graph. For convenience, our complete program is listed in one piece below. Figure 1.1 shows an example of the output that it produces. This is what you should see on your display when you run the program. Here we have used the initial values n_uranium(1) = 100 and t(1) = 0, along with a time constant of 1 s and a time step of 0.05 s. We will consider the choice of time step later.

---

[6]The *True Basic* documentation describes the options for this and the other graphics routines in more detail.

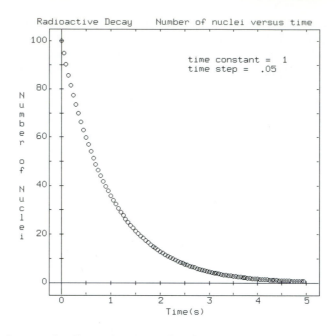

Figure 1.1: Output produced by our *True Basic* radioactive decay program. The initial number of nuclei was 100, and the time constant was 1 s.

For now we note only that our calculated values compare well with the exact result. This is illustrated in Figure 1.2, which shows the output of our program (the same results as those plotted in Figure 1.1) along with the exact result, Equation (1.2).

```
! Simulation of radioactive decay
! N. Giordano   10-1-94
program decay
   option nolet                    ! can omit the let keyword
   library "sgfunc*", "sglib*"  ! the graphics routines are found here
   dim n_uranium(100), t(100)    ! declare the arrays we will need
   call initialize(n_uranium,t,tau,dt)    ! use subroutines to do the work
   call calculate(n_uranium,t,tau,dt)
   call display(n_uranium,t,tau,dt)
end
! initialize variables
sub initialize(nuclei(),t(),time_constant,dt)
   input prompt "initial number of nuclei -> ": nuclei(1)
   t(1) = 0
   input prompt "time constant -> ": time_constant
   input prompt "time step -> ": dt
end sub
sub calculate(n_uranium(),t(),tau,dt)
   for i = 1 to size(t)-1              ! now use the Euler method
      n_uranium(i+1) = n_uranium(i) - (n_uranium(i) / tau) * dt
      t(i+1) = t(i) + dt
   next i
end sub
```

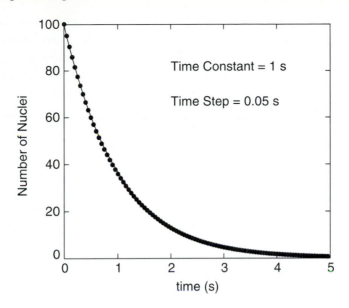

Figure 1.2:   Circles indicate the numerical solution to the radioactive decay problem. These are the same results as shown in Figure 1.1. The solid line is the exact solution Equation (1.2).

```
sub display(n_uranium(),t(),tau,dt)
            ! first set up title and label axes for graph
    call settitle("Radioactive Decay    Number of nuclei versus time")
    call sethlabel("Time(s)")
    call setvlabel("Number of Nuclei")
    call datagraph(t,n_uranium,4,0,"black")  ! the graph is produced here
    set cursor 5,30                          ! reposition cursor
    print "time constant = ";tau
    set cursor 6,30
    print "time step = ";dt
end sub
```

1.4   Testing Your Program

The title of Section 1.3 was a little misleading. It was concerned with producing a program that runs without any *True Basic* syntax errors, such as undeclared arrays, spelling errors, or variables omitted when calling a subroutine. However, we should not really consider it to be a working program until we are convinced that its output is correct! Checking a program is not always a trivial task, but there are some general guidelines. After a program has been debugged so that *True Basic* runs it without any complaints about the syntax, there are several things you should do to verify that the results of the program are correct.

1. *Does the output look reasonable?* Before you perform any calculation you should always have at least a rough idea of what the result should be. The first thing you should do when considering the results from any program is ask whether or not they are consistent with your intuition and

instincts. This exercise can also improve your overall understanding of the problem. When you show your result to someone else, you should always be able to convince them that it makes sense.[7]

2. *Does your program agree with any exact results that are available?* Since we knew the analytic solution for our radioactive decay problem, we were able to compare our numerical values with the exact result. While such a comparison will not be possible for most of the numerical calculations you will encounter, exact results are sometimes available in certain limits, that is, for special values of the parameters. You should always run your program in those limits to check that it gives the correct answer. This is a necessary, although not sufficient, test that a program is correct in the general case.

3. *Always check that your program gives the same answer for different "step sizes."* Our decay program involved a time-step variable, dt, and most other numerical calculations involve similar step- or grid-size parameters. Your final answer should be independent of the values of such parameters.

Checking your program should not be viewed as a trivial, last minute job. It is not unreasonable to spend as much time checking a program as it takes writing it. After all, a result is not much good if you don't trust it to be correct.

1.5   Numerical Considerations

The issue of numerical errors is central to the computational solution of any problem. Indeed, this is such an important topic that there are *many* books devoted to this area. Questions such as how to design or choose the best algorithm for a particular problem and how to estimate the numerical errors associated with an algorithm are central topics in many computer science and applied mathematics courses. We could easily spend *a lot* of time discussing the Euler method and all the other algorithms we will be using in this book. However, while this would certainly be an instructive thing to do, it would leave us with very little time to explore the *physics* that can be done with these algorithms. Since in this book our emphasis will be on the physics, much must be left unsaid about numerical methods. This does not mean that we view numerical methods as unimportant, but just that there is only so much time in a day (or in a course), so to speak. Nevertheless, we will be making some comments about the choice of algorithms, their numerical uncertainties, and their stability. We will attempt to blend these discussions with the physics as we go, since in many cases they will also be closely related to the physics of the problem.

With our radioactive decay program, errors were introduced by the *approximation* used to estimate the solution of the differential equation (1.7). Errors were also produced by the finite numerical precision of *True Basic*. The latter are known as round-off errors and are almost always present when numbers are represented by a finite number of digits. Fortunately, this is not usually a severe problem, as most modern computer language systems employ a large number of significant digits. (For example, *True Basic* stores typically 14 or more significant digits.) Nevertheless, in order to be as safe as possible, you should always use double precision variables in Fortran, C, and other languages where this is an

---

[7]One definition of a physicist is "a person who can calculate anything to within an order of magnitude." This is perhaps a bit overstated, but you should usually be able to anticipate an answer with this sort of accuracy.

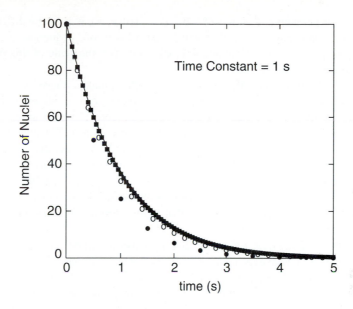

Figure 1.3: Numerical solution of the radioactive decay problem using the Euler method for different values of the time step. The time constant was 1 s, and the time steps were: filled circles, 0.5 s; open circles, 0.2 s; squares, 0.05 s. The solid curve is the exact solution.

option. Even with so many significant digits, however, there is no guarantee that these errors will be negligible, as the numerical solutions to certain types of problems are inherently sensitive to round-off errors. It is hard to give any general rules about what to watch for, but we will discuss such difficulties when they arise in several problems later in this book.

In attacking the radioactive decay problem we were led to treat time as a discrete variable; that is, we converted the differential equation (1.1) into a difference equation (1.7), which enabled us to compute estimates for N_U at the discrete times $n\Delta t$, where n is an integer. Such a "discretization" of time, or space, or both, is a common practice in numerical calculations, and brings up two related questions: (1) How do we know that the errors introduced by this discreteness are negligible, and (2) how do we choose the value of such a step size for a calculation? Again, there are no general answers to these questions. All we can do is give some guidelines, which can be illustrated using our radioactive decay problem.

The first guideline is that a calculation should *always* be repeated using several different values of the step size. Figure 1.3 shows the results from our radioactive decay calculation using three different values of the time step. The time constant τ was taken to be 1 s, and the symbols show the numerical results for time steps of 0.5, 0.2, and 0.05 s. Also shown is the exact solution (the solid line). Because of the nonzero step size, our program only yields results at discrete values of t, which is why the calculated points become more dense as the time step is reduced. We see that as the time step is made smaller, the calculated values converge quickly to the exact solution. This is not surprising, since intuition tells us that our approximations should become better as Δt is reduced. Being more quantitative, we already noted that the terms dropped in our derivation of (1.6) are of order $(\Delta t)^2$. In addition, the number of time steps required varies as $(\Delta t)^{-1}$. The total error is proportional to the product of the number of time steps and the error per step and is thus of order Δt. Hence, we expect the difference between the numerical (Euler) and exact results to be cut in half for each factor of 2 reduction of Δt. It is clear from Figure 1.3 that the numerical results become extremely close (on the scale of this figure) to the exact solution for time steps below about 0.05 s.

For our decay problem we have the exact solution, which makes it easy to evaluate the accuracy of our numerical results. However, we will not usually be this fortunate, so it is important to consider how to evaluate our results when the exact result is not available. In such cases you should always check that the calculated result converges to a fixed value (or curve) as the step size is made smaller. A closely related matter concerns the choice of step size in the first place; that is, what is a reasonable value? Here, yet again, there are no hard and fast rules. Ideally, you should use a step size that is small compared to any characteristic time scales in the problem. In our decay problem this time scale is τ, since its value determines how fast N_U varies. Our recommendation is that you pick the time step to be a small fraction of τ. We see from Figure 1.3 that a time step that is a few percent (or less) of this characteristic scale is a good choice.

One more important issue concerning numerical precision will be encountered later in this book. There are situations in which what appears to be a very reasonable numerical approach can be inherently unstable. For example, we will find in Chapter 3 that the Euler method, which we have found to work well for the radioactive decay problem, fails miserably when applied to problems involving oscillatory motion. The message here is that there is no best method for solving ordinary differential equations or any other particular class of problems. You must apply your understanding of the theory behind an algorithm (as discussed, for example, in a numerical methods book such as Press et al. [1986]) and your ingenuity (and also this book!) to choose the appropriate method for any particular problem.

1.6   Programming Guidelines and Philosophy

In our construction of the radioactive decay program we noted that writing a program is necessarily an individualistic endeavor. Nevertheless, there are certain guidelines that are generally recommended, some of which were touched on above. All of these guidelines have essentially the same purpose: To make the program as easy to understand as possible.

- *Program structure.* Use subroutines to organize the major tasks and make the program more readable and understandable. The `main` program for the decay problem was basically an outline of the program; we recommend this style for *all* programs. Use subroutines and functions to perform any jobs that take more than a few lines of code, or that are required repeatedly.

- *Use descriptive names.* Choose the names of variables and subroutines according to the problem at hand. Descriptive names make a program easier to understand, as they act as built-in comment statements.

- *Use comment statements.* Include comment statements to explain program logic and describe variables. A short subroutine that uses descriptive variable names should not need a large number of comment statements.

- *Sacrifice everything for clarity.* This a bit overstated, but not much! It is often tempting to write a critical piece of code in a very compact or terse manner in the belief that this will make the program run faster. This compactness nearly always comes at the price of clarity and readability;

there are many famous pieces of code in Fortran and C that come to mind here. It is always better to take a few more lines, or a few more variables, to do a job, if it makes the code more understandable. It is also a good idea to make the code look as much as possible like the associated physics equation. This will save time later when you are checking your program. The importance of the execution speed of a program is, in our experience, almost always oversold. In this book we will generally write our programs without worrying much about program efficiency. If you want to "tune-up" a program to make it run faster, this should be done only *after* it is known to be correct. Moreover, modern language packages often do a good job of optimizing code without the programmer even knowing it!

- *Take time to make the graphics presentable.* In almost all cases, numerical results should be presented graphically. The axes should be labeled clearly (including units, where appropriate) and parameter values given directly on the graph.

Exercises[8]

1. The velocity of a freely falling object near Earth's surface is described by the equation

$$\frac{dv}{dt} = -g , \qquad (1.8)$$

where v is the velocity and $g = 9.8 \text{ m/s}^2$ is the acceleration due to gravity. Write a program that employs the Euler method to compute the solution to (1.8); that is, calculate v as a function of t. For simplicity, assume that the initial velocity is zero—that is, the object starts from rest—and calculate the solution for times $t = 0$ to $t = 10$ s. Repeat the calculation for several different values of the time step, and compare the results with the exact solution to (1.8). It turns out that for this case the Euler method gives the exact result. Verify this with your numerical results and prove it analytically.

2. The position of an object moving horizontally with a constant velocity, v, is described by the equation

$$\frac{dx}{dt} = v . \qquad (1.9)$$

Assuming that the velocity is a constant, say $v = 40$ m/s, use the Euler method to solve (1.9) for x as a function of time. Compare your result with the exact solution.

3. It is often the case that the frictional force on an object will increase as the object moves faster. A fortunate example of this is a parachutist; the role of the parachute is to produce a frictional force due to air drag, which is larger than would normally be the case without the parachute. The physics of air drag will be discussed in more detail in the next chapter. Here we consider a very simple example in which the frictional force depends on the velocity. Assume that the velocity of an object obeys an equation of the form

$$\frac{dv}{dt} = a - bv , \qquad (1.10)$$

---

[8]Throughout this book, exercises labeled with a * are more challenging than others in that section. Exercises with ** are even more challenging.

where a and b are constants. You could think of a as coming from an applied force, such as gravity, while b arises from friction. Note that the frictional force is negative (we assume that $b > 0$), so that it opposes the motion, and that it increases in magnitude as the velocity increases. Use the Euler method to solve (1.10) for v as a function of time. A convenient choice of parameters is $a = 10$ and $b = 1$. You should find that v approaches a constant value at long times; this is called the terminal velocity.

*4. Consider a radioactive decay problem involving two types of nuclei, A and B, with populations $N_A(t)$ and $N_B(t)$. Suppose that type A nuclei decay to form type B nuclei, which then also decay, according to the differential equations

$$\frac{dN_A}{dt} = -\frac{N_A}{\tau_A} , \tag{1.11}$$

$$\frac{dN_B}{dt} = \frac{N_A}{\tau_A} - \frac{N_B}{\tau_B} ,$$

where τ_A and τ_B are the decay time constants for each type of nucleus. Use the Euler method to solve these coupled equations for N_A and N_B as functions of time. Explore the behavior found for different values of the ratio τ_A/τ_B.

*5. Consider again a decay problem with two types of nuclei A and B, but now suppose that nuclei of type A decay into ones of type B, while nuclei of type B decay into ones of type A. The corresponding rate equations are then

$$\frac{dN_A}{dt} = \frac{N_B}{\tau} - \frac{N_A}{\tau} , \tag{1.12}$$

$$\frac{dN_B}{dt} = \frac{N_A}{\tau} - \frac{N_B}{\tau} ,$$

where for simplicity we have assumed that the two types of decay are characterized by the same time constant, τ. Solve this system of equations for the numbers of nuclei, N_A and N_B, as functions of time. Consider different initial conditions, such as $N_A = 100$, $N_B = 0$, etc., and take $\tau = 1$ s. Show that your numerical results are consistent with the idea that the system reaches a steady state in which N_A and N_B are constant. In such a steady state, the time derivatives dN_A/dt and dN_B/dt should vanish.

6. Population growth problems often give rise to rate equations that are first order. For example, the equation

$$\frac{dN}{dt} = a N - b N^2 , \tag{1.13}$$

might describe how the number of individuals in a population, N, varies with time. Here the first term aN corresponds to the birth of new members, while the second term $-bN^2$ corresponds to deaths. The death term is proportional to N^2 to allow for the fact that food will become harder to find when the population N becomes large. Begin by solving (1.13) with $b = 0$ using the Euler method, and compare your numerical result with the exact solution. Then solve (1.13) with $a = 10$, $b = 3$. Give an intuitive explanation of your results.

References

KERNIGHAN, B. W. and P. J. PLAUGER. 1978. *The Elements of Programming Style*. 2d ed. New York: McGraw-Hill. A very nice discussion of how to write clear, readable, and efficient programs in any language.

PRESS, W. H., B. P. FLANNERY, S. A. TEUKOLSKY, and W. T. VETTERLING. 1986. *Numerical Recipes*. Cambridge: Cambridge University Press. An excellent all-purpose reference on numerical methods and why they work.

2

Realistic Projectile Motion

In this chapter we consider several problems involving the motion of objects through the atmosphere. The problems are all described by ordinary differential equations in which initial values are given and all can be solved using the Euler method, which was introduced in the last chapter. These problems are good examples of interesting physics involving the mechanics of macroscopic objects, which can't be solved analytically, but can be easily tackled with a computer.

We begin with a discussion of the motion of a bicycle traveling on flat terrain. We will find that air resistance must be included if we are to obtain a realistic description of the problem, and this leads us to a simple but fairly accurate model of the drag force due to the atmosphere. Next we treat projectile motion in two dimensions as we consider the trajectory of a shell fired by a large cannon. Again, the effect of air resistance is important, but now its variation with altitude plays a key role. We proceed to the national pastime, baseball, and consider the trajectory of a batted ball and the motion of thrown balls (curve balls and knuckleballs). To model a batted ball we are led to consider air resistance a little more realistically than in the earlier problems, while for a thrown ball we must also include spin dependent forces. These themes are developed further in our discussion of the motion of golf balls, where we answer the eternal question: "Why do golf balls have dimples?"

2.1 Bicycle Racing: The Effect of Air Resistance

The bicycle is an extremely efficient form of transportation, a fact that is well known to anyone who rides one. Our goal in this section is to understand the factors that determine the ultimate speed of a bicycle and to estimate this speed for a realistic case. We will begin by ignoring friction; we'll have to add it eventually, of course, but let us first understand how to deal with the simpler case without friction.

Our equation of motion is Newton's second law, which can be written in the form

$$\frac{dv}{dt} = \frac{F}{m} \, , \tag{2.1}$$

where v is the velocity, m is the mass of the bicycle-rider combination, t is the time, and F is the force on the bicycle that comes from the effort of the rider (here we will assume that the bicycle is moving on flat terrain). Dealing properly with F is complicated by the mechanics of a bicycle, since the force exerted by the rider is transmitted to the wheels by way of the chainring, gears, etc. This makes it very difficult to derive an accurate expression for F. However, there is another way to attack this problem that avoids the need to know the force. This alternative approach involves formulating the problem in terms of the power generated by the rider. Physiological studies of elite racing bicyclists have shown that these athletes are able to produce a power output of approximately 400 watts over extended periods of time ($\sim$ 1 h). Using work-energy ideas we can rewrite (2.1) as

$$\frac{dE}{dt} = P \, , \tag{2.2}$$

where E is the total energy of the bicycle-rider combination, and P is the power output of the rider. (This assumes implicitly that very little energy is lost to friction in the bicycle itself; we'll include other sources of friction in a moment.) For a flat course the energy is all kinetic, so $E = \frac{1}{2}mv^2$, and $dE/dt = mv(dv/dt)$. Inserting this into (2.2) yields

$$\frac{dv}{dt} = \frac{P}{mv} \, . \tag{2.3}$$

If P is a constant, (2.3) can be solved analytically. Rearranging gives

$$\int_{v_0}^{v} v' \, dv' = \int_{0}^{t} \frac{P}{m} \, dt' \, , \tag{2.4}$$

where v_0 is the velocity of the bicycle at $t = 0$. Integrating both sides and solving for v then leads to

$$v = \sqrt{v_0^2 + 2 P t / m} \, . \tag{2.5}$$

While this is the correct solution of the equation of motion (2.2), it cannot be the whole story, since it predicts that the velocity will increase without bound at long times. We will correct this "unphysical" result in a moment, when we generalize our model to include the effect of air resistance. The new term we will add to the equation of motion will require us to develop a numerical solution, so with that in mind we consider a numerical treatment of (2.3). We begin with the finite difference form for the derivative of the velocity

$$\frac{dv}{dt} \approx \frac{v_{i+1} - v_i}{\Delta t} \, , \tag{2.6}$$

where we have assumed small, discrete time steps of size Δt and taken v_i to be the velocity at time $t_i \equiv i \, \Delta t$, where i is an integer (this should be familiar from Chapter 1). Inserting this into (2.3) we obtain, after a little rearranging

$$v_{i+1} = v_i + \frac{P}{mv_i} \Delta t \, . \tag{2.7}$$

The approximation made in (2.6) leads to correction terms here that are proportional to $(\Delta t)^2$ (and higher powers).

Given the velocity at time step i (i.e., v_i), we can use (2.7) to calculate an *approximate* value of the velocity at the next step, v_{i+1}. Hence, if we know the initial velocity, v_0, we can obtain v_1, then v_2, and so on, and thereby estimate the velocity at all future times. This is just the Euler method, which we encountered in Chapter 1. There are more sophisticated methods for numerically solving differential equations of this form, and a few of them are described in Appendix 1. In this book we will only rarely encounter problems for which the Euler method, or simple variants, are not adequate. However, you should be aware that: (1) methods that are more powerful[1] than the Euler method exist; (2) these more powerful methods can certainly be used to solve all of the problems in this book where we use the Euler method; and (3) if you are going to do this sort of thing for a living it is worth your while to learn about these other methods. In taking what some purists might consider a quick-and-dirty approach (our use of the Euler method), we are *not* trying to minimize the importance of other algorithms. Our intent is merely to use the simplest numerical method (which will give the correct solution, of course) appropriate for the job, so that we can emphasize the *physics* of our problems and not let the numerical techniques get in the way. Students and instructors are encouraged to follow their own tastes here, and with all of the other problems discussed in this book, and to use the methods with which they feel most comfortable.

A program that performs this calculation is listed below. The overall structure is similar to the one we used in the nuclear decay problem in Chapter 1. The `main` program references the graphics libraries and declares the arrays `t()` and `velocity()`, which hold values for the time and velocity, respectively. The `initialize` subroutine initializes the necessary variables, which all have names that fit the problem. `dt` is the time step, `power` is the power output of the bicyclist P, and `mass` is the mass of the bicycle-rider combination. The routine `calculate` then uses the Euler method to calculate the velocity as a function of time. After the calculation is finished, the `mat redim` statement is used to resize the arrays to make them exactly the length used in the calculation (`nmax`). This is handy when using the *True Basic* graphics routines, but may not be needed if you use a different language package. The `display` routine is not listed here. It is very similar to that used in the nuclear decay problem in Chapter 1 and is included in the complete listing of this program, which is given in Appendix 4.

```
! Simulation of velocity vs. time for a bicyclist
! 10-1-94  N. Giordano
! assume no air resistance
program bike
    option nolet
    library "sglib*","sgfunc*"
    dim t(5000),velocity(5000)
    call initialize(t,velocity,dt,power,mass,nmax)
    call calculate(t,velocity,dt,power,mass,nmax)
    call display(t,velocity)
end
```

---

[1]By "more powerful" we mean that they yield more accurate solutions for a given amount of computer time, or that they are more stable in a numerical sense.

```
! t() = time      v() = velocity
! dt = time step      power = rider power
! mass = mass of rider + bicycle
sub initialize(t(),v(),dt,power,mass,nmax)
   t(1) = 0
   v(1) = 4              ! m/s - all units are SI
   dt = 1               ! second
   power = 400          ! watts
   mass = 70            ! kg
   tmax = 200           ! seconds
   nmax = tmax / dt   ! total number of time steps required
end sub
sub calculate(t(),v(),dt,pmax,mass,nmax)
   for i = 2 to nmax
      t(i) = t(i-1) + dt
      v(i) = v(i-1) + pmax * dt / (mass * v(i-1))      ! Euler method
   next i
   mat redim t(nmax),v(nmax)      ! trim arrays to the size actually used
end sub
```

We are now ready to compute a numerical solution. We assume that the bicycle starts with a velocity of $v_0 = 4$ m/s (about 10 mph) and take $P = 400$ W, the value obtained from physiological measurements of well-trained athletes, as mentioned above. The last point to consider is the choice of Δt. Roughly speaking, Δt should be sufficiently small that the velocity changes only a little during such an interval. What it means to be "sufficiently" small is hard to say, in general. A useful rule of thumb is to begin with a time step that is about 1 percent of any time scales in the problem, and then repeat the calculation with several smaller values.[2] Smaller time steps will give smaller correction terms [e.g., in (2.7)] and thus more accurate results, but the calculation will take a computational time proportional to $(\Delta t)^{-1}$, so there is a tradeoff here. For our bicycle problem it will turn out that time steps smaller than about 1 s are adequate. It is usually instructive to repeat a calculation using different values of the time step so as to observe how the solution converges to the correct one as Δt is reduced.

The results for our frictionless bicycle are shown in Figure 2.1, where we have used a mass of 70 kg for the bicycle-rider combination (elite bicycle racers tend to be rather slender). We see immediately that, as anticipated above, our model has a serious problem; the velocity reaches 45 m/s (about 100 mph) in less than 3 min. While this performance would not be particularly impressive for a car, it is certainly not within reach of any known bicycles (or bicyclists). We also see that v appears to grow indefinitely, and this makes the origin of our problem clear. We have not included any sources of dissipation, so given our assumption of constant power exerted by the rider, the kinetic energy will increase without limit. If we want to have a realistic model, we must add some mechanism for energy loss.

For a well-tuned bicycle traveling at more than about 5 or 10 mph, the energy lost to friction in the hubs and tires is negligible compared to that caused by air resistance, that is, atmospheric drag. Thus, a reasonably realistic model of the motion of a bicycle need only consider this one source of friction. As we will come to appreciate in later sections, the physics of air resistance is a very complicated problem.

---

[2]While the "characteristic" time scale is often not a unique or precise quantity, in some cases it is easy to estimate. For example, in the radioactive decay problem in Chapter 1 it was the time constant τ of the decay. In the present problem, one natural choice is the time it takes to attain a velocity of the order of terminal velocity (see Figure 2.2).

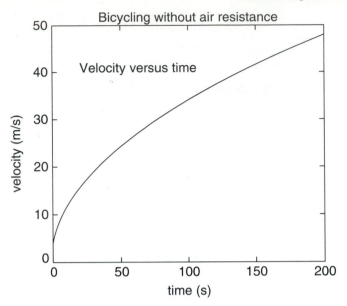

Figure 2.1: Velocity as a function of time for our bicycle problem, assuming no air resistance. The mass of the bicycle-rider combination was 70 kg, the initial velocity was 4 m/s, and the time step was 0.1 s. Here and in the other figures in this chapter, the results at each time step are connected to obtain an essentially smooth curve.

In general, this force can be written in the fairly innocent form

$$F_{\text{drag}} \approx - B_1 \, v \, - \, B_2 \, v^2 \, . \tag{2.8}$$

You will no doubt notice that (2.8) bears a strong resemblance to a Taylor expansion. At extremely low velocities the first term dominates, and its coefficient B_1 can be calculated for objects with simple shapes. This is known as Stokes' law and is considered in most elementary mechanics texts. However, at any reasonable velocity the v^2 term in (2.8) dominates for most objects. Moreover, B_2 cannot be calculated exactly for objects as simple as a baseball, and certainly not for a complicated object like a bicycle. We can, however, make an *approximate* estimate of B_2, as follows. As an object moves through the atmosphere, it must push the air in front of it out of the way. The mass of air moved in time dt is $m_{\text{air}} \sim \rho A v \, dt$, where ρ is the density of air and A the frontal area of the object. This air is given a velocity of order v, and hence its kinetic energy is $E_{\text{air}} \sim m_{\text{air}} v^2/2$. This is also the work done by the drag force (the force on the object due to air resistance) in time dt, so $F_{\text{drag}} v \, dt = E_{\text{air}}$. Putting this all together we find

$$F_{\text{drag}} \approx - C \rho A v^2 \, . \tag{2.9}$$

C is known as the drag coefficient, and our simple argument predicts that it is equal to $\frac{1}{2}$. However, we caution that our calculation was only approximate; while we expect it to give the correct functional dependence of F_{drag} on A and v, we certainly do not expect the precise value it predicts for C to be correct. The best way to determine the drag coefficient of any particular object is via wind tunnel measurements, or similar experiments.

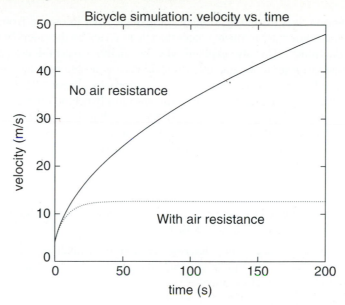

Figure 2.2:   Velocity as a function of time for our bicycle problem, with and without air resistance. The drag coefficient was 0.5, the frontal area 0.33 m², the mass of the bicycle-rider combination 70 kg, the initial velocity 4 m/s, and the time step 0.1 s.

It is easy to include this drag force in our calculation; Equation (2.9) contributes another term to the right-hand side of (2.7), which becomes

$$ v_{i+1} \; = \; v_i \; + \; \frac{P}{m v_i} \, \Delta t \; - \; \frac{C \rho A v_i^2}{m} \, \Delta t \; , \tag{2.10} $$

and we can use the Euler method to obtain v as a function of t as before. The program given above can again be used, provided that we add the drag term to the Euler equation in the `calculate` subroutine (a task we will leave to the reader).

The result obtained from solving (2.10) is shown in Figure 2.2, where we have assumed a frontal area of $A = 0.33$ m², which is a typical estimate for a rider in a racing crouch. We obtain an ultimate (i.e., terminal) velocity of approximately 13 m/s (about 30 mph), which is in reasonable accord with the performance of an elite racer.[3]

Besides giving a good estimate of the speed of a bicycle racer, our model provides some insight into racing strategy. It is clear from Figure 2.2 that reducing the air resistance is the key to increasing the speed for a given power exertion or decreasing the power required to maintain a given speed. This is, of course, why bicycle racers often ride in a pack. The idea is to let the riders at the front of the pack break the wind, and thereby lower the effective frontal area for those in the pack who "draft" off those

---

[3]It is interesting to note that the 1995 record for the distance traveled by bicycle in 1 h is a little more than 55 km. This corresponds to an average velocity of approximately 15 m/s, which is within about 15 percent of our result for the terminal velocity.

in front. For this reason, it is extremely difficult for a single rider to escape from a large group; the energy required of the single rider is much greater than that exerted by the riders in the pack (assuming they share time at the front).[4] This also explains why the relatively recent development of "aerobars," handle bars that allow the rider to assume an extremely narrow profile and thereby reduce his frontal area, enables an isolated rider to go faster than with conventional handlebars. This is useful in individual events such as time trials and triathalons, where following closely behind other riders is not allowed.

With a little work to include air resistance, we have developed a simple but reasonably accurate model of bicycle performance. Both our model and the numerical approach can be easily generalized to include other factors, which will be our job in the following sections.

Exercises

1. Compare the exact solution for the velocity as a function of time without air resistance with the numerical results in Figure 2.1 and show that they agree.

2. Investigate the effect of varying both the rider's power and frontal area on the ultimate velocity. In particular, for a rider in the middle of a pack, the effective frontal area is about 30 percent less than for a rider at the front. How much less energy does a rider in the pack expend than does one at the front, assuming they both move at a velocity of 13 m/s?

*3. Generalize the model to treat motion through mountainous terrain. A steep hill is one with a 10 percent grade (that is, $\tan \theta = 0.1$, where θ is the angle the hill makes with the horizontal). Calculate how fast our bicyclist can travel up and down such a slope. Does racing strategy change in these situations? Determine what conditions (the steepness of the grade and the rider's frontal area) would be required for a bicycle to reach a velocity of 70 mph. This is reportedly the speed that professional riders sometimes attain on steep descents.[5]

*4. You might wonder why we did not let our bicycle begin from rest, but instead gave it a nonzero initial velocity. The reason for this is that (2.7) breaks down when $v_i = 0$, since then the term involving P is infinite.[6] If $v_i = 0$, then for a nonzero P the derivative dv/dt is, according to (2.3), infinite. This is difficult to handle in a numerical approach, and it also doesn't make sense from a physical point of view. The problem arises from our assumption that the bicyclist maintains a constant power output. This assumption must break down when the bicycle has a very small velocity, since it would then require that the rider exert extremely large forces (recall that the instantaneous power is the product of the force and the velocity). At low velocities it is more realistic to assume that the rider is able to exert a constant force. To account for this we can modify our bicycle model so that for small v there is a constant force on the bicycle, F_0, which leads to the equation of motion

$$\frac{dv}{dt} = \frac{F_0}{m} . \tag{2.11}$$

---

[4]Estimates are that the effective frontal area is reduced by approximately 30 percent for a rider in the middle of a pack, as compared with a rider at the front.

[5]It is interesting to also include the effect of a tail wind in this calculation, as discussed in the section on the motion of a batted baseball.

[6]The problem is also evident from (2.3), and thus is not a product of the Euler method.

The corresponding Euler equation is

$$v_{i+1} = v_i + \frac{F_0}{m} \Delta t ,$$ (2.12)

and the difficulty that occurs when $v = 0$ is eliminated.

Rewrite your bicycle program to incorporate (2.12). That is, use the Euler method with (2.12) when the velocity is small, and (2.7) when v is large. Let the crossover from small to large v occur when the power $(= F_0 v)$ reaches P. Use the same parameters as in Figure 2.2, and take $F_0 = P/v^*$ where $v^* = 7$ m/s (this corresponds to a force approximately twice that found when the bicycle is traveling at its maximum velocity, which seems like a reasonable approximation).

2.2   Projectile Motion: The Trajectory of a Cannon Shell

The Euler method we used to treat the bicycle problem can easily be generalized to deal with motion in two spatial dimensions. To be specific, we consider a projectile such as a shell shot by a cannon. We have a very large cannon in mind, and the large size will determine some of the important physics. If we ignore air resistance, the equations of motion, which are again obtained from Newton's second law, can be written as

$$\frac{d^2 x}{dt^2} = 0$$ (2.13)

$$\frac{d^2 y}{dt^2} = -g ,$$

where x and y are the horizontal and vertical coordinates of the projectile, and g is the acceleration due to gravity. These are second-order differential equations, as opposed to the first-order equations we have encountered so far, so we must generalize our approach a bit. We have seen that with a first-order equation, such as (2.1), it is possible to use a finite difference approximation for the derivative (2.6) to obtain a simple algebraic equation containing the variable of interest at two adjacent time steps. However, if we were to take the same approach with one of the equations in (2.13) and write a finite difference approximation to the second derivative, we would obtain a more complicated algebraic equation involving our variable at three time steps. We will see how this works out in Chapter 6 (and later), as sometimes this is the best approach. However, in the present case it is possible to avoid this complication by recasting the differential equations in the following way.

Let us write each of these second-order equations as two first-order differential equations

$$\frac{dx}{dt} = v_x$$ (2.14)

$$\frac{dv_x}{dt} = 0$$

$$\frac{dy}{dt} = v_y$$

$$\frac{dv_y}{dt} = -g ,$$

where v_x and v_y are the x and y components of the velocity. While we now have twice as many equations to deal with (four altogether), we can use our standard Euler approach to solve each one. To use the Euler method, we write each derivative in finite difference form, as in (2.6), which leads to

$$x_{i+1} = x_i + v_{x,i}\,\Delta t \qquad (2.15)$$

$$v_{x,i+1} = v_{x,i}$$

$$y_{i+1} = y_i + v_{y,i}\,\Delta t$$

$$v_{y,i+1} = v_{y,i} - g\,\Delta t \;.$$

Given the initial values of x, y, v_x, and v_y, we can use (2.15) to estimate their values at later times. These estimates are *approximate*, since there are correction terms to (2.15) that are of order $(\Delta t)^2$ and higher. By choosing Δt to be sufficiently small, we will usually be able to make these corrections negligible. However, their existence should not be forgotten.

In our treatment of the bicycle problem we found that air resistance was very important, so we now add that to the model. As was the case with a bicycle, we will assume that the magnitude of the drag force on our cannon shell is given by

$$F_{\text{drag}} = -B_2\,v^2\;, \qquad (2.16)$$

where $v = \sqrt{v_x^2 + v_y^2}$ is the speed of the shell. This force is always directed opposite to the velocity, so we must consider the vector components as illustrated in Figure 2.3. We find

$$F_{\text{drag},x} = F_{\text{drag}}\cos\theta = F_{\text{drag}}\,v_x\,/\,v\;, \qquad (2.17)$$

with a similar expression for $F_{\text{drag},y}$.

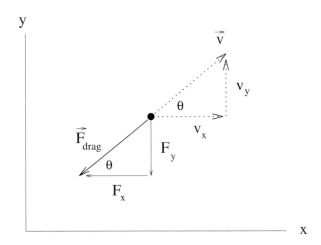

Figure 2.3: Components of the force due to air resistance on an object moving with a velocity $\vec{v}$. The direction of the drag force is opposite to $\vec{v}$.

The components of the drag force are thus

$$F_{\text{drag},x} = -B_2 \, v \, v_x \tag{2.18}$$
$$F_{\text{drag},y} = -B_2 \, v \, v_y \, .$$

Adding this force to the equations of motion leads to

$$x_{i+1} = x_i + v_{x,i} \, \Delta t \tag{2.19}$$

$$v_{x,i+1} = v_{x,i} - \frac{B_2 \, v \, v_{x,i}}{m} \Delta t$$

$$y_{i+1} = y_i + v_{y,i} \, \Delta t$$

$$v_{y,i+1} = v_{y,i} - g \, \Delta t - \frac{B_2 \, v \, v_{y,i}}{m} \Delta t \, .$$

The complete listing of a program that computes the trajectory of our cannon shell is given in Appendix 4; below we list the subroutine that performs the actual calculation. The arrays x() and y() are used to store the trajectory of the shell, while vx and vy hold the velocity components (since we only plan to plot the trajectory, we don't need to save the velocity results in arrays). Each time through the for loop we calculate the next values of position and velocity using (2.19). This process is continued until y becomes negative, which means the shell struck the ground somewhere during the previous time step. We then exit the loop and interpolate between the last two calculated positions to estimate where the shell struck the ground. The arrays are also redimensioned to the size actually used, in preparation for plotting.[7]

```
! x() and y() are the position of the projectile
! dt = time step   v_init = initial speed   theta = launch angle
! B_m = proportional to drag force = B2/m
sub calculate(x(),y(),dt,v_init,theta,B_m)
    option angle degrees          ! use degrees rather than radians
    x(1) = 0
    y(1) = 0
    vx = v_init * cos(theta)       ! initial velocity components
    vy = v_init * sin(theta)
    nmax = size(x)     ! this is the number of elements in the array x()
    for i = 2 to nmax
        x(i) = x(i-1) + vx * dt            ! Euler method equations
        y(i) = y(i-1) + vy * dt
        f = B_m * sqr(vx^2 + vy^2)         ! drag force from air resistance
        vy = vy - 9.8 * dt - f * vy * dt   ! Euler method for velocity
        vx = vx - f * vx * dt
        if y(i) <= 0 then exit for         ! shell has hit the ground
    next i
    a = -y(i) / y(i-1)                     ! interpolate to find landing point
    x(i) = (x(i) + a*x(i-1)) / (1+a)
    y(i) = 0
    mat redim x(i),y(i)
end sub
```

---

[7]The *True Basic* graphics routines plot all of the points in the input arrays, so resizing the arrays in this way avoids plotting any unused points at the ends of the original arrays.

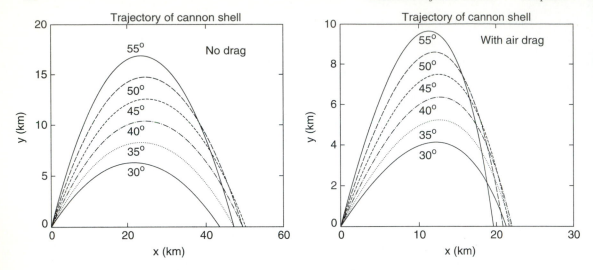

Figure 2.4: Left: trajectory of a cannon shell without air resistance. We assumed an initial speed of 700 m/s, and the firing angles are indicated. Right: trajectory of the same cannon shell, but now with air resistance included, with $B_2/m = 4 \times 10^{-5}$ m^{-1}.

Results for the trajectory are shown in Figure 2.4, where we have assumed an initial velocity of 700 m/s, which is appropriate for a large cannon shell. The plot on the left shows the results without air resistance,[8] while on the right we show results with air resistance for $B_2/m = 4 \times 10^{-5}$ (m^{-1}), which is a value appropriate for a very large cannon shell.[9] There are two important points to note from these results. First, air resistance decreases the range *a lot*, approximately by a factor of 2. The second point concerns the behavior as a function of firing angle. You probably have learned in your introductory mechanics course that without air resistance the maximum range occurs for $\theta = 45°$, and this is indeed observed in Figure 2.4. However, when air resistance is included, the maximum range occurs at a lower firing angle. For the parameters we have used here, the largest range with atmospheric drag is obtained with a firing angle of approximately 37°. This is in accord with our intuition that the longest range is obtained by shooting low into the "wind."

Our calculations clearly show that air resistance plays a major role in the problem. However, there is another important piece of physics that we have not yet accounted for. From Figure 2.4 we see that the shell travels to a very high altitude, where the air density will be lower than at sea level. We saw in our discussion of the drag on a bicycle that the force from air resistance is proportional to the density of the air, so the drag force at high altitudes will be less than that at sea level. To investigate the

---

[8]For this case the trajectory can also be calculated analytically. We will leave it to the reader to verify that the trajectories we have obtained numerically agree with the analytic results.

[9]See Chapter 5 of Bennett (1976) for a description of the cannon for which this value of B_2 was measured. The shells were approximately 10 cm in diameter. We emphasize that this value of B_2 was measured via "experimental" observations, and not estimated using the value $C = \frac{1}{2}$ in (2.9). We will see in the next section that the drag force for rapidly moving objects, such as cannon shells and baseballs, is more complicated than implied by (2.9).

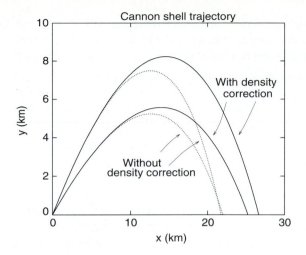

Figure 2.5: Trajectory of a cannon shell with (solid curves) and without (dotted curves) the effect of the lower air density at high altitudes taken into account. In all cases the air resistance was included with $B_2/m = 4 \times 10^{-5}$ m^{-1}, and the initial speed was 700 m/s. The lower two curves were for a firing angle of 35°, while for the top curves it was 45°.

magnitude of this effect we note that the density of the atmosphere varies as

$$\rho = \rho_0 \exp(-y/y_0), \qquad (2.20)$$

where y is the altitude, $y_0 = 1.0 \times 10^4$ m, and ρ_0 is density at sea level ($y = 0$). The drag force due to air resistance is proportional to the density, so

$$F^*_{\text{drag}} = \frac{\rho}{\rho_0} F_{\text{drag}}(y = 0), \qquad (2.21)$$

where $F_{\text{drag}}(y = 0)$ is the force at sea level [given by (2.16)], and F^*_{drag} is the drag force at altitude. Putting this into the calculation is straightforward; we replace B_2 in (2.19) with $B_2\rho/\rho_0$. We will leave it to you to modify the program given above. Some results are shown in Figure 2.5 where we compare trajectories with and without the variation of ρ with altitude taken into account. We see that for this cannon, the decrease of ρ at high altitudes increases the range by about 20 percent. In addition, the maximum range now occurs for a firing angle slightly *larger* than 45°. Hence, to get the longest range for a projectile such as this, it is best to take advantage of the reduced drag at high altitudes.

Exercises

1. Use the Euler method to calculate cannon shell trajectories ignoring both air drag and the effect of air density (actually, ignoring the former automatically rules out the latter). Compare your results with those in Figure 2.4, and with the exact solution.

2. In our model of the cannon shell trajectory we have assumed that the acceleration due to gravity, g, is a constant. It will, of course, depend on altitude. Add this to the model and calculate how much it affects the range.

3. Calculate the trajectory of our cannon shell including both air drag and the reduced air density at high altitudes so that you can reproduce the results in Figure 2.5. Perform your calculation for different firing angles and determine the value of the angle that gives the maximum range.

*4. Generalize the program developed for the previous problem so that it can deal with situations in which the target is at a different altitude than the cannon. Consider cases in which the target is higher and lower than the cannon. Also investigate how the minimum firing velocity required to hit the target varies as the altitude of the target is varied.

*5. In warfare you generally want to hit a particular target (as opposed to having the cannon shells land indiscriminately). However, this is not easy, since very small changes in any of the parameters can lead to large changes in the landing site of the shell. Investigate this by calculating how much the range of the cannon shell considered in this section would change if the initial speed is increased by 1 percent. Also compute the change in the range if there is a slight (10 km/h) wind (this effect can be added using the methods developed in the next section). You should find that even these relatively small changes alter the landing site by quite significant amounts.

2.3 Baseball: Motion of a Batted Ball

The game of baseball has fascinated fans of the game, and also physicists (some of us are both), for many years. There have probably been more books and papers written on the physics of baseball than any other sport, which is perhaps justified considering the wide variety of physical principles that are important in different aspects of the game. In this section we will consider the trajectory of a batted ball. Our goal is to understand how far a *real* baseball should be expected to travel when hit by a "typical" power hitter. The most important ingredient in our model will be the effect of atmospheric drag, and we will employ a somewhat more realistic model of the drag force than was used in previous sections. We will also see that wind and atmospheric density have smaller, but quite significant effects on the game. In the next few sections we will depart from our usual exclusive use of SI units and use also the units of feet and miles per hour (mph), which are so closely tied with how many of us (or at least the author) usually think about the sport.

The basic equations of motion for a baseball are the same as those of the cannon shell, (2.19), and we will again use the Euler method in our simulations. Before we go too far, however, it is interesting to estimate the distance a baseball would travel in a vacuum, that is, without atmospheric drag. This range can be calculated analytically, or numerically, by using (2.19) with $B_2 = 0$. A good power hitter can give the ball an initial speed of about 110 mph (49 m/s), and if it is hit at an initial angle of 45° starting from a height of 1 m, the range in a vacuum would be 248 m, or approximately 815 ft. So far as I know, no one has ever hit a baseball that far (except, perhaps, in the presence of a tornado). A typical outfield fence is 350–400 ft from home plate, and from practical experience we know that a 500-ft home run is an exceptionally long one.[10] Thus, it is clear that baseball in a vacuum would be a very different game than the one we are used to watching.

The force on a baseball due to air resistance is given by a form similar to (2.9). However, it turns out that the drag coefficient C for a baseball is not independent of v. Wind tunnel measurements with real baseballs show that C is actually a strong function of v, as illustrated in Figure 2.6, which shows

---

[10]Chapter 4 of Adair (1990) has a nice discussion of the distances traveled by the longest known home runs.

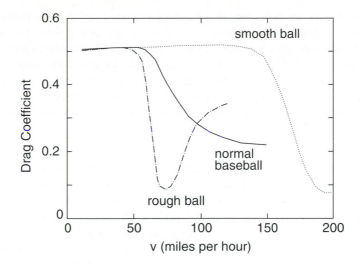

Figure 2.6:   Variation of the drag coefficient, C, with velocity for normal, rough, and smooth baseballs. Note that for a normal ball the drag force is equal to the weight of the ball at a velocity of approximately 95 mph. From R.K. Adair, *The Physics of Baseball.*

a plot of the drag coefficient as a function of the speed of the ball. At low speeds, C is close to the value of $\frac{1}{2}$ predicted by the simple argument we gave in the derivation of (2.9). However, as the speed increases, C drops substantially, and it is more than a factor of 2 smaller at high speeds. This does *not* mean that the drag force is lower at high speeds; F_{drag} is proportional to the product Cv^2, and this quantity[11] is a monotonically increasing function of v.

The behavior of C can be understood qualitatively as follows. At low speeds the air flow around the ball is "well behaved" and orderly. However, at high speeds the flow becomes turbulent, and it turns out that an object is able to "slip" through the air more easily in this case than when the flow is nonturbulent. This makes the drag coefficient smaller at high speeds when the flow pattern is turbulent, than at low speeds when it is nonturbulent. Such behavior is quite general and is important for other objects as well (we will consider the interesting case of a golf ball later in this chapter). We see from Figure 2.6 that this transition occurs at a speed of about 80 mph for an ordinary baseball. This is a common speed for both a batted and a pitched ball, so the velocity dependence of C must be considered in any realistic modeling. The figure also shows the variation of C for balls that are rougher or smoother than typical baseballs, and the behavior is quite different in these cases. For a rough ball the transition to turbulent flow occurs at a lower velocity than for a regular ball, so the drop in C takes place sooner, while the opposite trend is observed for a smooth ball (a ball without stitches would qualify as smooth). This will turn out to have important implications for the motion of the pitch known as a knuckleball, since the stitches on the ball are equivalent to a sort of roughness.

---

[11]A plot of F_{drag} as a function of velocity is given in Chapter 2 of Adair (1990) (it could also be derived from the data given in Figure 2.6). While it does not appear to happen in the case of a baseball, it is possible that for certain objects the drag force might become smaller as the speed is increased. Some of the consequences of such behavior are discussed by Adair.

In order to calculate the trajectory of a baseball, we need to solve the Euler equations (2.19), including the velocity dependence of the drag force. The variation of C observed in Figure 2.6 is clearly a complicated function. For our numerical work it is convenient to have an (admittedly approximate) analytic representation of this function. Taking the results for the drag coefficient from Figure 2.6 and adding in the appropriate factors of air density, and so on, it turns out that the drag factor for a normal baseball is described reasonably well by the function (now using SI units)

$$\frac{B_2}{m} = 0.0039 + \frac{0.0058}{1 + \exp\left[(v - v_d)/\Delta\right]}, \tag{2.22}$$

with $v_d = 35$ m/s and $\Delta = 5$ m/s. Using this parameterization of the drag we can construct a program to calculate the trajectory of our batted baseball. The program is very similar to the one given earlier for the cannon shell problem, so we will leave the details to the exercises.

A typical result for the trajectory is shown as the solid curve in Figure 2.7. Recalling that the range in a vacuum would be more than 800 ft, we see that air resistance has an *enormous* effect. The range of our power hitter is now approximately 120 m, or about 395 ft, which is in much better accord with the size of typical major league ballparks.[12] It turns out that with air resistance described by (2.22), the maximum range is largest for angles near 35°. This is much lower than the 45° angle that gives the maximum range without air resistance. The trajectory is seen to be noticeably nonparabolic[13] (in a vacuum it would be an exact parabola), which is also in agreement with our everyday experience.

Let us next add the effect of the wind. We will assume that it is blowing in a horizontal (x) direction and has a constant magnitude and direction during the flight of the ball.[14] In this case the components of the drag force become

$$F_{\text{drag},x} = -B_2 \mid \vec{v} - \vec{v}_{\text{wind}} \mid (v_x - v_{\text{wind}}) \tag{2.23}$$
$$F_{\text{drag},y} = -B_2 \mid \vec{v} - \vec{v}_{\text{wind}} \mid v_y ,$$

where v_{wind} is the velocity of the wind, and a positive value corresponds to a tailwind. The derivation of (2.23) is understood most easily if you consider the drag force (2.18) in the reference frame at rest with respect to the wind. In that frame the drag force is just (2.18). Transforming into the batter's reference frame then requires that we subtract the velocity of the wind from $\vec{v}$, which yields (2.23).

We can include the wind in our program using (2.23), an exercise we will leave to the reader. Some results from such a calculation are shown in Figure 2.7, where we compare the trajectories calculated with a tail wind and a head wind (both 10 mph) with the result for still air. This relatively modest breeze alters the range by approximately ±25 ft, which is more than enough to turn a routine fly ball out into a home run, or a home run into a long out. The wind can thus have a pronounced effect on the game,

---

[12]In writing a program to determine the range, it is advisable to locate the place where the ball strikes the ground by using an interpolation procedure, similar to that used in our work on the cannon shell problem. The program "knows" that the ball has landed when $y_n < 0$. You could just take x_n to be the range, but this would overestimate the landing point by as much as $v_{x,n} \Delta t$, which can be significant when you want to consider small differences in the range. A better method is to interpolate between (x_n, y_n) and (x_{n-1}, y_{n-1}), assuming the trajectory to be a straight line, to get a much improved estimate of where $y = 0$.

[13]This can be seen by noting that the ball reaches its maximum height at about $x = 70$ m while it strikes the ground at $x = 120$ m in the absence of any wind.

[14]It is not difficult to treat the case of a swirling wind like that found in most stadiums, but we'll leave that for the interested student. Such an effect would certainly be important in developing a model of judging and catching a fly ball.

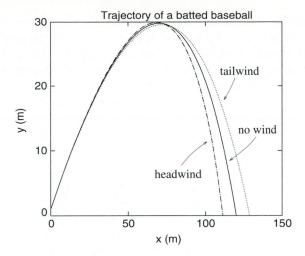

Figure 2.7:   Calculated trajectory of a baseball hit at an initial velocity of 110 mph, with the effects of atmospheric drag included. Solid curve: no wind; dotted and dot-dashed curves: a tailwind and headwind of 10 mph. In all cases we assume that the initial velocity makes an angle of 35° with the horizontal.

as any fan who has been to Wrigley Field or Candlestick Park can verify.[15] It is interesting that major league parks are oriented so that the generally prevailing westerly breeze, which averages about 5 mph in the United States, is at the batter's back and thus favors a home run. As in most sports, offense is favored over defense; that is, the hitter over the pitcher.

It is also interesting to consider the effect of altitude. This can be added to the model just as we did in the case of the cannon shell, with the only difference being that we don't have to worry about density changes during the flight of the ball. The results for the range of our home-run hitter at several altitudes are shown in Table 2.1. The highest major league park is currently in Denver (altitude ≈ 5280 ft). Our long fly ball will travel about 31 ft farther there than at sea level. This is a substantial difference and suggests that home-run hitters should enjoy playing in Denver. The next highest major league park is in

Table 2.1:   Calculated range of a batted ball at various altitudes. In all cases we have assumed an initial velocity of 110 mph, that there is no wind, and that the ball is hit at an initial angle of 35° with respect to the horizontal. (Pike's Peak is a mountain in Colorado.)

Location	Altitude (feet)	Range (feet)
sea level	0	390
Atlanta	1,000	396
Denver	5,280	421
Pike's Peak	14,110	473

[15]These two baseball parks are notorious for being very windy. Note: Candlestick Park is now named 3Com Park.

Atlanta (altitude $\approx$ 1000 ft), and here the effect of the altitude is to add about 6 ft to the range. We also note that if a ballpark is ever built on Pike's Peak, home runs there will be very interesting to watch.

One of the conclusions that can be drawn from our results for the range of a batted baseball is that atmospheric drag simply must be taken into account to get an accurate picture of the range and trajectory of a fly ball. Air resistance reduces the range of a home-run hitter by more than a factor of 2. For the statisticians, it seems clear that playing in Denver will significantly enhance a hitter's record and be unfair to a pitcher's earned-run average.[16] There are a number of other effects that can be added to our model, and a nice qualitative discussion of many of them is given by Adair (1990). One more comment concerning the "philosophy" of numerical simulations is appropriate here. It is not realistic to expect our model to be accurate in a truly quantitative sense. There are just too many complications. Besides the approximation involved in our parameterization of the drag factor, we must expect that this force will vary somewhat from ball to ball, and that it will also be a function of the humidity and other similar factors. Factors such as these will almost certainly add (or subtract) a few feet or perhaps more to the range. The usefulness of our model is *not* that we can use it to calculate the range of a home run with great precision. Rather, it should give us insight into the relative importance of different effects, and enable us to estimate *changes* in the range as a result of the wind, or other factors. We will have more to say concerning the philosophy of model building in physics during the course of this book. That said, the predictions of our model are certainly consistent with what is observed on the ballfield.

Exercises

1. Construct a program to calculate the trajectory of a baseball, as in Figure 2.7. Use it to investigate the following questions:
   (a) Calculate the range at sea level, with no wind, of a ball hit at 110 mph for different initial angles. Determine to within $1°$ the angle that gives the maximum range.
   (b) Determine the initial angles that give the maximum range for a ball hit at 110 mph into a 25-mph head wind, and with a 25-mph tail wind. What are the maximum ranges in the two cases?
   (c) In all of our calculations we have assumed that the initial velocity is 110 mph, a value typical for a good power hitter. How much does the range depend on this value? Calculate the range for initial velocities of 120 and 100 mph. How does the range scale with the initial kinetic energy of the ball and why?
   (d) Calculate how much a fastball slows down on its way to home plate. Assume a pitch that leaves the pitchers hand at 100 mph and find its speed when it crosses home plate, which is 60.5 ft away.

*2. Consider the effect of a crosswind on the trajectory of a fly ball. How much will a wind of 10 mph directed at right angles to the initial velocity alter the place where one of the fly balls in Figure 2.7 lands?

*3. Calculate the range for the smooth and rough balls described by the drag functions in Figure 2.6.

4. Estimate the initial speed required to hit a home run 550 ft at sea level in the absence of any wind. How far would this ball travel on Pike's Peak?

---

[16] Although the reduced density at altitude will add slightly to the velocity of a fastball.

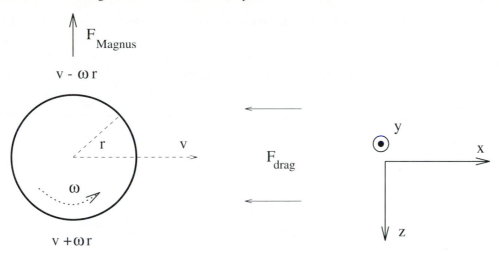

Figure 2.8: Forces acting on a spinning ball. The ball is moving from left to right, and the rotation axis is directed along y, out of the page. The lower edge of the ball has a speed relative to the air of $v + \omega r$, which is larger than that of the the top edge, $v - \omega r$, so the drag force on the bottom part of the ball is larger. This figure corresponds to a sidearm curve ball (see Figure 2.9) as viewed from above. After Adair (1990).

2.4   Throwing a Baseball: The Effects of Spin

To treat the problem of a thrown or pitched ball we must deal with two different effects. One effect is the spin of the ball; this will turn out to dominate the motion of a curve ball. The other effect concerns the difference in the drag coefficients for rough and smooth balls, which we encountered in Figure 2.6, and this will be crucial for the behavior of a knuckleball. We begin with the curve ball.

The origin of the force that makes a spinning ball curve can be appreciated if we recall that the drag force has the form $F_{\mathrm{drag}} \sim v^2$, where v is the speed of the object relative to the air. For a ball spinning about an axis perpendicular to the direction of travel, this speed will be different on opposite edges of the ball, as illustrated in Figure 2.8.

Because of the spin, the lower edge of the ball in Figure 2.8 will have a larger velocity relative to the air than will the upper edge. This will result in a larger drag force on the lower part of the ball than on the top edge. When the forces on the bottom and top parts of the ball are then added, there will be a component of the force in the $-z$ direction (upward in Figure 2.8), perpendicular to the (center of mass) velocity. This is known as the Magnus force and is believed to be the dominant spin-dependent force for objects such as baseballs.[17] We expect this force to be proportional to B_2 in (2.16), but the precise value of the coefficient of proportionality is hard to estimate since it is determined from averaging the appropriate component of the drag force over the curved face of the ball. Rather than trying to perform

---

[17]The Bernoulli effect is sometimes mentioned as the origin of the spin-dependent force on baseballs. See the discussion by Adair (1990) for more on both this and the Magnus force.

this averaging, we will simply observe that the spin-dependent force in this simple geometry will have the functional form[18]

$$F_M = S_0 \, \omega \, v_x \,, \tag{2.24}$$

where ω is the angular speed of the ball and the numerical coefficient S_0 takes care of averaging the drag force over the face of the ball, as just discussed. We will determine the value of S_0 through experimental measurements.[19] Since the drag coefficient of a baseball depends on its speed (see Figure 2.6), we must also expect that S_0 will depend on v. However, for simplicity we will assume that S_0 is a constant in the following. Over the velocity range that is usually of interest to a pitcher, 50–110 mph, we estimate from the data given in Adair (1990) that $S_0/m \approx 4.1 \times 10^{-4}$, where $m = 149$ g is the mass of the ball (note that S_0/m is unitless). The magnitude of the Magnus force (2.24) is about one-third the weight of the ball for a typical curve ball.

To calculate the trajectory of a curve ball, we have to consider motion in three dimensions. We will let x be the axis running from home plate to the pitcher, z be the horizontal direction perpendicular to x, and y be the height above the ground, as in Figure 2.8. The equations of motion for a sidearm curve ball are then

$$\frac{dx}{dt} = v_x \tag{2.25}$$

$$\frac{dv_x}{dt} = -\frac{B_2}{m} v \, v_x$$

$$\frac{dy}{dt} = v_y$$

$$\frac{dv_y}{dt} = -g$$

$$\frac{dz}{dt} = v_z$$

$$\frac{dv_z}{dt} = -\frac{S_0 \, v_x \, \omega}{m} \,.$$

Here we assume that the axis of rotation is parallel to y, that is, perpendicular to the ground. These equations of motion include the effects of atmospheric drag on the largest component of the velocity (v_x), with a velocity dependent coefficient (2.22), but we haven't included it for v_y or v_z, since the forces are much smaller in these cases.

We can again use the Euler method to solve (2.25), and some typical results are shown in Figure 2.9. Here and below we assume that ω is a constant; that is, the ball's rotation rate does not decrease significantly during the course of the pitch. The ball begins on a trajectory that would carry

---

[18] The general vector form is $\vec{F}_M = S_0 \vec{\omega} \times \vec{v}$.

[19] In a sense we have swept all of our ignorance, that is, the complicated problem of averaging F_{drag} over the curved face of the ball, into the constant S_0. By then obtaining S_0 from experiment, you might conclude that we are giving in to the problem, and in a sense we are. However, even in taking this approach it still seems fair to say that we "understand" the physics contained in S_0; it is only that the mathematics required to calculate its value is more complicated than we wish to tackle at this time.

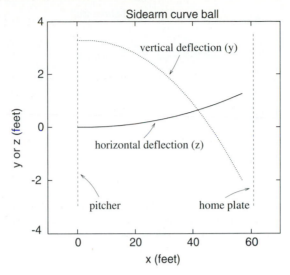

Figure 2.9:   Trajectory of a sidearm curve ball. The pitch traveled from left to right, with the y axis vertical. The z axis is horizontal, and perpendicular to the line between the pitcher and home plate. The solid curve shows the horizontal (z) displacement, which is due to the Magnus force, while the dashed curve shows the vertical (y) displacement, which is due solely to gravity. The ball was thrown with an initial velocity of 70 mph in the x direction, and was spinning at 30 revolutions/s, with $\vec{\omega}$ parallel to the y axis.

it over the center of the plate ($z = 0$), but the Magnus force deflects it by nearly a foot, which would take it well outside. The dotted curve shows how much the pitch falls during its trip to the plate. We have taken the initial velocity to be purely horizontal, and it turns out that the vertical deflection due to gravity is so great that it would cause this pitch to bounce in front of the plate. One conclusion here is that gravity has a significant effect on the trajectory, which in this case is larger than the effect of the spin. The fact that a curve ball is so much harder to hit than a fastball thrown at the same velocity implies that a hitter is able to estimate very rapidly and accurately the deflection due to gravity. This is probably because the trajectories of all fastballs are basically similar.

In Figure 2.10 we show the trajectories of several other pitches. The solid line shows an overhand curve. The axis of rotation is now horizontal, so that the Magnus force is (to a good approximation) vertical. The dotted curve shows the trajectory of a similar pitch, the only difference being this one is *not* spinning, so the deflection due to the Magnus force alone is now evident. The additional break due to the Magnus force is seen to be a little less than 1 ft, which is similar to that found for the sidearm curve ball. Note that we have given these two pitches a small, upward, initial velocity so that unlike the example in Figure 2.9, they cross the plate in or near the strike zone. Also shown as the dot-dashed curve in Figure 2.10 is the trajectory of a 95-mph fastball. This has much less downward deflection due to gravity, since it travels to the plate in about 70 percent of the time taken in the other cases.

We next consider one of most entertaining pitches, the knuckleball. Unlike other pitches, this one is thrown with very little spin. Even so, its trajectory typically exhibits one or two rapid and large displacements in directions perpendicular to the line connecting the pitcher with home plate (the x direction). These displacements are different from pitch to pitch, making it extremely difficult for the

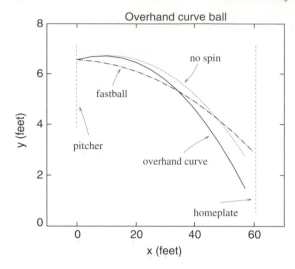

Figure 2.10:   Trajectories of several pitches. The pitches travel from left to right, and for these pitches the deflection of the ball is purely in the vertical (y) direction. The solid curve shows the break of an overhand curve ball ($\vec{\omega}$ is along $-z$), which is due to both gravity and the Magnus force. We have assumed the same velocity and the same angular velocity as with the sidearm curve in Figure 2.9. The dotted curve shows the break due to gravity alone; that is, we have assumed a pitch thrown at the same velocity, but with no spin. The dot-dashed curve shows the trajectory of a 95-mph fastball for comparison.

hitter to judge where to swing in order to make contact with the ball. In fact, the motion is so irregular that even the pitcher cannot predict exactly how the pitch will move or curve.

The origin of the lateral force on a knuckleball can be appreciated from Figure 2.6. Suppose that a moving ball is not spinning at all and is oriented such that a stitch is exposed on one side while the other side is smooth (no stitches exposed). Since the drag force is greater for a smooth ball than for a rough one, there will be an imbalance of forces on the two sides of the ball, giving a net force in the direction of the rough side. It turns out that this force is large enough to make the pitch curve as much or more than a typical curve ball. Now, if the ball rotates just a little as it moves toward home plate, so that the exposed stitch moves to the opposite side of the ball, the lateral force will reverse direction and the ball will then curve in the *opposite* direction. This is a knuckleball.

A curve ball is difficult to throw, since it requires the pitcher to impart a large amount of spin on the ball. At the other extreme, a knuckleball is difficult to throw since it requires the pitcher to impart *very little* spin on the ball. A well-thrown knuckleball might complete only half of a revolution on its way to the plate, so a stitch (i.e., rough surface) will be exposed for a significant amount of time.[20]

This force due to the effective roughness of the ball could in principle be estimated from the drag coefficients in Figure 2.6, but it is clearly preferable to obtain it from specially designed experiments. Fortunately Watts and Sawyer (1975) have performed wind tunnel measurements of this force, and a schematic of their results is shown in Figure 2.11. As anticipated, the lateral force is a function of the

---

[20]If the ball completes too many (several) rotations on the way to the plate, this lateral force will oscillate rapidly in direction, and cancel out the effect.

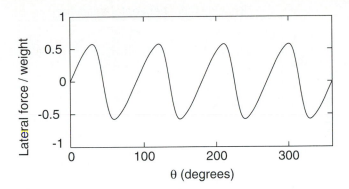

Figure 2.11:   Approximate horizontal force on a baseball traveling without spinning at a speed of 65 mph as a function of the angular orientation of the ball. The angle θ is measured about an axis that is vertical, and perpendicular to the center of mass velocity of the ball, which is horizontal. The four oscillations of the force for each complete revolution of the ball correspond to the four times the stitches pass by an observation point. These results are estimated from the data given by Watts and Sawyer (1975). Here we have expressed the force in terms of the weight of the ball, and scaled it as appropriate for a pitch thrown at 65 mph (the measurements were performed at a lower speed).

angular orientation of the ball. In this case the angle is measured about an axis such that stitches pass by any one point four times for each complete revolution of the ball. Hence there are four maxima and four minima in the lateral force for each revolution ($\Delta\theta = 360°$). The magnitude of this force is approximately one-half the weight of the ball at a speed of 65 mph. Besides the magnitude of the force, the nonsinusoidal shape of the curve is also worth noting (its not a plotting error!). The rapid variation of the force at certain angles no doubt contributes to the apparently irregular trajectory of this pitch. To calculate the trajectory of a knuckleball, we treat it as a projectile moving horizontally with a drag coefficient given by (2.22), and assume that it spins very slowly. We now have to keep track of the angular orientation of the ball, and we do this with the equation of motion $d\theta/dt = \omega$. For simplicity we will assume that the ball spins about a vertical axis so that the deflection due to the force in Figure 2.11 will be purely horizontal. Thus, the rotation angle θ is measured with respect to this vertical axis. This leads to another Euler equation

$$\theta_{i+1} = \theta_i + \omega\,\Delta t\,, \qquad\qquad (2.26)$$

with ω taken as constant during the course of the pitch (but adjustable from one pitch to the next). As the ball travels to home plate, θ varies with time, thereby altering the lateral force. The force in Figure 2.11 is given approximately by the function

$$\frac{F_{\text{lateral}}}{mg} = 0.5\left[\sin(4\theta) - 0.25\sin(8\theta) + 0.08\sin(12\theta) - 0.025\sin(16\theta)\right]. \qquad (2.27)$$

This expression is simply an empirical choice[21] that has a form close to the wind tunnel results of Watts and Sawyer (1975). Putting this all together, the trajectory can now be calculated. Two parameters

---

[21]Our choice of this particular function to describe the data of Watts and Sawyer (1975) was motivated by the form of a Fourier series that has a period of $\pi/2$. For more on this topic see Appendix 2.

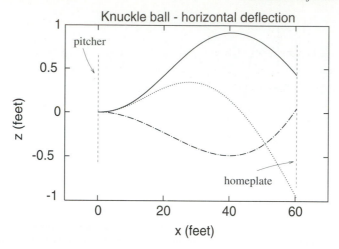

Figure 2.12: Calculated horizontal deflections of several knuckleballs, traveling from left to right. All had a velocity of 65 mph, with an angular velocity of 0.2 revolutions/s (with $\vec{\omega}$ parallel to the vertical direction, y). The different pitches had different initial orientations of the stitches.

control the behavior, the angular velocity of the ball, ω in (2.26), and its initial angular orientation. Some typical trajectories calculated for $\omega = 0.2$ rev/s are shown in Figure 2.12, where we have considered three different initial orientations. Our model reproduces the expected behavior very well. Typical deflections are a foot or more and are comparable to or even larger than those found for curve balls. The multiple deflections in the trajectory make it no surprise that catchers do not enjoy trying to stay in front of these pitches. The trajectories become more complicated if the rotation rate is increased, but the deflections are smaller since the direction of lateral force then varies more rapidly.

Exercises

1. Investigate the trajectories of knuckleballs as a function of the angular velocity ω, the initial angular orientation, and the (center of mass) velocity.

2. Calculate the effect of backspin on a fastball. How much does an angular velocity of 1000 rpm (typical for a fastball) affect the trajectory?

3. Model the effect of backspin on the range of a batted ball. Assume an angular velocity of 2000 rpm.

4. Calculate the effect of the knuckleball force on a batted ball. Assume that the ball is a line drive hit at an initial speed of 90 mph and an angle of 20° and that the ball does not spin at all (clearly a gross assumption). Let the rough side of the ball always face one side, which is perpendicular to the direction the ball is hit, and use Figure 2.11 to estimate the magnitude of the lateral force. With all of these assumptions, calculate the lateral deflection of the ball. Such balls hit with very little spin are observed by outfielders to effectively "flutter" from side to side as they move through the air.

*5. Calculate the trajectory of a batted ball hit with side spin. That is, let the rotation axis be vertical, corresponding to a ball that is hit so that it "hooks" or "slices." This is commonly encountered in a ball hit near one of the foul lines. Calculate how much a spin angular velocity of 2000 rpm would cause a line drive to curve. Is this consistent with your experiences? If not, calculate what angular velocity would be required.

**6. Estimate the value of S_0 in (2.24) by averaging F_{drag} as given in Figure 2.6 over the face of the ball. Don't be afraid to make some approximations, such as assuming that one side of the ball is completely rough while the other is smooth, in the sense of Figure 2.6. You might also want to perform your averaging numerically, using the integration methods discussed in Chapters 5 and 7.

*7. Estimate the velocity dependence of S_0 from the data given in Adair (1990). Use your results to calculate what effect this has on the trajectory of a typical curve ball.

2.5   Golf

We conclude this chapter with a treatment of the motion of a golf ball. While all of the ingredients we will need for our simulations have already been touched on in our discussions of cannon shells and baseballs, there are still some interesting lessons to be learned.

We again use a coordinate system in which y is the height of the ball above the ground, x is the horizontal direction in the same plane as the ball's initial velocity, and with z horizontal and perpendicular to the velocity. The equations of motion for the golf ball are then

$$\frac{dv_x}{dt} = -\frac{F_{drag,x}}{m} - \frac{S_0\,\omega\,v_y}{m} \tag{2.28}$$

$$\frac{dv_y}{dt} = -\frac{F_{drag,y}}{m} + \frac{S_0\,\omega\,v_x}{m} - g \,,$$

with the usual equations for dx/dt and dy/dt. Here we have assumed that the ball is hit with backspin with an angular velocity of ω, so that the spin axis is along z and thus perpendicular to both x and y. We have encountered all of these variables before, including the atmospheric drag, F_{drag}, and the Magnus force, which is proportional to the product of ω and the velocity. The magnitudes of these forces have been estimated from measurements with real golf balls. The drag force is given by an expression of the form (2.9), and it turns out that the drag coefficient C varies with velocity in a manner that is qualitatively similar to what we observed for a baseball in Figure 2.6. At low speeds $C \approx \frac{1}{2}$, but this coefficient drops sharply with increasing speed, with C measured to be $\approx 7.0/v$ (with v in m/s) at high speeds (see Erlichson [1983]). We will include the behavior in these two limits in our modeling by assuming that

$$F_{drag} = -C\,\rho\,A\,v^2 \,, \tag{2.29}$$

with $C = \frac{1}{2}$ for speeds up to $v = 14$ m/s, and $C = 7.0/v$ at higher velocities. Our drag force will thus be a continuous function of v, although it will have a discontinuous derivative (dF_{drag}/dv) at $v = 14$ m/s. This behavior is qualitatively similar to that of a baseball, but the transition to a reduced drag coefficient, that is, to turbulent flow, occurs at a much smaller velocity.

A golf ball is hit with a significant amount of backspin, and the associated Magnus force gives a large upward (vertical) force. In fact, the initial Magnus force can actually be larger than the force of gravity. This is apparent to any (physics) student of golf, since the initial trajectory of a well-hit drive has upward curvature. Using the measurements discussed by Erlichson, we estimate $S_0\omega/m \approx 0.25 \text{ s}^{-1}$ for a typical case. It is believed to be a good approximation to assume that ω does not change significantly over the course of the trajectory. In our simulations we will assume that $\vec{\omega}$ is constant (in both magnitude and direction), so the Magnus force then varies only as $\vec{v}$ changes.

The equations of motion (2.28) can (yet again) be solved with the Euler method. The programming is similar to what we have encountered previously in this chapter, so we will leave it to the exercises. Some results are shown in Figure 2.13, where we have assumed an initial velocity of 70 m/s (about 230 feet/s), which is a typical value for an average player. The maximum range is approximately 215 m (approximately 235 yards), in reasonable accord with our expectations, so the model seems to capture the essential physics. It turns out that the maximum range occurs with an initial angle of only 9°, much reduced from the 45° that would be found for a simple projectile in a vacuum. This shows the importance of the Magnus force.

We also consider several hypothetical cases in Figure 2.13. If we increase the spin on the ball by 50 percent, as might occur with an iron shot, for example, the trajectory is much higher even for our 9° initial angle, although for the parameters considered here the range is almost unchanged. If we put no spin on the ball, the range drops dramatically to about 112 m, again assuming an initial angle of 9°. Thus, as any golfer knows, the spin is indeed extremely important.

It is especially interesting to consider the case of a smooth ball, that is, a ball *without* dimples. This can be modeled with a constant drag coefficient, $C = \frac{1}{2}$, independent of the speed.[22] This case has the shortest range of all, only about 94 m. (Note: We have still assumed that the ball is spinning, with the same Magnus force, the same value of S_0, as above.) Now we can understand why a golf ball has dimples. They cause the transition to turbulent flow to occur at very low velocities, with a corresponding drop in the drag coefficient. This, in turn, allows a golf ball to be hit much farther than would otherwise be possible (thereby inflating the ego of the golfer). While it is probably too late to change such a familiar aspect of the game, the use of a smooth ball would have some advantages. For example, golf courses could be made much smaller and the players wouldn't have to walk as far.

Exercises

1. Model the behavior of a ping-pong ball. The drag force can be estimated from (2.9) with $C = \frac{1}{2}$ (since the ball is smooth). The Magnus acceleration of a ping-pong ball is $\approx S_0 \, \vec{\omega} \times \vec{v}/m$, where $S_0/m = 0.040$ (in SI units, with ω in rad/s and v in m/s; see the discussion in Bennett [1976]). Assume $v = 3$ m/s, and angular velocities in the range 1–10 revolutions per second (better yet, try to measure ω in your own experiment).

2. Calculate the trajectory for a hooking or slicing golf ball by giving the ball sidespin, with the same angular velocity used in the calculations in Figure 2.13.

3. Investigate the trajectory of the topspin lob in tennis. Topspin is also important for ground strokes and serves. See Štěpánek (1988) for a discussion of the relevant parameters.

---

[22]This amounts to assuming that the transition to turbulent flow occurs at a velocity above that used in our calculation, 70 m/s. As with baseballs, we would expect that even for a smooth ball there must eventually be a transition to turbulent flow, but we do not know of any accurate studies of where this transition occurs. Thus, our modeling of a "smooth" golf ball is less quantitative than our simulations for a ball with dimples. Even so, these uncertainties do not affect our main conclusion, which is that the dimples substantially increase the range of the ball.

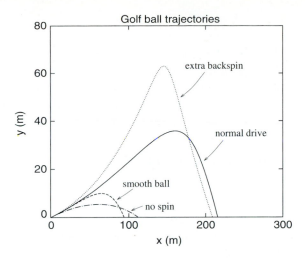

Figure 2.13: Several calculated trajectories of golf balls. In all cases the initial velocity was 70 m/s, at an angle 9° from the horizontal. Solid curve: result for a normal drive (the calculation includes the effect of air resistance and backspin); dotted curve: same as a normal drive, but with 50 percent more backspin to provide more lift; dot-dashed curve: without any backspin; dashed curve: normal amount of backspin, but for a smooth ball.

4. Calculate the effects of air drag, wind, or spin (or all three) for your favorite sports projectile. De Mestre (1990) gives a handy table of the relevant parameters for a wide variety of objects.

References

ADAIR, R. K. 1990. *The Physics of Baseball*. New York: Harper and Row, and also *Physics Today* May 1995, p. 26. For the arm-chair physicist baseball fan.

ARMENTI, A., JR. 1992. *The Physics of Sports*. New York: American Institute of Physics. A useful collection of articles on a wide variety of sports.

BENNETT, W. R., JR. 1976. *Scientific and Engineering Problem-Solving with the Computer.* Englewood Cliffs: Prentice-Hall. An entertaining discussion of trajectories in a windy environment plus more.

DE MESTRE, N. 1990. *The Mathematics of Projectiles in Sport.* Cambridge: Cambridge University Press.

ERLICHSON, H. 1983. "Maximum Projectile Range with Drag and Lift, with Particular Application to Golf." *Am. J. of Phys.* **51**, 357. Essential numbers for the drag and Magnus forces on a golf ball. Although his interpretation is a bit different than ours, the results are the same.

ŠTĚPÁNEK, A. 1988. "The Aerodynamics of Tennis Balls—the Topspin Lob." *Am. J. of Phys.* **56**, 138. A scholarly look at one of my favorite games.

WATTS, R. G. and E. SAWYER. 1975. "Aerodynamics of a Knuckleball." *Am. J. of Phys.* **43**, 960. Very useful wind tunnel results for the forces on a knuckleball.

3

Oscillatory Motion and Chaos

Examples of oscillatory phenomena can be found in many areas of physics, including the motion of electrons in atoms, the behavior of currents and voltages in electronic circuits, and planetary orbits. Perhaps the simplest mechanical system that exhibits such motion is a pendulum, consisting of a mass that is connected by a string to some sort of support so that it is able to swing freely in response to the force of gravity. In the idealized case, ignoring friction and assuming that the angle the string makes with the vertical is small, such a pendulum undergoes what is known as simple harmonic motion. The main features of this motion are common to many types of oscillating systems, making it a paradigm in elementary physics textbooks. However, elementary-level treatments usually do not consider the behavior of a *real* pendulum, that is, a pendulum that has some friction and is allowed to swing to large angles. The motion of such a pendulum exhibits many features not found in the simple harmonic case. Perhaps the most important of these features is the possibility of chaotic behavior, which is the central topic of this chapter.

In the next several sections we will explore some of the interesting effects that occur in real oscillatory systems. We begin with a simple pendulum and consider how to treat simple harmonic motion numerically. We then generalize our pendulum model to include the effects of friction and nonlinearities and find that they give rise to the possibility of chaotic behavior. While the term chaos probably has some intuitive meaning for all of us, it is not easy to give a precise definition of this notion (especially one that would make a physicist or a mathematician happy). We will, therefore, spend some time in formulating such a definition, and this will lead us to consider several key issues. The remainder of the chapter is devoted to the study of a variety of other systems that exhibit chaotic behavior.

3.1 Simple Harmonic Motion

One example of a simple pendulum is a particle of mass m connected by a massless string to a rigid support. We let θ be the angle that the string makes with the vertical and assume that the string is

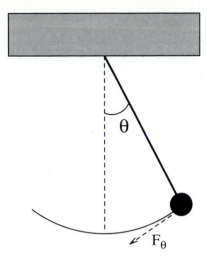

Figure 3.1:   A simple pendulum, consisting of a mass connected by a string to a fixed point on a support, such as a ceiling.

always taut, as in Figure 3.1. We also assume that there are only two forces acting on the particle, gravity and the tension of the string. It is convenient to consider the components of these forces parallel and perpendicular to the string. The parallel forces add to zero, since we assume that the string doesn't stretch or break, while the force perpendicular to the string is given by

$$F_\theta = -m\,g\,\sin\theta\,, \tag{3.1}$$

where g is the acceleration due to gravity, and the minus sign reminds us that the force is always opposite to the displacement from the vertical, where $\theta = 0$.

Newton's second law tells us that this force is equal to the mass times the acceleration of the particle along the circular arc that is the particle's trajectory, that is, $F_\theta = md^2s/dt^2$. The displacement along this arc is $s = \ell\,\theta$, where ℓ is the length of the string. If we now assume that θ is always small so that $\sin\theta \approx \theta$, we obtain the (probably familiar) equation of motion

$$\frac{d^2\theta}{dt^2} = -\frac{g}{\ell}\,\theta\,. \tag{3.2}$$

This is the central equation of simple harmonic motion. It is easy to verify that it has the general solution

$$\theta = \theta_0\,\sin(\Omega\,t + \phi)\,, \tag{3.3}$$

where $\Omega = \sqrt{g/\ell}$, and θ_0 and ϕ are constants that depend on the initial displacement and velocity of the pendulum. We see that the motion of a simple pendulum is indeed very simple. The oscillations are sinusoidal with time and continue forever without decaying, which is not surprising since there is no friction in the model. The oscillations have an angular frequency, Ω, which is a function of the length of the string (and g, of course), but is independent of m and the amplitude of the motion.

We now consider a numerical approach to this problem. You might wonder why this is necessary, since the analytic solution is already in hand. However, this is just a warm-up exercise, as we will soon be turning our attention to slightly more complicated oscillatory problems for which exact results are not available. Our basic equation of motion is the second-order differential equation (3.2), which we want to solve for θ as a function of t. It is convenient to rewrite this as two first-order differential equations

$$\frac{d\omega}{dt} = -\frac{g}{\ell}\theta \, , \tag{3.4}$$

$$\frac{d\theta}{dt} = \omega \, ,$$

where ω is the angular velocity of the pendulum. This should look familiar, as we took a very similar approach in the projectile problems in Chapter 2. There we used the Euler method to solve a similar set of equations, so let us consider the same algorithm here. We convert (3.4) into difference equations, using a time step Δt so that time is discretized with $t = i\Delta t$, where i is an integer. Letting θ_i and ω_i be the angular displacement and velocity of the pendulum at time step i, the equations in (3.4) become the difference equations

$$\omega_{i+1} = \omega_i - \frac{g}{\ell}\theta_i \, \Delta t \, , \tag{3.5}$$

$$\theta_{i+1} = \theta_i + \omega_i \, \Delta t \, .$$

These are closely analogous to the difference equations we obtained when using the Euler method in Chapters 1 and 2. As in those problems, we use the values of θ and ω at time step i to estimate the values at step $i + 1$, then repeat the process for steps $i + 2, i + 3, \ldots$.

In constructing a program to implement this approach, we use arrays to hold the values of θ, ω, and t. A partial program listing is given here (a complete listing is in Appendix 4), where we show the main program and the `calculate` subroutine that employs the Euler algorithm.

```
! motion of a simple pendulum    N. Giordano    10-1-94
! theta() = pendulum angle    omega() = pendulum angular velocity t() = time
! length = length of string     dt = time step
program pendulum
    option nolet
    library "sgfunc*","sglib*"
    dim theta(1000), omega(1000), t(1000)
    call initialize(theta,omega,t,length,dt)
    call calculate(theta,omega,t,length,dt)
    call display(theta,omega,t,length,dt)
end
! initialize variables
! theta() = pendulum angle    omega() = pendulum angular velocity
sub initialize(theta(),omega(),t(),length,dt)
    input prompt "initial pendulum angle (in radians) -> ": theta(1)
    input prompt "initial angular velocity of pendulum (in radians/s) -> ": omega(1)
    t(1) = 0
    input prompt "length of pendulum (in m) -> ": length
    input prompt "time step -> ": dt
end sub
```

```
! use the Euler method
sub calculate(theta(),omega(),t(),length,dt)
    i = 0
    g = 9.8
    period = 2 * pi / sqr(g/length)     ! period of pendulum
    do
        i = i + 1
        t(i+1) = t(i) + dt
        omega(i+1) = omega(i) - (g/length) * theta(i) * dt   ! Euler method
        theta(i+1) = theta(i) + omega(i) * dt
    loop until t(i+1) >= 5 * period     ! follow the oscillations for 5 periods
    mat redim omega(i+1),theta(i+1),t(i+1)
end sub
```

Here the general program structure is the same as the structure we have employed in previous problems. After declaring the arrays that will hold the calculated values of θ, ω, and t, we use one subroutine to initialize our variables, a second subroutine (`calculate`) to do the calculation, and a third one to display the results. Again, we choose descriptive variable names, making it easy to translate the physics (3.5) directly into program statements. We carry out the calculation for times up to 5 times the period of the pendulum, although that value could be changed to suit your taste.

Some results from program `pendulum` are shown in Figure 3.2. The behavior we see there is very peculiar; while the motion is basically oscillatory, the amplitude of the oscillations *grows* with time. This is contrary to the exact solution, (3.3), and should also be at odds with your intuition. Since the model does not contain any source of energy nor does it include any friction, the total energy of the pendulum should remain constant. However, our program doesn't seem to appreciate this fact!

It turns out that the difficulty lies with our use of the Euler method. As was emphasized when we first introduced this method in Chapter 1, it provides us with an approximate estimate of the solution to our differential equation, (3.2). Again, the emphasis is on the word *approximate*. We have not performed an explicit analysis of the errors involved in this approximation, but we do know that the errors involved in using the Euler method become smaller as the time step is made smaller. You might, therefore, think that the erroneous behavior seen in Figure 3.2 could be corrected by simply using a smaller value of Δt in our program. Reducing Δt will indeed make the errors smaller, but it turns out that the energy of the pendulum will increase with time for *any* nonzero value of Δt.

At this point you might sense a contradiction. If the errors get smaller when Δt is reduced, how can the calculated behavior be defective for all values of Δt? The results in Figure 3.2 show that for our Euler solution both the amplitude of the oscillations and the total energy increase with time. If the calculation were repeated with a smaller value of Δt (a job we will leave for the exercises), the *rate* of this increase would be smaller. However, for all nonzero values of Δt we would find that the energy increases with time, and hence the Euler solution is, in that sense, always incorrect.

This is our first encounter with a numerical method that is inherently unstable. But if this method is unstable, how did we manage to get away with using it for the problems in Chapters 1 and 2? The answer to this is that a method can only be termed "suitable" or "unsuitable" (i.e., "good" or "not good") in the context of a particular problem. In the problems treated in Chapters 1 and 2 the Euler method also yielded (in most cases) solutions that did not quite conserve energy.[1] However, in those situations

---

[1] A notable exception was the constant acceleration problem considered in Chapter 1, for which the Euler method gives the exact solution.

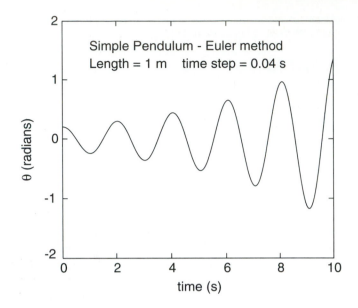

Figure 3.2: θ as a function of time for our simple pendulum, calculated using the Euler method with program pendulum. Here, and in most of the other figures in this chapter, we have connected the calculated values with solid lines.

the errors were negligible on the scales relevant for those particular problems. In contrast, for problems involving oscillatory motion we often want to consider the behavior for many periods of oscillation. In order to be useful in such cases, a numerical method must conserve energy over the long haul.[2] The Euler method is not a good choice for these types of problems.

We are thus led to consider other methods for solving ordinary differential equations of this type. This is such an important class of problems that we devote Appendix 1 to a discussion of several different numerical approaches, including the Runge-Kutta and Verlet methods. While those work well in dealing with the oscillatory problems encountered in this chapter, it turns out that a simple modification of the Euler method yields an algorithm that is also quite suitable. This modification yields what is known as the Euler-Cromer method, as Cromer was the first to carefully discuss the algorithm and show why it works. To appreciate the Euler-Cromer method, we reconsider our pendulum program. Given below is a *modified* version of the calculate subroutine.

---

[2]More precisely, the numerical algorithm must *itself* not contribute or remove energy from the system.

```
! use the Euler-Cromer method
sub calculate(theta(),omega(),t(),length,dt)
    i = 0
    g = 9.8
    period = 2 * pi / sqr(g/length)
    do
        i = i + 1
        omega(i+1) = omega(i) - (g/length) * theta(i) * dt
        theta(i+1) = theta(i) + omega(i+1) * dt
!                       this change    ^^   makes it the Euler-Cromer method
        t(i+1) = t(i) + dt
    loop until t(i+1) >= 5 * period
    mat redim omega(i+1),theta(i+1),t(i+1)
end sub
```

The only change in the subroutine is emphasized by the new comment statement and can be appreciated as follows. With the Euler method, the *previous* value of ω and the *previous* value of θ are used to calculate the new values of both ω and θ. However, with the Euler-Cromer method, the *previous* values of ω and θ are used to calculate the new value of ω, but the *new* value of ω is used to calculate the new value of θ. This is such a minor change in the algorithm that you are probably surprised that it makes any difference. Indeed, for many problems it makes no significant difference. However, for problems involving oscillatory motion the Euler-Cromer method conserves energy *exactly* over each complete period of the motion and thus avoids the difficulties we found in Figure 3.2. Figure 3.3 shows a stable oscillation obtained with the Euler-Cromer algorithm (the parameters used here were the *same* as those used in the calculation shown in Figure 3.2). This numerical solution is very stable; these calculated oscillations would persist until our patience runs out. There are other numerical methods besides the

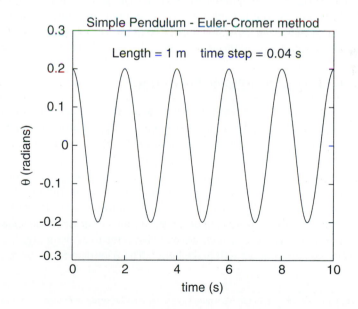

Figure 3.3: θ as a function of time for a simple pendulum calculated using the Euler-Cromer method.

Euler-Cromer algorithm that yield accurate solutions for oscillatory problems. Appendix 1 contains a description and discussion of the advantages and disadvantages of two other methods.

Exercises

1. Investigate the stability of the Euler-Cromer method. Modify our program so that it also calculates the total energy, kinetic plus potential, of the pendulum as a function of time. Show that the energy is conserved over each complete cycle of the motion.

2. Repeat the previous problem using the Runge-Kutta method described in Appendix 1. Compare the accuracy of the Runge-Kutta method with that of the Euler-Cromer algorithm using the same time step.

3. Use the Euler method to simulate the motion of a pendulum as in Figure 3.2. Study the behavior as a function of the step size, Δt, and show that the total energy always increases with time.

*4. For simple harmonic motion, the general form for the equation of motion is

$$\frac{d^2x}{dt^2} = -k\,x^{\alpha}\,, \tag{3.6}$$

with $\alpha = 1$. This has the same form as (3.2), although the variables have different names. Begin by writing a program that uses the Euler-Cromer method to solve for x as a function of time according to (3.6), with $\alpha = 1$ (for convenience you can take $k = 1$). The program we developed in this section can be modified to accomplish this. Show that the period of the oscillations is independent of the amplitude of the motion. This is a key feature of simple harmonic motion. Then extend your program to treat the case $\alpha = 3$. This is an example of an *anharmonic* oscillator. Calculate the period of the oscillations for several different amplitudes (amplitudes in the range 0.2 to 1 are good choices), and show that the period of the motion now depends on the amplitude. Give an intuitive argument to explain why the period becomes longer as the amplitude is decreased.

3.2   Chaos in the Driven Nonlinear Pendulum

Now that we have a numerical method that is suitable for the simple pendulum problem, we are ready to take on a slightly more complicated and also more interesting situation. In deriving (3.2) we made several simplifications. First, we assumed that the amplitude of the oscillation would always be small, which allowed us to expand the $\sin\theta$ term in (3.1). In this section we will not make this assumption; this will enable us to treat situations in which the mass swings to large angles or even all the way around the pivot point of the pendulum.[3] Second, we will include the effect of friction. The manner in which friction enters the equations of motion depends on the origin of the friction. Possible sources of friction include the effective bearing, where the string of the pendulum connects to the support, air resistance, etc. In many cases the frictional force, which we will also refer to as damping, is proportional to the velocity, and that is the assumption we will make here.[4] The frictional force we will employ thus has

---

[3]To allow such motion in a real pendulum we would have to replace the string in Figure 3.1 with a rigid rod.

[4]Note, however, that other functional forms are possible. For example, in the case of air resistance, we noted in Chapter 2 that while the drag from air resistance is proportional to v for very small velocities, it varies as v^2 in many cases of practical interest. We will leave the investigation of the behavior with other forms for F_{friction} to the inquisitive reader.

the form $-q(d\theta/dt)$, since the velocity of the pendulum is $\ell(d\theta/dt)$. Here q is a parameter that is a measure of the strength of the damping, and the minus sign guarantees that this force will always oppose the motion of the pendulum. A third ingredient we wish to add to our model is a driving force; that is, an external force acting on the pendulum. The form of this force will depend on how the force is applied. A convenient choice is to assume that the driving force is sinusoidal with time with amplitude F_D and angular frequency Ω_D (which is not to be confused with the natural frequency of the simple pendulum, Ω). This might arise, for example, if the pendulum mass has an electric charge and we apply an oscillating electric field. Putting all of these ingredients together, we have the equation of motion[5]

$$\frac{d^2\theta}{dt^2} = -\frac{g}{\ell}\sin(\theta) - q\frac{d\theta}{dt} + F_D\sin(\Omega_D t). \tag{3.7}$$

Our model for a nonlinear, damped, driven pendulum, (3.7), contains some very rich and interesting behavior. We will only be able to touch on a few of its intriguing properties here, although you can explore others through the exercises. Let us begin by examining the behavior of θ as a function of time for several typical cases. First we must construct a program to calculate a numerical solution, since there is no known exact solution to (3.7). Our program is similar in form to the one we used to study the simple pendulum. The only major difference is that we must use a slightly more complicated equation for ω. We again rewrite (3.7) as two first-order differential equations and obtain

$$\frac{d\omega}{dt} = -\frac{g}{\ell}\sin(\theta) - q\frac{d\theta}{dt} + F_D\sin(\Omega_D t), \tag{3.8}$$

$$\frac{d\theta}{dt} = \omega.$$

These can be converted into difference equations for θ_i and ω_i at time step i, as we did in (3.5). These difference equations can then be translated into a program. The complete listing is given in Appendix 4; below we give only the subroutine that does the work of calculating θ and ω.

```
! use the Euler-Cromer method for a damped, nonlinear, driven pendulum
sub calculate(theta(),omega(),t(),length,dt,q,drive_force,drive_frequency)
   i = 0
   g = 9.8
   period = 2 * pi / sqr(g/length)   ! period of the corresponding simple
   do                                ! pendulum
      i = i + 1
      t(i+1) = t(i) + dt                  ! use the Euler-Cromer method
      omega(i+1) = omega(i) - (g/length) * sin(theta(i)) * dt
         - q * omega(i) * dt + drive_force * sin(drive_frequency * t(i)) * dt
      theta(i+1) = theta(i) + omega(i+1) * dt
      if theta(i+1) > pi then theta(i+1) = theta(i+1) - 2 * pi ! keep theta in
      if theta(i+1) < -pi then theta(i+1) = theta(i+1) + 2 * pi! range -pi to pi
   loop until t(i+1) >= 10 * period
   mat redim omega(i+1),theta(i+1),t(i+1)
end sub
```

---

[5]Note that, strictly speaking, the parameter F_D in (3.7) is not the actual force since other factors of m and l also enter. However, F_D is proportional to the driving force, so when we speak of larger drive forces this will mean larger values of F_D, etc.

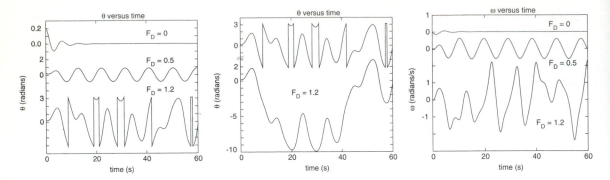

Figure 3.4: Left: behavior of θ as a function of time for our driven, damped, nonlinear pendulum, for several different values of the driving force. The vertical "jumps" in θ occur when the angle is reset so as to keep it in the range $-\pi$ to $+\pi$; they do not correspond to discontinuities in $\theta(t)$. Center: behavior of $\theta(t)$ for $F_D = 1.2$ with and without these "resets." Right: corresponding behavior of the angular velocity of the pendulum, ω. The parameters for the calculation were $q = 1/2$, $\ell = g = 9.8$, $\Omega_D = 2/3$, and $dt = 0.04$, all in SI. The initial conditions were $\theta(0) = 0.2$ and $\omega(0) = 0$.

This subroutine is organized much like the `calculate` routine for our simple pendulum program, but there are several differences of note. First, the equation for `omega(i+1)` is more complicated since we have a different equation of motion. Second, we have two `if` statements that keep an eye on the value of `theta(i+1)`. Recall that our pendulum can now swing all the way around its pivot point, which corresponds to $|\theta| > \pi$. Since θ is an angular variable, values of θ that differ by 2π correspond to the *same* position of the pendulum. For plotting purposes it is convenient to keep θ in the range $-\pi$ to π, and that is accomplished with the two `if` statements. If θ becomes less than $-\pi$, then its value is increased by 2π; likewise, if it becomes greater than $+\pi$, its value is decreased by 2π. This procedure keeps $-\pi \leq \theta \leq +\pi$, which will be handy although not absolutely necessary in some of our analyses. Finally, note that we again use the Euler-Cromer method.

Some typical results for θ and ω as functions of time, as calculated with our program, are shown in Figure 3.4 where we plot the behavior for several different values of the driving force, with all of the other parameters held fixed. With a driving force of zero the motion is damped and the pendulum comes to rest after only a few oscillations. These damped oscillations have a frequency close to the natural frequency of the undamped pendulum, Ω, and are a vestige of simple harmonic motion. With a small driving force, $F_D = 0.5$, we find two regimes. The first few oscillations are affected by the decay of an initial transient as in the case of no driving force. That is, the initial displacement of the pendulum leads to a component of the motion that decays with time and has an angular frequency of $\sim \Omega$. After this transient is damped away, the pendulum settles into a steady oscillation in response to the driving force. The pendulum then moves at the driving frequency, Ω_D, *not* at its natural frequency, with an amplitude determined by a balance between the energy added by the driving force and the energy dissipated by the damping. In a sense, the motion of the pendulum can be viewed as an interplay of the two frequencies Ω and Ω_D, the natural frequency of the pendulum and the frequency of the driving force.

The behavior changes radically when the driving force is increased to $F_D = 1.2$. Now the motion is no longer simple, even at long times. The vertical jumps in θ are due to our resetting of the angle to keep it in the range $-\pi$ to π and thus correspond to the pendulum swinging "over the top." To make this clear, the center plot in Figure 3.4 shows $\theta(t)$ for $F_D = 1.2$, with and without this resetting of the angle. We see that the pendulum does not settle into any sort of repeating steady-state behavior, at least in the range shown here. We might suspect that we have not waited long enough for the transients to decay and that a steady oscillation might be found if we simply waited a little longer. This is not the case; for this value of the driving force the behavior *never* repeats. This is an example of *chaotic* behavior, which will be our main concern for the rest of this chapter.

It is important to appreciate the behavior illustrated in Figure 3.4. At low drive the motion is a simple oscillation (after the transients have decayed), which would, if we were sufficiently patient, repeat forever. On the other hand, at high drive the motion is chaotic; it is a very complicated nonrepeating function of time. But what does it really mean to be chaotic? Your intuition probably tells you that chaotic behavior is random and unpredictable, and the behavior of our pendulum at high drive certainly has that appearance. However, if the behavior is truly unpredictable, then how was our program able to calculate it? This conundrum can be put another way when we realize that the behavior of our pendulum is described by the differential equation (3.7). From the theory of such equations we know that once the initial conditions (at $t = 0$, for example) are specified, the solution for θ is then *completely determined* for all future times. Indeed, we took this for granted in constructing our program. But how can the behavior be both deterministic and unpredictable at the same time?

We are thus faced with an apparent contradiction between analytic theory (the theory of differential equations) and numerical calculations (our program). Since our only evidence, so far, that the pendulum can be chaotic is from our numerical results, we might be tempted to suspect that we have made some sort of programming error, or that we have somehow misinterpreted the meaning of the numerical results. For example, we could imagine that if we waited long enough, a (predictable) pattern might emerge even at high drive, including at $F_D = 1.2$ in Figure 3.4. Indeed, how could such behavior ever be ruled out? Rather than pursue the question in this way, let us raise another possibility; namely, that the behavior is deterministic *and* unpredictable at the same time! This may seem to be impossible, but we will now show how to reconcile these two, apparently contradictory notions.

Let us consider the stability of the solutions to our pendulum equation of motion. We imagine that we have two *identical* pendulums, with exactly the same lengths and damping factors. We set them in motion at the same time with the same driving forces. The only difference is that we start them with *slightly* different initial angles. We thus must calculate the angular positions of two pendulums, θ_1 and θ_2, and we can do this using a program very similar to the one described above (an exercise we will leave to the reader). Some results for $\Delta\theta \equiv |\theta_1 - \theta_2|$ are shown in Figure 3.5 for two different values of the drive amplitude. The smaller value of F_D is the one for which we found simple oscillatory motion in Figure 3.4. To understand these results we first call your attention to the very sharp dips that occur approximately every 3 s. These dips in $\Delta\theta$ occur when one of the pendulums reaches a turning point. $\Delta\theta$ will vanish near each turning point since the trajectories $\theta_1(t)$ and $\theta_2(t)$ must then cross. It is more useful to focus on the plateau regions away from these dips in Figure 3.5. These plateau values of $\Delta\theta$ exhibit a steady and fairly rapid decrease with t. This means that the motion of the two pendulums becomes more and more similar, since the difference in the two angles approaches zero as the motion proceeds. (Indeed, this angular difference decreased by *six orders of magnitude* after about a dozen oscillations.) This in turn means that the motion is *predictable*. If, for some reason, we did not know the initial conditions of one of the pendulums, we could still predict its future motion since our results show that $\theta(t)$ converges to a particular solution (that of the other pendulum). This is what our intuition tells us to expect for predictable, nonchaotic motion.

In contrast, for the larger value of F_D we find that $\Delta\theta$ increases rapidly and irregularly with t; this trend is indicated by the dashed line on the right in Figure 3.5. This is usually described by saying that

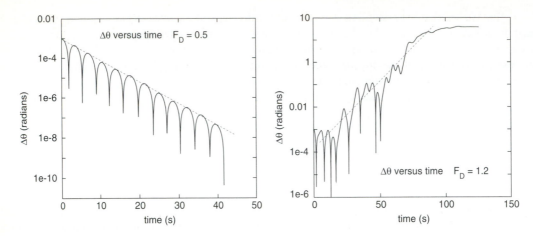

Figure 3.5: Results for $\Delta\theta$ from our comparision of two identical pendulums. The parameters were the same as in Figure 3.4. The initial values of θ for the two pendulums differed by 0.001 rad. On the left are results for low drive, while the results on the right were obtained from the chaotic regime. The dashed lines indicate the overall trends, that is, that $\Delta\theta$ decreases approximately exponentially for low drive, and increases roughly exponentially at high drive.

the two trajectories, $\theta_1(t)$ and $\theta_2(t)$, *diverge* from one another. Note that this divergence is extremely rapid at short times ($t < 75$ in Figure 3.5). $\Delta\theta$ saturates (i.e., stops changing) at long time periods, but this is only because it has reached a value of order 2π and simply can't get any larger! We have used a logarithmic scale in Figure 3.5, so the increase of $\Delta\theta$ with time is *very* rapid. The irregular variation of $\Delta\theta$ cannot be described by any simple function. However, if we were to repeat this calculation for a range of different initial values of θ_1 (keeping $\Delta\theta(0)$ fixed) and average the results, we would find a much smoother behavior, such as the dashed line in Figure 3.5. This line corresponds to the relation $\log(\Delta\theta) \sim \lambda t$, which implies

$$\Delta\theta \approx e^{\lambda t} . \tag{3.9}$$

It turns out that this functional form for $\Delta\theta$ is very common and the parameter λ is known as a Lyapunov exponent.[6]

For our pendulum the numerical results show that λ is positive at high drive, which means that two pendulums that start with nearly, but not exactly, the same initial conditions will follow trajectories that diverge exponentially fast.[7] Since we can never hope to know the initial conditions or any of the other pendulum parameters exactly, this means that the behavior at $F_D = 1.2$ is for all practical purposes unpredictable. Our system is thus both deterministic and unpredictable. Put another way, a system can obey certain deterministic laws of physics, but still exhibit behavior that is unpredictable due to an extreme sensitivity to initial conditions. *This* is what it means to be chaotic. One more point should

---

[6]In general, systems such as a pendulum possess several different Lyapunov exponents. In order to be chaotic, at least one of these exponents must be positive. The accurate extraction of the values of the Lyapunov exponents from results such as those computed in this section is a somewhat complicated procedure. For one approach to this extraction see Wolf et al. (1985).

[7]Similar results would be found if the two pendulums had slightly different lengths or driving forces, or if any other of the parameters were different.

be noted from Figure 3.5. The behavior of $\Delta\theta$ can be described by a Lyapunov exponent in both the chaotic and nonchaotic regimes. In the former case $\lambda > 0$, while in the latter, $\lambda < 0$. The transition to chaos thus occurs when $\lambda = 0$.

Now that we have seen how $\theta(t)$ for our pendulum can be unpredictable, you might give up all hope of developing a useful theoretical description of the chaotic regime. However, it turns out that this view is too pessimistic. It is possible to make certain accurate predictions concerning θ, even in the chaotic regime! To demonstrate this we need to consider the trajectory in a different way. Instead of plotting θ as a function of t, let us plot the angular velocity ω as a function of θ. This is sometimes referred to as a *phase-space* plot. Since we have already constructed a program to calculate θ and ω, it is straightforward to modify it to make the desired plot; results for two values of the drive amplitude are shown in Figure 3.6.

With a small driving force the trajectory in phase space (ω-θ space) is easy to understand in terms of the behavior we found earlier for $\theta(t)$. For short times there is a transient that depends on the initial conditions (in this case we started at $\theta = 0.2$ with $\omega = 0$), but the pendulum quickly settles into a regular orbit in phase space corresponding to the oscillatory motion of both θ and ω. It can be shown that this final orbit is independent of the initial conditions; this is also what our results for the Lyapunov exponent imply. The behavior in the chaotic regime is a bit more surprising. The phase-space trajectory exhibits many orbits that are nearly closed and that persist for only one or two cycles. While this pattern is certainly not a simple one, it is not completely random, as might have been expected for

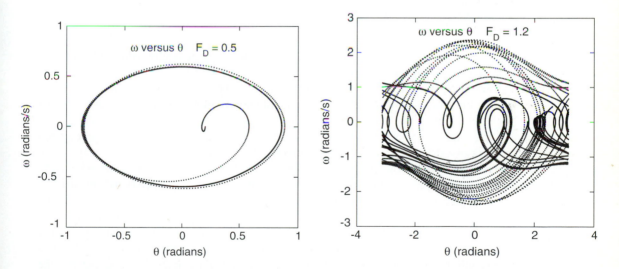

Figure 3.6: Results for ω as a function of θ for a pendulum. The parameters were the same as in Figure 3.4. For high drive (on the right), many trajectories go beyond $|\theta| = \pi$ and thus "jump" from $\theta = \pi$ to $\theta = -\pi$, or vice-versa in this plot.

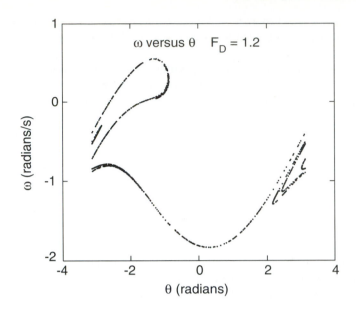

Figure 3.7:   More results for ω as a function of θ for a pendulum; here we only plot points at times that are in phase with the driving force. The parameters were the same as in Figure 3.4. This surface of points is known as a strange attractor.

a chaotic system. This is a common property of chaotic systems; they generally exhibit phase-space trajectories with significant structure.

If we examine these trajectories in a slightly different manner we find a very striking result. In Figure 3.7 we show the same type of phase-space graph, but here we plot ω versus θ only at times that are *in phase* with the driving force. That is, we only display the point when $\Omega_D t = n\pi$, where n is an integer.[8] This is an example of what is known as a *Poincaré section* and is a very useful way to plot and analyze the behavior of a dynamical system. The motivation for plotting the results in this way can be appreciated from an analogy with the function of a stroboscope. It sometimes happens that we want to examine an object that is rotating at a high rate. A good example is an old-fashioned (vinyl) record as it is rotated on a record player. When in operation, the record rotates too fast for a human eye to read the label. However, if the record is illuminated with a light source (a stroboscope), which is turned on and off at the frequency of the record player, our eye will receive input only when the record has a particular orientation; as a result we will be able to read the label as if the record were not moving at all. The key point is that things will look simpler when we observe them at a rate (i.e., frequency) that matches the problem. This lesson can be applied to the pendulum by observing the behavior, that is, recording the values of θ and ω, at a rate that matches the drive frequency, and this is effectively what we have done in the Poincaré section shown in Figure 3.7. If we had constructed this plot in the nonchaotic regime,

---

[8]When constructing this plot numerically you must be careful to account for the fact that time increases in steps of size Δt. Thus, the points in Figure 3.7 were actually plotted when $|t - n\pi/\Omega_D| < \Delta t/2$.

with $F_D = 0.5$ for example, it would yield a single point (after allowing the initial transient to decay), since at any particular point of the drive cycle we would always find the same values of θ and ω.

   The result of such a stroboscopic plot is very different in the chaotic regime, Figure 3.7. It turns out that except for the initial transient this phase-space trajectory is the same for a wide range of initial conditions. In other words, even though we cannot predict the behavior of $\theta(t)$, we do know that the system will possess values of ω and θ, which put it on this surface of points. The trajectory of our pendulum is drawn to this surface, which is known as an attractor. Actually, there are attractors in both the nonchaotic and chaotic regimes; the single point that would be found with $F_D = 0.5$ would also be an attractor. While the attractors have simple forms in the nonchaotic case, they have a very complicated structure in the chaotic regime. The "fuzziness" of the chaotic attractor in Figure 3.7 is not due to numerical uncertainties or plotting errors. It is a property of the attractor. Chaotic attractors have a *fractal* structure and are usually referred to as *strange attractors*.[9] We will discuss the nature of fractals at some length in Chapter 7.

   There is much more that the damped, nonlinear, driven pendulum can tell us about chaos, and we will explore a few of these lessons in the exercises. Our key results are: (1) it is possible for a system to be both deterministic and unpredictable—in fact, this is what we mean by the term chaos; and (2) the behavior in the chaotic regime is not completely random, but can be described by a strange attractor in phase space. We will amplify and expand on these themes in the following sections.

Exercises

1. Study the effects of damping by starting the pendulum with some initial angular displacement, say $\theta = 0.5$ radians, and study how the motion decays with time. Use $q = 0.1$ and estimate the time constant for the decay. Compare your result with approximate analytic estimates for the decay time. Note: Any of the exercises in the section can be conveniently done with either the Euler-Cromer algorithm or the Runge-Kutta method described in Appendix 1.

2. Calculate $\theta(t)$ for $F_D = 0.1$, 0.5, and 0.99, with the other parameters as in Figure 3.4. Compare the waveforms, with special attention to the deviations from a purely sinusoidal form at high drive.

3. In constructing the Poincaré section in Figure 3.7 we plotted points only at times that were in phase with the drive force; that is, at times $t \approx 2\pi n/\Omega_D$, where n is an integer. At these values of t the driving force passed through zero [see (3.7)]. However, we could just as easily have chosen to make the plot at times corresponding to a maximum of the drive force, or at times $\pi/4$ out-of-phase with this force, etc. Construct the Poincaré sections for these cases and compare them with Figure 3.7.

4. Write a program to calculate and compare the behavior of two, nearly identical pendulums. Use it to calculate the divergence of two nearby trajectories in the chaotic regime, as in Figure 3.5, and make a qualitative estimate of the corresponding Lyapunov exponent from the slope of a plot of $\log(\Delta\theta)$ as a function of t.

5. Repeat the previous problem, but give the two pendulums slightly different damping factors. How does the value of the Lyapunov exponent compare with that found in Figure 3.5?

---

[9]Physicists like to use provocative names.

6. Study the shape of the chaotic attractor for different initial conditions. Keep the drive force fixed at $F_D = 1.2$ and calculate the attractors found for several different initial values of θ. Show that you obtain the same attractor even for different initial conditions, provided that these conditions are not changed by too much. Repeat your calculations for different values of the time step to be sure that it is sufficiently small that it does not cause any structure in the attractor.

*7. Investigate how a strange attractor is altered by small changes in one of the pendulum parameters. Begin by calculating the strange attractor in Figure 3.7. Then change either the drive amplitude or drive frequency by a small amount and observe the changes in the attractor.

*8. Construct a very high-resolution plot of the chaotic attractor in Figure 3.7, concentrating on the region $\theta > 2$ rad. You should find that there is more structure in the attractor than is obvious on the scale plotted in Figure 3.7. In fact, an important feature of chaotic attractors is that the closer you look, the more structure you find. We will see later that this property is related to fractals. It turns out that a strange attractor is a fractal object. Hint: In order to get accurate results for a high resolution plot of the attractor, it is advisable, in terms of the necessary computer time, to use the Runge-Kutta method.

3.3   Routes to Chaos: Period Doubling

We have seen that at low driving forces the damped, nonlinear pendulum exhibits simple oscillatory motion, while at high drive it can be chaotic. This raises an obvious question: Exactly how does the transition from simple to chaotic behavior take place? It turns out that the pendulum exhibits transitions to chaotic behavior at several different values of the driving force. We have already observed in Figure 3.4 that one of these transitions must take place between $F_D = 0.5$ and 1.2. However, this transition is not the clearest one to study numerically, so we will instead consider the behavior at somewhat higher driving forces.[10]

Figure 3.8 shows results for θ as a function of time for several values of the driving force calculated using the Euler-Cromer program described earlier. At these high values of the drive the pendulum often swings all the way around its support; this can be seen from the vertical steps in θ as our program resets[11] this angle to keep it in the range $-\pi$ to π. These steps notwithstanding, the behavior in Figure 3.8 is a periodic, repeating function of t in all three cases (after the initial transients have damped away). The drive frequency used here was $\Omega_D = 2/3$ so the period of the driving force was $2\pi/\Omega_D = 3\pi$, and this is precisely the period of the motion found at $F_D = 1.35$. Hence, in this case, the pendulum moves at the same frequency as the driving force.

The behavior at $F_D = 1.44$ is a bit more subtle. While we again have periodic motion, the period is now *twice* the drive period. This can be seen most clearly by comparing the θ-t waveforms at $F_D = 1.35$ and 1.44, and noticing that in the latter case the bumps alternate in amplitude. Our pendulum has already surprised us on several occasions, and we might be tempted to add this behavior to our list of pendulum puzzles. However, this surprise is a very special and important one. When a nonlinear

---

[10]The pendulum exhibits an extraordinarily rich behavior, some of which we discuss later. Unfortunately, we only have time to explore a small portion of the chaotic regime here. We will, therefore, limit ourselves to one value of both the drive frequency and damping, and only certain ranges of the drive amplitude. The interested reader is encouraged to investigate other parameter values. Additional results are also described by Baker and Gollub (1990).

[11]This distraction can be avoided by plotting ω instead of θ. We will leave this to the exercises.

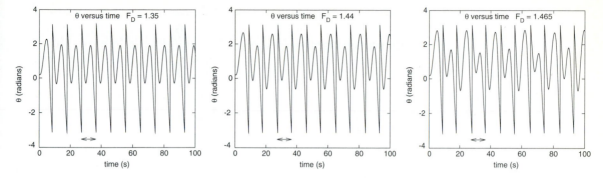

Figure 3.8:   Results for θ as a function of time for our pendulum for several different values of the drive amplitude. The other parameters were the same as in Figure 3.4 except that here we used a time step of 0.01. The horizontal arrows show the period of the driving force. In the middle plot the period is twice the drive period, since the values at the maxima alternate between $\theta \approx 1.9$ and 2.6. On the right the period is four times the drive period, as the maxima alternate between the values $\theta \approx 1.69, 2.82, 1.52$, and 2.72.

system is excited or driven by a single frequency stimulus, the response is, in general, not limited to the driving frequency. If Ω_D is the drive frequency, the nonlinear response will usually contain components at $2\Omega_D$, $3\Omega_D$, etc., at all harmonics. This process is known as mixing and is manifest by the generation of responses at integer multiples of the driving frequency. Such a nonlinear response is standard and well understood, and its key property is that it contains frequencies that are equal to or greater than the drive frequency. Hence, the periods of these harmonics will be smaller than the drive period. In contrast, our pendulum is now exhibiting a response at $\Omega_D/2$ (a lower frequency!), a *subharmonic*, which is unlike any standard mixing effect.

Returning to Figure 3.8, a careful look at the results for $F_D = 1.465$ shows that they exhibit a period that is four times the driving period. The pattern should now be evident. If we were to increase the drive amplitude further, the period would double again as the pendulum would switch to a motion that has a period eight times that of the drive. This period-doubling cascade would continue if the drive were increased further.

But if the period keeps on doubling, what about the transition to chaos? A nice way to appreciate how this transition comes about is with what is known as a *bifurcation diagram*. In Figure 3.9 we show a bifurcation diagram for θ as a function of drive amplitude, which was constructed in the following manner. For each value of F_D we have calculated θ as a function of time. After waiting for 300 driving periods so that the initial transients have decayed away, we plotted θ at times that were in phase with the driving force[12] as a function of F_D. Here we have plotted points up to the 400th drive period. This process was then repeated for the range of values of F_D shown in the figure.[13]

To understand the bifurcation diagram we start at $F_D = 1.35$. We have already seen that in this case the motion has the same period as the drive, so if we observe θ at a particular time in the drive cycle we will always find the same value. Our bifurcation diagram thus consists of a single point; there is just

---

[12] Just as we did in constructing the Poincaré section in Figure 3.7.

[13] We have chosen to study this range of F_D because it exhibits period-doubling in an especially clear manner. Results for other values of F_D are shown by Baker and Gollub (1990), or you can calculate them for yourself.

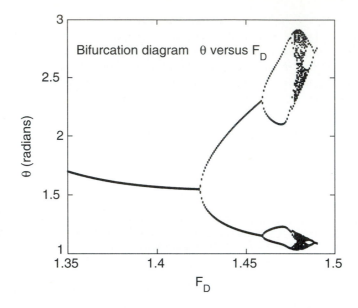

Figure 3.9: Bifurcation diagram for our pendulum. The parameters used for the calculation were the same as in Figure 3.8.

one value of θ for this value of F_D, although that point will be plotted many times. We will refer to this as period-1 behavior, since the θ-t waveform has the same period as the driving force. If the motion is period-2, then the values of θ that are plotted will alternate between two values. This is just the alternation we saw at $F_D = 1.44$ in Figure 3.8, and it leads to two points on the bifurcation diagram. The pattern should now be clear: Motion that is period n will yield n points on the bifurcation diagram for that value of F_D. From Figure 3.9 we see that the behavior is period 1 up to approximately $F_D = 1.424$, where there is a transition to period-2 motion. This persists up to the transition to period-4 behavior at $F_D \approx 1.459$. This process continues, although the resolution of our diagram makes it difficult to follow the behavior past period 8. This period-doubling cascade ultimately ends in a transition to chaotic behavior.

We have now obtained at least a qualitative understanding of how the transition from regular to chaotic behavior occurs for one particular system, the pendulum, in one particular range of parameters (i.e., drive force, drive frequency, damping strength, etc.). But how general is this behavior? Is it only found in the pendulum, or does it occur in other systems? These are the kinds of questions that physicists often ask. We tend to look for (and like to discover) patterns and principles that occur widely and apply to many different systems. For example, the motion of macroscopic objects can, with only a few exceptions, be described by Newton's laws of motion. Likewise, classical (as opposed to quantum) electromagnetic phenomena can be described by Maxwell's equations. Because of their near-universal applicability we feel that these "laws" of physics provide us with a better understanding of the world. We don't want to get too philosophical here, and we also don't want to be pressed into a discussion of what the term understand really means, but we hope that this gives the reader some appreciation for why it is important to look hard for universal aspects in any problem or result. With that in mind, we now restate the question posed at the beginning of this paragraph. Is the period-doubling route to chaos universal in any way, or do all systems have their own particular way of making this transition?

While there is not yet a complete theory of chaos in the sense of Newton's laws or Maxwell's equations, the answer to this question seems to be the following. Many systems have been found to exhibit chaotic behavior, but there appears to be only a few ways in which the transition from simple to chaotic behavior can occur. The periodic-doubling scenario that we have observed with the pendulum is one of these few known routes to chaos. You can then ask if this periodic-doubling procedure itself has any properties that are universal. The answer to this is yes (why else would we raise the question?!), as we will now explain.

Returning to our bifurcation diagram, Figure 3.9, we note that the spacing between period-doubling transitions becomes rapidly smaller as the order of the transition increases. For example, the period-2 regime extends from $F_D \approx 1.424$ to 1.459, while the period-4 regime extends only from about 1.459 to 1.476, and the same trend is found for higher periods.[14] Let us define F_n to be the value of the driving force at which the transition to period-2^n behavior takes place. The shrinkage of the size of the periodic windows can be described by a parameter δ_n, where

$$\delta_n \equiv \frac{F_n - F_{n-1}}{F_{n+1} - F_n} . \tag{3.10}$$

The observation that the windows become smaller as n increases means that $\delta_n > 1$. It has been found that as n becomes large, δ_n approaches a constant that is known as the Feigenbaum δ. That is, the rate of shrinkage approaches a constant in the limit $n \to \infty$. Moreover, it turns out that essentially all systems that exhibit the period-doubling route to chaos appear to possess the same value of $\delta \approx 4.669 \ldots$. Hence, there are indeed some universal aspects associated with the transition to chaos. There are, as we have hinted above, several other known routes to chaos, and a few of them can also be found in the pendulum. However, rather than making this chapter the story of the pendulum, we will next consider several other chaotic systems.

Exercises

1. Calculate Poincaré sections for the pendulum as it undergoes the period-doubling route to chaos. Plot ω versus θ, with one point plotted for each drive cycle, as in Figure 3.7. Do this for $F_D = 1.4$, 1.44, and 1.465, using the other parameters as given in connection with Figure 3.8. You should find that after removing the points corresponding to the initial transient the attractor in the period-1 regime will contain only a single point. Likewise, if the behavior is period n, the attractor will contain n discrete points.

2. Calculate the bifurcation diagram for the pendulum in the vicinity of $F_D = 1.35$ to 1.5. Make a magnified plot of the diagram (as compared to Figure 3.9) and obtain an estimate of the Feigenbaum δ parameter.

*3. Investigate the bifurcation diagrams found for the pendulum with other values of the drive frequency and damping parameter. Warning: This can easily become an ambitious project!

---

[14] In order to see this clearly we would need to examine the bifurcation on a much finer scale than in Figure 3.9.

*4. A very popular mathematical model that exhibits chaotic behavior is the logistic map. This map is defined by the relation

$$x_{i+1} = \mu \, x_i \, (1 - x_i) \,. \qquad\qquad (3.11)$$

You can interpret x_i as the size of a population of animals in generation i and μ as a parameter that determines their reproductive rate. This model has been adopted by many different fields, with different interpretations. Its connection with physics is a bit remote, but it is nevertheless studied extensively by physicists as a (mathematically) simple chaotic system. In the logistic map the parameter μ plays the role that the driving force plays in the pendulum, while x is roughly analogous to θ.

Begin by calculating x as a function of i for several values of μ in the range 0 to 4. Note that x is restricted to values in the range 0 to 1. You should find that for $\mu < 3$, x is a constant (independent of i) after the initial transient has decayed away. For larger values of μ you should observe a sequence of period-doubling transitions, with a chaotic regime beginning at $\mu \approx 3.57$. It is also interesting to compute the bifurcation diagram (the analog of Figure 3.9 for the pendulum). Estimate the value of the Feigenbaum δ parameter and compare it with that quoted above for the pendulum. The article by May (1976) and the book by Baker and Gollub (1990) contain good introductions to the logistic map.

3.4   The Lorenz Model

The pendulum model we have considered is a very simple system, yet it exhibits extremely rich behavior. It is thus not surprising that other slightly more complicated systems are also capable of chaotic behavior. When we think of chaotic or unpredictable behavior, an example that naturally comes to mind is the weather. Because of the economic importance of having accurate weather predictions, a good deal of effort has been devoted to this problem. While much of this effort has gone into computer modeling of Earth's atmosphere, much has also been devoted to understanding the weather problem from a more fundamental point of view. It was work of this kind by the atmospheric scientist E. N. Lorenz (1963) that provided a major contribution to the modern field of chaos.

Lorenz was studying the basic equations of fluid mechanics, which are known as the Navier-Stokes equations; they can be thought of as Newton's laws written in a form appropriate for a fluid. These are a complicated set of differential equations that describe the velocity, temperature, density, etc., as functions of position and time, and they are very difficult to solve analytically in cases of practical interest. Of course, this is just the type of problem where a computational approach can be useful, and that is precisely what Lorenz did. The specific situation he considered was the Rayleigh-Bénard problem, which concerns a fluid in a container whose top and bottom surfaces are held at different temperatures. It had long been known that as the difference between these two temperatures is increased, the fluid can undergo transitions from a stationary state (no fluid motion) to steady flow (nonzero flow velocities that are constant in time, also referred to as convection) to chaotic flow. Lorenz did his work more than 30 years ago, so the computational power available to him was not very impressive by today's standards. This prompted him to consider a greatly simplified version of the Navier-Stokes equations as applied to this particular problem. Indeed, he grossly oversimplified the problem as he reduced it to only three equations

$$\frac{dx}{dt} = \sigma\,(y - x)\,, \tag{3.12}$$

$$\frac{dy}{dt} = -x\,z + r\,x - y\,,$$

$$\frac{dz}{dt} = x\,y - b\,z\,.$$

These are now known as the Lorenz equations (or equivalently, the Lorenz model).[15] As noted above, the Navier-Stokes equations, from which those in (3.12) are derived, involve the state of the fluid as a function of position and time. Hence, a complete description of the Rayleigh-Bénard problem must involve a *large* number of variables. The Lorenz variables x, y, and z are derived from the temperature, density, and velocity variables in the original Navier-Stokes equations, and the parameters σ, r, and b are measures of the temperature difference across the fluid and other fluid parameters. However, it is not particularly useful to insist on interpreting x, y, and z in that manner, since the simplifications made in reducing the problem to only three variables means that we cannot expect our results to apply to any real system. Rather, the behavior exhibited by these equations is indicative of the *type* of behavior that could be expected of the Rayleigh-Bénard problem or any other problem involving the Navier-Stokes equations. For brevity we shall often refer to the latter as the weather problem. Any behavior we find in the Lorenz model will certainly be found in the weather problem. Moreover, it makes strategic sense to attack the Lorenz model first, since if we can't solve that, we would have no hope of making headway on the weather problem.

With this in mind, we plunge ahead and consider solutions to the Lorenz equations. They are just three, coupled, differential equations that are very similar to those we have already encountered in connection with the pendulum [for example, (3.4)]. We will, therefore, not discuss the program construction in detail; it is basically the same approach we employed in the previous sections, but with the pendulum equation of motion replaced by the Lorenz equations. However, we will make a few general comments about the numerical aspects of the problem. We saw in our work on the pendulum that the Euler method does not conserve energy for oscillatory problems. The Lorenz equations exhibit oscillatory solutions for certain parameter values, which could cause us to worry about using the Euler method. We might, therefore, want to use the Euler-Cromer method here, but since that algorithm is designed for second-order differential equations, it is not directly applicable to the Lorenz model. However, it turns out that the Euler algorithm can actually be used to treat the Lorenz problem, for the following reason. Several of the terms in the Lorenz equations play the same role as the damping term in the pendulum equations of motion, while other terms are analogous to the driving force. If the time step in the Euler algorithm is sufficiently small, the energy lost (or added) through the error terms associated with the Euler method can be made much smaller than the energy lost to the effective damping, or added by the effective driving force. In this situation the Euler method provides an accurate

---

[15]While these do not appear to resemble our pendulum's equation of motion, the two systems are both nonlinear (note the terms involving products such as xz and xy), and as we saw with the pendulum, this is very important.

solution, as can be verified directly by simply repeating the Euler calculation with different time steps (or by comparing with the solution generated with the Runge-Kutta method). This exercise, which we will leave to the reader, reveals that the Euler solution is accurate for the time steps we have employed in the computations described below. This is another example of a point we made earlier; the suitability of an algorithm depends upon the problem.

Returning to the Lorenz problem, there are three parameters in (3.12), σ, b, and r, and the behavior we find depends on their values. We will follow custom (and also Lorenz [1963]) and use $\sigma = 10$ and $b = 8/3$. According to some authors these values correspond to cold water, but given the highly simplified nature of the model you shouldn't take this claim seriously! The parameter r is a measure of the temperature difference between the top and bottom surfaces of the fluid. For small r the effective force on the fluid is small in the sense that there is very little heat carried by the fluid. As r increases this force increases, so r plays a role analogous to F_D in the pendulum problem. Results for z as a function of time are shown in Figure 3.10, which shows the behavior at three different values of the force r (x and y exhibit qualitatively similar behavior). At $r = 5$ there is an initial transient, and after it decays away z is a constant, independent of t. The same behavior is seen at $r = 10$, although the transient takes a little longer to decay. These two cases correspond to steady convective motion in the original fluid; in this process the warm fluid produced at the bottom surface of the container rises and the cooler fluid returns from the top. This steady convection is the analog of regular nonchaotic motion of the pendulum. The behavior is completely different at $r = 25$. Here the initial transient is roughly periodic, but it gives way to an irregular, that is, chaotic time dependence after $t = 20$ or so. There are not many exact results available for the Lorenz model, but it is known that the transition from steady convection to chaotic behavior takes place at $r = 470/19 \approx 24.74$. This is consistent with our

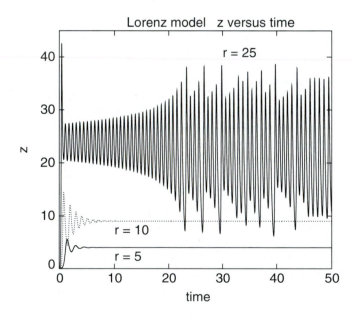

Figure 3.10:   Variation of the Lorenz variable z as a function of time. The calculation was performed using the Euler method with a time step of 0.0001. The initial conditions were $x = 1$, $y = z = 0$.

numerical results, although we have not attempted to locate this transition accurately here; we leave that for the exercises!

The chaotic behavior seen at $r = 25$ after the initial transient has decayed certainly appears to be very random and unpredictable. However, we learned in dealing that of the pendulum that looks can be deceiving. In that case we found that a Poincaré section can reveal underlying regularities that are not obvious from the time dependence alone. With this motivation we consider how to construct such a phase-space plot for the Lorenz model. The situation here is a little more complicated than that of the pendulum, since we now have three variables to deal with, x, y, and z, as opposed to only two in the pendulum problem (θ and ω). There are several ways to proceed. Perhaps the simplest way is to imagine that x, y, and z are coordinates in some abstract space and recognize that we are dealing with a trajectory in this space. We can then obtain a projection of this trajectory by simply plotting z as a function of x (for example); this gives a projection onto the x–z plane. Such a projection for the chaotic case $r = 25$ is shown in Figure 3.11. In this trajectory the system undergoes approximately periodic oscillations (roughly circular orbits) on one side of the line $x = 0$, then moves to the opposite side of this line and undergoes a new series of oscillations, etc.

The phase-space plot in Figure 3.11 certainly gives some hints of an underlying regularity, but we would like to have more than hints. With the pendulum we saw that the Poincaré sections in the chaotic regime revealed the attractors in a particularly clear way, as with the strange attractor in Figure 3.7. Might there be a similar sort of underlying attractor for the Lorenz model? You will recall that to construct a Poincaré section for the pendulum we plotted ω as a function of θ at times that were in phase with the driving force. Hence, we essentially used the driving force as a timekeeper, which told us when to make the measurement. However, in the Lorenz model there is no direct analog to this

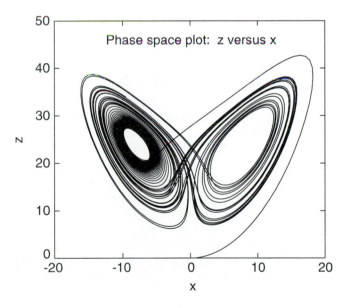

Figure 3.11: Trajectory of the Lorenz model projected onto the x–z plane, with $r = 25$. This was calculated using the Euler method with a time step of 0.0001 and the initial conditions $x = 1$, $y = z = 0$.

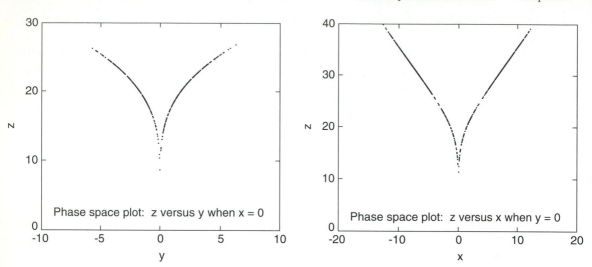

Figure 3.12: Phase-space plots for the Lorenz model with $r = 25$, calculated with a time step of 0.0001. Left: z versus y, with points plotted only when $x = 0$. Right: z versus x, with points plotted only when $y = 0$. The points were recorded only after $t = 30$, to allow for the decay of initial transients.

drive force with its sinusoidal time dependence, so we must take a slightly different approach. We already mentioned that the Lorenz variables x, y, and z can be viewed as specifying the trajectory of a particle moving in three dimensions. It is then natural (or at least it was to Lorenz!) to consider two-dimensional slices through this trajectory. To be more specific, we show on the left in Figure 3.12 a plot of z versus y when $x = 0$.[16] In our trajectory language, we are simply plotting the places where the trajectory intersects the y–z plane. The results in Figure 3.12 were obtained with $r = 25$, which, as we have already seen, places us in the chaotic regime. We see from the figure that even though the behavior is strongly chaotic, there is a very high degree of regularity in the phase-space trajectory. This attractor surface in phase space can be shown to be independent of the initial conditions. Hence, while the time-dependent behavior [e.g., $z(t)$] is unpredictable, we *can* predict with certainty that the system will be found somewhere on the attractor surface in phase space.

In the previous section we studied the period-doubling route to chaos in the pendulum. The Lorenz model exhibits this route to chaos, as do several others. A complete study of the model would take us too long here, so we refer the interested reader to Sparrow (1982), an entire *book* devoted to the Lorenz model. Here we will only explore one of the chaotic transitions exhibited by the model. Figure 3.13 shows the behavior of z at two values of r. At $r = 160$ we see periodic oscillations. While the waveform of these oscillations is certainly not simple, they are stable and persist forever. This corresponds to period-1 behavior, and is analogous to the results we found for the pendulum. If we were to examine the behavior as r is made smaller, we would observe period-doubling and eventually chaos (see the exercises for more on this). However, let us instead consider what happens as r is increased;

---

[16]Since t can take on only discrete values in our simulations, we can only determine that the system has crossed the plane $x = 0$ at some instant between two adjacent time steps. We then interpolate the position to construct the phase-space plots.

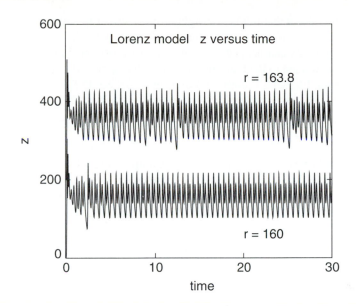

Figure 3.13:   Variation of the Lorenz variable z as a function of time, for high values of r.   Calculated using the Euler method with a time step of 0.0001.

this is also shown in Figure 3.13. The motion is seen to be approximately periodic for many cycles of oscillation, but these periodic stretches are interrupted by chaotic interludes (hiccups?). The behavior is thus chaotic, but in a sense it is only barely chaotic.

This is known as the intermittency route to chaos, and can be pictured as follows. Let r_c be the value of r at which this transition occurs. For r less than r_c the behavior is perfectly periodic, as found with $r = 160$. For values of r that are just a little beyond the transition, in our case just a little larger than r_c, the behavior is *almost* periodic with only an occasional chaotic interlude. As we go farther and farther into the chaotic regime these interludes occur more and more often, until eventually the underlying periodic behavior is unrecognizable. As we approach r_c, but still stay inside the chaotic regime, there are fewer and fewer interludes spaced farther and farther apart. At the transition the spacing between the interludes becomes infinitely long; that is, they no longer occur, and we are left with periodic motion.

The Lorenz model is a very rich and interesting chaotic system, and we will explore it in further detail in the exercises. Before we leave this topic we have a few comments concerning what the behavior of the Lorenz model implies about the weather problem. We have seen that the Lorenz model can exhibit chaotic behavior. Since it is a special case of the Navier-Stokes equations, we must expect that chaos is a general property of virtually all fluid systems. The weather problem is concerned with a complicated fluid system, our atmosphere, so we reach the not very surprising conclusion that the weather is a chaotic problem. From what we have learned about the extreme sensitivity of chaotic systems to initial conditions, we know that predicting the weather, therefore, must be an *inherently* difficult problem. Suppose that we construct an extremely detailed computer model of the atmosphere (this problem is not in the exercises). The model would take all atmospheric conditions, including the temperature, wind velocity, etc., as functions of position around the world at some particular time as input parameters, and then calculate how these conditions vary with time. However, assuming that the atmosphere is in its chaotic regime (and it appears that it is), any slight error in any of the initial conditions would rapidly lead to an enormous error in the predictions. This conclusion should be no surprise; we all know how bad current weather forecasts can be, and these are based largely on computer models (or the human equivalent!). This situation led to the butterfly metaphor that appeared in the title of a talk by Lorenz, "Predictability: Does the Flap of a Butterfly's Wings in Brazil Set Off a Tornado in Texas?"[17] This is just another reference to the extreme sensitivity of chaotic systems to their initial conditions.

Exercises

*1. Study period-doubling in the Lorenz model by examining the behavior for $r \leq 160$. Calculate the bifurcation diagram and extract the value of Feigenbaum's δ parameter. You should find a value similar to that calculated for the pendulum. Hint: While this problem can be done using the Euler method, it is probably advisable, in order to conserve computer time, to use the Runge-Kutta algorithm.

2. Continue the previous problem, and construct the phase-space plots as in Figures 3.11 and 3.12 in the different regimes.

3. Show that the Poincaré sections in Figure 3.12 are independent of the initial conditions. For example, compare the attractor found for $x(0) = 1$, $y(0) = z(0) = 0$ with that found for $x(0) = 0$, $y(0) = z(0) = 1$.

*4. Estimate qualitatively the Lyapunov exponent for a few trajectories of the Lorenz model near the transition to chaos at $r = 24.74 \ldots$. Try to observe this exponent change from negative in the nonchaotic regime, to positive in the chaotic regime.

*5. Explore the intermittency route to chaos for $r \geq 163$ in more detail. Begin by calculating z as a function of time for different values of r. Try $r = 163$ (which should be in the nonchaotic regime), and several larger values up to $r = 165$ or so. For the larger values of r you should observe chaotic "hiccups" like those found in Figure 3.13. Next calculate the average time between these hiccups and study how it diverges as the transition to chaos is approached. While the idea here is easy to explain, writing a program to detect hiccups is a bit tricky. One way to accomplish this is to construct a histogram of times between adjacent maxima in $z(t)$. In the oscillatory (nonchaotic) regime these times will all be the same. An odd value signals a hiccup.

---

[17]Given at a meeting of the American Association for the Advancement of Science in 1972. It seems fitting that the trajectory in Figure 3.11 bears some resemblance to a butterfly.

3.5   The Billiard Problem

So far we have considered two different chaotic systems, and you are probably willing to believe that there are many more. To get an appreciation for the different kinds of behavior that can be found, and also the common threads that run through this behavior, we will consider two more chaotic models in this chapter. Here we consider the problem of a ball moving without friction on a horizontal table. We imagine that there are walls at the edges of the table that reflect the ball perfectly and that there is no frictional force between the ball and the table. We can think of this as a billiard ball that moves without friction on a perfect billiard table.[18] The ball is given some initial velocity, and the problem is to calculate and understand the resulting trajectory. This is known as the stadium billiard problem.

Except for the collisions with the walls, the motion of the billiard is quite simple. Between collisions the velocity is constant so we have

$$\frac{dx}{dt} = v_x \, , \tag{3.13}$$

$$\frac{dy}{dt} = v_y \, ,$$

where v_x and v_y change only through collisions with the walls. These equations can be solved using our usual Euler algorithm. Note that since the velocity is constant (except during the collisions), the Euler solution turns out to give an exact description of the motion across the table. The most difficult part of the calculation is the treatment of the collisions. Since we have assumed that they are perfectly elastic, the reflections will be mirrorlike, which means that the angle of incidence will be equal to the angle of reflection. These angles are defined in terms of the incoming and outgoing velocity vectors, and the vector normal to the wall at the location of the collision. This geometry is shown in Figure 3.14, where we have drawn a curved wall; our arguments apply just as well to a straight wall.

A numerical solution for the billiard's motion thus consists of two parts. First, when the billiard is away from the wall its motion is described by (3.13). These equations of motion are used to integrate forward in time, calculating x and y as functions of time. After each time step we must check to see if there has been a collision with one of the walls, that is, if the newly calculated position puts the billiard off the table. When this happens the program must backtrack to locate the position where the collision occurred. There are several ways to do this. One way is to back the billiard up to the position at the previous time step and then use a much smaller time step [for example, a factor of 100 smaller than the time step used to initially integrate (3.13)], so as to move the billiard in much smaller steps. When the billiard then goes off the table (again), we take the location after that iteration to be the point of collision.[19] After locating the collision point, we need to do a little vector manipulation. The initial velocity vector $\vec{v}_i \equiv (v_x, v_y)$ is already known, since v_x and v_y are known. We must next obtain the

---

[18] We will ignore any complications associated with the angular momentum of the ball, so it is better to think of this as a particle sliding on a frictionless sheet of ice. It would thus be more accurate to term this the "hockey puck" problem, but the name billiard is already firmly attached to the model.

[19] This approach will always yield a collision point that is off the table by a small amount. We can imagine other ways to locate the collision point, but in most cases they will never locate the collision point exactly. We have found that the approach described here yields results that are essentially identical to other methods for locating the collision point. A different method will be considered in the exercises.

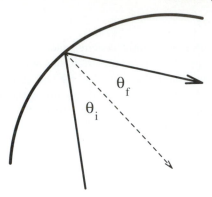

Figure 3.14:   Geometry for perfect reflection of the billiard from a wall. The angle of incidence is equal
to the angle of reflection, $\theta_i = \theta_f$.

unit vector normal to the wall at the point of collision, $\hat{n}$. It is then useful to calculate the components
of $\vec{v}_i$ parallel and perpendicular to the wall. These are just

$$\vec{v}_{i,\perp} = (\vec{v}_i \cdot \hat{n})\,\hat{n}\,, \qquad\qquad\qquad (3.14)$$

$$\vec{v}_{i,\parallel} = \vec{v}_i - \vec{v}_{i,\perp}\,.$$

Once we have the components of $\vec{v}_i$ we can reflect the billiard. A mirrorlike reflection reverses
the perpendicular component of velocity, but leaves the parallel component unchanged (we'll leave it
to the reader to show that this makes $\theta_f = \theta_i$ in Figure 3.14). Hence, the velocity after reflection from
the wall is

$$\vec{v}_{f,\perp} = -v_{i,\perp}\,, \qquad\qquad\qquad (3.15)$$

$$\vec{v}_{f,\parallel} = v_{i,\parallel}\,.$$

Some results are given in Figure 3.15 that show the first few bounces for a billiard on a square
table. When (if) you write your own program for this problem, a graphical display of the trajectory
is extremely useful in finding, and fixing, any errors. Two strong tests of the program are that the
reflections should indeed be mirrorlike (usually referred to as *specular*), and that the energy, which is
all kinetic for this problem, should be conserved. The trajectory on a square table is, as we might infer
from Figure 3.15, very regular; it has a very simple predictable pattern. This is confirmed in Figure 3.16,
which shows such a trajectory over a much longer time period.

Another way to graphically capture the regularity of the trajectory is with yet another phase-space
plot. In Figure 3.16 we show a plot of v_x versus x, but here we have not plotted every point of the
phase-space trajectory. Rather, we have constructed another type of Poincaré section by plotting the
points only when the billiard crosses the $y = 0$ axis.[20] We find two horizontal lines here; the billiard
trajectories are all parallel to one of two different directions, so only two different values of v_x occur.

---

[20]This should remind you of how we dealt with the Lorenz model.

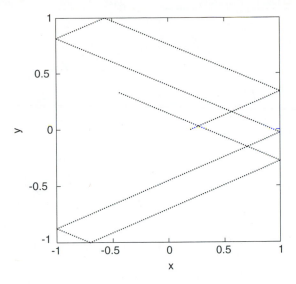

Figure 3.15: Trajectory of a billiard on a square table. Only the first few reflections are shown. The billiard started at $x = 0.2$, $y = 0$ with a speed of unity and with the velocity directed toward the upper right of the table. The time step was 0.01.

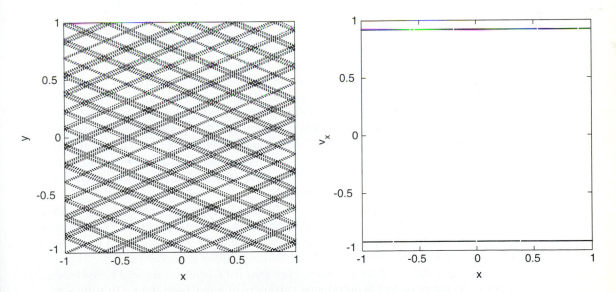

Figure 3.16: Left: trajectory of a billiard on a square table. This is a continuation of the trajectory shown in Figure 3.15. Right: corresponding Poincaré section derived from the trajectory shown on the left. Note that the phase-space plot was obtained from a much longer run of the program than was used for the trajectory plot. There are a few gaps visible in the phase-space plot; these would be filled in if the program were run for a longer period of time.

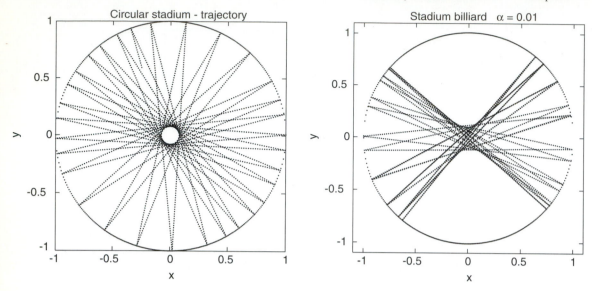

Figure 3.17:   Left: trajectory of a billiard on a circular table; right: trajectory of a billiard on a stadium-shaped table with $\alpha = 0.01$.

Since the billiard can cross the $y = 0$ axis anywhere, the values of x in this plot vary continuously from -1 to $+1$.

The behavior of the billiard gets more interesting when we consider other table shapes. There are many possibilities; here we will consider only one, the so-called stadium shape, which can be described as follows. Imagine a circular table of radius $r = 1$, as shown on the left side of Figure 3.17. Now cut the table along the x axis, and pull the two semicircular halves apart (along y), a distance $2\alpha r$. Then fill in these two open sections with straight segments. Thus $\alpha = 0$ yields a circular table, while nonzero values of α give a table with a more traditional stadium shape. Figure 3.17 compares trajectories for a circular table with those for a table with $\alpha = 0.01$. While the trajectories depend on the initial conditions (the initial values of x, y, and $\vec{v}$), the results for the circular table are always highly symmetric. On the other hand, the trajectory for the $\alpha = 0.01$ stadium is much more complicated and is definitely not symmetric, except for very special initial conditions (such conditions were not used in Figure 3.17).[21] This should remind you of chaotic motion.

The corresponding phase-space plots of v_x versus x (constructed as in Figure 3.16) are shown in Figure 3.18. The very ordered pattern for the circular table confirms our impression from the trajectories, that this is a nonchaotic system. However, for the $\alpha = 0.01$ stadium the phase-space plot is somewhat reminiscent of the chaotic attractor we found for the pendulum problem; it is indeed chaotic. Two more phase-space plots for other stadium shapes are shown in Figure 3.19, and both are seen to be chaotic.

A hallmark of a chaotic system is an extreme sensitivity to initial conditions. This property is also found in the billiard problem, as can be seen if we calculate the trajectories of two billiards with slightly different initial conditions. An example is shown in Figure 3.20 where we plot the distance

---

[21]Examples of such special, nonchaotic initial conditions are $x(0) = y(0) = 0$, with $\vec{v}$ parallel to either the x or y axis.

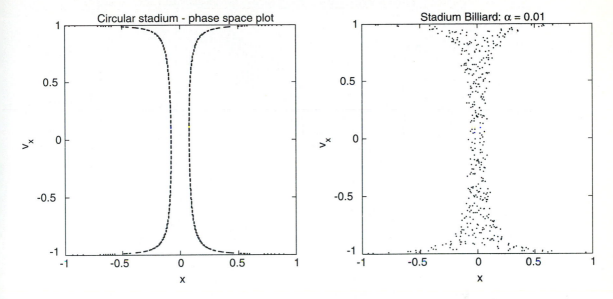

Figure 3.18: Phase-space plots for the trajectories shown in Figure 3.17. Left: for a circular-shaped table; right: for a stadium-shaped table with $\alpha = 0.01$. These were constructed by plotting points only when $y = 0$.

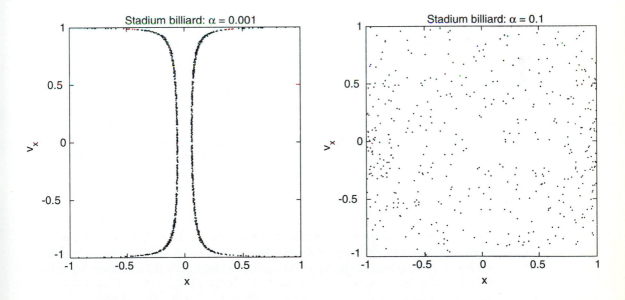

Figure 3.19: Phase-space plots for two more stadium-shaped tables. Left: for a table with $\alpha = 0.001$; right: table with $\alpha = 0.1$.

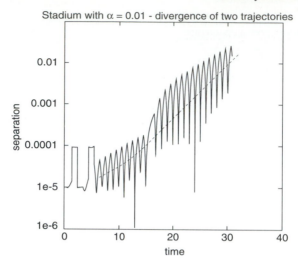

Figure 3.20:   Divergence of the trajectories of billiards started at slightly different initial conditions, for a stadium-shaped table with $\alpha = 0.01$. The dashed line is drawn to emphasize the rapid overall increase of the separation with time. The initial separation of the billiards was 1×10^{-5}.

between two billiards as a function of time. The billiards were on a chaotic table ($\alpha = 0.01$) and were given the same initial velocities, but were started a distance 1×10^{-5} apart (recall that the table has a radius of approximately 1 unit). The billiard separation shows a very sharp dip after about every one time unit. These dips occur when the billiards collide with the walls, as this causes their trajectories to cross. The overall separation is seen to increase very rapidly with time (note the logarithmic scale). The divergence of these trajectories can be described by a Lyapunov exponent, as we found for the pendulum.[22]

A remarkable feature of our results for the billiard problem is that the chaotic behavior is evident even for very small values of α. It turns out that the stadium billiard is chaotic for *any* nonzero value of α. In fact, only tables with very high symmetry are nonchaotic. The billiard problem may be relevant for describing the motion of gas molecules in a container. Our results suggest that for any realistically shaped container (i.e., any shape that is not extremely symmetric, such as the perfectly circular table) such motion is likely to be chaotic and thus unpredictable. This finding will be relevant to our discussion of entropy and the approach to equilibrium in Chapter 7.

Exercises

1. Investigate the Lyapunov exponent of the stadium billiard for several values of α. You can do this qualitatively by examining the behavior for only one set of initial conditions for each value of α you consider, or more quantitatively by averaging over a range of initial conditions for each value of α.

---

[22]To calculate the Lyapunov exponent quantitatively we would would have to average the behavior over different initial conditions, so as to smooth out the irregularities in Figure 3.20.

*2. Study the behavior for other types of tables. One interesting possibility is a square table with a circular interior wall located either in the center, or slightly off-center. Another possibility is an elliptical table.

*3. The key part of a program for the billiard program is the treatment of collisions with the wall of the stadium, and one way of doing this was described above. Another way is to use the exact solution of (3.13) to compute the trajectory and then solve analytically (using the equation that specifies the perimeter of the stadium) for the location of the collision. Write a program that uses this method and compare your results with those given in this section.

3.6   Bouncing Balls: A Chaotic Mechanical System

In order to convince you of the ubiquity of chaos, as if you needed more convincing, we devote this section to one more simple, mechanical, chaotic system. The system consists of two balls that move in response to gravity as illustrated in Figure 3.21. During the course of their motion they can collide with each other, and the bottom ball can also collide with the floor. Both of these collisions are assumed to be completely elastic, and the balls are constrained to move only along a vertical direction.

To construct a program to treat this problem, we first note that during the time the balls are in free fall (i.e., not colliding with each other or the floor) the equations of motion (simply Newton's second law) are

$$\frac{dv_1}{dt} = -g \, , \tag{3.16}$$

$$\frac{dx_1}{dt} = v_1 \, ,$$

$$\frac{dv_2}{dt} = -g \, ,$$

$$\frac{dx_2}{dt} = v_2 \, ,$$

where x_1 is the (vertical) position of ball number 1 and v_1 its velocity, etc., for ball number 2. We have encountered similar equations in previous problems, and it is natural to think of our standard approach, namely the Euler method. However, a better algorithm for this problem is the midpoint method. This

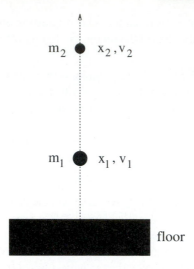

Figure 3.21:   Two balls moving in response to gravity.

is similar in spirit to both the Euler and Euler-Cromer algorithms. When applied to the system of equations (3.16) the midpoint method yields the difference equations

$$v_{1,i+1} \; = \; v_{1,i} \, - \, g \, \Delta t \,, \tag{3.17}$$

$$x_{1,i+1} \; = \; x_{1,i} \, + \, \frac{(v_{1,i+1} \, + \, v_{1,i})}{2} \, \Delta t \,,$$

$$v_{2,i+1} \; = \; v_{2,i} \, - \, g \, \Delta t \,,$$

$$x_{2,i+1} \; = \; x_{2,i} \, + \, \frac{(v_{2,i+1} \, + \, v_{2,i})}{2} \, \Delta t \,.$$

The treatment of v_1 and v_2 is the same as with the Euler method, which we have already found to yield the exact solution (for the velocity) in this case. However, x_1 and x_2 are handled a bit differently than they would be with the Euler method. For the Euler algorithm we use the *previous* value of the velocity to estimate the new value of position. With the midpoint method we use the *average* of the previous velocity and the new velocity to calculate the new value of position. It is not hard to show that for problems concerning motion in which the acceleration is constant, this approach yields the *exact* result for x. Hence, the midpoint method can be used to treat free fall exactly.

We must also deal with two types of collisions. The collision of the lower ball with the floor can be dealt with in the manner we used in the billiard problem. Since the collision is elastic, we simply reverse the velocity $v_1 \rightarrow -v_1$ when ball number 1 hits the floor, that is, when $x_1 \leq 0$; for simplicity we assume that the balls are point masses so that the center of the ball, x_1 in this case, is also the location of the edge of the ball. The collisions of the balls with each other are only a little more complicated. We know from elementary mechanics that when two objects undergo an elastic collision in one dimension, the velocities before (v_i) and after (v_f) are related by

$$v_{1,f} = \left(\frac{m_1 - m_2}{m_1 + m_2}\right) v_{1,i} + \left(\frac{2\,m_2}{m_1 + m_2}\right) v_{2,i} \,, \tag{3.18}$$

$$v_{2,f} = \left(\frac{2\,m_1}{m_1 + m_2}\right) v_{1,i} + \left(\frac{m_2 - m_1}{m_1 + m_2}\right) v_{2,i} \,,$$

where m_1 and m_2 are the masses of the two balls. Our program must check if x_2 is less than x_1 (recall that ball number 1 is the bottom one). If so, then the balls must have collided during the previous time step, and we use (3.18) to calculate the new velocities.

Before we consider the results of our program (this program is not given in Appendix 4; you'll have to write it yourself!), we should comment on the numerical approximations that are involved. We have already mentioned that the midpoint method provides the exact solution for both the velocity and position if the acceleration is constant, so there are no errors involved in our calculation of the motion during free fall. However, our treatments of the collisions are only approximate. For the collision with the floor we reverse the velocity of ball number 1 when $x_1 \le 0$. In general, this collision will effectively take place *below* the floor. The same worry applies to our treatment of the collisions between the balls. Our algorithm permits ball number 2 to move slightly below ball number 1 before the collision is handled. We might worry that these approximations could lead to serious errors. To check for this, we can repeat the calculation with different values of the time step to determine if this kind of error is, or is not, important. It turns out that it is not a significant source of error for this problem, but we must always be on guard.[23]

Now that we have described how to simulate the motion of our two balls, we show some results for the position of ball number 2 (the upper ball) as a function of time in Figure 3.22. The behavior depends on the ratio of the masses of the two balls. For balls of equal mass, the example on the left in Figure 3.22, the motion is periodic. All of the sharp dips in Figure 3.22 when ball number 2 approaches the floor do not quite reach the same level, but this is due to the discreteness of the time-step. Near the top of the trajectory, where the velocity is smaller and time-step discreteness thus not as important, the behavior of $x_2(t)$ is seen to be nicely periodic. In particular, x_2 always reaches the same value (ball number 2 reaches the same height), and this maximum occurs at evenly spaced time intervals. This is in sharp contrast to the results found with $m_2 = 2m_1$. In this case x_2 varies erratically (chaotically) with time. As the mass ratio is increased further, a very rich behavior is found; here we show results for $m_2 = 9m_1$, where a nearly, but not precisely, periodic variation is found.

By now you should be asking about phase-space plots. These can be produced in several ways. Here we choose to plot v_2 as a function of x_2 at times when the bottom ball hits the floor (we'll leave it to the exercises to investigate other ways of constructing Poincaré sections). As expected, we see that the attractor in phase-space is very simple in the nonchaotic case, $m_2 = m_1$, but very complicated in the chaotic regime, $m_2 = 2m_1$. With $m_2 = 9m_1$ we found nearly periodic behavior, and in this case the attractor displays very interesting structure that is in some ways intermediate between the other two cases considered in Figure 3.23. This is all we will say about the bouncing ball problem. Other facets of the problem are explored in the exercises.

---

[23] For this problem we could actually avoid these approximations by looking ahead and calculating the *exact* times and positions of the collisions. It is not hard to write such a program, and the results are essentially the same as those shown here.

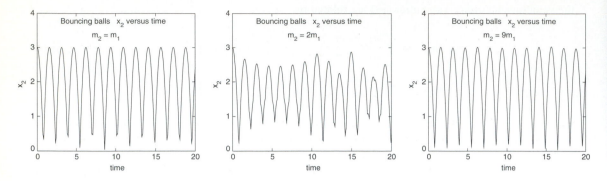

Figure 3.22: Results for x_2 as a function of time, for several different mass ratios. In each case we took $m_1 = 1$, $x_1(0) = 1$, $v_1(0) = 0$, $x_2(0) = 3$, and $v_2(0) = 0$. The time step was 0.0003. For convenience we take all of these quantities to be unitless.

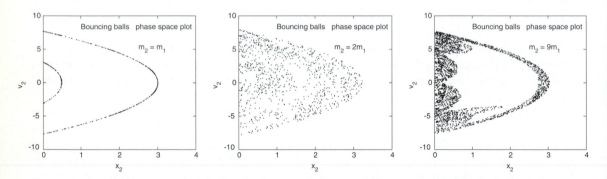

Figure 3.23: Phase-space plots corresponding to the $x_2(t)$ results in Figure 3.22. Here we have plotted v_2 versus x_2 each time ball number 1 hits the floor.

Exercises

1. Study the divergence of two nearby trajectories. Perform the calculation for different mass ratios and estimate qualitatively the corresponding Lyapunov exponents.

2. Construct a phase-space attractor by plotting v_2 as a function of x_2 at times when the two balls collide. Compare the results with the phase-space plots in Figure 3.23.

3. Compare the behavior when the heavy ball is on top with that found for the heavy ball on the bottom. Keep the mass ratio fixed.

*4. Add a third ball to the problem and investigate the behavior for different values of the masses.

*5. Write a program that implements collisions by looking ahead, that is, extrapolating the free-fall solutions (3.17) forward in time to determine where and when the next collision will take place. Then treat the collision as described above. Compare your results with the method used in this section.

3.7   Behavior in the Frequency Domain: Chaos and Noise

Our intuitive ideas concerning what it means to be chaotic usually include some connection with terms such as *random*, *unpredictable*, and *noisy*. We have already explored the first two notions; in this section we consider how chaotic behavior is connected with noise. For this we require several tools for dealing with time-dependent signals. These tools are discussed in Appendix 2 and rely on the Fourier transform.[24]

Our goal in this section is to Fourier analyze the time-dependent signals obtained in our simulations of the damped, nonlinear pendulum in Section 3.2. We will consider only the signals associated with the angular position of the pendulum, $\theta(t)$, although the same sort of analysis could be used with the angular velocity, $\omega(t)$. Such a signal can, in general, be a complicated function of time. Nevertheless, we show in Appendix 2 how it can always be decomposed into component waveforms that are simple sines and cosines.

A program to calculate this Fourier decomposition is given in Appendix 4 and employs the fast Fourier transform (FFT) algorithm. Here we will be concerned only with the frequency spectrum associated with $\theta(t)$, which can be derived using the power-spectrum program given in the appendix. Here the term *power* is used in the following sense. Typical signals of interest include the amplitudes of pressure waves, electrical voltages, and light waves. In such cases the square of the amplitude of a particular frequency component of the signal is proportional to the *intensity* of the signal at that frequency, which is in turn proportional to the power carried by the signal. An examination of the intensity as a function of frequency leads to the *power spectrum* discussed in Appendix 2. This term is commonly used, even in cases (such as the present one) where the connection with power and energy is not direct.[25]

The power spectra of several pendulum waveforms are shown in Figure 3.24, where we show the power spectrum of $\theta(t)$ as a function of frequency. The area under each peak in the spectrum is proportional to the effective power, that is, the sum of the squares of the corresponding Fourier components of the signal. At low drive, $F_D = 0.5$, the pendulum is in a period-1 state, in which the $\theta(t)$ waveform is very close to a simple sine wave. The FFT result shows a single peak at the frequency of this sine wave, that is, at the drive frequency. This is completely analogous to what we found for the FFT of a sine wave in Appendix 2. At somewhat higher drive $F_D = 0.95$, the behavior is again period-1, and we see that the power spectrum is again dominated by a single peak at the drive frequency. We also notice a very small peak at approximately three times the drive frequency (≈ 0.3 Hz). This peak is not a plotting error! It is produced by the nonlinearity of the waveform at this drive and is an example of the phenomenon of nonlinear mixing we mentioned earlier. The most interesting result is found in the chaotic regime, $F_D = 1.2$. The spectrum is now very complicated as the power is broadly

---

[24] Readers who are not familiar with the concept of Fourier analysis should review Appendix 2 before tackling this section.

[25] Although with the pendulum, the power spectrum of $\theta(t)$ will be closely connected with the kinetic energy of the system.

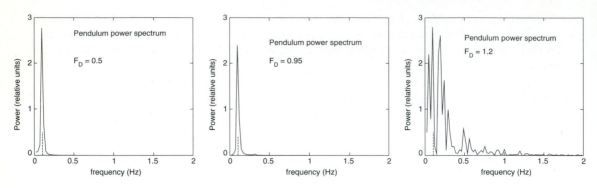

Figure 3.24:   Fourier analysis of the results for $\theta(t)$ for the nonlinear pendulum at different values of the driving force. At $F_D = 0.5$ and $F_D = 0.95$ the pendulum is in the period-1 regime, while for $F_D = 1.2$ it is chaotic. The dashed lines indicate the drive frequency.

distributed over a wide range of frequencies. This is just the noise that we intuitively expect to find in a chaotic system.

It is also interesting to examine the power spectra when the pendulum undergoes period-doubling on its way to the chaotic regime. Results from the period-2 regime are shown in Figure 3.25. There is a large peak at the drive frequency $\Omega_D/2\pi \approx 0.1$ Hz, with additional peaks at integer multiples of this frequency, as we again have the nonlinear mixing observed earlier. However, there is now a strong component at half this frequency, ≈ 0.05 Hz. This corresponds to a component with twice the period

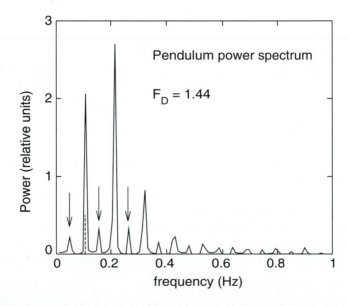

Figure 3.25:   Fourier analysis of the results for $\theta(t)$ for the nonlinear pendulum in the period-2 regime. The dashed line indicates the drive frequency. The arrows indicate the subharmonic (period-doubled) component, which appears at half the drive frequency, and some of its harmonics.

and is, therefore, the result of *period-doubling*. A similar analysis can be used to examine the behavior in the period-4, period-8, etc., regimes. If the behavior is period-n, there will be a spectral component at a frequency $1/n$ times the drive frequency. Hence, spectral analysis reveals the period-doubling route to chaos in an extremely clear manner.

The key result of this section is that much can be learned about the behavior of a system by examination of its frequency spectrum. Here we have used this approach to study the pendulum in and near its chaotic states. In later chapters we will use the same method in connection with several other problems.

Exercises

1. In Figure 3.24 we saw that at a relatively high drive, $F_D = 0.95$, there was a small, but noticeable response of the pendulum at three times the frequency of the driving force. Calculate the size of this component as a function of the drive force in the range $F_D = 0.95 - 1.00$. Try also to observe a component at five times the drive frequency. The process in which these signals at multiples of the drive frequency are produced is an example of mixing.

2. Analyze the behavior of the nonlinear pendulum in the period-4 regime and show that the spectral component with the lowest frequency has a frequency of one-fourth the drive frequency.

*3. We saw in connection with Figures 3.8 and 3.9 that every time a period-doubling threshold is crossed a new subharmonic component is added to the $\theta(t)$ waveform. The size of this component can be readily extracted using the Fourier transform. Calculate $\theta(t)$ for values of the drive amplitude near the period-2 transition in Figure 3.9. Then use the FFT to obtain the amplitude of the period-2 component as a function of F_D. Try to determine the functional form that describes the way in which this amplitude vanishes at the transition.

4. Analyze the power spectrum of $\omega(t)$ of the nonlinear pendulum for different values of the driving force.

5. Calculate the frequency spectra for the waveforms $z(t)$ for the Lorenz model. Compare the behavior in the chaotic, nonchaotic, intermittent, and period-doubled regimes.

References

CROMER, A. 1981. "Stable Solutions using the Euler Approximation." *Am. J. Phys.* **49**, 455. Discusses the Euler-Cromer method, and shows analytically that it conserves energy for oscillatory problems.

BAKER, G. L. and J. P. GOLLUB. 1990. *Chaotic Dynamics: an Introduction*. Cambridge: Cambridge University Press. A very readable introduction to chaotic behavior in simple systems. Discusses the logistic map extensively and also has a nice description of the damped nonlinear pendulum.

HILBORN, R. C. 1994. *Chaos and Nonlinear Dynamics: An Introduction for Scientists and Engineers*. Oxford: Oxford University Press. A thorough introduction to chaos. Goes into much more depth than we have had space to discuss in this chapter.

LORENZ, E. N. 1963. "Deterministic Nonperiodic Flow." *J. Atmos. Sci.* **20**, 130 The classic treatment of the Lorenz equations.

MAY, R. M. 1976. "Simple Mathematical Models with very Complicated Dynamics." *Nature* **261**, 459. A nice introduction to interated maps, such as the logistic map (3.11).

MOON, F. C. 1992. *Chaotic and Fractal Dynamics*. Redwood City: John Wiley & Sons. A nice discussion of a wide variety of chaotic systems. The overall level is somewhat more advanced than our treatment.

SPARROW, C. 1982. *The Lorenz Equations: Bifurcations, Chaos, and Strange Attractors*. New York: Springer-Verlag. Devoted entirely to the Lorenz model.

WOLF, A., J. B. SWIFT, H. L. SWINNEY, AND J. A. VASTANO. 1985. "Determining Lyapunov Exponents from a Time Series." *Physica* **16D**, 285. Estimating Lyapunov exponents quantitatively is not an easy task. This paper describes one way to do it.

4

The Solar System

In Chapter 2 we found that atmospheric drag plays a major role in the behavior of projectiles moving near the earth's surface. In some respects, this drag and other types of "friction" obscure the fundamental physical principles that govern the behavior.[1] If we want to study the essential consequences of these principles, it thus seems best to consider a system in which frictional forces are as small as possible. The solar system is just such a laboratory, and not surprisingly, studies of the motion of planets and moons provided major inspiration to the founders of classical mechanics.

In the present chapter we will consider several problems that arise in the study of planetary motion. We begin with the simplest situation, a sun and a single planet, and investigate a few of the properties of this model solar system. While a computational approach is not required in this case, the algorithm we develop will prove useful for later problems.

4.1 Kepler's Laws

Figure 4.1 shows our hypothetical solar system. There is one planet, which we will refer to as Earth, in orbit around the Sun and the only force in the problem is gravity. According to Newton's law of gravitation this force is given by

$$F_G = \frac{G M_S M_E}{r^2} , \qquad (4.1)$$

where M_S and M_E are the masses of the Sun and Earth, r the distance between them, and G is the gravitational constant. Let us assume that the Sun's mass is sufficiently large that its motion can be

---

[1]For example, Newton's first law is most clearly observed with systems in which friction is negligible.

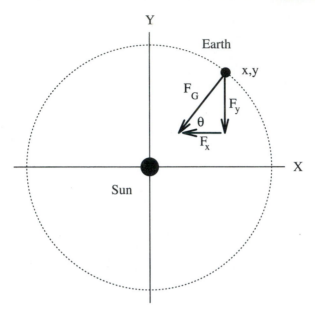

Figure 4.1:   Coordinate system for describing the motion of Earth in orbit around the Sun. The Sun is at the origin and Earth is located at coordinates (x, y).

neglected.[2] Our goal is to calculate the position of Earth as a function of time. From Newton's second law of motion we have

$$\frac{d^2x}{dt^2} = \frac{F_{G,x}}{M_E} \tag{4.2}$$

$$\frac{d^2y}{dt^2} = \frac{F_{G,y}}{M_E} ,$$

where $F_{G,x}$ and $F_{G,y}$ are the x and y components of the gravitational force. From Figure 4.1 we have

$$F_{G,x} = -\frac{G\,M_S\,M_E}{r^2}\cos\theta = -\frac{G\,M_S\,M_E\,x}{r^3} , \tag{4.3}$$

with a similar result for $F_{G,y}$. Here the negative signs remind us that the force is directed toward the Sun, which is located at the origin of our coordinate system.

We now follow our usual approach and write each of the second-order differential equations in (4.2) as two first-order differential equations

$$\frac{dv_x}{dt} = -\frac{G\,M_S\,x}{r^3} \tag{4.4}$$

_____

[2]This is a very good approximation for all of the problems we will be considering. However, it is not difficult to also allow for the Sun's motion. This will be explored in the exercises.

$$\frac{dx}{dt} = v_x$$

$$\frac{dv_y}{dt} = -\frac{G\,M_S\,y}{r^3}$$

$$\frac{dy}{dt} = v_y \, .$$

These can be converted into difference equations that can be solved numerically. However, before we proceed with that, it is useful to consider the choice of units. One option is to simply use SI units. There is no difficulty with this, except that meters and seconds do not match the scale of the problem. For example, the radius of Earth's orbit is $\sim 1.5 \times 10^{11}$ m. If we were to use SI units, a graph showing this orbit around the Sun would have labels of 1×10^{11}, 2×10^{11} m, etc. This would be awkward, though not impossibly so. It is much more convenient to use *astronomical units*, AU, which are defined as follows. One astronomical unit of length, known simply as 1 AU, is the average distance between the Sun and Earth ($\approx 1.5 \times 10^{11}$ m). It is convenient to measure time in years (1 year $\approx 3.2 \times 10^7$ s) since this unit matches the solar system better than, say, seconds. For the remainder of this chapter we will, therefore, use astronomical units for distance, and measure time in years, unless specifically noted otherwise.

To complete our system of units we also need the corresponding unit of mass. This is easily derived if we recall that Earth's orbit is, to a very good approximation, circular. For circular motion we know that the force must be equal to $M_E v^2 / r$, which leads to

$$\frac{M_E\,v^2}{r} = F_G = \frac{G\,M_S\,M_E}{r^2}\,, \tag{4.5}$$

where v is the velocity of Earth. Rearranging we find

$$G\,M_S = v^2\,r = 4\,\pi^2\,\text{AU}^3/\text{yr}^2\,, \tag{4.6}$$

where we have used the fact that the velocity of Earth is $2\pi r/(1\text{ yr}) = 2\pi$ (since $r = 1$ AU, again making the approximation that Earth's orbit is circular). Since G and M_S appear only as a product in (4.4) there is no need to express either term separately.

We next convert the equations of motion (4.4) into difference equations in preparation for constructing a computational solution. We find

$$v_{x,i+1} = v_{x,i} - \frac{4\,\pi^2\,x_i}{r_i^3}\,\Delta t \tag{4.7}$$

$$x_{i+1} = x_i + v_{x,i+1}\,\Delta t$$

$$v_{y,i+1} = v_{y,i} - \frac{4\,\pi^2\,y_i}{r_i^3}\,\Delta t$$

$$y_{i+1} = y_i + v_{y,i+1}\,\Delta t\,,$$

where, as usual, Δt is the time step and the factors of $4\pi^2 (= GM_S)$ signal that we are using astronomical units. Note that we have used the Euler-Cromer method. That is, we use the *previous* values of position and velocity to update the velocities, while the *previous* values of position and the *new* values of velocity are used to update the positions. As we discussed in Chapter 3, the Euler method is not a good choice for oscillatory problems, and planetary motion is just such a problem. If we were to use the Euler method here we would find that the energy of the planet would grow with time, and it would spiral away from the Sun. This difficulty is avoided with the Euler-Cromer method, since it conserves energy exactly over the course of each orbit.

We can use the techniques developed in previous chapters to translate (4.7) into a suitable program. The result is listed below.

```
! Planetary motion with the Euler-Cromer method
! N. Giordano   10-1-94
program kepler
   option nolet          ! don't need the graphics libraries for this program
   call initialize(x,v_x,y,v_y,dt)    ! set up initial conditions
   call calculate(x,v_x,y,v_y,dt)     ! do the calculation
end
! initialize variables
sub initialize(x,v_x,y,v_y,dt)
   input prompt "initial x position -> ": x
   input prompt "initial y position -> ": y
   input prompt "initial x velocity -> ": v_x
   input prompt "initial y velocity -> ": v_y
   input prompt "time step -> ": dt
                             ! now set up window for plotting
   aspect = 1.33            ! aspect ratio of screen - yours may be different
   r = 1.4 * sqr(x^2+y^2) ! pick a scale a bit larger than the planet's radius
   set window -r,r,-r/aspect,r/aspect  ! set window coordinates
   set color "black"
   clear
   plot -r,0;r,0                         ! plot axes
   plot 0,-r*aspect;0,r*aspect
end sub
! x,y = position of planet
! v_x,v_y = velocity of planet
! dt = time step
sub calculate(x,v_x,y,v_y,dt)
   do                          ! use Euler-Cromer method
      r = sqr(x^2 + y^2)
      v_x = v_x - (4 * pi^2 * x * dt) / r^3
      v_y = v_y - (4 * pi^2 * y * dt) / r^3
      set color "black"        ! keep trail of the planet black
      plot x,y
      x = x + v_x * dt
      y = y + v_y * dt
      set color "red"          ! current location of the planet is red
      plot x,y
   loop until key input        ! loop until any key is hit
end sub
```

The program employs two subroutines. As usual, `initialize` sets the time step and initial conditions. It now also prepares the screen for plotting. Rather than using `datagraph` as we have in all of our previous programs, we have chosen to use the `plot` command. This plots points directly on the screen, and we use it to display the planet's position as we loop through the calculation (this also eliminates the need for arrays to store the results prior to plotting). However, we must first set up the coordinate system, and this is accomplished with the `set window` command. The arguments

Table 4.1: Some useful planetary data. For all of the planets except Mercury and Pluto the orbits are very nearly circular. The orbits for Mercury and Pluto are noticeably elliptical (i.e., they deviate substantially from circular), and in these cases the entry under radius gives the semimajor axis of the ellipse (see Figure 4.3). Note that the mass of the Sun is 2.0×10^{30} kg.

planet	mass (kg)	radius (AU)	eccentricity
Mercury	2.4×10^{23}	0.39	0.206
Venus	4.9×10^{24}	0.72	0.007
Earth	6.0×10^{24}	1.00	0.017
Mars	6.6×10^{23}	1.52	0.093
Jupiter	1.9×10^{27}	5.20	0.048
Saturn	5.7×10^{26}	9.54	0.056
Uranus	8.8×10^{25}	19.19	0.046
Neptune	1.03×10^{26}	30.06	0.010
Pluto	$\sim 6.0 \times 10^{24}$	39.53	0.248

to `set window` are the minimum and maximum x, and minimum and maximum y coordinates of the screen. We choose these so that a circular orbit with a radius estimated from the initial conditions will fit comfortably on the screen. The variable `aspect` allows for the fact that the horizontal and vertical dimensions of the screen may not be the same. By setting it to the value appropriate for your screen, a circular orbit will appear as circular on the screen.

The `calculate` subroutine updates the velocity and position and plots the results as it proceeds through the loop. By changing colors before using the `plot` command we are able to display the current location of the planet in red, while its trail is black. Note again that we use the Euler-Cromer method. The loop in `calculate` terminates when any key is hit, through the `if key input` statement. This statement causes *True Basic* to check to see if a keystroke has been entered since the last `input` statement. If so, the test is satisfied.[3]

Our program can be used to simulate the motion of any planet. For your convenience, Table 4.1 lists orbital data for the planets in our solar system. The entry under "eccentricity" refers to the shape of each orbit and will be discussed further in the next section.

We have used our planetary orbit program to simulate the motion of Earth, and the results are shown in Figure 4.2. To perform this calculation we need to specify the initial conditions. As we have already noted, Earth's orbit is circular to a very good approximation. From Table 4.1 we see that the radius of the orbit is 1.00 AU (which we already knew from the definition of astronomical units), so for our simulation we have chosen an initial x coordinate of 1.0 and a y coordinate of zero. It is crucial that we also choose the proper initial velocity. A value that is too small will yield a narrow elliptical orbit oriented along the x axis, while a value that is too large will lead to an ellipse stretched along y. To estimate the value required to yield a circular orbit we recall that Earth completes one orbit in one year. The velocity is thus $2\pi r/1 = 2\pi$ AU/yr.

---

[3]Note that this occurs whether the return key has been hit or not. `if key input` checks for *any* keystroke. This is a handy feature of *True Basic*.

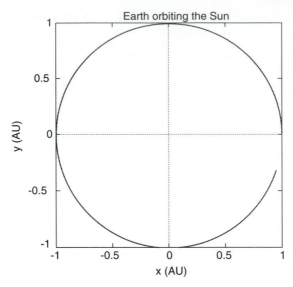

Figure 4.2: Results for a simulation of Earth orbiting around the Sun. The Sun was located at the origin ($x = 0$, $y = 0$), and the points on a circle with radius 1 AU (which are so close together that they partially overlap) show the calculated path of Earth. The time step was 0.002 yr, and the initial conditions were $x = 1$, $y = 0$, $v_x = 0$, $v_y = 2\pi$ (in AU and AU/yr, respectively). The program was stopped just before one orbit was completed.

Using these initial conditions we obtain the nicely circular orbit shown in Figure 4.2. If we had let the program run for many orbits, we would have found that the calculated path of Earth repeats itself to within the size of the points in the figure. We will see below that this repeatability is a general feature of orbits in a two-body solar system; that is, a system with one planet and one sun. The result in Figure 4.2 also demonstrates that the Euler-Cromer method is quite suitable for solar system calculations, and we will use it throughout this chapter.[4]

We can use our program to investigate Kepler's laws for planetary motion. You may recall that Johannes Kepler was a 17th century astronomer who performed a very careful study of the planetary data acquired earlier by Tycho Brahe. Kepler showed that Brahe's observations were consistent with the following three statements:

1. All planets move in elliptical orbits, with the Sun at one focus.

2. The line joining a planet to the Sun sweeps out equal areas in equal times.

3. If T is the period and a the semimajor axis of the orbit (Figure 4.3), then T^2/a^3 is a constant (i.e., the same constant for all of the planets). Note that for a circular orbit, a is just the radius of the orbit.

It can be shown analytically that all three of Kepler's laws are consequences of the fact that the gravitational force follows an inverse-square law, (4.1), and we will have more to say about such

---

[4]Other methods, such as the Runge-Kutta and Verlet methods discussed in Appendix 1, also work well for this problem.

Table 4.2: Confirmation of Kepler's third law. The results were obtained using the planetary orbit program to calculate the orbital periods of several planets.

planet	T^2/a^3 (yr^2/AU^3)
Venus	0.997
Earth	0.998
Mars	1.005
Jupiter	1.010
Saturn	0.988

matters in Section 4.2. Here we want to consider how our planetary orbit program can be used to confirm Kepler's third law. For simplicity we consider only the planets whose orbits are circular (we'll deal with the case of elliptical orbits in a later section). Table 4.1 gives the distance from the Sun, and by choosing the initial velocity appropriately[5] we can obtain circular orbits and thus simulate the motion of any of the planets. It is convenient to modify the program slightly to print out the value of the time when a planet passes a particular point on the orbit (such as where it crosses the x axis), as this makes it easier to accurately determine the period of an orbit. We'll leave this job to the reader. Table 4.2 lists the calculated values of T^2/a^3 for the planets Venus through Saturn. These planets all have orbits that are very nearly circular, so a is just the orbital radius listed in Table 4.1. According to Kepler's third law, T^2/a^3 should be a constant, and in astronomical units this constant is unity. Our numerical results are in agreement with this prediction and thus confirm Kepler's third law. The time steps used in these calculations were 0.001 yr for Venus, Earth, and Mars and 0.005 yr for Jupiter and Saturn, and this is the cause of the (small) deviations of the calculated values of T^2/a^3 in Table 4.2 from the ideal value of unity. We will leave it to the exercises to confirm Kepler's third law for noncircular orbits.

Exercises

1. Investigate the results obtained from the planetary motion program with different values of the time step. Show that for simulations of Earth, time steps greater than about $\Delta t = 0.01$ yr do not lead to satisfactory results. For such large time steps the orbits are not stable (i.e., not repeating). This is in accord with our general rule of thumb (Chapter 1) that the time step should be no larger than 1 percent or so of the characteristic time scale of the problem. In this case the characteristic time scale is the period of one orbit.

2. Change the planetary motion program so that it uses the Euler method. Show that Earth always spirals away from the Sun no matter how small the time step is made. Compare your results with those obtained using the Euler-Cromer method.

---

[5] As we have already noted, choosing the proper initial conditions is essential. Here we have used the initial positions given in Table 4.1 and chosen the initial velocity by trial and error so as to give a circular orbit, in accord with the actual orbits of these planets. The same values of the initial velocities could have been obtained from arguments like those used to obtain (4.5), but in a way this would be begging the question in a "test" of Kepler's third law. Our point here is simply to show that our planetary motion program correctly reproduces Kepler's third law for the particular case of circular orbits.

3. Modify the planetary orbit program so that you can use it to verify Kepler's second law for the case of an elliptical orbit. As part of this problem you might also check quantitatively that the orbits are indeed elliptical.

4. Investigate the orbit of Halley's comet. This comet has an orbital period of 76 yr and a distance of closest approach to the Sun of 0.59 AU. Use trial and error to determine its maximum orbital speed and maximum distance from the sun. How does its maximum distance compare with the orbit of Pluto?

5. Extend your (Euler-Cromer) orbit program so that it calculates the energy (kinetic, potential, and total) of the planet, and also the angular momentum. Consider the following issues.
   (a) Begin with a circular orbit and show that both the kinetic and potential energy are constants. The angular momentum should also be a constant.
   (b) Consider an elliptical orbit. An orbit with an initial position 1 AU from the Sun and a velocity of 5 AU/yr is a convenient choice. Show that while the kinetic and potential energies now vary as the planet moves through its orbit, their sum (the total energy) is a constant. Also show that the angular momentum is a constant during the course of the orbit. Prove that these results are direct consequences of the fact that the force of gravity is conservative, and is a central force (i.e., it acts along the line that runs between the Sun and the planet).

6. Consider a planet that begins a distance of 1 AU from the Sun. By trial and error, determine what its initial velocity must be in order for it to escape from the Sun. Compare your estimate with the exact result (which you should also calculate).

*7. Consider a hypothetical solar system consisting of a sun and one planet in which the mass of the sun is not much greater than the mass of the planet. Now you must allow for the motion of both the planet and the sun. Extend your planetary motion program to include this effect. You will have to deal with a set of equations such as those in (4.7) for both objects. Investigate the possible types of orbital motion found in such a system. Begin with a double star system in which the two objects are of equal mass. Then explore the behavior when the masses are unequal. Hint: In order to obtain the simplest orbits, it is best to pick initial conditions such that the total linear momentum is zero. While this problem can be handled with a stationary sun together with the concept of a reduced mass, this calculation is a necessary prelude to the study of orbits of planets in binary star systems, which we will consider in a later exercise.

4.2   The Inverse-Square Law and the Stability of Planetary Orbits

We mentioned in the previous section that Kepler's laws follow directly from the functional *form* of the gravitational force. A crucial point is that this force varies as the inverse of the square of the distance between the two objects. An inverse-square dependence is also found for the electric force between two charges (Coulomb's law), and this raises some interesting questions. Is there anything special or profound about the inverse-square dependence, or is it just an accident? Does the force vary exactly as $1/r^2$, or might it really go as $1/r^{2.0000000001}$? To answer the first question it is necessary to consider how the force "gets from one of the objects to the other." Or, to put it another way, how do the masses

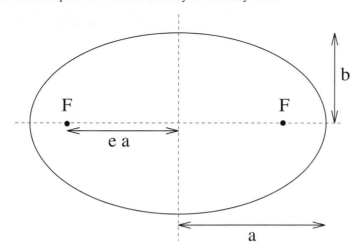

Figure 4.3: Hypothetical elliptical orbit. A sun lies at one of the foci of the ellipse; both foci are labeled F. The semimajor and semiminor axes are a and b, and the eccentricity is e. This drawing is not to scale.

know about each other? A useful classical picture involves lines of force or (equivalently) field lines.[6] Here we imagine that gravitational field lines emanate from all objects that have mass and that these lines radiate outward to infinity, that is, they never terminate. The number of such lines is proportional to the mass of the object, and the force felt by a second, nearby object is proportional to the number of lines that intersect it. As the separation between the two objects is increased, the number of intersecting field lines drops because the lines are spreading out over an ever larger surface area as they move away from their source.

The inverse-square law follows naturally from this field-line picture. The area of a sphere of radius r that surrounds an object is proportional to r^2. Since a fixed number of lines, say N, emanate from an object, the density of these field lines as they cut through such a sphere is proportional to N/r^2. The inverse-square law is thus a direct consequence of the field-line picture together with the geometry of the Euclidean space in which we live.[7]

These arguments concerning the inverse-square law have all been theoretical. We should also consider what the real world has to say about this matter. Since, as noted above, Kepler's laws are predicted to be a direct consequence of the inverse-square law, we can use experimental tests of Kepler's laws to determine if gravity really does follow an inverse-square law. One way to accomplish this can be seen in Figure 4.3, which shows the geometry of a hypothetical elliptical orbit. Among other things, Kepler's laws tell us that the orientation of such an orbit does not change with time. More precisely, if we have a solar system consisting of a sun and one planet, and that planet follows an elliptical orbit, it is predicted that the orientation of the axes of the ellipse does not change with time.

---

[6]A quantum mechanical picture would, of course, be somewhat different. However, an inverse-square law has profound implications in that case as well.

[7]Again, this a classical picture.

Now let us suppose that the force law deviates slightly from an inverse-square dependence.[8] To be specific, suppose that the gravitational force is of the form[9]

$$F_G = \frac{G\, M_S\, M_E}{r^\beta}.$$ (4.8)

If $\beta = 2$, then we have an inverse-square law, but we also want to consider the motion of our planet for values of β that are different from 2. The behavior of elliptical orbits with this force law can be simulated with the planetary motion program given above by simply changing the exponent of r in the equations for the velocity.

Figure 4.4 shows a result for $\beta = 2$, that is, an inverse-square law. We have chosen the initial conditions to give an elliptical orbit, and it is seen that, as advertised, the sun is *not* at the center of the orbit. This is expected, since according to Kepler's first law the sun should be at one focus of the ellipse. The other point to note about this result is that we have plotted the position over the course of many orbits. The calculated orbit is seen to accurately retrace itself, demonstrating that the orientation of the ellipse does not change with time. This confirms some of the things we have claimed concerning Kepler's laws.

Interesting things happen when we make β different from 2. Results for $\beta = 3.00$, an *inverse-cube* law, are shown in Figure 4.5. The behavior is *very* different from the inverse-square case. A planet in this solar system would not even follow a stable (i.e., repeating) orbit.[10] The hypothetical planet in Figure 4.5 passes very near its sun and is then, because of numerical errors (due to the time step being too large during the close approach with the sun), ejected from the solar system. The result for $\beta = 2.50$ is not quite as dramatic; the planet is seen to follow an approximately elliptical path, with the axes of the ellipse rotating through an angle of nearly $360°$ after only three orbits.

As β is made closer to 2 the orbits become somewhat more stable, although even for $\beta = 2.01$ the ellipse still rotates significantly after only a few orbits. Indeed, comparing these results with those for $\beta = 2$ we see that the behavior is *extremely* sensitive to deviations from an inverse-square law (see Figure 4.6). This suggests that we might be able to use observations of planetary orbits to determine by what amount (if any) nature deviates from a perfect inverse-square law.

Such an experiment would not be as simple as our calculations here suggest. You may have noticed that in our discussions of Kepler's laws we have often referred to a two-body solar system consisting of a sun and just one planet. Of course, the real world is not that simple. There are nine planets to worry about, and any complete simulation would have to include the gravitational force of each planet on all of the others. We will study this problem in later sections. Here we only note that the forces from the other planets can also cause an elliptical orbit to rotate with time.[11] Hence,

---

[8]As we will discuss shortly, general relativity leads to such deviations, although they have a functional form that is different from (4.8). We will consider the effect of general relativity on elliptical orbits in the next section.

[9]Note that if the value of β is different than 2, this will alter the units of G. For simplicity we will assume here that r is always measured in AU and use $GM_S = 4\pi^2$ throughout.

[10]You might think that if the orbit was perfectly circular with $r = 1$ AU, then, since $r^2 = r^3$ in this case, such an orbit with $\beta = 3$ would be stable. However, it turns out that for this value of β, *any* small deviations of r away from unity (as from round-off errors in a calculation, or the effects of other planets in a real solar system) are rapidly amplified, and such an orbit is still unstable.

[11]This should not be surprising, since all of the planets orbit in the same direction (i.e., their angular momentum vectors are parallel), so the mutual attraction from gravity tends to drag the lighter planets along with the heavier ones.

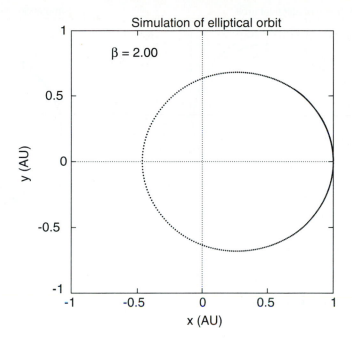

Figure 4.4: Elliptical orbit calculated for a force law with $\beta = 2$. The time step here, and in all of the calculations shown in this section, was 0.001 yr. We also used the same initial conditions in all of these simulations. The sun is at the origin.

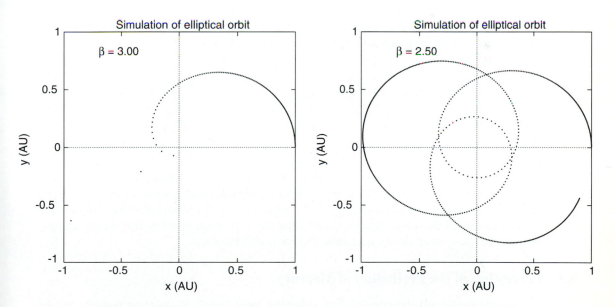

Figure 4.5: Elliptical orbits calculated for a force law (4.8) with $\beta = 3$ (left) and $\beta = 2.50$ (right).

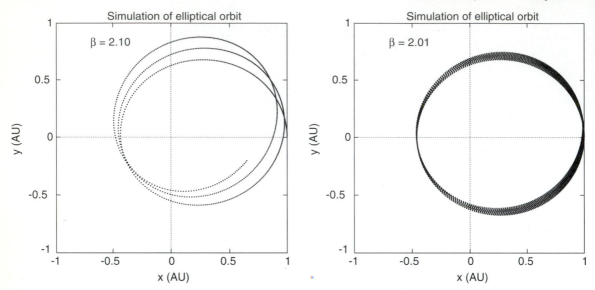

Figure 4.6:   Elliptical orbits calculated for a force law (4.8) with $\beta = 2.1$ (left) and $\beta = 2.01$ (right).

an experiment aimed at determining β through deviations from Kepler's laws would have to account carefully for the effects of the other planets.

Exercises

1. Verify Kepler's third law for elliptical orbits. Run the planetary motion program with initial conditions chosen to give orbits that are noncircular. Calculate T^2/a^3 and compare with the values given in Table 4.2.

*2. In this section we saw that orbits are unstable for any value of β that is not precisely 2 in (4.8). A related question, which we did not address (until now), is *how* unstable an orbit might be. That is, how long will it take for an unstable orbit to become obvious. The answer to this question depends on the nature of the orbit. If the initial velocity is chosen so as to make the orbit precisely circular, then the value of β in (4.8) will make absolutely no difference. Of course, in practice it is impossible to construct an orbit that is exactly circular, so the instabilities when $\beta \neq 2$ will always be apparent given enough time. Even so, orbits that start out as nearly circular will remain almost stable for a longer period than those that are highly elliptical. Investigate this by studying orbits with the same value of β (say, $\beta = 2.05$) and comparing the behavior with different values of the ellipticity of the orbit. You should find that the orientation of orbits that are more nearly circular will rotate more slowly than those that are highly elliptical.

4.3   Precession of the Perihelion of Mercury

In Section 4.2 we mentioned the possibility of using the solar system in an experiment to test the accuracy of the inverse-square law. In fact, such an experiment essentially has already been performed.

Astronomy is a precise science. We mentioned earlier that Kepler inferred his laws from observations made by Tycho Brahe. What we didn't mention was that Brahe's observations were all made *by eye*; the telescope had not yet been invented! With the availability of telescopes and improvements in timekeeping, astronomical observations became even more precise.[12] This prompted impressive advances in celestial mechanics, the branch of physics concerned with the motion of planets and other objects in the universe. You might think that Kepler's laws provide all of the information a celestial mechanic would ever require, but this is far from the case. In a solar system with more than one planet there will be deviations from Kepler's laws. For our solar system these deviations are small, so Kepler's laws form an extremely useful starting point for discussing the planets we know. Nevertheless, there are deviations from these laws. These deviations come from a number of sources, including the effects of the planets on each other. It turns out that this is a problem for which very few exact results are known (even today). One of the jobs of a celestial mechanic is to calculate such effects.

We have noted several times that most of the planets have orbits that are very nearly circular. The planets whose orbits deviate the most from circular are Mercury and Pluto, and this leads to interesting consequences in both cases. For Mercury it was known by the early part of the 19th century that the orientation of the axes of the ellipse that describes its orbit rotate with time. This is known as the precession of the perihelion of Mercury (the perihelion is the point in an orbit when a planet is nearest the Sun). The magnitude of this precession is approximately 566 arcseconds per century (an arcsecond is 1/3600 of a degree). That is, Mercury's perihelion makes one complete rotation every $\approx 230,000$ years. That such a small effect can be measured so accurately is a striking demonstration of the precision of astronomical measurements. This deviation from Kepler's law was of great interest to celestial mechanics, and by the middle of the 19th century it had been calculated that the gravitational forces of the other known planets[13] lead to a precession of 523 arcseconds/century. Jupiter, which is by far the largest planet, is responsible for most of this. Perhaps most amazing is the fact that this calculation of the precession was performed "by hand" in a numerical computation involving log tables and the like, long before computers were available!

While the precision of both the experimental measurement and the theoretical calculation of the precession of Mercury's perihelion are very impressive, the fact remained that they did not agree. It was realized, of course, that this disagreement might be evidence for some interesting new physics, and various solutions to this puzzle were proposed. One of the most popular (for a while at least) was the suggestion that there might be another planet whose orbit was inside that of Mercury. However, such a planet was never found. It was also suggested that there might be a large amount of dust orbiting near the Sun, whose gravitational attraction was affecting Mercury, but again this proposal was never confirmed.

This troubling discrepancy was not explained until 1917 when Einstein developed the theory of general relativity. That theory deals with the geometry of space and views gravity in a much more complicated manner than our simple picture of Euclidean space and the inverse-square law (4.1). Nevertheless, general relativity leads to a similar prediction for the force due to gravity, provided that the two objects are not too close together (or equivalently, not too massive). However, if the separation between the two objects is made small enough, general relativity predicts deviations from

---

[12] Astronomers have to measure not only *where* an object is located, but also *when* it is there.

[13] At that time only eight planets were known. Pluto was not discovered until 1930, but it is too small and too far away to have a significant effect on Mercury.

the inverse-square law. It turns out that the Sun and Mercury are close enough for these deviations
to just be significant, and Einstein showed that they precisely account for the previously unexplained
43 arcseconds of precession. This was one of the first triumphs of the theory of general relativity.

The precession due to general relativity can be calculated analytically, although to do so is fairly
complicated. However, it is actually very straightforward to deal with this problem computationally
(which is why we have devoted a section to it!). All we have to do is simulate the orbital motion using
the force law predicted by general relativity and measure the rate of precession of the orbit, much as
we did in the previous section. However, the precession rate is fairly small, so we have to design our
simulation with that in mind (we don't want to have to compute the motion for 230,000 years).

The force law predicted by general relativity is

$$F_G \approx \frac{G \, M_S \, M_M}{r^2} \left(1 + \frac{\alpha}{r^2} \right) , \tag{4.9}$$

where M_M is the mass of Mercury and[14] $\alpha \approx 1.1 \times 10^{-8}$ AU^2. The force is seen to be an inverse-square
law with a very small additional piece[15] that is proportional to $1/r^4$. The effects of this tiny deviation
from an inverse-square law are too small to measure easily in a computer simulation. The approach we
take here is to calculate the rate of precession as a function of α, with values of α that are much larger
than the actual value for Mercury. It will turn out that the rate of precession is given by $C\alpha$, where C is
a constant that we will calculate. After we have obtained the value of C, we can then estimate the rate
of precession for $\alpha = 1.1 \times 10^{-8}$, which is the case that we are really interested in.

To carry out this approach we first need to modify our planetary motion program to employ the
force law (4.9), with α as an adjustable parameter. We will leave this job for the exercises. Next we need
to determine the initial conditions required to obtain the orbit of Mercury. This is important, since the
behavior depends on both the size of the orbit and also its eccentricity. The length of the semimajor axis
(see Figure 4.7) for Mercury's orbit is $a = 0.39$ AU. The corresponding velocity, v_1, which we require
as an initial condition for the simulation, can be estimated in either of two ways. One is to calculate
the motion for different trial values of v_1 and adjust its value until the eccentricity of the resulting orbit
agrees with the known value, $e = 0.206$. A second approach is to make use of the conservation of both
energy and angular momentum over the course of an orbit to calculate v_1. This approach can be carried
out with the help of Figure 4.7.

Conservation of total energy (kinetic plus potential) implies that the energies at points 1 and 2 in
Figure 4.7 are the same. Thus

$$-\frac{G \, M_S \, M_M}{r_1} + \frac{1}{2} M_M v_1^2 = -\frac{G \, M_S \, M_M}{r_2} + \frac{1}{2} M_M v_2^2 . \tag{4.10}$$

The terms on the left-hand side of this equation are just the potential and kinetic energies at point 1 in
Figure 4.7, and the terms on the right are the corresponding energies at point 2 (here we don't need to
worry about the extremely small contribution of the general relativistic term in the potential). Since the

---

[14]α can be expressed in terms of the speed of light, the mass of the Sun, the eccentricity of the orbit, and other similar
parameters (see Goldstein [1990], Chapter 11). This general relativistic effect is most noticeable for Mercury because it is the
planet closest to the Sun.

[15]The term involving α in (4.9) is actually just the first of a series of such terms, which can be written as an expansion in
powers of r^{-1}. For Mercury it is accurate to stop with the first correction term, as we have done here.

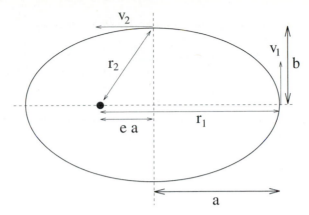

Figure 4.7:   Definition of the parameters necessary for a calculation of the initial conditions needed for a simulation of Mercury's elliptical orbit. Points 1 and 2 are the places where the orbit crosses the x and y axes, respectively.

force of gravity is a central force, it exerts no torque on the planet. Hence, the angular momentum at point 1 is equal to that at point 2, which yields

$$r_1 \, v_1 \; = \; b \, v_2 \, . \tag{4.11}$$

We thus have two equations involving the unknowns v_1 and v_2. After several lines of algebra (we'll leave that to you) we find

$$v_1 \; = \; \sqrt{2\,G\,M_S \left[\frac{b^2}{a^2(1+e)^2 - b^2} \right] \left[\frac{1}{\sqrt{e^2 a^2 + b^2}} - \frac{1}{a + ea} \right]} \; = \; \sqrt{\frac{G\,M_S\,(1-e)}{a\,(1+e)}} \, , \tag{4.12}$$

where in the last step we have used the fact that $b = a\sqrt{1 - e^2}$. Inserting the values of a and e given above yields $v_1 = 8.2$ AU/yr, and this is one of our initial conditions. The other is the distance from Mercury to the Sun, which is $r_1 = (1 + e)a = 0.47$ AU.

Now that the initial conditions are known we can simulate the motion of Mercury. The result obtained using the force law (4.9) with $\alpha = 0.01$ is shown in Figure 4.8. This value of α is *much* larger than the true value for Mercury, and it is seen that the ellipse precesses very noticeably in this case. The lines drawn from the Sun to the orbit show the orientation of the long axis of the ellipse. They are drawn from the origin (which is where the Sun is located) to the points on each orbit that are farthest from the Sun. These points are found by monitoring the distance of Mercury from the Sun and noting when its time derivative changes from positive to negative. These lines are very useful for our calculation, since the angles they make with the x axis are the amounts the orbit has precessed.

The next step is to calculate the angle of precession as a function of time for a particular value of α. A plot of this angle, which is the angle the radial lines in Figure 4.8 make with the x axis as a function of time is shown in Figure 4.9. We see that the precession angle θ varies linearly with time. This means that the precession rate is a constant, which is what we have assumed implicitly all along.

The rate of precession, $d\theta/dt$, is the slope of the line in Figure 4.9. To obtain this slope we have two choices. One is to simply draw in a line by hand through the points and estimate its slope. A

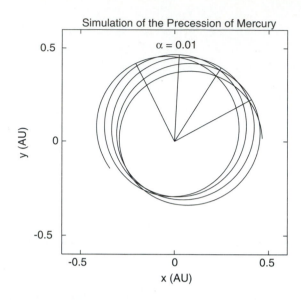

Figure 4.8: Simulated orbit for Mercury orbiting the Sun. The force law (4.9) was used, with $\alpha = 0.01$. The time step was 0.0001 yr. The program was stopped after several orbits. The solid lines emanating from the Sun (i.e., the origin) are drawn to the points on the orbit that are farthest from the Sun, so as to show the precession of the orientation of the orbit.

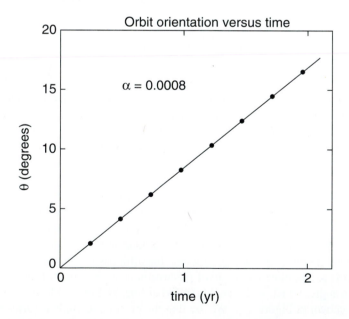

Figure 4.9: Precession of the axis of Mercury's orbit as a function of time, calculated for $\alpha = 0.0008$. The time step was 0.0001 yr. The solid line is a least-squares fit.

much better approach is to calculate the equation of the best-fit line. By this we mean the line that comes closest to passing through all of the points. If we had somehow been able to perform a perfect calculation of θ as a function of t, all of our points would lie exactly on a line. Alas, things are not this simple. Numerical errors (due to the nonzero value of the time step, etc.) will cause the points to deviate from such an ideal result. We would, therefore, like to somehow choose a line that comes as close as possible to all of the points (sort of a grand compromise). The conventional way to choose this line is with the method of least squares, which is discussed in Appendix 3. This is a very powerful method of "fitting" straight lines (or, more generally, smooth curves) to noisy data; here the data are our results for θ. This least-squares line is determined in the following way. Since, as we have already mentioned, the data do not all fall precisely on a single line, any line we imagine will deviate somewhat from at least some of the points. In our specific case, the values of θ defined by any line will in general deviate somewhat from the calculated values in Figure 4.9. With the method of least squares we choose a line so as to minimize the sum of the squares of these deviations. This approach is discussed at greater length in Appendix 3, where we show how to calculate the slope and intercept of the least-squares line. It turns out that there is a unique solution for this problem. That is, there is one and only one least-squares line. Moreover, it is not hard to calculate.

Let us now return to the precession of the perihelion of Mercury. The solid line in Figure 4.9 is the least-squares line for these calculated values of $\theta(t)$. The equation of this line was obtained using the least-squares subroutine that is part of the *True Basic* scientific graphics library, so it took us very little effort to modify our program to include it. If you are using a different language package, or just prefer to do things for yourself, Appendix 4 contains the listing of a least-squares program. We see from Figure 4.9 that the least-squares line does indeed provide an excellent fit to the results for $\theta(t)$. The slope of this best-fit line then gives the precession rate for this particular value of α. We can now repeat the calculation with different values of α and obtain the best-fit precession rate in each case. The results of such a calculation are shown in Figure 4.10 where we plot the precession rate as a function of α. We see that the precession rate itself varies linearly with α. We can again use the method of least squares to describe these results, and the best-fit line is also shown in Figure 4.10. The slope of this line is 1.11×10^4 degrees per year per unit α. Now we are finally ready to finish off our calculation. Since we have found that the precession rate varies linearly with α and we have calculated the coefficient of proportionality, we can extrapolate to the case $\alpha = 1.1 \times 10^{-8}$ predicted by the theory of general relativity. This yields a precession rate of $1.1 \times 10^{-8} \times 1.11 \times 10^4 \approx 1.2 \times 10^{-4}$ degrees/year, which is also equal to ≈ 43 arcseconds/century, in agreement with the experimental result mentioned at the beginning of this section.

Our study of the precession of the perihelion of Mercury has illustrated several useful techniques. One is the use of extrapolation to deal with situations in which the effects of interest are too small to conveniently estimate directly with a numerical approach. Of course, you must have some confidence in how the extrapolation should be made. In the present case we were able to show that a linear extrapolation as a function of α is appropriate. The second useful technique we have introduced is the method of least squares. We will use it again in later chapters.

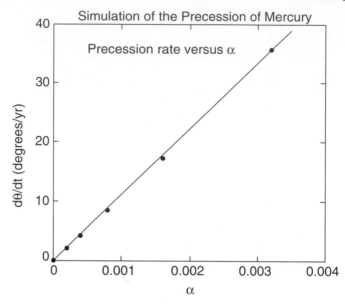

Figure 4.10:   Precession rate of Mercury as a function of α. The solid line is a least-squares fit, which yielded a slope of 1.11×10^4 degrees per year per unit α.

Exercises

1. Calculate the precession of the perihelion of Mercury, following the approach described in this section.

*2. Investigate how the precession of the perihelion of a planet's orbit due to general relativity varies as a function of the eccentricity of the orbit. Study the precession of different elliptical orbits with different eccentricities, but with the same value of the perihelion. Let the perihelion have the same value as for Mercury, so that you can compare it with the results shown in this section.

4.4   The Three-body Problem and the Effect of Jupiter on Earth

To this point all of our planetary simulations have involved two-body solar systems. It is now time to consider some of the things that can happen when there are three or more objects in the solar system. The problem of two objects interacting through the inverse-square law (4.1) can be solved exactly (as we have already mentioned), leading to Kepler's laws. However, if we add just one more planet to give what is known as the three-body problem, an analytic theory becomes *much* more difficult. In fact, there are very few exact results in this case, even though it has been studied extensively for several centuries. Indeed, the three-body, or more generally the n-body problem, is *the* problem of celetial mechanics.

In this section we consider one of the simplest three-body problems, the Sun and two planets, which we will take to be Earth and Jupiter. We know that without Jupiter, Earth's orbit is stable and

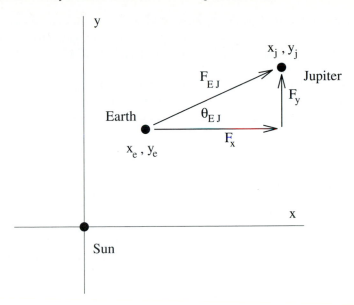

Figure 4.11:   Components of the gravitational force due to Jupiter, located at x_j, y_j, with Earth at x_e, y_e. The Sun is at the origin.

unchanging with time.[16]   Our objective is to observe how much effect the gravitational force from Jupiter has on Earth's motion. We consider Jupiter since it is the largest planet in the solar system.

To carry out this simulation we must modify our planetary-motion program to include two planets and the gravitational force between them. The magnitude of the force between Jupiter and Earth is given by our now familiar inverse-square law, with the Sun replaced by Jupiter

$$F_{E,J} \;=\; \frac{G\,M_J\,M_E}{r_{EJ}^2}\;, \tag{4.13}$$

where M_J is the mass of Jupiter and r_{EJ} the distance between Earth and Jupiter. Splitting this into components yields (see Figure 4.11)

$$F_{EJ,x} \;=\; -\frac{G\,M_J\,M_E}{r_{EJ}^2}\,\cos\theta_{EJ} \;=\; -\frac{G\,M_J\,M_E\,(x_e - x_j)}{r_{EJ}^3}\;, \tag{4.14}$$

for the x component of the force, with a corresponding result for the y component. Here x_e and x_j are the coordinates of Earth and Jupiter (the Sun remains at the origin), and θ_{EJ} is the angle defined in Figure 4.11. The total force on Earth in the x direction will be the sum of the forces of gravity from the Sun (4.3) and Jupiter (4.14), yielding the equation of motion for the x component of Earth's velocity, $v_{x,e}$

$$\frac{dv_{x,e}}{dt} \;=\; -\frac{G\,M_S\,x_e}{r^3} \;-\; \frac{G\,M_J\,(x_e - x_j)}{r_{EJ}^3}\;, \tag{4.15}$$

---

[16]Ignoring general relativity, whose effect is much smaller for Earth than it is for Mercury.

where r is again the distance from Earth to the Sun. We can convert this and the corresponding result for $v_{y,e}$, into difference equations, just as we did in (4.7). The only thing left to do is calculate GM_J in the appropriate units. Here it is simplest to just use the result $GM_J = GM_S(M_J/M_S) = 4\pi^2(M_J/M_S)$, with M_J and M_S given in Table 4.1.

Our program to calculate the orbits of two planets is listed below. Actually, we only give the calculate subroutine, as the initialization follows the same pattern as in our program for a single planet in Section 4.1.

```
! x_earth,y_earth = position of earth
! v_x_earth,v_y_earth = velocity of earth
! x_jupiter,y_jupiter = position of jupiter
! v_x_jupiter,v_y_jupiter = velocity of jupiter
! m_e = mass of earth
! m_j = mass of jupiter
! m_s = mass of sun
! dt = time step
sub calculate(x_earth,v_x_earth,y_earth,v_y_earth,x_jupiter,v_x_jupiter,
                           y_jupiter,v_y_jupiter,m_s,m_e,m_j,dt)
   do                            ! use the Euler-Cromer method
      r = sqr(x_earth^2 + y_earth^2)
      r_j = sqr(x_jupiter^2 + y_jupiter^2)
      r_ej = sqr((x_earth-x_jupiter)^2 + (y_earth-y_jupiter)^2)
      v_x_earth = v_x_earth - 4 * pi^2 * x_earth * dt / r^3
                  - 4 * pi^2 * (m_j/m_s) * (x_earth-x_jupiter) * dt / r_ej^3
      v_y_earth = v_y_earth - (4 * pi^2 * y_earth * dt) / r^3
                  - 4 * pi^2 * (m_j/m_s) * (y_earth-y_jupiter) * dt / r_ej^3
      v_x_jupiter = v_x_jupiter - 4 * pi^2 * x_jupiter * dt / r_j^3
                  - 4 * pi^2 * (m_e/m_s) * (x_jupiter-x_earth) * dt / r_ej^3
      v_y_jupiter = v_y_jupiter - (4 * pi^2 * y_jupiter * dt) / r_j^3
                  - 4 * pi^2 * (m_e/m_s) * (y_jupiter-y_earth) * dt / r_ej^3
      set color "black"      ! keep trail of the planet black
      plot x_earth,y_earth
      plot x_jupiter,y_jupiter
      x_earth = x_earth + v_x_earth * dt
      y_earth = y_earth + v_y_earth * dt
      x_jupiter = x_jupiter + v_x_jupiter * dt
      y_jupiter = y_jupiter + v_y_jupiter * dt
      set color "red"           ! current location of the planets are red
      plot x_earth,y_earth
      plot x_jupiter,y_jupiter
   loop until key input         ! loop until any key is hit
end sub
```

The organization is the same as in our earlier program, except that we now have to update the velocities and positions of two planets each time through the main loop. We have used the names earth and jupiter for the planets, but with suitable initial conditions they could be any two planets (real or imagined). A note about program efficiency should also be made here. You may have noticed that the Euler-Cromer equations in calculate contain factors such as $4\pi^2 M_J/M_S$. The way we have written the code, these factors may be recomputed each time through the loop. However, we could have arranged to calculate them just once at the beginning of the program, thereby saving some time during each iteration. As we have noted in previous chapters, it is usually our policy to sacrifice speed for clarity. You might argue that with the proper use of comment statements the reduction of clarity can be made very small. While this is correct, we would argue in response that the increase in program

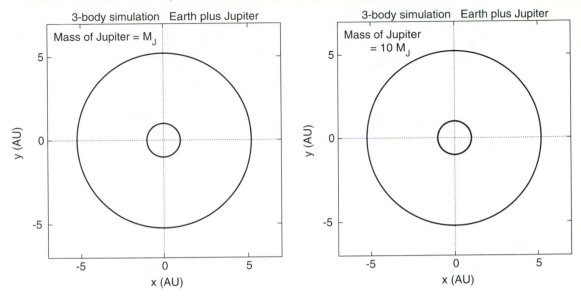

Figure 4.12:   Simulation of a solar system with two planets, Earth and Jupiter. Left: Jupiter has its true mass; right: the mass of Jupiter has been set to 10 times its true mass.

speed is probably also very small. Indeed, most modern compilers and interpreters would probably recognize that our factors of $4\pi^2 M_J/M_S$ do not have to be recomputed each time and would store them accordingly. Hence, we would have both our clarity and efficiency. In any case, if you do insist on expending extra effort to make a program execute as fast as possible, we have two recommendations. First, don't spend much time at this until *after* the program is working. Second, use a profiling tool or other means to determine which part(s) of the program is limiting the overall speed. Chances are that only one routine or loop will need to be tuned, so you might as well concentrate your efforts on it.

Some results from this simulation are shown in Figure 4.12. Using parameters appropriate for Earth and Jupiter, we find that both of the planets follow stable circular orbits. Thus, Jupiter has a negligible effect on Earth (at least on this scale). This should not be terribly surprising; we know that Earth has been orbiting the Sun for several billion years, so the orbit must be fairly stable! We can also use our simulation to calculate what would happen if the mass of Jupiter were somehow increased. Giving Jupiter a mass of $10M_J$, that is, 10 times its actual value, has no discernible effect on Earth (at least on the scale of this figure). However, if the mass of Jupiter is increased to $100M_J$, Figure 4.13, Earth's orbit is no longer a stable circle. Here we have plotted many orbits and they have overlapped to the point where Earth's path appears as a solid band in this plot. If we were to consider each orbit separately we would find that each is somewhat elliptical, with the orientation of the ellipse rotating with time. Giving Jupiter a mass of $1000M_J$ causes Earth's orbit to be completely unstable.[17]

The conclusion from this simulation is that Jupiter is (fortunately) too small to have a major influence on Earth. However, Jupiter is much closer to Mars, so there will be a larger effect in that case.

---

[17]This is not very realistic since Jupiter would then be about as massive as the Sun, and we would have a double-star system.

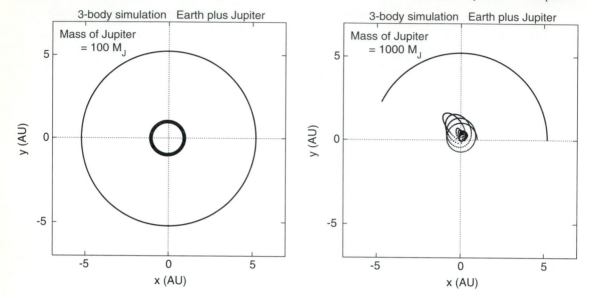

Figure 4.13:   Simulation of a solar system with two planets, Earth and Jupiter. Left: the mass of Jupiter has been set to 100 times its true mass; right: the mass of Jupiter has been set to 1000 times its true mass. Here we stopped the simulation before Jupiter had completed even half an orbit, as the motion of Earth was unstable.

We will leave it to the exercises to investigate this issue. In the next section we will consider the effect of Jupiter on the asteroids that orbit the Sun in the region between Mars and Jupiter.

Exercises

1. Investigate the effect of Jupiter on Mars.

2. Explore the orbits of a planet in a double-star system. Write a program that computes the motion of both stars along with that of the planet, including the gravitational forces of both stars on the planet and on each other. Explore the nature of the planetary orbits, and try to discover stable, repeating ones. Hint: First consider the case of two stars of equal mass, and pay special attention to planetary orbits that are especially symmetric with respect to the orbits of the stars.

*3. In our discussion of the precession of the perihelion of Mercury we mentioned that the other planets cause most of the observed precession. As the largest planet, Jupiter is responsible for most of this. Calculate the precession of the perihelion of Mercury due to Jupiter. We suggest that you perform the calculation by giving Jupiter a mass that is much larger than its true value, and then extrapolate to obtain the final result.

4.5   Resonances in the Solar System: Kirkwood Gaps and Planetary Rings

Table 4.1 gives the distances between the nine planets and the Sun. It is interesting to note that these distances grow in a seemingly regular manner, with the spacing between adjacent planets increasing as

Table 4.3: Comparison of the actual semimajor axes of the planetary orbits, a, with the predictions of the Titus-Bode formula.

Planet	a (actual) (AU)	Titus-Bode (AU)
Mercury	0.39	0.40
Venus	0.72	0.70
Earth	1.00	1.00
Mars	1.52	1.60
???	–	2.80
Jupiter	5.20	5.20
Saturn	9.54	10.00
Uranus	19.19	19.60
Neptune	30.06	38.80
Pluto	39.53	77.20

we go outward from the Sun. In fact, this pattern can be described by what is known as the Titus-Bode formula (see Peterson [1993]). According to that formula, the distances from the planets to the Sun are closely related to the sequence of integers

$$0, 3, 6, 12, 24, \ldots \tag{4.16}$$

which is obtained by starting with the integers 0 and 3 and letting each succeeding term be just twice the term before. To derive the distance from a planet to the Sun, the corresponding term in this sequence is added to 4 and the result divided by 10 (in AU). In this formula, the first planet is Mercury, the second Venus, etc. The values calculated from the Titus-Bode formula are given in Table 4.3, where we also list the actual planetary distances for comparison.

The agreement is quite respectable for the planets Mercury through Uranus, although we might well be skeptical that the Titus-Bode formula simply describes a trend, but doesn't contain any real physics. On the other hand, it is interesting to note that Uranus was discovered *after* the Titus-Bode formula was proposed. The predictions for Neptune and Pluto are not as good, but nothing is perfect. Perhaps the most striking result in Table 4.3 is that a planet is missing. We don't mean this literally, of course; the point is that the formula predicts a planet between Mars and Jupiter, but none is known in that region. Now, if you don't believe in the Titus-Bode formula, you would not find this to be disturbing. However, 200 years ago, when the formula was first proposed, some astronomers did take it seriously. It was, therefore, the source of some excitement when, in about 1800, a "planet" with an orbital radius of approximately of 2.8 AU was discovered. Unfortunately, many other objects with about the same orbital radii were subsequently discovered. It was eventually realized that these orbiting objects are much smaller than planets, and they were given the name asteroids.

As more and more asteroids were discovered, an interesting pattern in *their* orbital radii was found. In the mid-1800s, the astronomer Daniel Kirkwood plotted the number of asteroids as a function of their distance from the Sun[18] and found a result like that sketched in Figure 4.14. There are many

---

[18]More precisely, he plotted the probability density for finding an asteroid as a function of the orbital radius.

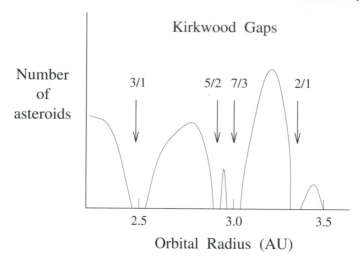

Figure 4.14: Schematic plot of the number of asteroids as a function of their distance from the Sun. The distances at which there are no asteroids are the Kirkwood gaps. For comparison, the orbital radii of Mars and Jupiter are 1.52 and 5.20 AU, respectively.

gaps in this distribution plot. That is, for some values of the orbital radius there are essentially no asteroids. These are now known as the Kirkwood gaps.

Kirkwood also showed that the gaps are associated with Jupiter. He did this by noting that a (hypothetical) asteroid that has a radius placing it in one of the gaps, would be in *resonance* with Jupiter. For example, the gap at approximately 3.3 AU corresponds to an orbital period[19] that is one half that of Jupiter's period. This is known as the 2/1 gap, since an asteroid placed there would complete two orbits every time Jupiter completes one. Similarly, there are Kirkwood gaps corresponding to 3/1, 5/2, and 7/3 resonances, and others as well.

The phenomenon of resonance is probably familiar to you, as it is found in many mechanical and electrical systems. For example, a lightly damped pendulum exhibits a resonance at its natural frequency of oscillation. If you were to excite a pendulum at this frequency, its amplitude of oscillation would become much larger than it would if another frequency was used. The same behavior would be found if an asteroid were somehow placed in one of the Kirkwood gaps. We have already discussed the gravitational force exerted by Jupiter on the other objects in the solar system. This force will be largest when the asteroid is closest to Jupiter and will tend to perturb the orbit of the asteroid. In most cases the asteroid will be in a completely different part of its orbit when Jupiter makes its closest approach, and the perturbations due to Jupiter will, therefore, tend to (at least roughly) cancel out. However, if the asteroid is in resonance with Jupiter, it will be at the same point (or points) in its orbit each time Jupiter comes closest. For example, an asteroid in the 2/1 gap will always be at one of two points on its orbit when Jupiter makes its closest approach, and these points will be at opposite ends of the orbit.

---

[19]The orbital period can be calculated using Kepler's third law.

Table 4.4:   Initial positions and velocities used for three hypothetical asteroids in the vicinity of the 2/1 Kirkwood gap. The initial conditions for Jupiter are also given.

Object	Radius (AU)	Velocity (AU/yr)
Asteroid number 1	3.000	3.628
Asteroid number 2	3.276	3.471
Asteroid number 3	3.700	3.267
Jupiter	5.200	2.755

As a result, the effects of Jupiter during each approach will accumulate and eventually lead to a *large* perturbation of the orbit.

This resonant effect can be studied with our planetary-motion program. We have already discussed how to modify the program to allow the simulation of two planets. The same procedure can be used to simulate any number of planets. We will leave the programming for the exercises, but do have a few suggestions. It is simplest to use arrays to store the positions and velocities of the planets and asteroids. The first element in each array would then contain the position or velocity of the first object, etc., for whatever number of objects you want to place in orbit. Also, since Jupiter is by far the largest orbiting object in this problem and the mass of an asteroid is very small by comparison, it is not necessary to include the gravitational force of each asteroid when computing Jupiter's motion (you can also ignore the interactions between asteroids). This approximation amounts to what is known as the *restricted n-body problem* and will make your program run faster without significantly affecting the physics of the problem.

To study the resonant behavior of asteroids near the 2/1 Kirkwood gap we have simulated the motion of three hypothetical asteroids, all placed in circular orbits. The initial positions and velocities of these asteroids, along with those of Jupiter, are given in Table 4.4.

The parameters for asteroid number 2 have been chosen to place it in the 2/1 gap, while the other asteroids are adjacent to this gap. The reason for including them in the simulation will become clear as we discuss the results, which are shown in Figure 4.15. The simulation was run for approximately 10 orbits of Jupiter (which is not shown in the figure), and only a portion of the calculated positions (about every 10th one) are shown. We see that the orbits of all three asteroids are somewhat "smeared out" in our plot. This means that the force of Jupiter has caused all three orbits to be elliptical, and the axes of all three ellipses precess with time. The interesting result is that the asteroid in the 2/1 gap, the one that is in resonance with Jupiter (shown on the left in Figure 4.15), is the one affected *most* strongly by Jupiter. This must be due to the resonance since the outermost asteroid (one of those shown on the right), which experiences the largest force from Jupiter, is affected *less* than the asteroid in the gap region.

Now that we have confirmed the importance of the resonance, it is interesting to consider how an asteroid, which is initially in the gap region, might be ejected from this orbit. One possibility is that the disturbance of the orbit seen in Figure 4.15 would simply grow with time, until the orbit becomes so elliptical that the asteroid has a close encounter with Mars, or some other planet. However, extensive numerical simulations carried out in the last 15 years or so give a somewhat different picture (more on this can be found in the references at the end of the chapter). These calculations show that an asteroid that begins with an orbit in a Kirkwood gap will follow an orbit that, though somewhat elliptical because of the effect of Jupiter, remains in resonance with Jupiter for a long period of time. Then, seemingly

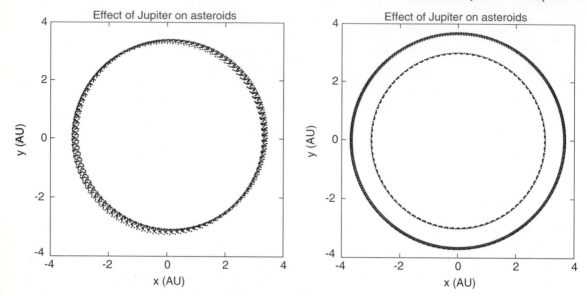

Figure 4.15: Simulation of the effect of Jupiter on three asteroids, showing only the asteroids (Jupiter's orbital radius is 5.2 AU). Left: an asteroid (number 2 in Table 4.4), which was chosen to be in the 2/1 Kirkwood gap, and was thus in resonance with Jupiter. Right: two asteroids (number 1 and number 3 in Table 4.4), chosen to be closer to and farther from Jupiter than the asteroid in the gap. The orbit of the asteroid in the gap is much more "smeared out," that is, much more affected by Jupiter, than are the other asteroids. The time step was 0.005 yr. Here we have not connected the calculated positions, which is why the trajectories appear as discrete points.

without warning, the orbit changes drastically over a relatively short period, taking the asteroid near Mars or Earth, which then pulls it far from its initial orbit.

Such strange and erratic behavior is actually very similar to what we studied in Chapter 3 (recall the intermittency route to chaos), and the motion of these gap asteroids is believed to be chaotic. This is a very intriguing result for the following reason. We have already seen that the two-body problem is governed by Kepler's laws. This *always* implies a perfectly regular, predictable orbital motion. However, the addition of one more object can lead to motion that is completely unpredictable, that is, chaotic. It is believed that there are a number of other instances of chaotic motion in our solar system. One of these will be considered in the next section, while others are discussed in the references.

The physics associated with the Kirkwood gaps is not limited to asteroids. You have probably seen pictures of the rings around Saturn. These rings are made up of a large collection of particles that orbit the planet. These particles have a distribution of orbital radii and hence effectively form a disk. However, for certain orbital radii there are essentially *no* orbiting particles. These gaps are analogous to the Kirkwood gaps in the asteroid distribution. In accord with that analogy, each gap in the ring system is associated with one of Saturn's moons. If a particle could somehow be placed in one of these gaps, it would be in resonance with a moon and would exhibit the behavior we have observed in our asteroid simulations.

Exercises

1. Simulate the motion of asteroids near the one of the Kirkwood gaps. The 2/1 and 7/3 gaps are good choices.

*2. Investigate how close an asteroid must be to the precise gap resonance in order to be effectively "in" the gap. That is, study the effective width of the resonances in Figure 4.14. Do this by performing the calculation of Figure 4.15 for several asteroids whose (circular) orbits are near that of asteroid number 2 in Table 4.4. Calculate how much the orbit is "smeared out" as a function of the initial orbital radius. Note: You will need to develop a quantitative measure of this "smearing."

4.6   Chaotic Tumbling of Hyperion

We mentioned in the previous section that the motion of asteroids located near the Kirkwood gaps is believed to be chaotic. Unfortunately, we were not able to demonstrate this explicitly; to do so would require a simulation of the motion for several million years or longer. Such a simulation is very involved (don't try this at home) and best left for a professional. It turns out that there is also good evidence, based largely on computer simulations, that the motion of Pluto is chaotic. This is another difficult simulation that we will not attempt here (nor will we leave it for the exercises). However, there is one case of chaos in our solar system that is accessible to a fairly simple simulation. It involves the motion of one of Saturn's moons, Hyperion.

Moons are very interesting objects. Most planets have them, with the larger planets such as Jupiter and Saturn having a great many each. You are probably most familiar with Earth's moon and know that it spins about its axis in such a way that it always keeps one particular side facing Earth. That is, its spin is synchronized with its orbital motion about Earth. It is believed that this synchronization came about in the following way. When first formed, a typical moon (such as Earth's moon) probably spun at a rate larger than one revolution per orbit. However, as time passed, a slight asymmetry in the Moon's mass distribution coupled with the fact that the gravitational force of Earth falls off with distance, led to a very small "stretching" and "compressing" of the Moon during each orbit. This dissipated a small amount of energy (essentially from friction), which caused the spin angular velocity to decrease. Eventually, this angular velocity matched the orbital motion, at which point an effect known as spin-orbit resonance came into play and added enough energy to the Moon's spinning motion during each orbit to counter the frictional losses. The spin and orbital motion were then synchronized, and this situation has persisted to the present time. It turns out that all of the moons in the solar system *except one* exhibit such synchronism. The exception is Hyperion.

The reason for Hyperion's different behavior is its very unusual shape, together with its highly elliptical orbit. While other moons (and planets) are approximately spherical, Hyperion is shaped more like an egg. Hence, it is roughly like an orbiting dumbbell, and anyone who has ever thrown a dumbbell, or something with a similar shape, knows that they can spin in a very erratic manner. Indeed, this is precisely what Hyperion seems to do. Not only is Hyperion's spin out of synchrony with its orbital motion, but careful astronomical observations suggest that Hyperion tumbles chaotically as it orbits Saturn.

To simulate the motion of Hyperion we will first make a few simplifying assumptions. Our goal will *not* be to perform a realistic simulation of Hyperion (you can read about such work in the references). Rather, our objective is simply to show that the motion of such an irregularly shaped moon

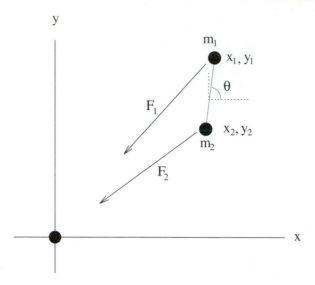

Figure 4.16: Simplified model of Hyperion in orbit around Saturn. Our "moon" consists of two particles, m_1 and m_2, connected by a massless rod. The dotted lines show the x and y directions and intersect the rod at the center of mass. θ is the angle that the rod makes with x. Saturn is at the origin.

can be chaotic. With that goal in mind we consider the model shown in Figure 4.16. We have two particles, m_1 and m_2, connected by a massless rod in orbit around a massive object located at the origin. To simulate this we have to extend our original planetary-motion program to include the rotation of the object about the axis perpendicular to the plane of the figure.

We let θ be the angle that the rod makes with the x axis and define the associated angular velocity $\omega = d\theta/dt$. Our program must calculate the variation of θ and ω, along with the position of the center of mass of the object, x_c and y_c. The motion of the center of mass can be calculated in precisely the manner we used in our first planetary motion program, as the equations of motion for x_c and y_c are unchanged. To calculate the behavior of θ and ω we will use the Euler-Cromer method. We, therefore, need the equation of motion for ω, which can be obtained from the torque on the moon.

There are two forces acting on each of the masses, the force of gravity from Saturn and the force from the rod. Since we are interested in the motion (and thus the torque) about the center of mass, the force from the rod does not contribute. The gravitational force on m_1 can be written as

$$\vec{F}_1 = -\frac{G\,M_S\,m_1}{r_1^3}\left(x_1\,\hat{\imath} + y_1\,\hat{\jmath}\right),\tag{4.17}$$

where M_S is the mass of Saturn, r_1 is the distance from Saturn to m_1, and $\hat{\imath}$ and $\hat{\jmath}$ are unit vectors in the x and y directions. The coordinates of the center of mass are (x_c, y_c), so that $(x_1 - x_c)\hat{\imath} + (y_1 - y_c)\hat{\jmath}$ is the vector from the center of mass to m_1. The torque on m_1 is then

$$\vec{\tau}_1 = \left[(x_1 - x_c)\,\hat{\imath} + (y_1 - y_c)\,\hat{\jmath}\right] \times \vec{F}_1,\tag{4.18}$$

with a similar expression for $\vec{\tau}_2$. The total torque on the moon is just $\vec{\tau}_1 + \vec{\tau}_2$, and this is related to the time derivative of ω by[20]

$$\frac{d\vec{\omega}}{dt} = \frac{\vec{\tau}_1 + \vec{\tau}_2}{I} \, , \tag{4.19}$$

where $I = m_1 \mid r_1 \mid^2 + m_2 \mid r_2 \mid^2$ is the moment of inertia. Putting this all together yields, after some algebra (which we will leave to the inquisitive reader),

$$\frac{d\omega}{dt} = -\frac{12\pi^2}{r_c^5} \, (x_c \, \sin\theta - y_c \, \cos\theta) \, (x_c \, \cos\theta + y_c \, \sin\theta) \, , \tag{4.20}$$

where r_c is the distance from the center of mass to Saturn.

To construct a program for this problem we must add a few lines to our planetary motion program so as to calculate ω according to (4.20), and θ using $d\theta/dt = \omega$. We will leave this to the exercises. Some results for θ and ω as functions of time are shown in Figures 4.17 and 4.18. Since we are not trying to do a quantitative simulation of the actual motion of Hyperion (our simple dumbbell model is too crude for that), we have chosen some slightly more convenient orbital parameters. After all, our goal is only to get a feeling for the kind of behavior that is possible. A truly quantitative simulation is, as they say, beyond the scope of this book.

Figure 4.17 shows the behavior when the orbit is circular. The abrupt vertical jumps in θ are simply due to the program "resetting" θ to keep it in the range $-\pi$ to π (as we did in our pendulum simulations). The behavior in Figure 4.17 is seen to be regular and repeatable; this is especially clear from the results for ω. We thus conclude that the motion is not chaotic when the orbit is circular. However, the results obtained for an elliptical orbit, Figure 4.18, are very different. The behavior seen in this case is very complicated and erratic, and certainly appears to be chaotic.

We learned in Chapter 3 that one essential feature of a chaotic system is an extreme sensitivity to initial conditions. We have, therefore, calculated the behavior of our model Hyperion for two slightly different initial conditions. Thus we obtained two separate results, $\theta_1(t)$ and $\theta_2(t)$, and a plot of $\Delta\theta \equiv \sqrt{(\theta_1 - \theta_2)^2}$ as a function of time is shown in Figure 4.19. Here we give results for both circular and elliptical orbits. In the circular case we see that while $\Delta\theta$ oscillates some with time, its overall magnitude grows only very slowly. Hence, these two trajectories, $\theta_1(t)$ and $\theta_2(t)$, stay near each other, and the motion is *not* chaotic (as we have already concluded). In contrast, we see that $\Delta\theta$ for the elliptical orbit grows rapidly, approximately exponentially, with time until it reaches a value of order π, and it can't get any larger than that. As we saw in Chapter 3, this extreme sensitivity to initial conditions is one of the hallmarks of chaotic behavior.

Our model for Hyperion is, as we have cautioned, a highly simplified version of the real thing. Our goal was to try to understand the types of motion that are possible, and the results clearly show that such a moon can tumble chaotically. This is perhaps the best, and computationally most accessible, example of chaotic motion in our solar system.

---

[20]The vector signs are not really needed here since all of the torques and angular momenta in this problem are along the z axis, that is, perpendicular to the plane of Figure 4.16.

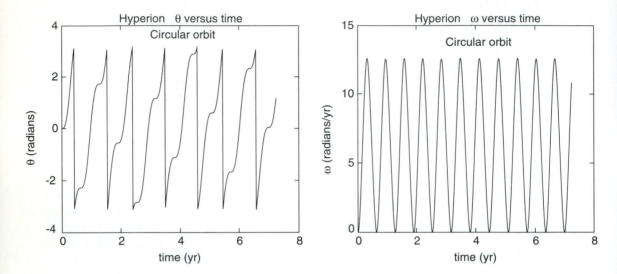

Figure 4.17:   Tumbling of Hyperion calculated assuming a circular orbit. This motion is not chaotic. The vertical "jumps" in $\theta(t)$ are due to the resetting of the angle from $+\pi$ to $-\pi$; these two angles correspond to the same angular orientation of the moon. For simplicity we took $GM_S = 4\pi^2$ and an orbital radius of 1 AU. The time step was 0.0001 yr.

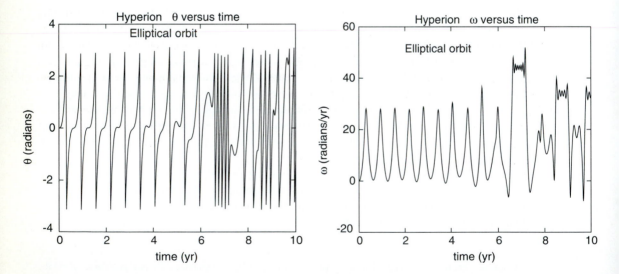

Figure 4.18:   Tumbling of Hyperion calculated assuming an elliptical orbit. The initial distance from Hyperion to Saturn was 1 AU and its initial velocity was 5 AU/yr (we again took $GM_S = 4\pi^2$). The time step was 0.0001 yr. The tumbling is now chaotic.

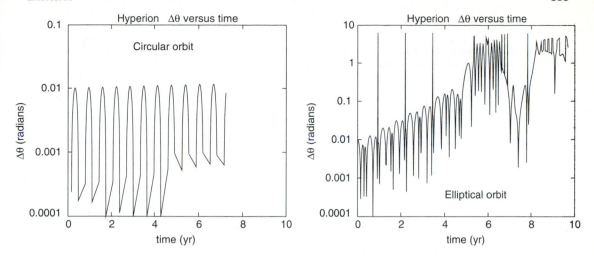

Figure 4.19: Divergence of two nearby trajectories of the tumbling motion of Hyperion. We plot the difference between two calculated results for $\theta(t)$ with different initial conditions. We used $\theta(0) = 0$ for one trajectory and $\theta(0) = 0.01$ for the other. In all cases the initial ω was zero. Left: calculated for a circular orbit (as considered in Figure 4.17); right: calculated for an elliptical orbit (the same ellipse as used in Figure 4.18).

Exercises

1. Study the behavior of our model for Hyperion for different initial conditions. Estimate the Lyapunov exponent from calculations of $\Delta\theta$, such as those shown in Figure 4.19. Examine how this exponent varies as a function of the eccentricity of the orbit.

2. Our results for the divergence of the two trajectories $\theta_1(t)$ and $\theta_2(t)$ in the chaotic regime, shown on the right in Figure 4.19, are complicated by the way we dealt with the angle θ. In Figure 4.19 we followed the practice employed in Chapter 3 and restricted θ to the range $-\pi$ to $+\pi$, since angles outside this range are equivalent to angles within it. However, when during the course of a calculation the angle passes out of this range and is then "reset" (by adding or subtracting 2π), this shows up in the results for $\Delta\theta$ as a discontinuous (and distracting) jump. Repeat the calculation of $\Delta\theta$ as in Figure 4.19, but do *not* restrict the value of θ. This should remove the large ($\Delta\theta \sim 2\pi$) jumps in $\Delta\theta$ in Figure 4.19, but the smaller and more frequent dips will remain. What is the origin of these dips? Hint: Consider the behavior of a pendulum near one of its turning points.

References

GOLDSTEIN, H. *Classical Mechanics*. 1980. Reading, MA: Addison-Wesley. Gives the form for the perturbation of the gravitational inverse-square law due to general relativity.

KLAVETTER, J. J. 1989. "Rotation of Hyperion. I. Observations." *The Astronomical Journal* **97**, 570; "Rotation of Hyperion. II. Dynamics." *The Astronomical Journal* **98**, 1855. Research articles that describe a detailed analysis of the motion of Hyperion.

PETERSON, I. 1993. *Newton's Clock: Chaos in the Solar System*. Freeman. A very entertaining account of the history of astronomical studies of the solar system.

WISDOM, J. 1987. "*Chaotic Dynamics in the Solar System*." *Icarus* **72**, 241. A readable, though advanced, discussion of simulations of several cases of chaotic motion in the solar system.

5

Potentials and Fields

5.1   Electric Potentials and Fields: Laplace's Equation

In regions of space that do not contain any electric charges, the electric potential obeys Laplace's equation

$$\frac{\partial^2 V}{\partial x^2} + \frac{\partial^2 V}{\partial y^2} + \frac{\partial^2 V}{\partial z^2} = 0 \, . \tag{5.1}$$

From a numerical perspective the situation here is a bit different from anything we have encountered so far in this book. All of our problems to this point have involved differential equations for which several initial conditions were given, and we were able to use the Euler method or something like it to calculate the behavior for later times. However, with Laplace's equation we are generally given some boundary conditions for V, which specify its value on a surface in x–y–z space. Alternatively, the boundary conditions might be given in terms of the electric field, which is proportional to the gradient of V. In either case our problem is to find the function $V(x, y, z)$ that satisfies both Laplace's equation and the specified boundary conditions. Most importantly, satisfying the boundary conditions will not be as easy as with the ordinary differential equations encountered in previous chapters.

While most ordinary differential equations can be dealt with using methods such as the Euler or Runge-Kutta approaches, there are no comparable "general purpose" algorithms for partial differential equations (PDEs). Instead there are many different algorithms, each designed for a particular class of PDEs. We will explore one such method in this and the following section, while others will be encountered in later chapters. The approach we will use is the relaxation method; it is convenient for dealing with the class of PDEs known as elliptic equations, of which Laplace's equation is one example.

As usual we discretize the independent variables, in this case x, y, and z. Points in our space are then specified by integers i, j, and k, with $x = i\Delta x$, $y = j\Delta y$, $z = k\Delta z$. Our goal is to determine the potential $V(i, j, k) \equiv V(i\Delta x, j\Delta y, k\Delta z)$ on this lattice of points.[1] The first step in reaching this goal is to rewrite (5.1) as a difference equation. We already know how to write a first derivative in finite-difference form. For example, at the point (i, j, k) the derivative with respect to x may be written as

$$\frac{\partial V}{\partial x} \approx \frac{V(i+1, j, k) - V(i, j, k)}{\Delta x}, \tag{5.2}$$

where the $\approx$ sign is there to remind you that this is only an approximation. This is not the only conceivable way to express the first derivative in finite-difference form. We could just as easily have written

$$\frac{\partial V}{\partial x} \approx \frac{V(i, j, k) - V(i-1, j, k)}{\Delta x}, \tag{5.3}$$

or

$$\frac{\partial V}{\partial x} \approx \frac{V(i+1, j, k) - V(i-1, j, k)}{2\,\Delta x}. \tag{5.4}$$

The "best" choice depends on the particular problem at hand.

Since here we are dealing with Laplace's equation (5.1), we are really after an expression for the second derivatives, so it is worth noting that (5.2) is effectively centered about the "imaginary" location $i + \frac{1}{2}$, while (5.3) is centered at $i - \frac{1}{2}$. Thus, it is natural to write the second partial derivative as

$$\frac{\partial^2 V}{\partial x^2} \approx \frac{1}{\Delta x} \left[\frac{\partial V}{\partial x}(i+\tfrac{1}{2}) - \frac{\partial V}{\partial x}(i-\tfrac{1}{2}) \right], \tag{5.5}$$

where the notation here is intended to indicate that the derivatives are to be evaluated at the locations $(i \pm \frac{1}{2})$. This leads to

$$\frac{\partial^2 V}{\partial x^2} \approx \frac{1}{\Delta x} \left[\frac{V(i+1, j, k) - V(i, j, k)}{\Delta x} - \frac{V(i, j, k) - V(i-1, j, k)}{\Delta x} \right], \tag{5.6}$$

and a little rearranging yields

$$\frac{\partial^2 V}{\partial x^2} \approx \frac{V(i+1, j, k) + V(i-1, j, k) - 2\,V(i, j, k)}{(\Delta x)^2}. \tag{5.7}$$

This expression is nicely symmetric in the way it treats $V(i+1, j, k)$ and $V(i-1, j, k)$, which will turn out to reduce the overall errors in our computations. The results for the other second partial derivatives have similar forms. Inserting them all into Laplace's equation and solving for $V(i, j, k)$ we find

$$V(i, j, k) = \frac{1}{6} [V(i+1, j, k) + V(i-1, j, k) + V(i, j+1, k) \tag{5.8}$$
$$+ V(i, j-1, k) + V(i, j, k+1) + V(i, j, k-1)]\,,$$

where we have assumed that the step sizes along x, y, and z are all the same ($\Delta x = \Delta y = \Delta z$).[2] In words, (5.8) simply says that the value of the potential at any point is the *average* of V at all of the

---

[1]Here we depart with what has been our usual convention (so far) and write $V(i, j, k)$ instead of $V_{i,j,k}$. The latter is a bit more cumbersome when there are two or more indices. In the remainder of this book we will use both of these notations (though not in the same problem!), with the choice being determined by convenience and (we hope) clarity.

[2]This assumption is not necessary, but does make the form of (5.8) a little simpler.

$$\overset{\text{Eq.(5.8)}}{V_0(i,j,k) \longrightarrow} \quad \overset{\text{Eq.(5.8)}}{V_1(i,j,k) \longrightarrow} \quad \overset{\text{Eq.(5.8)}}{V_2(i,j,k) \longrightarrow}$$

Figure 5.1:   Schematic flowchart for the relaxation algorithm.

neighboring points. The solution for $V(i, j, k)$ is the function that manages to satisfy this condition at *all* points simultaneously.

We now require a numerical strategy for determining this function, assuming only that V is known at the boundaries. We can't just start at one of the boundaries and work our way into and across the system, since according to (5.8) we need to know V at *all* of the neighbors in order to calculate its value at any particular point. The approach we take is to begin with some initial guess for the solution; call it $V_0(i, j, k)$. In general, unless we are extremely clever, the guess we make will not satisfy (5.8) everywhere. To obtain an improved guess, we use (5.8) to calculate new values of V, using V_0 on the right-hand side. This is illustrated pictorially in Figure 5.1. The guess V_0, together with (5.8) yields, a new and we hope improved guess, $V_1(i, j, k)$. We then repeat the procedure with V_1 to obtain an even better guess, V_2, etc. This iterative process is continued until our result satisfies some convergence criteria, which we will discuss shortly. The main point is that we can iterate with (5.8) to obtain a better and better solution. This general approach is called the *relaxation method* and is a useful way to deal with several important classes of partial differential equations. There are several different ways to implement the relaxation method, and some are much better than others with respect to speed of convergence, etc. The particular algorithm we have just described is known as the Jacobi method, and we will begin by applying it to several problems. We will then consider some other, more efficient relaxation algorithms.

In our description of the relaxation method we have assumed that each guess, V_n, is in some sense closer to the true solution than the previous guess, V_{n-1}. We will leave it to the references to explain in detail why this algorithm nearly always converges. It turns out that even the simplest relaxation algorithm, the Jacobi method outlined above, works reasonably well provided that the initial guess, V_0, is not too bad. In fact, as we will see shortly, even rather simple choices for V_0 are usually adequate.

We begin with the problem of calculating the electric potential inside the square box in Figure 5.2. For boundary conditions we assume that the face of the box at $x = -1$ is held at $V = -1$, while $V = +1$ on the face at $x = +1$.[3] We will assume that the sides of the box at $y = \pm1$ are nonconducting, so V on those faces will vary as we moves from $x = -1$ to $x = +1$. From the symmetry it is natural to suppose that the potential on these surfaces of the box will vary linearly with position[4] as we move from $x = -1$ to $x = +1$. We assume further that the box is infinite in extent along $\pm z$, so $V(i, j, k)$ is independent of k. We thus have only a two-dimensional problem. Our goal is to find $V(i, j)$.

A program to implement the relaxation method for this geometry is listed in full in Appendix 4. Below we give only the routines that deal specifically with the relaxation algorithm. We use a two-dimensional array v(i,j) to hold the values of the potential function, with i and j corresponding to the x and y coordinates. Here we have taken a slightly different approach to dealing with arrays than

---

[3]For convenience we will let V and x be unitless, although we could just as well give them units of volts and meters.

[4]For walls that are perfect insulators, the variation of V need not be linear as we assume here. However, if the walls have some small but nonzero conductivity, a linear variation would be found.

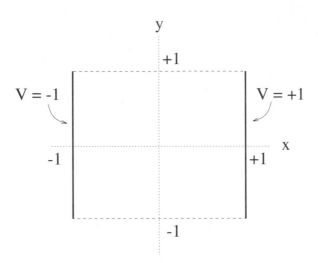

Figure 5.2:   Geometry and boundary conditions (at $x = \pm 1$) assumed by our program to solve Laplace's equation. The solid lines are the metallic walls of the box, while the dashed lines (at $y = \pm 1$) are insulating walls.

in previous programs. Since x and y can both have negative as well as positive values, it is convenient to let our array indices i and j do so as well. Then we can write $x = \text{i}\Delta x$ and $y = \text{j}\Delta y$. In *True Basic* the array indices normally run from 1 to the value requested in the dim statement. However, we can arrange for these indices to vary between any two specified values. In our initialize subroutine we use the statement mat redim v(-max to max, -max to max) so that the indices of the voltage array each run from -max to +max.[5] The variable max is an integer that is related to the number of lattice sites along x and y. We thus have 2max+1 grid sites along both x and y. The last part of initialize fills the array v(i,j) with the appropriate values of the potential at the boundaries (see Figure 5.2), along with our initial guess for the potential in the interior. Actually, we don't attempt to make a very good guess for V_0; we simply take $V = 0$ everywhere inside the box. We will see shortly that even with such a poor initial guess the relaxation algorithm converges rapidly to the correct solution.

The real work is done in the routines calculate and update, which are listed below. The update subroutine takes the guess for the solution in array v1 and uses the (Jacobi) relaxation algorithm, (5.8), to calculate a better guess, which is stored in the array v2. The new values cannot be stored directly in the original array since we would then be overwriting some of the values of v1(i,j) before we were finished using them. Note also that since for this problem the potential is independent of position in the z direction, the factor 6 in the denominator of (5.8) becomes a 4 in update.

---

[5]Note that the mat redim statement "resizes" an array that has already been declared using dim.

```
! calculate the electric potential and field lines
! between two parallel plates
! N. Giordano   10-1-94
! v() is the potential, max -> determines number of grid steps
! n = number of iterations of relaxation algorithm
sub calculate(v(,),max,n)
   dim v_tmp(0,0)
   mat redim v_tmp(-max to max,-max to max)
   for i = -max to max    ! initialize temporary array
      for j = -max to max        ! not absolutely necessary, but a
         v_tmp(i,j) = v(i,j)    ! good general habit
      next j
   next i
   i = 0
   do                         ! main loop - the real work is done here
      i = i + 1
      call update(v,v_tmp,max,diff,n)
      call update(v_tmp,v,max,diff,n)
   loop until i > 10 and diff < 1e-5
end sub
! use Jacobi relaxation algorithm to calculate new values of the potential
! old values are in v1, put new values into v2
! diff is average change in potential during the current iteration
sub update(v1(,),v2(,),max,diff,n)
   diff = 0
   for i = -max+1 to max-1
      for j = -max+1 to max-1
         tmp = v1(i,j)
         v2(i,j) = (v1(i-1,j) + v1(i+1,j) + v1(i,j+1) + v1(i,j-1)) / 4
         diff = diff + abs(tmp - v2(i,j))
      next j
   next i
   diff = diff / (2*max+1)^2
end sub
```

The `calculate` subroutine does two things: it declares an array `v_tmp` that is needed for temporary storage of the values of the potential and then calls `update` to obtain an improved guess for the solution. It actually calls `update` twice on each pass through its main loop, for the following reason. In the first call to `update` the array `v` contains the latest guess for the solution, and the improved guess is returned in `v_tmp`. For the next call `v_tmp` contains the latest guess, and the improved result is returned in `v`. Thus, two calls to `update` leave us with the latest guess stored back in the original array, `v`. The main loop in `calculate` terminates when the change in the potential, averaged over all sites (which is also calculated by `update`), is less than a specified value, chosen here to be 1×10^{-5}. In addition, we require that the loop be executed at least 10 times, to guarantee that the relaxation algorithm has time to get started. It is crucial to realize that this does *not* mean that the final result will be within 1×10^{-5} of the true solution. It only means that on average the potential function is changing by less than that amount with each iteration. Of course, using a smaller limit in the convergence test will make the final answer more accurate (and also require more computing time), but we must expect the true error in that answer to be somewhat larger than the error limit used to judge convergence. We will explore this point in the exercises.

The last subroutine in our program, `display`, takes care of plotting the results, first in a topographic form showing the equipotential lines, and then the electric field, which is calculated by differentiating v(i,j). The graphs are produced using some of *True Basic's* graphics routines, but of course you can substitute your favorite graphics programs here.

To give you some feeling for how the relaxation algorithm works, the results for the potential v(i,j), at several stages of the calculation, are printed out below. In this particular case we have taken max to be 3, so there are 7 rows and 7 columns in the array v(i,j). The layout is the same as in Figure 5.2, so the left-most column corresponds to $x = -1$, the right-most column to $x = +1$, and the top and bottom rows to $y = \pm 1$. The initial guess, V_0, satisfies the boundary conditions and assumes $V = 0$ in the interior of the box.

```
    Initial guess: V₀

-1.00 -.67 -.33  .00  .33  .67 1.00
-1.00  .00  .00  .00  .00  .00 1.00
-1.00  .00  .00  .00  .00  .00 1.00
-1.00  .00  .00  .00  .00  .00 1.00
-1.00  .00  .00  .00  .00  .00 1.00
-1.00  .00  .00  .00  .00  .00 1.00
-1.00 -.67 -.33  .00  .33  .67 1.00
```

After the first call to update, that is, one updating of our guess for the solution, we obtain V_1. We see that some of the zeros in the interior of v(i,j) have been replaced by values that bring it closer to solving Laplace's equation. That is, the values of v(i,j) are now closer to being equal to the average of the values in the neighboring sites. However, we still have a long way to go, so update must be used several more times.

```
    After 1 call to update: V₁

-1.00 -.67 -.33  .00  .33  .67 1.00
-1.00 -.42 -.08  .00  .08  .42 1.00
-1.00 -.25  .00  .00  .00  .25 1.00
-1.00 -.25  .00  .00  .00  .25 1.00
-1.00 -.25  .00  .00  .00  .25 1.00
-1.00 -.42 -.08  .00  .08  .42 1.00
-1.00 -.67 -.33  .00  .33  .67 1.00
```

After nine calls to update the relaxation algorithm has produced a very good guess for the potential. We will leave it to you to verify that each value of V in the interior is indeed very close to the average of the values at the neighboring sites, as required by (5.8).

```
    After 9 calls to update: V₉

-1.00 -.67 -.33  .00  .33  .67 1.00
-1.00 -.66 -.32  .00  .32  .66 1.00
-1.00 -.65 -.32  .00  .32  .65 1.00
-1.00 -.65 -.31  .00  .31  .65 1.00
-1.00 -.65 -.32  .00  .32  .65 1.00
-1.00 -.66 -.32  .00  .32  .66 1.00
-1.00 -.67 -.33  .00  .33  .67 1.00
```

The final results for the potential are plotted as equipotential contours[6] in Figure 5.3. These contours are simply lines drawn through the locations where the potential has a particular value (as

---

[6]These contours were drawn using a subroutine in the *True Basic* scientific graphics library. Other software packages should contain similar routines.

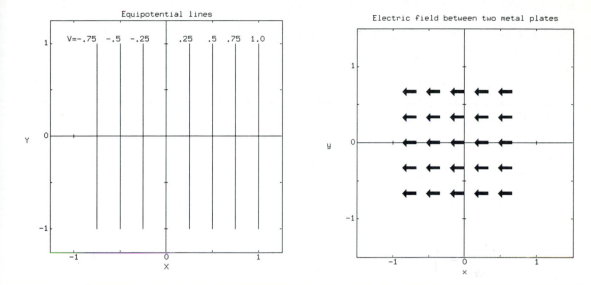

Figure 5.3: Left: equipotential lines inside the metal box in Figure 5.2. The value of V at each of the lines is given. Right: the corresponding electric field. Note that here and in later plots the size of each arrow is proportional to the magnitude of the field at the *tail* of the arrow.

given in Figure 5.3) and are not very exciting to look at. They are just evenly spaced, straight (vertical) lines, as we should have expected from the symmetry of the problem. These results for V can be used to obtain the electric field. To do this we use the fact that the component of E in the x direction is

$$E_x = -\frac{\partial V}{\partial x},\tag{5.9}$$

with corresponding relations for E_y and E_z. These derivatives can be estimated using our usual finite difference expressions, such as (5.2) or (5.4). In this case we have used a symmetric form for this derivative

$$E_x(i, j) \approx -\frac{V(i+1, j) - V(i-1, j)}{2\,\Delta x},\tag{5.10}$$

but a less symmetric form [such as (5.2) or (5.3)] would give essentially the same results.

The results for $\vec{E}$ are given in Figure 5.3, where we show a vector plot (again generated using a routine in the *True Basic* scientific graphics library). Here each arrow is oriented in the direction of $\vec{E}$ at that location, and the length of each arrow is proportional to the magnitude of the field. We find a uniform field directed from high potential ($x = +1$) to low potential ($x = -1$), as expected.

The simple problem treated above was intended to demonstrate how the relaxation method produces a solution to Laplace's equation. The method is very general and can be readily used in more complicated cases where an analytic solution is difficult or impossible. We now consider two such cases. The first is illustrated in Figure 5.4. It is an infinitely long, hollow prism, with metallic walls and a square cross-section. Inside this prism is a metal bar, also with a square cross-section. We assume that a voltage is applied between the bar and the outer walls, and we want to calculate the potential in

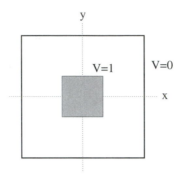

Figure 5.4: Schematic cross section of a hollow metallic prism with a solid, metallic inner conductor. The prism and inner conductor are presumed to be infinite in extent along z. The inner conductor is held at $V = 1$ and the walls of the prism at $V = 0$.

the space between them. The program we developed above can be used in this case; all we need to do is modify the `initialize` and `update` routines so as to take into account the different geometry. We will leave this task to the reader.

The results are given in Figure 5.5. Here we show the equipotential contours, a "three-dimensional" perspective plot of the potential, and the corresponding electric field. The results are consistent with our expectations based on the symmetry of the problem. These considerations tell us that the results should, after the appropriate rotation, be precisely the *same* in each quadrant in the x–y plane. The fact that our solution displays the expected symmetry gives us some extra confidence that we have not made any programming errors. However, we could have taken advantage of this symmetry to make the program execute faster. Since the result must be the same in all four quadrants, we really only need to consider one quadrant in the calculation. After obtaining a solution in one quadrant, the values for the other quadrants could then be obtained from the symmetry requirements. This approach would speed-up our program by (approximately) a factor of 4. Actually, for this problem we could do even better. Within each quadrant the solution must also be symmetric with respect to *reflection* about the line $y = \pm x$. Hence, our program really only needs to deal with half of one quadrant, leading to a speed-up by a factor of 8. However, this increased efficiency does come at a cost. Such a program would have to deal carefully with the values of V at the boundaries between the quadrants and along the lines $y = \pm x$. We will explore this problem in the exercises.

Another interesting use of the relaxation algorithm is the problem of the potential between two parallel capacitor plates. The case of infinite plates can, of course, be handled analytically using Gauss' law. However, here we are interested in what happens when the plates are *finite* in extent. The geometry of the problem is sketched in Figure 5.6. Again, we can modify our earlier program to handle this case. All we need to do is set up the proper boundary conditions for V. We set the plates to $V = \pm 1$, and the square boundary defined by $x = \pm 1$, $y = \pm 1$ surrounding the plates is set to $V = 0$. In analytic calculations we would generally apply the condition $V = 0$ at $x, y = \infty$, but that is usually not practical in a numerical treatment. Here, for simplicity, we apply this condition on the square boundary just described; we will have more to say about how to choose such boundary regions and their effects in the next section.

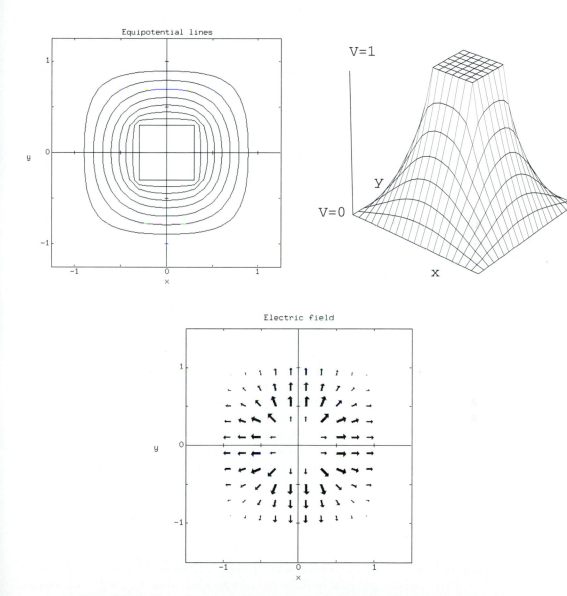

Figure 5.5:   Electric potential and field inside the prism in Figure 5.4. The sides of the prism in the x–y plane had lengths of 2 units, and the inner conductor had an edge length of 0.6 units. The spatial grid size was 0.1. Upper left: equipotential contours; upper right: perspective plot of the potential; bottom: electric field.

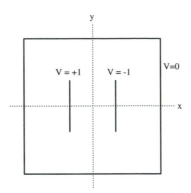

Figure 5.6: Schematic of two capacitor plates held at $V = 1$ (left plate) and $V = -1$ (right plate). The square boundary surrounding the plates is held at $V = 0$.

After specifying the boundary conditions on V, the application of the relaxation algorithm is the same as that outlined above. The results are given in Figure 5.7. They are again in accord with our expectations based both on symmetry[7] and the very schematic drawings given in many textbooks. The electric field is seen to be largest between the two plates. In that region the field is approximately uniform (although this is hard to verify with the rather coarse scale used for this plot) and is directed from high to low potential. The fringing fields at the edges of and outside the plates are also evident.

All of our calculations with the relaxation method have to this point used what is known as the Jacobi algorithm, according to which (5.8) is iterated as suggested in Figure 5.1. While this method is simple to describe and implement in a program, it does not have desirable convergence properties for large systems. We will not discuss speed of convergence and related issues here (see Press et al. [1985]). However, we do note that when the Jacobi method is applied to a two-dimensional problem (like those considered above) on an $L \times L$ grid, the number of iterations required for convergence scales as L^2. Hence, if the number of grid points is increased by a factor of 2, as might be desirable if we wanted to obtain a solution with better spatial resolution, the computational time increases as L^4. Here one factor of L^2 comes from the increase in the required number of iterations, while another factor of L^2 arises from the increased number of grid points that must be dealt with in each iteration.

As we have already hinted, the Jacobi method is not the last word in relaxation algorithms. Mathematically the Jacobi method can be expressed as

$$V_{\text{new}}(i, j) = \frac{1}{4} \left[V_{\text{old}}(i + 1, j) + V_{\text{old}}(i - 1, j) + V_{\text{old}}(i, j + 1) + V_{\text{old}}(i, j - 1) \right], \qquad (5.11)$$

where for simplicity we have assumed a two-dimensional problem and taken the grid sizes to be the same along x and y. Here V_{old} is the potential from the previous iteration, while V_{new} is the new value. In words, (5.11) states that only the old values of the potential are used to compute the values in the next iteration. One simple (though modest) improvement is the Gauss-Seidel method. The Gauss-Seidel method differs in that it uses the new values as they become available. The order in which they become

---

[7]As in the case of the field inside a square prism, this symmetry could be used to speed up the calculation.

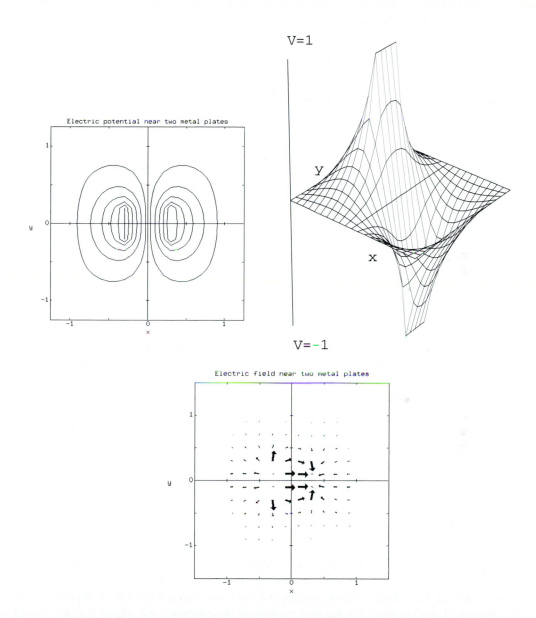

Figure 5.7:   Electric potential and field near near two capacitor plates. The plates were held at $V = +1$ (left plate) and $V = -1$ (right plate), while the square boundary surrounding the plates was held at $V = 0$. The plates are located at $x = \pm 0.3$ and the spatial step size was 0.1. For simplicity the box and plates were assumed to be infinite in extent along the z direction. Upper left: equipotential lines; upper right: perspective plot of the potential; bottom: electric field.

available depends on how you loop through the grid. If you move along each row (i) from small i to large i, beginning with the top row (small j), the Gauss-Seidel method can be written as

$$V_{\text{new}}(i, j) \;=\; \frac{1}{4}\left[V_{\text{old}}(i + 1, j) \,+\, V_{\text{new}}(i - 1, j) \,+\, V_{\text{old}}(i, j + 1) \,+\, V_{\text{new}}(i, j - 1)\right] . \qquad (5.12)$$

While the performance of the Gauss-Seidel algorithm is better than that of the Jacobi method, the improvement is only modest. It turns out that the number of iterations required for convergence with the Gauss-Seidel method is smaller, but only by a factor of 2. A factor of 2 is certainly useful, but we might have hoped for bigger things, such as a factor of L. A second bonus of the Gauss-Seidel method is that it does not require that we use two separate arrays to store the potential. Since the new values can be used as soon as they are calculated, there is no need to save the old values separately.

The problem with the slow convergence of the Jacobi and Gauss-Seidel methods can be overcome with a method known as *simultaneous overrelaxation*, which can be appreciated as follows. Let $V^*(i, j)$ be the new value of the potential calculated using the Jacobi method.[8] We can then think of

$$\Delta V(i, j) \;\equiv\; V^*(i, j) \,-\, V_{\text{old}}(i, j) , \qquad (5.13)$$

as the change recommended by the Jacobi algorithm. However, we have seen in our previous examples that this choice of $\Delta V(i, j)$ is too conservative, so to speed up convergence we will change the potential by a larger amount calculated according to

$$V_{\text{new}}(i, j) \;=\; \alpha \, \Delta V(i, j) \,+\, V_{\text{old}}(i, j) , \qquad (5.14)$$

where α is a factor that measures how much we "overrelax." Choosing $\alpha = 1$ yields the Jacobi method. It turns out that if $\alpha \geq 2$, the method does not converge, while $\alpha < 1$ corresponds to "underrelaxation." The algorithm known as simultaneous overrelaxation employs (5.14) with a value of α between 1 and 2. It remains for us to determine the best value of α; that is, the value that yields the fastest convergence. This is a question that requires a more detailed analysis than we can discuss here (see Press et al. [1986]), so we will only give a few pointers. For a problem on a two-dimensional square grid like the ones we have considered, the best choice for α is

$$\alpha \;\approx\; \frac{2}{1 + \pi/L} . \qquad (5.15)$$

If your problem uses a different grid geometry you should check Press et al. (1986), and the references they list on the subject, for guidelines on how to choose α. This method is not difficult to program, as it involves a relatively small change to the Jacobi (or Gauss-Seidel) algorithm. For this extra effort we gain in speed of convergence. The number of required iterations (for a given accuracy) now scales as L, so for problems with large grids ($L = 100$ is not unusual) the computational savings can be substantial. We will explore the simultaneous overrelaxation method in the exercises. As a final note we should point out that simultaneous overrelaxation is itself not the last word in algorithms, so if you need to solve really large problems of this type, it would pay to read more about these issues in the references.

---

[8]We could just as well have used the Gauss-Seidel method in this argument.

Exercises

1. Solve for the potential in the prism geometry in Figure 5.4.

*2. Use the symmetry of the problem described in Figure 5.4 to write a program that solves for V by calculating the potential in only half of one quadrant of the x–y plane.

*3. Use the symmetry of the capacitor problem (Figure 5.6) to write a program that obtains the result by calculating the potential in only one quadrant of the x–y plane.

4. Investigate how the magnitude of the fringing field of a parallel plate capacitor, that is, the electric field outside the central region of the capacitor in Figure 5.6, varies as a function of the plate separation.

5. Study the accuracy of the relaxation method by solving any of the problems considered in this section with several different values of the convergence (error) limit. Compare the results for V and $\vec{E}$, and estimate how the actual error in either of these quantities compares to the convergence limit.

6. Calculate the electric potential and field near a lightning rod. Model this as a very long and narrow metal rod held at a high voltage, with one end near a conducting plane. Of special interest is the field near the tip of the rod.

*7. Write two programs to solve the capacitor problem of Figures 5.6 and 5.7, one using the Jacobi method and one using the simultaneous overrelaxation algorithm. For a fixed accuracy (as set by the convergence test) compare the number of iterations, N_{iter}, that each algorithm requires as a function of the number of grid elements, L. Show that for the Jacobi method $N_{\text{iter}} \sim L^2$, while with simultaneous overrelaxation $N_{\text{iter}} \sim L$.

5.2   Potentials and Fields Near Electric Charges

In the last section we learned how to compute the electric potential and field in regions of space that are free of any electric charges. We next consider how to include charges in the problem. Laplace's equation applies only in charge-free regions. If we include charges we obtain Poisson's equation, which is given by

$$\frac{\partial^2 V}{\partial x^2} + \frac{\partial^2 V}{\partial y^2} + \frac{\partial^2 V}{\partial z^2} = -\frac{\rho}{\epsilon_0}, \tag{5.16}$$

where ρ is the charge density and the permittivity constant ϵ_0 takes care of the units (in SI units). To deal with this numerically we must add the charge density to the right-hand side of (5.8) and the result is

$$V(i, j, k) = \frac{1}{6}[V(i+1, j, k) + V(i-1, j, k) + V(i, j+1, k) + V(i, j-1, k) \tag{5.17}$$

$$+ V(i, j, k+1) + V(i, j, k-1)] + \frac{\rho(i, j, k)\,(\Delta x)^2}{6\,\epsilon_0},$$

where we have added the spatial indices to ρ to remind us that the charge density is, in general, a function of position. We have also assumed that the spatial-grid size is the same in all directions ($\Delta x = \Delta y = \Delta z$).

Any of the different versions of the relaxation method that we described in the previous section can be used to deal with (5.17). To generalize our program in order to handle this case, we employ a

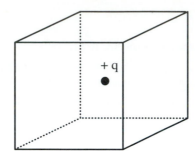

Figure 5.8:   Schematic of a point charge $+q$ located at the center of a metal box. The faces of the box
are all held at $V = 0$.

three-dimensional array to hold the charge density. In the program listing given in the previous section,
the line of update that calculates the new values of the potential for a three-dimensional problem then
becomes something like

```
v2(i,j,k) = (v1(i-1,j,k) + v1(i+1,j,k) + v1(i,j+1,k) + v1(i,j-1,k)
            + v1(i,j,k+1) + v1(i,j,k-1)) / 6 + rho(i,j,k) * dx^2 / 6
```

where the array rho contains the charge density per grid element and dx is the spatial step size.[9]

The relaxation algorithm works here just as it did with Laplace's equation. An instructive case is
that of a single-point charge in three dimensions. For our calculations we need to have some boundary
conditions for the potential, so we will place this charge at the center of a metal box whose walls are
held at $V = 0$ (Figure 5.8). The charge density is zero, except at the grid location at the center of the
box where it is given by rho(0, 0, 0) $= q/dx^3$. In the limit of a very large box we should recover
the result familiar to us from Coulomb's law. Results for the potential and electric field are shown in
Figure 5.9, where we have assumed a point charge of magnitude $q/\epsilon_0 = 1$. Both the electric field and
the potential fall off very rapidly as we move away from the charge.

Before we compare these results with the exact answer, we should comment on the overall symmetry of the equipotential lines. From the symmetry of the problem we would expect the potential to be
spherically symmetric, except near the faces of the box. However, even if we were to make the box very
large, our numerical solution would still impose a sort of cubic symmetry on the system, since the spatial
grid is cubic. This distorts the equipotential lines and gives them a distinctly noncircular shape when
projected as in Figure 5.9. This effect could be reduced by choosing a smaller grid size. An alternative
approach would be to use the symmetry of the problem. For example, the metal box could be replaced
with a spherical metal shell. Since the problem would then have full spherical symmetry (assuming we
keep the point charge at the center of the sphere), we could then rewrite Poisson's equation in terms of
the radial coordinate and obtain $V(r)$ with the relaxation algorithm. This approach would greatly speed
up our program and will be explored in the exercises. However, before we get too carried away with
exploiting all of the possible symmetries in each problem, we have a cautionary note. Highly symmetric
problems are generally the ones most amenable to analytic solution. The kinds of problems you are likely
to encounter in numerical work will be those with very little, if any, symmetry. Even so, recognition of
symmetries is important since they can at least provide a check on the correctness of a numerical solution.

---

[9]Here we have chosen units so that the factor ϵ_0 is unity, for convenience.

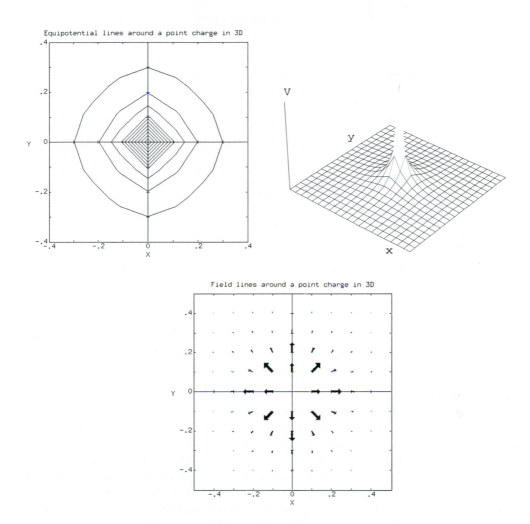

Figure 5.9: Results for the electric potential and field near a point charge located at the center of a metal box. The box had an edge length of 2 (x, y, and z all ran from -1 to $+1$) and the spatial step size was 0.1. Upper left: equipotential lines; upper right: perspective plot of the potential in the $z = 0$ plane; bottom: electric field (note that the length of each arrow is proportional to the field strength at the point where the base of the arrow is located). Also note that the arrows closest to the origin are "distorted"; the singularity at the origin together with the finite difference expression used to compute E makes the value smaller than it should ideally be. The plots on the upper left and right show only the potential and field near the center of the box.

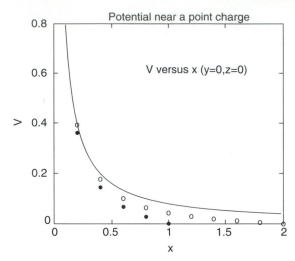

Figure 5.10: Numerical results for the potential near a point charge obtained using the Jacobi relaxation method compared with the exact result (the solid line). The open circles were obtained with a box of edge length 4 (so the face of the box was at $x = 2$), and the filled circles with a box of length 2. The magnitude of the charge was such that $q/\epsilon_0 = 1$ and the spatial grid size was 0.2 for both calculations.

Returning to the results in Figure 5.9, it is instructive to compare them quantitatively with the exact result for this case (Coulomb's law)

$$V(r) \; = \; \frac{q}{4\pi \epsilon_0 r} \; , \tag{5.18}$$

where $r = \sqrt{x^2 + y^2 + z^2}$ is the distance from the charge. This comparison is shown in Figure 5.10 where we plot the numerical solutions for boxes with edge lengths of 2 and 4. Near the charge, that is, as $x \to 0$, the numerical results agree with the exact solution. However, as x increases, the numerical results fall systematically below the exact result. This is because of the different boundary conditions assumed in the two cases. The analytic result, (5.18), assumes that $V = 0$ an *infinite* distance away, while our numerical solution takes $V = 0$ on the faces of the box, which are much closer. Indeed, we see that the numerical result for V goes smoothly to zero at the face of the box. Thus, the presence of the grounded box forces V to vanish faster than it would otherwise. In short, the numerical and analytic solutions differ because they are not dealing with the same problem.

This illustrates something that must always be kept in mind in numerical work. For many problems we would like to impose conditions on the behavior at "infinity," but this is often difficult to do in a numerical treatment. Therefore we impose these conditions at the boundaries of some suitable region; for the problem here this is just the box. We then hope that the finite size of the box will not distort or otherwise significantly affect the numerical solution near the center of the box, but we must always be on guard for such effects. In our problem involving the potential near a point charge, we have observed that the influence of the finite size of the box is felt even fairly near the center. The reason for this is the relatively slow spatial dependence in Coulomb's law. From (5.18) we find a $1/r$ dependence that means that the effect of the box will be felt at rather long distances from the face of the box. Fortunately, boundary effects often fall off much faster than this (the rate of fall off depends on the problem), so they aren't always as large as in the present case.

Exercises

1. Extend our treatment of a point charge in a metal box to deal with the case in which the charge is located near one face of the box. Study how the equipotential contours are affected by the proximity of a grounded surface (the face of the box).

*2. In spherical coordinates Poisson's equation has the form

$$\frac{1}{r} \frac{\partial^2}{\partial r^2} (r\,V) = -\frac{\rho}{\epsilon_0} \,, \tag{5.19}$$

where we have assumed a spherically symmetric problem so that V is a function only of the distance from the origin. Solve this equation numerically using the relaxation method for a point charge at $r = 0$, imposing $V = 0$ some large distance away. Compare your result with Coulomb's law, (5.18). Hint: This problem is made difficult by the factor of $1/r$ on the left side of (5.19) and its effect on constructing a numerical solution, especially when the charge distribution is a singular function at $r = 0$ as is the case for a point charge. One way to deal with this problem is to instead give the "point" charge a small but nonzero spatial size; that is, assume that there is a uniform charge density inside a small sphere of radius r_{min}. If you take this approach, be sure to pick a grid size smaller than r_{min}. Convenient parameter choices are $r_{min} = 0.2$ with a grid size of 0.025, and $V = 0$ imposed at $r = 5$, but you should also try other values. Compare your result for $V(r)$ with Figure 5.10.

*3. Investigate the performance of the simultaneous overrelaxation algorithm for a point charge in two and three dimensions. Hint: In two dimensions we know the optimum choice of the overrelaxation parameter, α in (5.15). In three dimensions you should determine the optimum choice of this parameter by observing the speed of convergence for different values of α. How sensitive is the convergence to the value of α?

5.3   Magnetic Field Produced by a Current

We now turn to several problems associated with magnetic fields. Our goal is to calculate the magnetic field produced by an electric current for several different geometries. Besides illustrating how to compute the magnetic field in cases that cannot easily be dealt with analytically, these problems will also introduce a few of the ideas involved with numerical integration.

We start with the simplest possible problem, the magnetic field produced by a straight wire. The geometry is sketched in Figure 5.11 where we define several variables that enter the Biot-Savart law for the magnetic field produced by a current I flowing in a wire segment $\vec{dz}$

$$d\vec{B} = \frac{\mu_0 I}{4\pi} \frac{\vec{dz} \times \vec{r}}{r^3} \,. \tag{5.20}$$

Here $\vec{r}$ is the vector that runs from the segment carrying the current to the point in question, and μ_0 takes care of the units (in SI). For this particular geometry the cross-product can be written in terms of

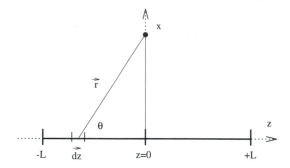

Figure 5.11: Geometry for computing the magnetic field near a straight wire. The wire is of length $2L$ and we consider the field at a point on the x axis. This axis is perpendicular to the wire and intersects the wire at its center. The current is assumed to flow from left to right, so at the point in question (the dot on the x axis) the field is perpendicular to the plane of the drawing and directed out of the plane.

the angle θ in Figure 5.11 yielding

$$dB = \frac{\mu_0 I}{4\pi} \frac{dz \, \sin\theta}{r^2} \, , \tag{5.21}$$

where we have dropped the vector symbols, since the field from each segment of the wire is directed perpendicular to the plane in Figure 5.11.

The total field is the integral of dB over the length of the wire. To compute this we follow our usual pattern of converting differentials into small differences; dz becomes Δz and the integral becomes a sum from one end of the wire to the other

$$B \approx \sum \frac{\mu_0 I}{4\pi} \frac{x \, \Delta z}{(z^2 + x^2)^{3/2}} \, , \tag{5.22}$$

where we have now expressed r and $\sin\theta$ in terms of x and z. This sum yields an *approximate* value for B, where the numerical error can be reduced by making Δz smaller. This is a very simple, but quite effective way to compute an integral numerically. It is similar to the method known as Simpson's rule, which is introduced in many calculus (and numerical analysis) textbooks. As a slight digression, we will now make a few general comments about numerical integration.

Integrating a function $f(x)$ can be viewed as the problem of finding the area under the corresponding curve, as illustrated in Figure 5.12. The approximation to the integral we used in deriving (5.22) yields in the general case

$$\int f(x) \, dx \approx \sum_i f(x_i) \, \Delta x \, , \tag{5.23}$$

where Δx is the size of the grid step along x and $x_i = i\Delta x$. Each term in this sum is the area of one of the rectangles in Figure 5.12. This approximation for the integral thus amounts to approximating the region of interest by a sequence of rectangles of width Δx and height $f(x_i)$. As Δx is made smaller these rectangles provide a better and better approximation to the true area.[10] The Simpson's rule method

---

[10] Assuming, of course, that the function is not pathological.

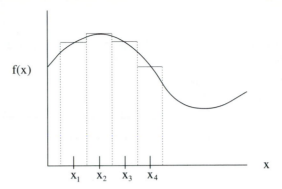

Figure 5.12: Geometrical interpretation of how the sum (5.23) approximates the area under a function $f(x)$.

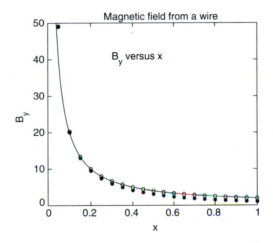

Figure 5.13: Magnetic field near a straight wire for a current I such that $\mu_0 I = 1$. Filled circles: for a wire of length 1; open circles: for a length of 10. The solid curve is the exact result for an infinite wire. The step size for the integration was $\Delta z = 0.1$.

for approximating an integral employs the same basic approach, except that it uses rectanglelike regions with arcs on one end (the arcs are chosen so as to approximate the function) instead of simple rectangles. We will leave it to the exercises for you to compare the relative accuracies of the two methods.

Returning to the problem of a magnetic field produced by a straight wire, the sum in (5.22) can be evaluated numerically and a full listing of such a program is given in Appendix 4. Figure 5.13 shows results for the field strength as a function of distance from the wire. Here we consider wires of two different lengths and also show the exact result for an infinitely long wire as obtained from Ampere's law, $B = \mu_0 I/(2\pi r)$. The results for the longer wire are seen to be in agreement with the infinite wire values, except at locations nearest the wire. These slight deviations are due to the finite grid size, Δz. As we approach the wire (i.e., for small x), we eventually reach the regime where the grid size is no longer small compared to x, and errors due to the finite grid become important. We will investigate in the exercises how these errors vary with grid size.

Exercises

1. Calculate the field from a straight wire using Simpson's rule (see Press et al. [1986]), and compare it with the result obtained from (5.22) for the same grid size, Δz.

2. Evaluate (5.22) for different grid sizes and compare the results with Ampere's law. Derive a rule of thumb concerning how small the grid size must be in comparison with the distance from the wire, in order for the calculated field to be within 5 percent of the exact result.

3. Calculate the value of π by using numerical integration to estimate the area of a circle of unit radius. Observe how your estimate approaches the exact value (3.1415926...) as the grid size in the integration is reduced.

5.4   Magnetic Field of a Solenoid: Inside and Out

We next consider the magnetic field produced by somewhat more complicated current arrangements. The first case we consider is a circular current loop. The field along an axis perpendicular to the plane of the loop and passing through its center, can be calculated analytically. However, the field at points off this axis cannot be evaluated in closed form. To calculate the field at a general location, we take the approach employed in the previous section and adapt the sum (5.21) to the case of a wire with a circular shape. We consider a circle of radius r lying in the x–y plane (Figure 5.14) and find

$$\vec{\Delta B} \approx \frac{\mu_0 I}{4\pi} \frac{\vec{\Delta r} \times \vec{L}}{L^3} . \tag{5.24}$$

The total field is the sum of these terms as we traverse the loop. This can be done by letting θ vary from 0 to 2π with $\Delta r = r\Delta\theta$.

   Implementing this calculation with a program requires a careful consideration of the terms in the cross product, since $\vec{\Delta r} \times \vec{L}$ generally will have nonzero components along x, y, and z. One version of such a program is given in Appendix 4. The calculation yields the three components of $\vec{B}$ as a function of position, so the question of how to best display the result requires a little thought. In Figure 5.15 we

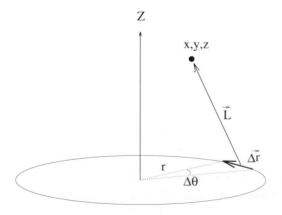

Figure 5.14:   Geometry of the current loop problem.

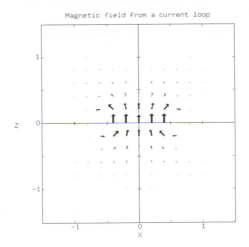

Figure 5.15:   Magnetic field near a current loop (this is the $y = 0$ plane in Figure 5.14). The radius of the loop was 0.5 and the step size $\Delta\theta$ was $2\pi/10$.

show the field lines in the plane perpendicular to plane of the loop, which cuts through the center of the loop. We see that the field lines circulate around the wire, as expected.

As noted above, these results for the field cannot be expressed analytically except on the axis of the loop (z). It is thus useful to check our calculations against the exact result in this case. For points on the z axis the magnetic field is directed along z, and the Biot-Savart law can be evaluated in closed form

$$B_z = \frac{\mu_0 \, I \, r^2}{\sqrt{2 \, (r^2 + z^2)}} . \tag{5.25}$$

This exact answer is compared with our numerical results in Figure 5.16. The results agree, which gives us some confidence in our program. As we have emphasized in connection with previous problems, it is always advisable to check numerical results against analytic calculations whenever possible. A program always gives an answer (once the syntax errors are removed), but that is no guarantee that it is correct!

Another interesting case is that of a solenoid. While the field along the axis of a solenoid can be calculated analytically using the Biot-Savart law, the field off the axis cannot be obtained in closed form. This field can be computed numerically using a program very similar to the one for the current loop. The only difference is that now the current follows a helical path, so $\vec{\Delta r}$ has three nonzero components. We will leave the programming for you. Some results are given in Figure 5.17, which shows $\vec{B}$ in both the x–z and x–y planes (the solenoid is centered on the z axis). The field near the z axis inside the solenoid is shown on the left. It is seen to be (relatively) large, uniform, and parallel to the axis of the solenoid (here the z axis), which is what we are all taught in our courses on electricity and magnetism.[11] The field outside the solenoid is often taken to be zero, since it is much smaller than the

---

[11] The magnitude of the field at the center of the solenoid has been checked against the analytic result (they agree).

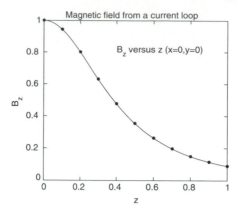

Figure 5.16: Magnetic field produced by a current loop, on the axis of the loop. The field is directed along the z axis in Figure 5.14. The radius of the loop was 0.5 and the step size $\Delta\theta$ was $2\pi/10$. For convenience, the current was chosen such that $\mu_0 I = 1$. The solid line is the exact result.

field inside (note that the effective scale on the right in Figure 5.17 is greatly magnified). That there is a field outside can be understood if we note that since the solenoid winding follows a helical path, there is also a component of the current *along* the z axis. This component is much smaller than the component that cuts the x–z plane, since there are many windings that cut this plane, but only one that cuts through the x–y plane. Nevertheless, the current along z is not zero, so there is a small field whose direction can be roughly estimated by modeling this current by a single wire that runs along z and using the right hand rule. Hence, the field outside the solenoid should circulate counterclockwise as viewed from the

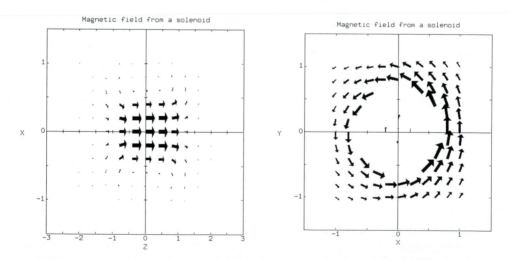

Figure 5.17: Magnetic field produced by a solenoid. Left: $\vec{B}$ in the x–z plane. The solenoid runs along the z axis and is 2 units long; its radius is 0.5 units. Right: $\vec{B}$ in the x–y plane ($z = 0$). The magnitude of B here is much smaller than in the plot on the left. The number of turns in the solenoid was 80 and the step size was $\Delta\theta = 2\pi/20$.

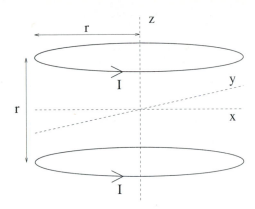

Figure 5.18: Helmholtz coils; two current loops that are parallel and whose separation is equal to their radius. This geometry is noteworthy because the field at the center (the origin) is particularly uniform.

large z end of the solenoid; this is precisely what is seen in Figure 5.17. It is interesting to note that the field outside the solenoid is *not* quite symmetric about the z axis. We have chosen the geometry of the solenoid such that the helix carrying the current pierces the x–y plane at $y = 0$, $x > 0$, making the field slightly larger on that side of the solenoid in the plot on the right in Figure 5.17.

Exercises

1. Write a program to calculate the magnetic field for your favorite current distribution. One possibility is a pair of loops of radius r, with one loop lying in the x–y plane and the other in the y–z plane. Another possibility is the solenoid considered in Figure 5.17.

2. Consider the magnetic field produced by a set of two coils that are both centered on the z axis, are both parallel to the x–y plane, and are both of radius r (see Figure 5.18). Let the separation between the coils also be r. These are called Helmholtz coils and are noteworthy because they produce a particularly uniform field near the point centered between them. Calculate numerically the field produced by these coils both on the z axis (where you can compare with the exact result from Biot-Savart law), and along the x axis.

3. Calculate the magnetic field both inside and outside a coil wrapped on a torus. Be sure to compare your result for B on the axis of the torus with the exact answer.

References

Press, W. H., B. P. Flannery, S. A. Teukolsky, and W. T. Vetterling, 1986. *Numerical Recipes*. Cambridge: Cambridge University Press. Chapter 17 discusses the relaxation method and analyzes its convergence properties. They also give a good description of Simpson's rule and related algorithms.

6

Waves

In this chapter we consider several topics associated with wave motion. While the central ideas in this discussion are applicable to virtually all types of waves, we will find it convenient (and interesting, we hope) to consider the particular case of waves on a string. After introducing and developing a solution for the wave equation in the ideal case (that is, for a perfectly flexible, frictionless string), we then extend our modeling to deal with waves in more realistic situations. This will lead us to several interesting issues that arise in connection with musical instruments.

6.1   Waves: The Ideal Case

The central equation of wave motion is

$$\frac{\partial^2 y}{\partial t^2} = c^2 \frac{\partial^2 y}{\partial x^2},$$
(6.1)

which is usually referred to as the wave equation. This equation arises in many situations, including waves on a string, electromagnetic waves, waves on the surface of a lake, and sound waves. Here we will use a language appropriate for waves on a string, although our methods and conclusions will apply to other cases as well. y is then the displacement of the string from its equilibrium (undisturbed) form, x is distance measured along the string, t is the time, and c is a parameter that turns out to be the speed with which a wave moves on the string. From direct substitution you can verify that solutions to (6.1) have the form $y = f(x \pm ct)$, which corresponds to waves traveling in either direction ($+x$ or $-x$) along the string. The function f describes the shape of the wave, and we will see shortly that it is determined by the initial conditions; that is, how the string is excited.

   Our main job in this section is to develop a numerical scheme for solving (6.1). Superficially, the partial differential equation (6.1) bears some resemblance to Laplace's equation, so we might think that an approach similar to the relaxation methods described in Chapter 5 would be useful. However, this turns out not to be the case, and we will see that the wave equation and Laplace's equation require rather different numerical treatments. After we develop an algorithm suitable for (6.1), we will use it to explore several aspects of wave motion. In later sections we move on to consider the spectral analysis of wave motion and also the behavior of more realistic models, including the stiffness of the string (which leads to an effect known as dispersion) and friction (i.e., damping).

To construct a numerical approach to the wave equation, we will, as usual, write it in finite difference form. We treat both x and t as discrete variables with $x = i\Delta x$ and $t = n\Delta t$. The displacement of the string is then a function of both i and n, which we write as $y(i, n) \equiv y(x = i\Delta x, t = n\Delta t)$ so that the first index of y specifies the spatial coordinate and the second index corresponds to time. We have already derived the needed expression for the second partial derivative (see the discussion of Laplace's equation in Chapter 5), and inserting it into the wave equation, (6.1), yields

$$\frac{y(i, n + 1) + y(i, n - 1) - 2\, y(i, n)}{(\Delta t)^2} \approx c^2 \left[\frac{y(i + 1, n) + y(i - 1, n) - 2\, y(i, n)}{(\Delta x)^2} \right]. \qquad (6.2)$$

This problem is in some respects similar to the initial-value problems we encountered in Chapters 1–4. In those cases we typically considered the time-dependent motion of an object using an equation of motion that was (usually) derived from Newton's second law. In order to obtain a solution for those differential equations we required some initial conditions, which were often the position and velocity at an initial time. To construct a solution of (6.2) we will also require some initial conditions. For simplicity we will assume that the displacement of the string at times prior to and including $t_n = n\Delta t$ is known. We then want to derive an expression for the displacement at the next time step, $t_{n+1} = (n + 1)\Delta t$. Rearranging (6.2) we can express $y(i, n + 1)$ in terms of y at previous time steps, with the result

$$y(i, n + 1) = 2\,[1 - r^2]\, y(i, n) - y(i, n - 1) + r^2\, [y(i + 1, n) + y(i - 1, n)] , \qquad (6.3)$$

where $r \equiv c\Delta t/\Delta x$. Thus if we know the string configuration at time steps n and $n - 1$, we can calculate the configuration at step $n + 1$. Typically, we might know the string configuration at $t = 0$, which we will refer to as $y_0(x)$. Since we are dealing with a second-order differential equation, we require two initial conditions.[1] Knowledge of the string configuration at two consecutive time steps is thus sufficient.[2] One natural choice, and the one that we will make here, is to assume that the string is held fixed with shape $y_0(x)$ prior to $t = 0$.

A program that calculates the motion of a string is given in full in Appendix 4. Below we list only the subroutine `propagate`, which implements (6.3). The variables `dt`, `dx`, and `c` are the time step, spatial grid size, and wave speed, and are set by the initialization routine. The parameter `r2` is the variable r^2 used in (6.3),[3] while the string displacement is stored in the two dimensional array `y(i,n)`. The spatial index, `i`, runs from 0 to `nmax`, corresponding to the `nmax + 1` spatial steps along x. The time index `n` can have the value of 1, corresponding to the previous time step, 2, for the current time

---

[1] Actually, we require two initial conditions for each (discrete) spatial element of the string.

[2] The initial position and velocity of the string would also suffice.

[3] As usual, we have sacrificed program efficiency for clarity. The variable `r2` could, of course, be evaluated in the initialization subroutine, and its value passed into `propagate`. This would avoid the need to evaluate it anew in each call to `propagate`. In practice, however, the extra time spent doing this is negligible, since `propagate` has to loop through the spatial index.

step, or 3, which is the "next" time step. `propagate` loops through the spatial index and calculates the string displacement at the next time step, placing the result in `y(i,3)`. In preparation for the next iteration it then shifts the values in `y(i,2)` into `y(i,1)`, and those in `y(i,3)` into `y(i,2)`.[4]

```
!   simulate waves on a string
!   N. Giordano   1-10-94
!   y(,) is a two dimensional array containing the displacement at
!      the current time step y(i,2), the previous time step y(i,1)
!      the next time step corresponds to y(i,3)
!   dt = time step      dx = spatial grid size    c = wave speed
!   nmax = number of spatial units
!   i runs from 0 to nmax, with the fixed ends at i=0 and i=nmax
sub propagate(y(,),dt,dx,c,nmax)
   r2 = (dt * c / dx)^2
   for i = 1 to nmax-1           ! calculate y at the next time step
      y(i,3) = r2 * (y(i+1,2) + y(i-1,2)) + 2*(1.0 - r2)*y(i,2) - y(i,1)
   next i
   for i = 1 to nmax-1           ! shift values of y "back" in time sequence
      y(i,1) = y(i,2)
      y(i,2) = y(i,3)
   next i
end sub
```

There is one more important issue that must be dealt with, namely how to treat the ends of the string. We have several options; perhaps the simplest choice is to treat the ends as fixed, that is, tied down so that they cannot move, and this is what we have done in `propagate`. This is accomplished by first initializing `y(i,n)` to be zero at the ends of the string (at `i=0` and `i=nmax`), and then restricting the main loop in `propagate` to the range between `i=1` and `i=nmax-1`. However, we could easily have assumed different boundary conditions, such as free ends, or ends that are intermediate between fixed and free. We will see shortly that the boundary conditions affect the manner in which waves are reflected when they reach the ends of the string.

Some results from our program are shown in Figure 6.1, where we have plotted the string displacement at different times. The uppermost plot is the initial ($t = 0$) displacement of the string. Here we have assumed a simple "gaussian pluck" of the string. That is, we have taken the initial string profile to be

$$y_0(x) = \exp[-k(x - x_0)^2],\tag{6.4}$$

where the displacement is centered at x_0, and k is a factor that determines the width of the gaussian envelope. In Figure 6.1 we use $x_0 = 0.3$ m and $k = 1000$ m^{-2}, and the string runs from $x = 0$ to 1 m. We have included units here as we will be appling some of these ideas to (semi-) realistic piano strings in the following sections.

While the initial displacement has a (single) gaussian profile, it quickly splits into two separate wavepackets, or pulses, which propagate in oppose directions along the string. This can be seen from the second and third traces in Figure 6.1, where the two wavepackets have the same shape (as they must, by symmetry) as they move apart. As t increases, the wavepacket on the left reaches the end

---

[4]This shifting could be avoided by simply treating the time index n in a "cyclical" manner. This is not hard to do, but we will leave it for the curious reader. We could easily spend a great deal of time streamlining and otherwise tinkering with our programs, but if we did, we would probably still be in Chapter 1.

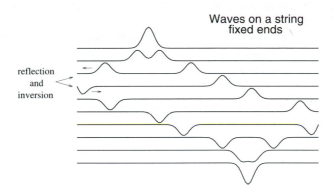

Figure 6.1:   Waves propagating on a string with fixed ends. The string had a length of 1 m and the simulation used the values $c = 300$ m/s, $\Delta x = 0.01$ m, and $\Delta t = \Delta x/c$. The initial string profile is given at the top, and successive traces (moving from top to bottom) show the string at progressively later times. An example of reflection and inversion of a wavepacket when it reaches the left end of the string is indicated.

of the string at $x = 0$, where it finds that the string is held fixed [$y(\text{end}) = 0$]. This wavepacket is reflected, but the reflection process also *inverts* the wave so that the displacement is now negative. This inverted wavepacket then travels toward the right. Meanwhile, the wavepacket on the right eventually encounters the opposite end of the string, and it too is inverted on reflection (the seventh trace from the top in Figure 6.1). These two inverted wavepackets then come together, and in the bottom trace they have overlapped so as to reform the initial string displacement (although it is now inverted).

The results in Figure 6.1 show that our numerical approach gives an accurate solution of the wave equation. Indeed, things seem almost too easy. It turns out that there are, in fact, some subtle numerical issues that we have managed to avoid so far. We have in previous chapters made several comments concerning the accuracy of finite difference approximations, and as a general rule we know that smaller step or grid sizes usually lead to smaller numerical errors. The problem we are dealing with here involves *two* step sizes, one for t and one for x, and the question now is how best to choose them. You may have noticed that the step sizes we used in Figure 6.1 satisfied the condition $c\Delta t/\Delta x = 1$; in other words, the factor $r \equiv c\Delta t/\Delta x$ in (6.3) was exactly 1. This was no accident. It turns out that when $r = 1$ the higher-order terms that are dropped in deriving (6.3) are largely (but not completely) canceled out. If we were to repeat the calculation with a smaller time step and the same value of Δx, the results would actually be *less* accurate; we will illustrate the nature of such errors shortly. However, reducing the spatial step size while keeping Δt fixed leads to a real disaster. For example, if we were to cut Δx in half but keep Δt fixed so that $r = 2$, the algorithm becomes *unstable*. In this case a wavepacket like the one in Figure 6.1 would grow with rapidly with time, and the calculated string displacement would *diverge*!

There are some numerical lessons to be learned here, and a full discussion of these issues could easily fill this chapter. We refer readers to the sources in the references (as well as the exercises) for further information, and will make only a few general observations here. Let us first consider what is so special about $r = 1$ and why larger values of r, that is, smaller values of the spatial grid size Δx, lead to numerical instabilities. Imagine that our string is initially at rest with $y = 0$ everywhere. We then arrange things so that at time step $n = 1$ the value of y at one of the spatial grid sites, $i = i_0$, is given a nonzero value, while $y = 0$ at all of the other sites. You can think of this as a very special way of plucking the string. The finite difference expression, (6.3), tells us that at time step $n = 2$ this "disturbance" will be felt at sites $i_0 \pm 1$. The string displacements $y(i_0, 2)$ and $y(i_0 \pm 1, 2)$ will be nonzero, but the displacements at all other values of i will still be zero. Similarly, at time step 3, the disturbance will propagate to sites $i_0 \pm 2$, etc. With our numerical scheme the disturbance will propagate precisely one spatial step for each time step. The velocity of the disturbance is thus $\Delta x / \Delta t$ and is, therefore, limited by our choice of step sizes. It is not possible for our algorithm to yield a disturbance that moves more than one spatial element per time step. Now, we know that a wave on the string will move at a speed of c, so if our numerical solution has any hope of describing such a wave, it must be able to handle disturbances that travel at this speed. However, if the step sizes are such that $\Delta x / \Delta t < c$, our algorithm will simply be incapable of yielding a wave moving at the proper velocity. This corresponds to $r > 1$, and so in this case our numerical algorithm must fail. This failure is manifested by the instability mentioned above; it turns out that a simulation with $r > 1$ yields waves whose amplitudes diverge rapidly with time. We will leave a study of this behavior to the exercises.

This simple argument involving propagation velocities explains why our algorithm requires $r \leq 1$. To analyze the performance of the algorithm for this range of r requires a bit more work, which can be reviewed in the sources in the references. There it is shown that when $r = 1$ the higher-order terms neglected in deriving (6.3) are (as we already noted) largely canceled. Thus, as a practical point, it is usually better to choose the step sizes such that $r = 1$ rather than, say, $r = 0.5$. However, values of r smaller than 1 still yield stable solutions, as we will illustrate in our next example.

Consider a string that is composed of two segments on which the waves have different velocities. This would arise, for example, if we tie together two strings of different thicknesses (i.e., different values for the mass per unit length). If we were dealing with electromagnetic (light) waves, this would correspond to light traveling from a material with one index of refraction into a material with a different index. We can model this problem with (6.3) and the program developed above by letting c be dependent on position. To be specific, we consider a string 1 m long described by a wave velocity c_1 for $0 \leq x \leq 0.5$, and c_2 elsewhere. This means that r in (6.3) has different values on the two halves of the string.

Some results from such a simulation are shown in Figure 6.2. Here the left-hand part of the string (the part to the left of the dotted line) has a wave velocity c_1, which is a factor of 2 larger than the velocity on the right. Hence, we have a light string on the left and a heavy string on the right (we won't worry about the knot in the middle). The wavepacket is initiated on the left side of the string, and immediately splits into left- and right-going components. When the right-going wavepacket hits the interface with the heavy string, it is partially reflected and partially transmitted. The reflected part is inverted, since the heavy string acts a little like a fixed boundary. The transmitted part is not inverted and is seen to travel more slowly on the heavy string, which is expected since $c_2 = c_1/2$. Careful examination of the shape of the wave packet in the heavy string shows a small "blip" trailing the main part of the packet. It turns out that this is due to the numerical errors, mentioned above, that arise when $r < 1$ (we will justify this claim in the exercises). While we are able to use $r = 1$ for the left part of the string, the algorithm forces us to then use $r = 1/2$ on the right side of the system, so these numerical errors cannot be avoided (at least with our simple algorithm). Nevertheless, these errors are not serious and our wave simulations give a nice picture of wave transmission and reflection at a boundary.

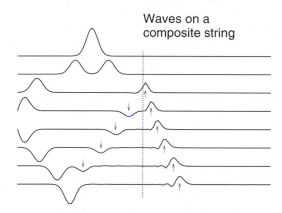

Figure 6.2: Waves propagating on a composite string with fixed ends. The string was 1 m long, with $c_1 = 300$ m/s on the left half of the string and $c_2 = 150$ m/s on the right half (the dotted line shows where the change in c occurs). We used $\Delta x = 0.01$ m and $\Delta t = \Delta x / c_1$. The arrows indicate pieces of the wavepacket that are reflected by, and transmitted through, the point where the propagation velocity changes.

The program we have developed for wave propagation can easily be extended to study a variety of other wave phenomena. Examples include reflection from a free end, superposition of waves, and standing waves. Some of these are explored in the exercises.

Exercises

1. Write a program to simulate wave motion on a string with free ends. Do this by using boundary conditions that always give the ends of the string the same displacement as the points that are one spatial unit in from the ends. Study how the waves are reflected from the ends of the string and compare the results with the behavior with fixed ends. You should find that the reflected wave packets are not inverted.

2. Compare the behavior calculated with different values of r. Observe the instabilities associated with $r > 1$ and the errors that arise when $r < 1$. It is especially instructive to compare the reflection of a wavepacket from a fixed end for different values of $r \leq 1$. The small errors that are introduced when $r < 1$ are then clearly visible as extra "bumps" (like the ones noted in connection with Figure 6.2) that are generated during each reflection.

*3. Set up a wavepacket that doesn't split up into two pieces (as we observed with our gaussian packet in Figure 6.1), but moves uniformly in one direction. Hint: In the simulations discussed (so far) in this section we have assumed that the string is at rest prior to $t = 0$. In order to construct a single wavepacket that does not immediately split you will have to properly specify both the initial displacement and velocity of the string.

4. Study the propagation of wavepackets with other shapes. For example, a guitar string that is plucked has an initial profile like that shown in Figure 6.3. Calculate how this excitation splits and moves with time.

Figure 6.3: Realistic excitation profile for a guitar string that is plucked. The initial string displacement consists of two straight lines, which join with different slopes at the excitation (plucking) point.

*5. Investigate the motion of a string for which one end is held fixed, while the other is made to oscillate. Do this by letting the string element at one end move according to $y(i = 0) = A \sin(\omega t)$. You should find that this generates a wave that propagates toward the opposite end of the string. This wave is then reflected, and it interferes with the initial wave. Confirm that the frequency of this wave ($f = \omega/2\pi$) and its wavelength are consistent with the parameter c in the wave equation. Also determine the values of ω that lead to standing waves.

6. An important feature of a linear equation is that the sum of two solutions is also a solution. One consequence of this is that two wavepackets will travel independently of each other. An especially clear way to demonstrate this is to set up a string with an initial profile such that there are two gaussian wavepackets, located at different places on the string. These wavepackets (or components of them) may then propagate toward each other and collide. Show that the wavepackets are unaffected by these collisions. That is, show that two such wavepackets pass through each other without changing shape or speed.

*7. The origin of the wave equation (6.1) is different for different types of waves. For electromagnetic waves it is a result of Maxwell's equations, while for waves on a string it follows from Newton's second law. One way to derive the wave equation for compressional waves on a solid rod is as follows. Model the rod as a collection of particles of mass m, as shown in Figure 6.4. Each mass is a small piece of the rod and is connected to adjacent pieces (masses) by springs. Let the position of mass m_i be y_i. The springs are unstretched and uncompressed when the masses are at their equilibrium positions, which we will take to be $y_i = 0$. Each mass experiences forces from the two springs to which it is connected (don't worry about the ends). The force from the spring to the left is just $F_i(\text{left}) = -k(y_i - y_{i-1})$ where k is the force constant of the spring, and the force from the spring on the right has a similar form. Write Newton's second law for mass m_i and show that it can be cast in the form (6.1), with $x = i\Delta x$ where Δx is the distance between masses. Find the value of c in terms of m, k, and Δx. Hint: The finite difference form for a second partial derivative will be useful. Also, note that this derivation assumes implicitly that the displacements y_i are all small compared to Δx.

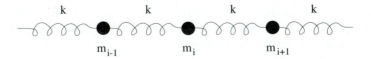

Figure 6.4: Model for compressional waves on a rod. Each small piece of the rod is modeled as a small mass m, connected to adjacent masses by springs with force constants k.

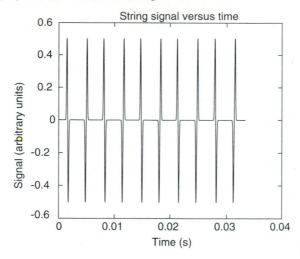

Figure 6.5:   Signal from a vibrating string. The string was excited with a gaussian initial pluck centered at the middle of the string, and the displacement a distance 5 percent from one end was recorded. The other parameters in the simulation were the same as in Figure 6.1.

6.2   Frequency Spectrum of Waves on a String

Vibrating strings are used in a variety of musical instruments, which makes it interesting to consider the frequency spectrum of waves on a string. We have already employed Fourier analysis of a time-dependent signal in connection with our study of oscillatory motion in Chapter 3, and the same sort of spectral analysis can be used to examine waves on a string.[5] Ideally we might want to perform such an analysis in connection with a model of a guitar or piano, in which case we would analyze the sound wave caused by plucking (in the case of a guitar) or striking (for a piano) a string. However, for a *real* musical instrument this is a very complicated process, since the sound is actually produced by the vibration of a wooden plate connected to the string.[6] A full treatment of the vibrations of such a plate coupled to a vibrating string is too involved to include here, so we will take a simplified approach.

We consider a string with fixed ends and imagine that we record the displacement of a particular point on the string as a function of time. An example of such a signal is given in Figure 6.5, where we show some results calculated using the program developed in Section 6.1. We see a series of pulses, each of which is produced when one of the wavepackets observed in Figure 6.1 moves past our observation point. Here the observation point, that is, the position at which the string position was recorded, was 5 percent from one end of the string. The pulses alternate in sign, since the wave is inverted when it is reflected. The pulses occur in closely spaced (inverted) pairs because the observation point is very near to one end.

As was discussed in Chapter 3 and in more detail in Appendix 2, this signal can be decomposed into Fourier components. That is, we can write the signal as a sum of sines and cosines with different

---

[5]Readers who are not familiar with Fourier analysis should examine Appendix 2 before attempting this section.

[6]The body of the guitar or the sound board in a piano.

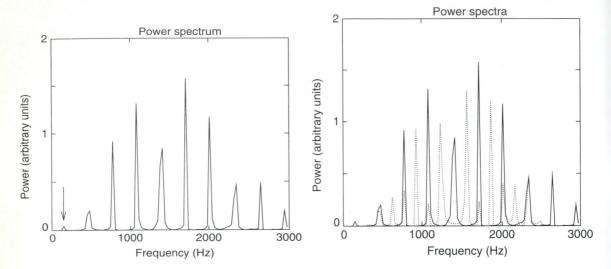

Figure 6.6: Left: power spectrum of the signal in Figure 6.5. Here the string was excited at the center. The arrow indicates the peak corresponding to the fundamental frequency of the string, which in this case is 150 Hz. Right: the dotted curve is the power spectrum obtained when the string was excited 5 percent from its center. For comparison, the solid curve shows the power spectrum found when the string was excited at the center (this is the result shown on the left).

frequencies and different amplitudes. The results of such an analysis can be displayed in several ways. For this problem it is most convenient to consider the power spectrum. This is just the sum of the squares of the Fourier components (the sine and cosine components) at each frequency, as a function of the frequency.[7] The power spectrum calculated for the signal in Figure 6.5 is shown in Figure 6.6, where we find a series of regularly spaced peaks.

These peaks can be understood in terms of the standing waves that are found for a string with fixed ends, as illustrated in Figure 6.7. The standing wave with the longest wavelength is the one shown at the top, and has a wavelength $\lambda_1 = 2L$, where L is the length of the string. The other standing waves have wavelengths of $L, 2L/3$, etc. These standing waves can be thought of as the basic *spatial* Fourier components of the string motion, just as the time-dependent sine waves discussed in Chapter 3 and Appendix 2 are the basic Fourier components in a frequency analysis. Each of these standing waves has a specific wavelength, which means that they also have a specific *frequency*, since the wavelength and frequency of a wave (even a standing wave) are related by $\lambda f = c$. The allowed wavelengths are $\lambda = 2L/m$, where m is an integer, so the possible frequencies are just $mc/(2L)$. This is why the peaks seen in the spectral analysis in Figure 6.6 occur at regularly spaced frequencies. Each of these peaks corresponds to a particular value of m.

For the parameters used in this simulation, the lowest frequency peak in the spectrum should occur at $c/(2L) = 150$ Hz, and we do, indeed, find a peak at this frequency (albeit a small one), as

---

[7]As a first approximation, the sound wave produced by a vibrating string will have an amplitude proportional to that of the string (there would also be a frequency-dependent coefficient of proportionality that we won't worry about here). With these approximations, the power carried by the sound wave is proportional to the power spectrum considered here (hence the name).

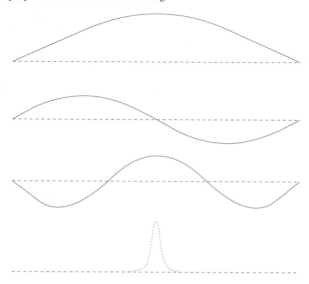

Figure 6.7: Solid curves show possible standing waves on a string with fixed ends. The dotted curve at the bottom shows one choice for the initial wavepacket, a gaussian function centered at the middle of the string.

shown on the left in Figure 6.6. There are also substantial peaks at 450, 750, 1050 Hz, etc., so there is certainly a very regular pattern. However, our standing wave argument suggests that the peaks should be spaced by $c/(2L)$, but the "peaks" at 300, 600, 900 Hz, etc., are either missing or extremely small compared to the adjacent peaks. To understand this behavior we need to consider how the string is excited, that is, how the initial wavepacket is setup. As we have already mentioned, the standing waves are the spatial Fourier components for our problem. We can, therefore, write our initial wavepacket, the gaussian curve at the bottom in Figure 6.7, as a sum of these standing waves. In fact, for our ideal string the magnitudes of these components do not change with time, so once we have determined the Fourier components for the initial wavepacket, we also have them for all later times. The wave moves, of course, because the different Fourier components have different frequencies. However, the relative *magnitudes* of these components do not change with time (we will develop these ideas further in Section 6.4).

Now let us consider in a little more detail the spatial Fourier components for our initial gaussian wavepacket. This wavepacket is located at the center of the string and is also *symmetric* with respect to the center of the string. This symmetry will be preserved in the Fourier components. That is, the only Fourier components with significant amplitudes will be those that are nonzero at the center of the string and are symmetric about the center. Thus we see that the Fourier components, which have zero amplitude (nodes) at the center, will not be present in our initial wavepacket. The standing waves that are not present have wavelengths $L, L/2, L/3, \ldots$ and for the particular simulation in Figure 6.6, their frequencies are 300, 600, 900, ... Hz. This is why these frequencies are missing in our spectrum.

The argument, then, is that the *symmetry* of the initial wavepacket causes certain frequencies to be suppressed. To convince you that this is indeed the case, we have repeated the simulation with an initial wavepacket whose peak is located 5 percent away from the center of the string, and the results are shown for comparison on the right in Figure 6.6. The peaks are now (almost) all spaced by 150 Hz, as expected for the string in this simulation. The only peaks missing here are those with nodes located 5 percent away from the center of the string. The message of this exercise is that the frequencies that are excited will be those whose spatial modes have the same *symmetry* as that of the initial wavepacket.

It turns out that a situation of this kind occurs in pianos. When you press a key on a piano, a complicated mechanical linkage is engaged that sets a "hammer" into motion. These hammers are essentially felt-covered mallets that strike one or more steel strings, the vibrations of which lead to the desired musical tone. The lowest frequency vibration of the string(s) is referred to as the frequency of the note, although as we have seen, many higher frequencies will also be generated. These harmonics are, for an ideal string such as the one considered here, integer multiples of the lowest, or fundamental, frequency.[8]

If we were to perform a Fourier analysis of the sound signal associated with a particular note, we would find a spectrum similar to that seen in Figure 6.6. There would be many peaks at regularly spaced frequencies. While the fundamental frequency is just the frequency of the first peak, the harmonics play an absolutely crucial role. It is not hard to arrange for a piano, a guitar, and a violin to all play the same note, that is, a note with the same fundamental frequency. However, most people would have no trouble in distinguishing the different instruments. This is because each produces a distinctive pattern of harmonic components. The relative strengths of the harmonics, and how they vary with time during the course of the note, are different for different instruments. Our ear (really our brain) makes use of these differences to identify the instruments.

Taking this argument one more step, when a piano designer assembles plans for a piano, the placement of the hammers is a crucial issue. This is because the striking point (the place where the hammer contacts the string) affects the spectrum of the vibrations. Nowadays, in most pianos the strike points are approximately 1/8 of the way from one end of the string. Using the arguments connected with Figure 6.7, this implies that vibrations that have a node at this location will not be excited by the hammer. Piano designers, and listeners, have apparently decided that minimizing these particular harmonics leads to the most pleasing tone. Precisely why that is the case is not obvious.

Exercises

1. Perform a spectrum analysis of waves on a string in which one end is free to move while the other is held fixed. Assume an initial gaussian wavepacket located 40 percent from one end. Explain the peaks in the spectrum in terms of the allowed standing waves. Note that because the ends are free, these standing waves will be different from those found with fixed ends (Figure 6.7).

2. Devise an initial string displacement that gives rise to a vibration in which the only frequency present is the one corresponding to the Fourier component with a wavelength of $2L/3$, where L is the length of the string.

3. Devise an initial string displacement that gives rise to vibrations in which the vibrational frequencies are all higher than the frequency of the Fourier component with a wavelength of $2L/5$, where L is the length of the string.

---

[8]We will consider these harmonics in more detail in Section 6.3.

4. Gaussian initial string displacements are convenient for the calculations of this section, but are not very realistic. When a real string, such as a guitar string, is plucked, the initial string displacement is more accurately described by two straight lines that start at the ends of the string (we assume fixed ends) and end at the excitation point, as illustrated in Figure 6.3. Compare the power spectrum for a string excited in this manner with the results found above for a gaussian initial wavepacket.

5. Consider the power spectra for waves on a string as a function of where the string vibration is observed, x_0. Some standing waves will have nodes at x_0, and the corresponding frequencies will not appear in the power spectrum, even though these waves may be excited on the string as a whole. Demonstrate this by comparing spectra obtained for values of x_0, which are 10 percent, 40 percent, and 50 percent from the end of the string. Hint: It is helpful in each case to consider initial gaussian excitations located at different spots along the string.

*6. The peaks in the power spectra in Figure 6.6 vary greatly in size, with the peaks at the lowest and highest frequencies being much weaker than the peaks at intermediate frequencies ($\sim$ 1000–2000 Hz). Explain qualitatively why this is the case

6.3   Motion of a (Somewhat) Realistic String

In our studies of vibrating strings we have so far treated only the case of an ideal string. Of course, real strings will have some frictional losses (damping), as well as some stiffness. To get a feeling for how these affect the vibrations, we will in this section consider the effect of stiffness (leaving damping to the exercises). The phenomena of damping and stiffness are not limited to waves on a string. For example, the same physics (and a similar equation) is encountered when dealing with electromagnetic waves in a lossy medium or sound in the atmosphere.

The physical origin of stiffness in the case of waves on a string can be understood as follows. In using the wave equation, (6.1), we assume that the string is perfectly flexible. The only force then arises from the string tension, and this force is directed along the string. While strings can be made to be very close to this ideal limit, there will always be a stiffness force that opposes bending of the string. This is the case, for example, with a thick metal bar; the vibrations of such an object are very different from those of a flexible wire.

Stiffness can be added to the model by adding a term[9] to our original wave equation (6.1)

$$\frac{\partial^2 y}{\partial t^2} = c^2 \left(\frac{\partial^2 y}{\partial x^2} - \epsilon L^2 \frac{\partial^4 y}{\partial x^4} \right) , \tag{6.5}$$

where ϵ is a stiffness parameter and L is the length of the string. The fourth partial derivative can be written in a finite difference form, using the same approach that we used to obtain the second partial derivative in Chapter 5. The result is

$$\frac{\partial^4 y}{\partial x^4} \approx \frac{y(i+2,n) - 4\,y(i+1,n) + 6\,y(i,n) - 4\,y(i-1,n) + y(i-2,n)}{(\Delta x)^4} . \tag{6.6}$$

---

[9]The origin of the new term in (6.5) is discussed in Chaigne and Askenfelt (1994).

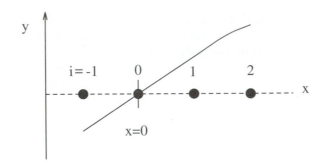

Figure 6.8: Hinged boundary conditions at the end of a string. The "real" string ends at $x = 0$ (spatial step $i = 0$). The displacement at $i = -1$ is only imaginary and is taken to be $-y(i = +1)$.

The fourth derivative thus involves the value of y at distances up to ± 2 spatial units away from the point where the derivative is centered. Inserting this into (6.5) leads, after a little algebra, to

$$
\begin{aligned}
y(i, n+1) = \; & [2 - 2r^2 - 6\epsilon r^2 N^2]\, y(i, n) - y(i, n-1) \\
& + r^2[1 + 4\epsilon N^2]\,[y(i+1, n) + y(i-1, n)] \\
& - \epsilon r^2 N^2\,[y(i+2, n) + y(i-2, n)] \;,
\end{aligned} \tag{6.7}
$$

where $N = L/\Delta x$ is the number of spatial units along the string. Equation (6.7) thus yields the string displacement at time step $n + 1$ in terms of the displacement at previous time steps. Extending our program to handle this equation is straightforward; we simply need to modify one line in the `propagate` subroutine. There is a slight complication, however. Equation (6.7) involves the displacement at sites ± 2 units away from the site in question, whereas without stiffness only sites displaced by ± 1 unit were involved. Now, when the program approaches the end of the string, that is, the last mobile section of the string, we need to know the displacement at the end and also the displacement one unit *past* the ends. The simplest way to deal with this problem is to assume that the ends of the string are "hinged." That is, we take the displacement at each end to be zero and assume that there are phantom locations one unit beyond the ends, which have displacements that are opposite the displacements at locations one unit inside the ends. This is illustrated in Figure 6.8. Here the real string terminates at $x = 0$ (corresponding here to spatial step $i = 0$ and a fixed end), but the program allows it to effectively extend to $i = -1$. The displacement of this phantom point is $y(i = -1) = -y(i = +1)$. This simple treatment of the boundary conditions will be adequate for our work and is actually the procedure used in detailed modeling of piano strings (see the references for more on this).[10]

The simulations of our stiff string can be carried out as before. Here we will focus our attention on an issue that is relevant to musical instruments. Figure 6.9 shows the power spectra calculated for several cases that correspond roughly to piano strings (this note would be in the upper bass region of

---

[10]You might object that such hinged boundary conditions are not very realistic. In our defense we have the following comments. First, we could assume some sort of clamped boundary conditions, which would amount to conditions on the spatial derivatives of y. The most realistic way to do this would depend on precisely how the string is fastened to its support. Second, in many instruments hinged boundary conditions seem to be a reasonable approximation (see Chaigne and Askenfelt [1994]). Third, if we want to construct a truly accurate model of a real musical instrument (or other type of string), life can quickly get very complicated.

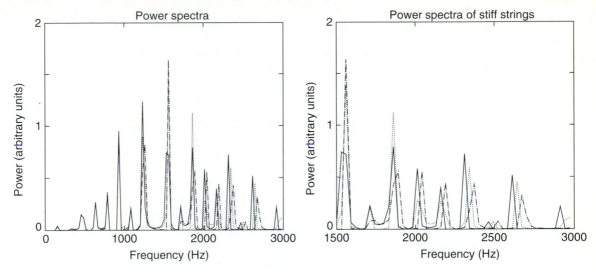

Figure 6.9: Power spectra for "realistic" strings. Solid curves: no stiffness; dotted curves: $\epsilon = 1 \times 10^{-5}$; dot-dashed curves: $\epsilon = 2 \times 10^{-5}$. In all cases the string was excited 5 percent off center, the displacement 5 percent from one end was analyzed, and we used $\Delta t = \Delta x/(4c)$ to ensure stability for all values of ϵ employed. The plot on the right shows the high frequency region on an expanded scale.

the keyboard).[11] Here we compare results for three separate simulations; a perfectly flexible string (stiffness $= \epsilon = 0$), a string with a stiffness similar to that found in a good grand piano ($\epsilon = 1 \times 10^{-5}$), and a string with a somewhat higher stiffness. Overall, the spectra are very similar; the peaks are regularly spaced and the spacing is very close to the expected value, which is 150 Hz for this string. However, careful examination of the region above about 2000 Hz shows that the peaks for the stiff strings are shifted systematically to higher frequencies when compared with those of the ideal string.

We have already seen that for an ideal string the frequencies of the standing waves are spaced by $c/(2L)$, independent of the frequency. However, for the stiff string this separation increases as we move to higher frequencies. This effect is known as *dispersion* and occurs because the stiffness causes the wave speed to now be *frequency dependent*. Physically this can be understood as follows. The higher frequencies correspond to standing waves with shorter wavelengths.[12] In order for it to move with a shorter wavelength, the string must be bent more severely. A stiff string resists bending and this extra resistance makes the string effectively tighter, leading to a higher wave velocity and a higher frequency.

Thus, for a real string the "harmonics" are not arranged harmonically. Indeed, they are usually called *partials* for this reason. The effect seen in Figure 6.9 is, in fact, a significant effect in pianos and other stringed instruments. The frequencies of the partials deviate by a small amount from the ideal harmonic spacing, and this deviation contributes to the characteristic piano sound. Perhaps most importantly, it affects chords since these involve notes that, in the ideal case, are harmonically related.

---

[11] Note that in this simulation we used $r < 1$. It turns out that the numerical stability condition involving r is altered by the stiffness term in the wave equation. Values of r less than unity are now required for stability; this is discussed in the references.

[12] It is important to note that the concepts of normal modes and superposition, which are at the heart of these arguments, still apply here since even with the stiffness term included the wave equation (6.5) is linear.

For example, a chord might involve two notes for which the second harmonic of one is very close in frequency to the third harmonic of the other. For a real string these harmonics, that is, partials, will not have quite the same frequencies, and this will affect the way the chord sounds.[13]

There are three other points that we should mention regarding this simulation. First, the shift of the partials to higher frequencies (higher than pure harmonics) is known as *octave stretching*, and is well known to piano designers and technicians. This term arises in the following way. Two notes that are an octave apart would, in the perfectly harmonic case, differ in frequency by precisely a factor of 2. For a well-tuned piano the second partial of the lower note will have approximately the same frequency as the fundamental (first partial) of the upper note. However, because of the shift produced by the string stiffness, the second partial of the lower note will be slightly more than a factor of 2 higher than its fundamental frequency. Hence, the effective size of an octave separation is stretched slightly and is greater than the value of 2 that would be found for a perfectly flexible string.

A second point concerns piano design. The effects of string stiffness depend on the length of the string. Essentially, this is because a short string will (other factors being similar) need to bend more than a long one. For this reason the shifting of the partials away from the harmonic "ideal" is greater for shorter strings. Since smaller pianos have shorter strings, the effect is generally largest in small pianos, and this is one reason why a large piano is preferred over a small one.[14] Interestingly, however, we would *not* like to see octave stretching eliminated altogether. This stretching contributes an essential element to the characteristic piano sound. After all, in an organ there is no octave stretching (there is no problem with stiff strings in that case), and most of us have no problem discerning an organ from a piano.

Our third point is a numerical one. We saw earlier that when solving the wave equation it is best from a numerical standpoint, to choose the parameter r to be unity, as this led to the best and most stable solutions. However, when the wave equation is generalized to include stiffness, the value of r at which our algorithm becomes unstable is reduced. Accordingly we chose $r = 1/4$ in the simulation of Figure 6.9. The problem of numerical stability is discussed further in Chaigne and Askenfelt (1994).

Exercises

1. Derive the finite difference approximation for the fourth partial derivative (6.6).

*2. Perform the calculations described in this section. One interesting possibility is to compare the size of the octave stretching, that is, the magnitude of the deviations from a purely harmonic spectrum, for short (treble) and long (bass) strings. The relevant string parameters for a good grand piano are given in Table 6.1.

---

[13]Our discussion here is a bit oversimplified, since we are ignoring how the strings are tuned (i.e., equal versus just temperament), etc. However, these complications do not change our basic point.

[14]Note that the stiffness parameter ϵ in (6.5) is a function of L. Thus, contrary to the way it may first appear from this equation, the effect of stiffness is actually smaller with a longer string (all else being the same). We have used this admittedly poor choice of notation in order to be consistent with the literature on piano string simulation.

Table 6.1:   Some parameters describing the properties of a strings in a typical grand piano. The note $C4$ is middle C, while $C2$ is two octaves lower and $C7$ is three octaves higher in frequency. The parameter b is associated with damping, as discussed in the next problem. After Chaigne and Askenfelt (1994).

Note	f (Hz)	L (m)	c (m/s)	ϵ (unitless)	b (s^{-1})
$C2$	65.4	1.9	250	7.5×10^{-6}	0.5
$C4$	262	0.62	330	3.8×10^{-5}	0.5
$C7$	2093	0.09	380	8.7×10^{-4}	0.5

**3. None of the wave models we have considered so far include friction (i.e., damping), hence none of these waves would decay away with time. To make our simulations more realistic, add damping to the wave equation. This can be accomplished by adding a term $-2b(\partial y/\partial t)$ to the right-hand side of (6.5), corresponding to a frictional force proportional to the velocity of the string. Derive a new difference equation that includes this term and calculate the wave pattern as a function of time. Warning: This is not a trivial calculation, but it is straightforward; for some background see Chaigne and Askenfelt (1994). You can also listen to your calculated signals if you have access to the appropriate hardware. They don't sound too bad, but they aren't quite the same as the real thing.

6.4   Waves on a String (Again): Spectral Methods

In this section we reexamine the problem of waves on a string using a different computational approach. This approach relies heavily on ideas associated with the Fourier transform and is usually placed under the general heading of "spectral methods." These methods avoid the use of a finite difference expansion and, instead, do most of their work in Fourier space.

We have already seen several instances in which it is useful to decompose a time-dependent signal into its Fourier components. A typical example was the displacement of a vibrating string at a particular location along the string, $y(x, t)$. We learned how to use a Fourier transform to write such a function in the frequency domain as a collection of sines and cosines with different frequencies. This is a central theme of Appendix 2 and was an essential computational tool in Section 6.2. As we have hinted in our discussion of standing waves on a string, the concept of Fourier analysis is not limited to time-dependent functions, but can be applied in a natural way to *space-dependent* functions, as well. When discussing the string displacement *at a particular time*, it is useful to consider a Fourier decomposition in term of sines and cosines that are functions of *space* instead of time. This is illustrated in Figure 6.10, which shows at the top a hypothetical string displacement given by our usual gaussian form (6.4). This function can be written as a sum of sines and cosines, the largest of which are plotted in Fig 6.10. We have already seen how to use Fourier techniques to write a function in the time domain. Here we have used the same techniques to write the initial string displacement $y_0(x)$ in terms of sines and cosines that are functions of x. Mathematically this decomposition has the form

$$y_0(x) = \sum_i \left[A_i \sin\left(\frac{2\pi x}{\lambda_i}\right) + B_i \cos\left(\frac{2\pi x}{\lambda_i}\right) \right], \tag{6.8}$$

where the wavelengths λ_i determine the spatial variations of our sines and cosines. The values of λ_i

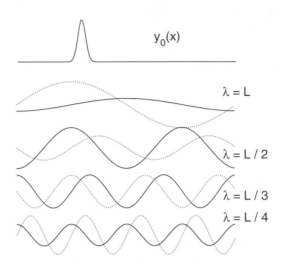

Figure 6.10: Top: string displacement at $t = 0$, given by the function $y_0(x)$ in (6.4); bottom: the first few spatial Fourier components of $y_0(x)$. The solid lines are the cosine components, while the dotted lines are the sine components. The corresponding Fourier wavelengths are indicated. The string was 1.0 m long, the spatial step size was $\Delta x = 0.01$ m, and there were $N = 128$ points used in the FFT.

for the Fourier components of our gaussian displacement function are given next to the components in Figure 6.10.

This expansion is completely analogous to the Fourier sums involving time-dependent functions that we have employed in our work with the pendulum and the vibrating string. The spatial transform we need here can also be computed using the fast Fourier transform (FFT) algorithm. Indeed, that is how we calculated the components in Figure 6.10. Computationally the problem is essentially the same as when dealing with a time-dependent function. You will recall that for functions of time we had N values of our signal that were obtained at points spaced in time by Δt. The FFT then yielded the Fourier components at frequencies $n/(N \Delta t)$, where the integer n varied from 0 to $N/2 - 1$. For a function of space we require values of the signal at N points that are evenly spaced in space. For a spatial step size Δx the FFT then gives the Fourier components at wavelengths $\lambda_n = N \Delta x / n$, where n runs from 0 to $N/2 - 1$. Figure 6.10 shows the spatial Fourier components calculated using the FFT for the gaussian pluck plotted at the top of the figure. In this case we employed $N = 128$ points in our FFT, so the Fourier decomposition yielded the sine and cosine components at $N/2 = 64$ wavelengths. Figure 6.10 shows only the first few components, that is, those with the longest wavelengths. We will consider how the magnitudes of these components vary with λ in a moment.

Now that we have split up our signal into its Fourier components, the next problem is deciding what to do with them. Each component has a particular value of λ. For an ideal string the waves have a speed c, so each of these components will also have a particular frequency, $f_n = c/\lambda_n$. Another way of saying this is as follows. Suppose that we started the string off with a shape that was given exactly by one of the Fourier components in Figure 6.10, say the sine component with $\lambda = L$. The string would then vibrate with the frequency of this Fourier component, $f = c/L$. Each point on the string would undergo simple harmonic motion about $y = 0$ with this frequency, and the amplitude of vibration would be the initial displacement of the string[15] at that value of x. The string would be just a collection of simple harmonic oscillators, one for each point on the string, all oscillating at the same frequency, f. If instead the string were given an initial displacement with a shape corresponding to a different Fourier wavelength, say $\lambda = L/3$, the frequency would then be $f = c/\lambda = 3c/L$, but the basic behavior would be the same. Each point on the string would undergo simple harmonic motion at this frequency.

In general, the initial displacement of the string will not be so simple as to be given by only a single Fourier component. We have already seen that for our gaussian pluck there are many components present. To describe this more complicated case we appeal to the principle of superposition, which tells us that for an equation that is *linear*, the sum of two solutions is also a solution. The wave equation for our problem (6.1) is, indeed, linear since it contains only factors proportional to the first power of y. It is easy to verify in this case by direct substitution that the sum of two or more solutions is also a solution. Now imagine that we have all of the Fourier components for our gaussian initial shape. Each of these is a solution to the wave equation, so their sum is also. If we move forward in time, letting each component vibrate at its particular frequency, and then sum up the displacements corresponding to each component, we will again have a solution to the wave equation. This solution will, in fact, describe the way our string vibrates in response to the initial gaussian displacement. We have thus solved the wave equation.

This approach is sometimes referred to as a spectral method and is most useful if the time dependence of each Fourier component is easy to calculate. This time dependence is required in order to effectively propagate each component forward in time. The solution is then the sum of these individual components at the time (or times) of interest. For our problem of a wave on a string, the mathematical expression of these ideas is as follows. If $Y_r(k)$ and $Y_i(k)$ are the real (cosine) and imaginary (sine) Fourier components for wavelength $\lambda_k = L/k$, each will have the corresponding frequency $f_k = c/\lambda_k$. The string displacement at time t will then be[16]

$$ y(x, t) = \sum_{k=0}^{N/2-1} \left[Y_r(k) \cos\left(\frac{2\pi x}{\lambda_k}\right) + Y_i(k) \sin\left(\frac{2\pi x}{\lambda_k}\right) \right] \cos(2\pi f_k t) . \tag{6.9} $$

At $t = 0$ the factor $\cos(2\pi f_k t)$ is unity and we simply have the sum of our original Fourier components. For $t > 0$, each component vibrates according to its individual frequency f_k.

To illustrate how this method works in practice we reconsider the problem of a vibrating string. We have already described in Figure 6.10 the FFT of an initial displacement given by a gaussian function. Performing the sum (6.9) gives the results for a vibrating string shown in Figure 6.11. The behavior is seen to be essentially identical to that which we obtained using finite difference methods to solve the wave equation in Figure 6.1. The initial gaussian displacement splits into two pulses that propagate in opposite directions. The only difference between this solution and the finite difference result occurs when one of the pulses reaches the end of the string. In Section 6.1 we assumed that the ends of the string were held fixed, and this caused the pulses to be reflected (and inverted) when they reached the ends. However, these boundary conditions were not put into our spectral calculation. In fact, in using a Fourier decomposition we have implicitly assumed that the string has *periodic* boundary conditions.

---

[15] This assumes that the string is initially at rest.

[16] We assume here that the string is initially at rest. To allow for a nonzero initial velocity, a phase factor would have to be added to the last (time-dependent) cosine factor.

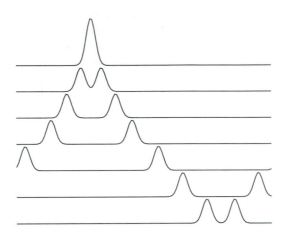

Figure 6.11: Solution for a vibrating string obtained using the spectral method. The top curve shows the string at $t = 0$, while the other traces (moving down the plot) show the string profile at progressively later times. Note that when the left traveling pulse reaches the end of the string (in the plot which is third from the bottom), it reappears at the far right (in the plot second from the bottom) due to the effectively periodic boundary conditions.

That is, we have assumed that the two ends of the string are connected as if the string formed a large closed loop. This assumption can be seen mathematically from the spatial periodicity of the sines and cosines in (6.9). For our calculated solution in Figure 6.11 we observe that when the left-going pulse reaches the (left) end of the string, it simply reappears at the right end, just as if the two ends were connected. Spectral methods can be extended to include such boundary effects, but that is a problem we will leave for the exercises.

Now that we have described spectral methods and illustrated them in one case, you might ask "why bother?" Have we gained anything from this approach? The answer is "maybe." For the particular calculation illustrated in Figure 6.11 we took $N = 128$, which means we had to calculate the displacements of 128 places along the string. Since we also had N Fourier components, evaluating (6.9) every time step was still a tall order (although we could imagine using an FFT to do this calculation). The utility of spectral methods arises in situations where some of these Fourier components are very small and can be neglected. It turns out that in many cases of physical interest the Fourier amplitudes decrease rapidly with N. Figure 6.12 shows these amplitudes for our gaussian displacement, and we see that they become very small at short wavelengths. For λ^{-1} greater than about 0.2 m^{-1} the amplitudes are extremely small compared to the first few components. The reason these components are so small is that their wavelengths are *much* smaller than the scale over which the initial string displacement varies. Since these short wavelength components have very small Fourier amplitudes, we can, to a very good approximation, simply ignore them in computing the spectral sum (6.9). In fact, we already did this (without telling you) in Figure 6.11; in that calculation we used only half of the Fourier components.

This simplification is very common when dealing with spectral methods. We can often ignore all but the first few Fourier components, leading to a great simplification and speed up of the calculation. This will, of course, lead to some numerical errors in the final result. However, these errors are not as serious as some of the others we have encountered in this chapter, as they do not grow with time.

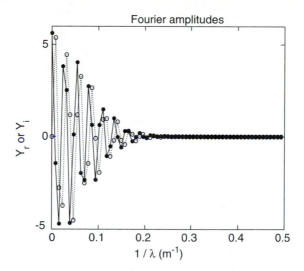

Figure 6.12:   Fourier amplitudes for the gaussian displacement in Figure 6.10. The solid symbols (and solid line) are the real (cosine) components, and the open symbols (and dotted line) are the imaginary (sine) components. Note that the horizontal axis is the *inverse* of λ, so the long wavelength components are on the left.

In Figure 6.11 these errors were very small since the Fourier components that were neglected were themselves very small. However, we can only push things so far. To illustrate what happens when we use too few Fourier components, Figure 6.13 shows the results calculated using only $N/4$ and $N/8$ spectral components. The basic behavior is the same as that found with the more accurate calculation, Figure 6.11. However, we now see undulations in the string well away from the two pulses. The Fourier components we have dropped here were small, but not completely negligible, and this is the kind of error introduced when they are omitted.

Spectral methods are potentially useful in problems that are linear, that is, in which the principle of superposition applies. Fortunately, this is the case in many problems in physics. We will employ them again in Chapter 10 in our dealings with quantum mechanics.

Exercises

1. Write a program that uses the spectral approach to solve the problem of waves on a string. Reproduce the results in Figure 6.11.

2. Use a broader initial wavepacket than we employed in the calculation in Figure 6.13, and show that the errors introduced by using a (relatively) small number of Fourier components is reduced. That is, show that for a given desired error we can use fewer Fourier components if the initial wavepacket is made broader. Explain why this is the case.

*3. Build fixed-end boundary conditions into the spectral method. Hint: Use only Fourier components that automatically yield a displacement of zero at the ends of the string.

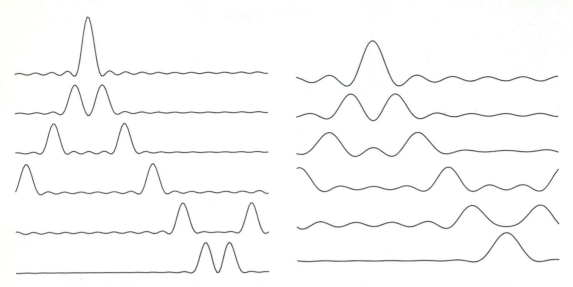

Figure 6.13: Effect of limiting the number of Fourier components in the spectral treatment of a vibrating string. Left: using $N/4$ spectral components; right: using $N/8$ spectral components. In both graphs the top curves show the string at $t = 0$, while the other traces (moving from top to bottom) show the string profile at progressively later times.

References

CHAIGNE, A., and A. ASKENFELT. (1994). "Numerical Simulations of Piano Strings I and II." *J. Acoustical Society of America* **95**, 1112, 1631. These papers describe state-of-the-art simulations of the motion of piano strings.

PRESS, W. H., B. P. FLANNERY, S. A. TEUKOLSKY, and W. T. VETTERLING. 1986. *Numerical Recipes*. Cambridge: Cambridge University Press. Chapter 17 discusses the problem of numerical stability with regards to the wave equation.

7

Random Systems

7.1 Why Perform Simulations of Random Processes?

In all of our work to this point we have considered systems that are *deterministic*. These are systems that are described by some mathematical rule, such as a differential equation with boundary conditions, which has a uniquely determined solution. For example, with projectile motion the rules are the differential equations derived from Newton's second law. Given some initial conditions, the motion of the projectile is completely determined, that is, predictable, for all future times. Similarly, for problems involving the electric potential the relevant rule is Poisson's equation. Once the boundary conditions on the electric potential and the charge distribution are specified, there is a unique solution for V.

In this chapter we consider a different class of systems that are known as random or stochastic. A typical case is diffusion, which describes such processes as the spreading of a drop of cream in your morning coffee. Let us consider what happens if we start with a cup of black coffee and then delicately place a drop of cream at the center. Now, assuming that you resist the urge to stir the coffee, the white mass of cream will slowly spread to fill the cup, and eventually the coffee will take on a uniform brownish color. At the molecular level this process would be described in the following way. The drop of cream contains $\sim 10^{23}$ molecules, which for simplicity we will refer to as "cream molecules."[1] If we were somehow able to watch or follow one particular cream molecule as it moved through the coffee, we would find that it undergoes a complicated trajectory. Roughly speaking, it would move for a short period in a straight line (according to Newton's first law), between collisions with other cream molecules and with coffee molecules. Each collision would cause an abrupt change in our cream molecule's velocity, and it would then move on with this new velocity until the next collision.

---

[1]Even though we know that a proper chemical description would be more complicated, this simpleminded point of view is all we need here.

Our goal is to construct a useful theoretical description of the way the cream mixes with the coffee. We could *in principle* accomplish this by writing down the equations of motion for all of the molecules (cream plus coffee) in the cup. This would give $\sim 10^{23}$ differential equations which we could *in principle* solve (using, perhaps, the Euler method) to tell us everything there is to know about our cup of coffee. However, this approach is flawed for two reasons. First, while this calculation would be possible in principle, it certainly is not possible *in practice*. It seems highly unlikely that we will have a computer powerful enough for this computation any time soon. Second, even if we did have such a computer, the results of the calculation would be the positions and velocities of our $\sim 10^{23}$ molecules as a function of time. While these numbers would describe how the cream mixes with the coffee in great detail, it is not obvious that they would give us any real understanding of the process. By "understanding" we mean an intuitive picture that would allow us to apply what we have learned from the calculation to other similar situations. For example, if our computation showed that the cream was well mixed in, say, 20 seconds, could we then predict how long the mixing would take in a cup that was twice as large?

Our point is that such a complete computational solution of the problem would give far more information than we want or need to understand the mixing process. What we really require is a *statistical* description, or theory, of the behavior. We don't care about the detailed trajectory of every cream molecule. It is enough for us to know the trajectory of an average molecule. Since the number of particles involved is very large, the statistical fluctuations away from this average will turn out to be small, and if we are careful we can also estimate these fluctuations using statistical arguments.

This discussion of the cream-in-your-coffee problem was intended to introduce you to a situation in which a statistical approach provides precisely the type of information we are after. But where does the concept of randomness come into the problem? Each cream molecule follows a complicated trajectory as it collides repeatedly with other molecules. Such a trajectory can be described by what is known as a "random walk." This is a process in which a particle (the walker) moves one step at a time, according to certain rules. In the model appropriate for our cream molecule, the walker's steps correspond to the motion of the molecule between collisions. Each collision changes the direction of the velocity of the molecule, and this is modeled by letting the direction of each step in the walk be random. Hence, our random walker follows a zig-zag path that is similar to the effectively random trajectory of a cream molecule. Of course, the trajectory of a molecule is not really random since, in principle, we could have calculated the motion of all the other molecules in the cup and then predicted the precise times of the collisions, etc. However, we have already seen that this is not feasible, so we will treat these collisions as effectively *random* processes. The large number of molecules (and collisions) in the problem will make this a very good approximation; we will return later to the question of how good this approximation really is. In any case, we hope that you are now convinced that it makes sense to model the motion of a molecule of cream in a cup of coffee by a random walk.

7.2   Generation of Random Numbers

Now that you believe in, or at least appreciate, the utility of simulating a random process, there is one more issue that we must deal with before considering some specific problems. A computer is, in some ways, the epitome of a deterministic system. How can we possibly hope to get a computer (program) to do anything random? The short answer to this is: With a random number generator. All computer languages[2] contain a mechanism, usually a built-in function, for producing a sequence of random numbers; these should really be termed pseudorandom numbers, as we will explain shortly. *True Basic* has the function rnd, which returns a different random number each time it is used. With the rnd function these numbers are distributed uniformly in the range 0–1 (that is, all values in this range are equally likely). Other languages contain similar functions, although they sometimes have different ranges. We'll see how to use these functions to carry out simulations of random systems in the next few sections. However, you may find this short answer to be a bit unsatisfying, since we didn't explain how the computer language (compiler, interpreter, or whatever) actually generates the random numbers. There are several different numerical schemes for generating sequences of pseudorandom numbers. A popular and well-tested scheme employs an equation of the form

$$x_{n+1} = (a\, x_n + b)\, \mathrm{mod}\, m\, . \tag{7.1}$$

The arithmetic here is performed modulo m, with m typically 16 or 32, so that only the lowest 16 or 32 bits are kept in the calculation of x_{n+1}. Here x_n is the nth random number in the sequence, and a and b are carefully chosen constants.

This generator, which is known as a linear congruential generator, works as follows. First, an initial random number, called the *seed*, is selected. The value of the seed is usually chosen in one of two ways. One is to simply use a default value that is built into the language. If you make this choice, you will get the same seed and the same sequence of random numbers each time you run your program. It is probably not fair to call this particular sequence random since it is obtained repeatedly, and you would generally not want to use it in your simulations. However, it is very useful in the debugging process since you can use it as you search for programming errors. Such errors are easier to find if they are reproducible! Once you are convinced that your program works correctly, you will usually want to use a different choice for the seed each time you run your program. In *True Basic* you would use the randomize command to pick a "random" seed, which is different each time it is used (I don't know exactly how *True Basic* chooses the seed in this case, but it probably uses the time-of-day clock). Other languages have a similar mechanism for choosing or setting the seed.

Once a seed x_0 is selected, (7.1) allows you to calculate the next random number in the sequence, x_1, and from this you can obtain x_2, x_3, etc. It turns out that with the proper choice of the constants a and b in (7.1), the sequence of numbers will be random in the sense that they are evenly distributed over their allowed range (which might be $2^{16}-1$ or $2^{32}-1$, etc., depending on the way the high-order bits are treated), with no significant correlations between different members of the sequence.[3] Many person-years of work have been devoted to establishing these facts and to learning how best to choose the values of a and b.

The *reason* why the sequence of numbers obtained from (7.1) behaves randomly is also very interesting. It turns out that it is an example of a chaotic system! It is closely related to what is known as the logistic map, an equation whose solutions are known to exhibit chaotic behavior. The logistic map arises in problems related to population growth and several other areas; it is discussed a little in Chapter 3, and more extensively in Baker and Gollub (1990). The analogy to chaos can be appreciated from the following argument involving the nonlinear pendulum studied in Chapter 3. Suppose that we

---

[2]At least every one that the author has encountered.

[3]While they are the standard workhorse in this area, the linear congruential scheme is certainly not the last word in random-number generators. There is a nice discussion of their flaws in the book by Press et al. (1986).

perform a simulation of such a pendulum in the chaotic regime. We learned in Chapter 3 that, in this case, the behavior of $\theta(t)$ is a wildly varying function. If we choose the pendulum parameters to make the behavior as chaotic as possible,[4] the value of θ at evenly spaced intervals[5] would be a good candidate for a random sequence of numbers in the range $-\pi$ to π. Choosing the optimum pendulum parameters would not be trivial—this is also why choosing a and b in (7.1) is important—but this illustrates how a chaotic (yet deterministic) system can yield a sequence of pseudorandom numbers.[6]

Random number generators that are built into computer languages, such as `rnd`, usually yield numbers that are uniformly distributed over some range. For example, `rnd` generates numbers that are greater than or equal to zero and less than unity, while the function `rand()` in C returns integers in the range[7] from 0 to $2^{31}-1$. Nearly all of our stochastic simulations will involve random numbers that are uniformly distributed, so these functions are just what we need in most cases. However, there are instances in which random numbers that are described by a *nonuniform* distribution are required. For example, radioactive decay is characterized by a Poisson distribution, while the distribution of velocities in an ideal gas follows a Maxwell distribution. Let us now consider how we can generate random numbers that follow such a specific nonuniform distribution.

There are two useful methods for accomplishing this. The first approach, which is known as the transformation method, makes use of a fundamental property of probabilities. Consider a collection of variables $\{x_1, x_2, \ldots\}$ that are distributed according to the function $P_x(x)$. That is, the probability of finding a value that lies between x and $x + dx$ is $P_x(x)dx$. If y is some function of x, then

$$|P_x(x)\,dx| \;=\; |P_y(y)\,dy|\,, \tag{7.2}$$

where $P_y(y)$ is the probability distribution that describes the collection $\{y_1, y_2, \ldots\}$. In our case the x variables will be generated by `rnd`, or by a similar generator that yields uniformly distributed numbers, so $P_x = \text{constant} \equiv C$. We thus have

$$P_y(y) \;=\; P_x(x)\left|\frac{dx}{dy}\right| \;=\; C\left|\frac{dx}{dy}\right|. \tag{7.3}$$

In order to obtain a sequence characterized by a distribution P_y, we must be able to evaluate the function $y = f(x)$, whose derivative is $|dy/dx|^{-1} = P_y$.

To see how this works in practice we consider the Poisson distribution, $P_y(y) = \exp(-y)$. The transformation function is then $y = f(x) = -\ln(x)$, as you can verify by evaluating the derivative dx/dy. The procedure is then to take a sequence of random numbers, $\{x_1, x_2, \ldots\}$, which follow a uniform distribution (as produced by `rnd`), and calculate $y_i = -\ln(x_i)$. The resulting sequence of numbers $\{y_1, y_2, \ldots\}$ should obey the Poisson distribution. That this is indeed the case is illustrated in Figure 7.1, which shows the distribution $P_y(y)$ for sequences of different lengths. For example, the

---

[4]The careful reader might complain that based on what we learned about chaotic systems in Chapter 3, the phrase "as chaotic as possible" is not very well defined. However, this notion can be made fairly precise using the concept of entropy introduced in the exercises in Section 7.7. See also the discussion of entropy in Baker and Gollub (1990).

[5]It would probably be best to choose the intervals to be different from the drive period.

[6]The term *pseudorandom* is often used, since the sequence of numbers obtained from (7.1), or equations like it, is deterministic.

[7]Strictly speaking, the range of integers generated by `rand()` depends on the length of integers and long integers for the particular compiler in question. The range given here is appropriate for nearly all current 32-bit machines.

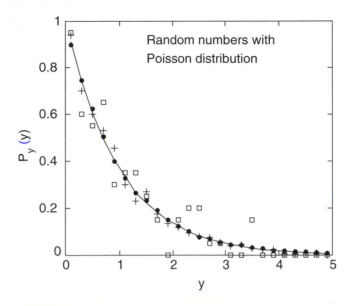

Figure 7.1:   Distributions of random numbers produced with the transformation method. The distribution was designed to have a Poisson form. Open squares: distribution calculated with the first 100 numbers; pluses: with 1000 numbers; filled circles: with 10^4 numbers; smooth curve: with 10^5 numbers. On this scale, the smooth curve is indistinguishable from the Poisson distribution $P_y = \exp(-y)$. These distributions were obtained by first generating a sequence of pseudorandom numbers containing the stated number of entries, and then constructing a histogram of the number of entries as a function of y. The histogram bins were of size $\Delta y = 0.2$.

squares show the distribution calculated for a sequence containing 100 values. The result follows the general form of the Poisson distribution (the solid curve), although there is some statistical *scatter*, which we will discuss in detail in a moment. As the length of the sequence is increased, that is, as more y values are used to calculate the distribution, the results converge to the Poisson form.

The transformation method is useful when the function $f(x)$ can be easily evaluated. However, there are cases when the desired distribution may not be known in analytic form.[8] Such problems can be handled with an algorithm known as the rejection method. We first use the `rnd` generator (or one like it) to produce a sequence of numbers $\{y_1, y_2, \ldots\}$ distributed uniformly in the range of interest, y_{min} to y_{max}. Now, suppose that our goal is to produce a sequence of numbers that are distributed according to the function P_y in Figure 7.2. We then proceed through the sequence $\{y_1, y_2, \ldots\}$ and accept entries with a probability proportional to P_y. That is, we start with y_1 and evaluate $P_y(y_1)$. A new random number p_{test} is then generated (with `rnd`, for example), which is distributed uniformly in the range 0 to $P_y(max)$ where $P_y(max)$ is the maximum value of P_y. If $P_y(y_1) < p_{test}$, we remove y_1 from the sequence; otherwise it is kept. This process is repeated with $y_2, y_3, \ldots$. The numbers that remain in the

---

[8]Or the transformation function may not be easily evaluated, or even expressible, in closed form.

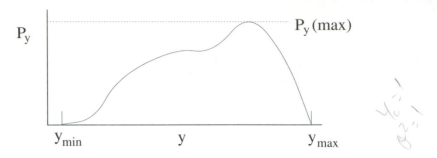

Figure 7.2: Schematic distribution function for use with the rejection method. The probability of obtaining a particular value of y is proportional to $P_y(y)$.

end will be distributed according to P_y. In terms of Figure 7.2, the probability that a number y_n passes this test is proportional to the "height" of the function $P_y(y_n)$.

An interesting feature of the rejection method is that it requires only that the function P_y be evaluated. This evaluation may be analytic or numerical, so the distribution function can be very irregular in form, as was intended with the illustration in Figure 7.2. In addition, both the generation of the original sequence and the rejection test require random numbers distributed uniformly, which are easily obtained with rnd (or a similar generator).

To demonstrate the rejection algorithm we have used it to generate numbers distributed according to the gaussian distribution

$$P_y = B \exp\left[(y - y_c)^2/\sigma^2\right] , \tag{7.4}$$

where the constant B is chosen to make P_y properly normalized.[9] This distribution is centered at y_c and has a width σ. Figure 7.3 shows the calculated distributions obtained with sequences of varying lengths. The shorter sequences exhibit the intuitively expected statistical fluctuations, while the longer sequences converge accurately to the desired gaussian form.

In our examples involving the transformation and rejection methods, we noted the statistical fluctuations associated with finite (that is, short) sequences of random numbers. We will come across such fluctuations often in our dealings with stochastic processes, so this is a good time to consider them in a little more detail. To be specific we will consider a sequence of random numbers generated using the rnd function of *True Basic*, although our methods and conclusions are widely applicable (as will, we hope, become clear). Suppose that we generate a sequence of N numbers and want to determine if they are indeed distributed uniformly, as advertised. One way to test for uniformity is to divide the allowed range into bins and compute the number of values that fall into each bin. An example of such a test is shown in Figure 7.4. Here we have generated a sequence of $N = 1000$ random numbers using rnd and calculated how they are distributed among 10 bins that encompass the range 0–1. If the numbers are uniformly distributed, the average number that falls into each bin should be $N/10 = 100$, and we see that the bin occupancies do indeed cluster around this value, the dotted line in Figure 7.4. Thus, at a crude level the rnd generator seems satisfactory. However, there are fluctuations about the

---

[9]Such normalization is actually not required by the rejection algorithm. In fact, it is usually convenient to choose the maximum value of P_y to be unity.

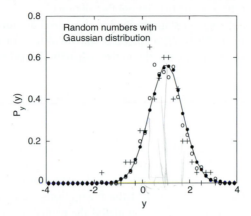

Figure 7.3: Distributions of random numbers obtained with the rejection method. The distribution was designed to have a gaussian form, (7.4), centered at $y = 1$ with a width of unity. Pluses: distribution calculated with the first 100 numbers; open circles: with 1000 numbers; filled circles: with 10^4 numbers; smooth curve: with 10^5 numbers. On the scale used here this curve is indistinguishable from (7.4). These distributions were constructed in the same manner as those in Figure 7.1.

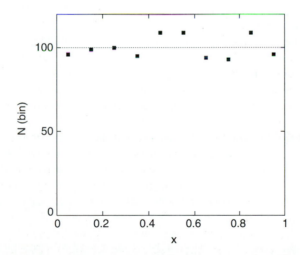

Figure 7.4: Measured distribution of $N = 1000$ random numbers generated using the *True Basic* `rnd` function. The range 0–1 was divided into 10 bins, and the number of values that fell into each bin was tabulated. Each bin had a width of $\Delta x = 0.1$, and the occupancy was plotted at the value of x corresponding to the center of the bin. That is, the occupancy of the bin that covers $x = 0$–0.1 was plotted with an abscissa $x = 0.05$, etc. The dotted line shows the ideal (theoretical) value for each bin, $N/10 = 100$.

ideal value for each bin. How can we tell if these fluctuations are too large or too small? That is, how do we know that they are just the expected statistical fluctuations?

This question is a central issue in statistics and is discussed at great length in many textbooks (see, for example, Press et al. [1986]). The standard statistical test for determining if an observed distribution is consistent with a model (that is, theoretical) distribution is based on what is known as the chi-square statistic

$$\chi^2 = \sum_i \frac{(N_i - n_{\text{ideal}})^2}{n_{\text{ideal}}} . \tag{7.5}$$

Here N_i is the number of events that are *measured* to fall into bin i, and n_{ideal} is the number of events that the theoretical model *predicts* should fall into each bin.[10] The quantity χ^2 is thus a quantitative measure of how much the observed distribution differs from the theoretical one. We should not expect this difference to be zero, since our intuition tells us that there will always be some fluctuations for such a stochastic problem. On the other hand, if the fluctuations are extremely large, we should be suspicious! It turns out that statisticians have calculated the probability of finding a particular value of χ^2, assuming that the process involves random variables that have a *normal* distribution.[11] This probability is related to what is known as the incomplete gamma function, $P(a, x)$. This function is displayed in many texts;[12] its behavior for several values of a is shown in Figure 7.5. This probability function involves two parameters; one of them is proportional to χ^2 ($x = \chi^2/2$), while the other is related to the number of degrees of freedom in the problem, ν ($a = \nu/2$). For the case considered in Figure 7.4, ν is equal to one less than the number of bins.[13] Since there is an unknown value of the occupancy for each bin, you might have thought that ν would be equal to the number of bins. However, ν is one less than this because the bin occupancies are not all independent. The total length of the sequence was specified ahead of time, so the occupancy of the last bin, for example, could have been calculated from the other occupancies.

Returning to Figure 7.5, $P(\nu/2, \chi^2/2)$ is the *probability* for finding a χ^2 that is smaller than the observed value. In other words, if we were to repeat this test many times, the chance of finding a χ^2 that lies far to the right of where $P(\nu/2, \chi^2/2) \sim 0.5$ should be small. If this is not the case, then we should suspect trouble, as the observed fluctuations are larger than the expected statistical fluctuations. It is appropriate that this test be a statistical one. After all, we are dealing with a random process, so some fluctuations are to be expected.

To complete our test of the rnd function, the graph on the right in Figure 7.5 shows the *distribution* of χ^2 values found by performing a bin test, such as that seen in Figure 7.4, many times. Here we have used 11 bins, so the number of degrees of freedom is 10. We see that the most likely value of χ^2 is near $x = \chi^2/2 \sim 4.5$. Since $\nu = 10$ for this case, the curve shown on the left for $P(a, x)$, with $a = \nu/2 = 5$, is appropriate. This theoretical curve has a value of 0.5 for $x = \chi^2/2 \sim 4.5$. Statistical

---

[10]These theoretical values could vary from bin to bin, but we will ignore that (largely notational) complication here.

[11]Here the term *normal* refers to an underlying gaussian process. As we will see later in this chapter when we discuss the central limit theorem such a distribution generally arises in connection with random processes. For now we note only that such a distribution will be found in virtually all processes in which each of the randomly generated values is independent of the others.

[12]See, for example, Press et al. (1986). There is unfortunately no convenient closed-form analytic expression for this function. Note also that here we follow convention in our definitions of x and a.

[13]For the commonly encountered problem of fitting a function containing n parameters to a collection of m data values, $\nu = m - n$.

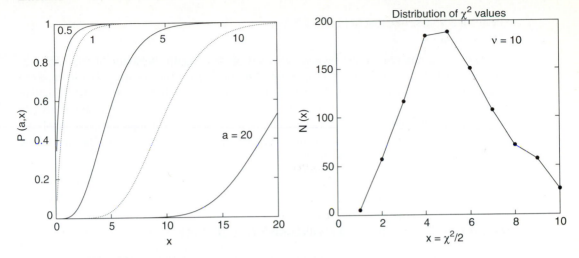

Figure 7.5: Left: incomplete gamma function, $P(a, x)$. For the χ^2 test, $x = \chi^2/2$ and $a = \nu/2$, where ν is the number of degrees of freedom. Right: distribution of χ^2 values found by performing 1000 bin tests, as in Figure 7.4. Here we used 11 bins so that $\nu = 10$ ($a = 5$), and each sequence contained 1100 numbers generated using rnd. This distribution was constructed in a manner similar to that employed in Figure 7.1.

theory thus predicts that in half of our measurements, that is, for half of the bin tests, we should find a value of χ^2 that is smaller than ~ 9. This theoretical prediction is in agreement with the distribution of χ^2, which was actually *measured* and which is shown on the right in Figure 7.5. Hence, the rnd generator passes the χ^2 test.

This is all we will say about the generation and testing of random numbers; see the references for more on the subject. For our purposes the random-number generator in *True Basic* is sufficient. However, for really serious numerical work you should always test your random-number generator extensively. Professionals generally write their own generators so that they know exactly what they are getting.

Exercises

1. Use the rejection method to generate a sequence of random numbers distributed according to $P_y(y) = 1/y$.

*2. Use the transformation method to generate a sequence of random-numbers distributed according to $P_y(y) = 1/y^2$.

3. Perform some statistical tests of your random-number generator. Possibilities include:
   - Generate a long sequence of random numbers and calculate the average of the squares of these numbers. Compare your result with the ideal value.
   - A random-number generator may pass distribution tests, such as the χ^2 test, but still be unsatisfactory. One way this can happen is if consecutive values are correlated. For example, numbers that are well below the mean value may tend to be followed by numbers that are also below the mean. Look for such correlations between the random numbers by computing the average of the product of adjacent numbers in the sequence.

- Perform a χ^2 test like that in Figure 7.5.
- Devise your own tests.

4. Design and test a random-number generator based on the chaotic behavior of the nonlinear pendulum model studied in Chapter 3. Use the value of θ at regular (or irregular) intervals to determine the value of the random number. For convenience, scale the values of θ to obtain numbers n in the range 0–1. Then calculate the averages $< n >$ and $< n^2 >$. You should also do a bin test like the one in Figure 7.4. If you are industrious, you could also perform a χ^2 analysis. Study the performance of your generator for different values of the driving force. Be sure to pick values of the drive that place the system in the chaotic regime.

*5. Repeat the previous problem, but use the chaotic billiards of Chapter 3 to generate the random numbers.

7.3   Introduction to Monte Carlo Methods: Integration

Our first problem involving the use of random numbers involves integration. Strictly speaking this is more of a numerical methods application than a physics problem. However, it is included here because it nicely illustrates many ideas that will be used extensively in later sections and chapters.

Consider a square dart board that contains a circular region in its interior, as shown in Figure 7.6. Now assume that you throw darts at the board and are accurate enough that all of the darts hit the board, but with locations that are distributed randomly (and uniformly) over the surface of the board. The probability that a dart lands in any particular region is then proportional to the area of that region. Hence, the fraction of darts that land inside the circular region will be proportional to the ratio of the area of the circle to the area of the entire board.

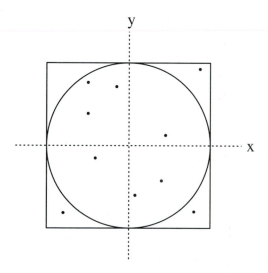

Figure 7.6:   Hypothetical square dart board, with an inscribed circle. The dots show where the first few darts might land.

This observation is the basis of the Monte Carlo method for evaluating an integral. Here the integral of interest is just the area of the circle in Figure 7.6. To simulate this dart-throwing process, we use random numbers to select the places where the darts strike the board. Let us consider only the portion of the dart board that lies in the upper-right quadrant in Figure 7.6, so that as far as our program is concerned the board lies in the range $0 \leq x \leq 1, 0 \leq y \leq 1$. For our first dart, we pick values of x and y at random from this range. We then test to see if this point (x, y) satisfies the condition $y \leq \sqrt{1 - x^2}$, that is, if the point lies within the circle. This process is repeated for a large number of such points, N_{total}, and we calculate how many of the darts land within the (quarter) circle, N_{under}. The area under this curve is $N_{\text{under}}/N_{\text{total}}$ times the area of the square, and the area of the square is unity. A subroutine that carries out this simulation is listed below (the complete program is given in Appendix 4).

```
! calculate area of circle with radius = 1
! consider only portion in first quadrant
! n_total = number of points (darts) to generate     value = integral
sub calculate(n_total,value)
   n_under = 0
   for i = 1 to n_total
      x = rnd        ! generate the coordinates of a random point
      y = rnd
      if y <= sqr(1 - x^2) then n_under = n_under + 1
                       ! check if point is within the quarter-circle
   next i
   value = n_under / n_total
end sub
```

Figure 7.7 shows some results for this integral as a function of the number of darts used in the simulation. Here we have multiplied the result by a factor of 4 to obtain the area of the entire circle, for which the exact answer is π. Figure 7.7 shows the results for two different runs of our program. In each case we generated a grand total of $\sim 10^7$ random points and plotted the estimate for the area at several values of N_{total} as the calculation proceeded. The numerical result for the integral will, of course, exhibit statistical fluctuations; this is, after all, a random process.[14] However, as N_{total} increased, the calculated area approached more and more closely to the exact result. The two different runs of the program produced slightly different results due to these statistical fluctuations, but both converged to the exact result as N_{total} became large.

In order to understand the accuracy of the Monte Carlo method, we must consider these statistical fluctuations in a little more detail. As we have already hinted in Section 7.2, random processes often give rise to gaussian distributions (see Reif [1965] for a nice discussion of this topic). These distributions are characterized by a mean value and a width [as in (7.4)], and the way in which these two quantities vary with N_{total} is intimately connected with the statistical accuracy of Monte Carlo integration. As illustrated in Figure 7.7, the value of such an integral fluctuates about some particular value. Here that value was π; this is the mean value of the associated distribution. That is, if we were to repeat the integration many times (using the same number of darts each time), we would find a collection of different values whose average was $\sim \pi$. This collection of values would be distributed around the mean with a typical spread

$$\sigma = \left[\frac{1}{N_{\text{trials}}} \sum_{i=1}^{N_{\text{trials}}} (I_i - \bar{I})^2 \right]^{1/2}, \tag{7.6}$$

---

[14]A random process is amenable to various statistical tests, such as the χ^2 test described in the Section 7.2.

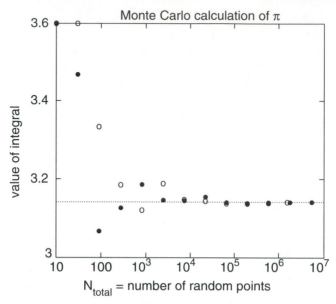

Figure 7.7: Area of a circle with a radius of unity calculated with the Monte Carlo method, as a function of the number of random points used to compute the integral, N_{total}. The dotted line is the exact result, π. The filled and open circles show the results of two independent simulations.

where N_{trials} is the number of values involved (the number of times the integral was evaluated), I_i is the value found in ith trial, and $\bar{I}$ is the average value. Combining the values for N_{trials} different evaluations will give a more accurate value of the integral. Intuitively we know that the accuracy will become better as N_{trials} is increased, or equivalently, as N_{total} is increased as in Figure 7.7 (in this example N_{total} is effectively proportional to N_{trials}). It turns out that a gaussian distribution of a collection of random variables, in this case the N_{trials} values of the integral, has the very general property that the statistical uncertainty in the overall average is given by $\sigma/(N_{trials}^{1/2}) \sim N_{trials}^{-1/2}$. Hence, if we want to double our accuracy we must increase N_{trials} by a factor of 4.

These arguments describe a key feature of the Monte Carlo method. The accuracy here and in other examples we consider below varies as $N^{-1/2}$, where N is the number of samples or trials. In Chapter 5 we discussed the use of Simpson's rule to calculate integrals, and it is interesting to compare the numerical efficiency of Simpson's rule with that of the Monte Carlo approach. In d dimensions[15] a Simpson's rule evaluation that employs a total of N grid points requires that the range in each dimension be split into $\sim N^{1/d}$ intervals of spacing $\Delta x \sim N^{-1/d}$. It turns out that the numerical error associated with Simpson's rule varies as $N(\Delta x)^{d+2} \sim N^{-2/d}$ (see Press et al. 1996). Hence, for low-dimensional integrals the error associated with Simpson's rule decreases more rapidly with N than it does with the Monte Carlo approach. That is, for a given amount of computer time Simpson's rule will yield a more accurate answer. However, as the dimension of the integral increases the Monte Carlo approach eventually wins out, since for large d the Monte Carlo error, which is proportional to $N^{-1/2}$, decreases

---

[15] In Chapter 5 we applied Simpson's rule to one dimensional integrals, but it can be readily extended to higher dimensions.

more rapidly with N than does the Simpson's rule uncertainty. The arguments here show that the Monte Carlo method is more efficient for values of d above about 4. Integrals that involve such high dimensions are not uncommon in physics and are often handled with the Monte Carlo method.

Exercises

1. Evaluate the area under a circle using Simpson's rule (see Chapter 5 and Press et al. [1986] for a refresher on this algorithm), and compare it with the Monte Carlo method. Show that Simpson's rule is more efficient (in terms of computer time) in this case.

2. Use the Monte Carlo method to compute the transcendental number e. Hint: Consider the integral of $1/x$ from $x = 1$ to 10.

3. Use the Monte Carlo method to compute the volume of a sphere. Be sure to compare your result with the exact answer.

7.4 Random Walks

In Section 7.1 we argued that the motion of a molecule in solution is analogous to a random walk. It turns out that such walks arise often in simulations of random processes, and in this section we will consider the simulation of several different types of random walks.

The simplest situation involves a walker that is able to take steps of length unity along a line. This one dimensional random walk is illustrated schematically in Figure 7.8. The walker begins at the origin, $x = 0$, and the first step is chosen at random to be either to the right or left, each with probability $1/2$. For the specific walk in Figure 7.8 the first step was to the right, so the location after the first step was $x_1 = +1$. The next step was then chosen, and again the probabilities for stepping left or right are both $1/2$. In this example the step went left, so $x_2 = 0$. This process can be repeated, and the position as a function of step number will be obtained. In a physical process such as the motion of a molecule in solution, the time between steps is approximately a constant, so the step number is roughly proportional to time. We will, therefore, often refer to the walker's position as a function of time.

A subroutine that implements a random walk in one dimension is given below (the full program is listed in Appendix 4). Here we generate a random number in the range between 0 and 1 using the rnd function and compare its value to $1/2$. If it is less than $1/2$, our walker moves right, otherwise it steps to the left. This process is then repeated to generate x_n as a function of n.

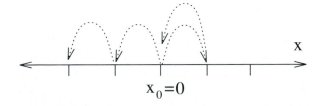

Figure 7.8:   Sketch of a random walk in one dimension. The walker began at $x = x_0 = 0$, and each step is indicated schematically by a dotted arrow. Here the first step happened to be to the right, while the next three steps were to the left.

```
! x2ave(n) contains the average of x^2 at step n
! n_walks = total number of walkers
! n_steps = number of steps taken by each walker
sub calculate(x2ave(),n_walks,n_steps)
   plot_flag = 1
   for i = 1 to n_walks
      x = 0                       ! current location of the walker
      for j = 1 to n_steps
         if rnd < 0.5 then
            x = x + 1
         else                     ! just use an else statement
            x = x - 1             ! DO NOT generate another new value using rnd
         end if
         if plot_flag = 1 then plot j,x !plot each walk until a keystroke occurs
         if key input then   ! after this just accumulate <x^2> for later display
            plot_flag = 0
            get key z
         end if
         x2ave(j) = x2ave(j) + x^2
      next j
   next i
   for i = 1 to n_steps                    ! normalize x2ave when finished
      x2ave(i) = x2ave(i) / n_walks
   next i
end sub
```

Some typical results are given in Figure 7.9 where we show two different walks, obtained in two separate runs of the program. The two walkers move erratically, which is why this process is sometimes referred to as a drunkard's walk. Several quantitative results can be obtained from these simulations. Perhaps the most basic is the distance a walker travels after n steps. Since a walker is as likely to step left as right, this average, which we denote by $< x_n >$, must be zero. Here the angular brackets indicate an average over different walkers and is calculated by simulating a large number of independent walkers and averaging their values of x_n.

A more interesting and informative quantity is $< x_n^2 >$, the average of the square of the location after n steps. Some results for this quantity are shown on the right in Figure 7.9. We see that they are well described by a straight line, that is

$$< x^2 > = D t , \qquad (7.7)$$

where t is the time, which here is just equal to the step number; the factor D is known as the diffusion constant. It is useful to compare this result with the behavior of a free particle, that is, one that is moving at a constant velocity and is not impeded by collisions with other particles. For such a particle we know that $x = vt$, so its distance from the origin (its starting point) grows linearly with time. A random walker behaves differently; according to (7.7) its root-mean-square distance from the origin grows only as $\sqrt{< x^2 >} \sim t^{1/2}$. Hence, a random walker escapes from the origin much more slowly than would a free particle.[16]

---

[16]The reader might object to this conclusion on the grounds that for small t the random-walk result $\sim t^{1/2}$ is larger than the constant velocity result $\sim t$. However, a comparison of these expressions at very small t is not appropriate. At such very short times the walker's first step has not yet "finished," so it, too, moves at a constant velocity. Hence, (7.7) applies only after several steps.

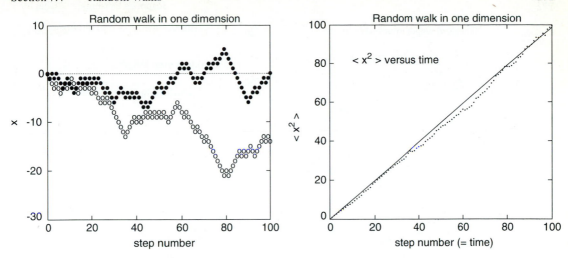

Figure 7.9: Left: x versus step number, that is, time, for two random walks in one dimension. Right: $<x^2>$ as a function of step number (which is proportional to time) for a collection of one-dimensional random walks. The step length was unity and the results for 500 walkers were averaged. The points are the calculated values and the straight line is a least-squares fit to the form (7.7).

Motion of the sort described by (7.7) is also known as diffusion, and we will explore the connection between random walks and diffusion in somewhat more detail later in this chapter. However, a few comments regarding (7.7) should be made here. First, to follow up on a discussion that we began in Section 7.1, it turns out that this result tells us a lot about how fast a drop of cream will mix with coffee if we change the size of the cup. Mixing will be roughly complete[17] when $<x^2>$ is equal to the diameter of the cup. If we double that diameter then from (7.7), we see that it will take *four* times as long for the cream to mix. A second interesting point concerns the value of the diffusion constant, D. This is the slope of the $<x^2>$ versus t plot in Figure 7.9, which we see is approximately unity. The value of D can, in fact, be calculated analytically. Writing the position after n steps, x_n, as a sum of n separate steps gives

$$x_n = \sum_{i=1}^{n} s_i \,, \tag{7.8}$$

where s_i is displacement for the ith step. For this problem $s_i = \pm 1$ with equal probabilities. We can then write

$$x_n^2 = \sum_{i=1}^{n} \left(\sum_{j=1}^{n} s_i\, s_j \right) \,. \tag{7.9}$$

---

[17]We will make these ideas more quantitative below.

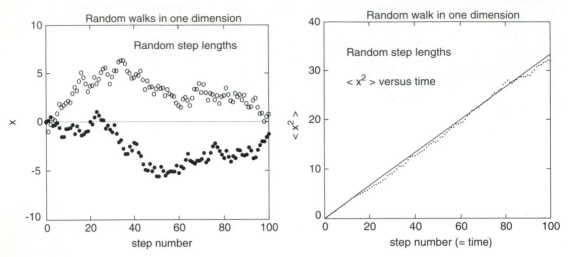

Figure 7.10: Left: x versus step number (that is, time) for two random walks in one dimension. Here the steps were of random lengths in the range -1 to 1. Right: $< x^2 >$ as a function of time for a collection of these one-dimensional random walks. The results for 500 walks were averaged.

Since the steps are independent of each other, the terms $s_i s_j$ with $i \neq j$ will be ± 1 with equal probability. If we average x^2 over a large number of separate walks this will leave only the terms s_i^2. Thus we find

$$< x_n^2 > = \sum_{i=1}^{n} s_i^2 = n , \qquad (7.10)$$

where we have used the fact that $s_i^2 = 1$. Since n is also equal to time, this is identical to (7.7) with $D = 1$.

Up to this point we have considered the simplest random-walk model. There are many ways to generalize the model to make it more realistic. One way is to allow the steps to be of random length. Some results for this case, again with a one-dimensional walker, are shown in Figure 7.10. We again find diffusive behavior, that is, $< x^2 >$ is described by (7.7), but with a different value of the diffusion constant. The value of D in this case can again be calculated analytically, a job we will leave for the exercises.

Another obvious generalization is to allow the walker to move in three dimensions, and results for this case are shown in Figure 7.11. For this simulation we have restricted the steps to be of unit length along either $\pm x$, $\pm y$, or $\pm z$. Diffusive behavior is again found. There are many other interesting generalizations of the random-walk model. We will explore a few of them in the exercises and also later in this chapter.

Exercises

1. Calculate the diffusion constant analytically for the random-walk simulations in Figures 7.10 and 7.11.

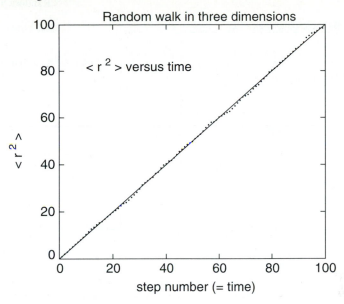

Figure 7.11: $< r^2 >$ as a function of step number (that is, time) for a collection of three-dimensional random walks ($r^2 \equiv x^2 + y^2 + z^2$). The step length was unity and the results for 500 walks were averaged.

2. Simulate a random walk in three dimensions allowing the walker to make steps of unit length in random directions; don't restrict the walker to sites on a discrete lattice. Show that the motion is diffusive, that is, $< r^2 > = Dt$. Find the value of D.

*3. Investigate the behavior of a random walk in which the probabilities for different step directions are not equal. For example, consider a one-dimensional walk with $p_{\text{left}} = 0.25$ and $p_{\text{right}} = 0.75$. In what sense is the motion still diffusive?

**4. The calculated values for $< x^2 >$ in Figure 7.9 do not agree perfectly with the theoretical prediction (7.7) with $D = 1$. Instead, these values exhibit statistical fluctuations about the theoretical curve. Show that these fluctuations follow a gaussian form. Apply the χ^2 test to demonstrate that their magnitude is consistent with the expected statistical fluctuations.

7.5   Self-Avoiding Walks

In the random-walk models we have considered so far, each step was completely independent of all prior steps. Indeed, this is what we would expect for truly random behavior. However, in some physical processes this assumption is not appropriate. Consider a long flexible molecule, such as a polymer. Under certain conditions these molecules tend to "coil up" into a very compact form. Suppose we want to construct a model to describe the shape of such a molecule. A random walk is an obvious candidate for such a model. Each link in the polymer chain corresponds to one step in the walk, and since the polymer is flexible (the angles between successive links are usually not rigidly fixed, but can take on

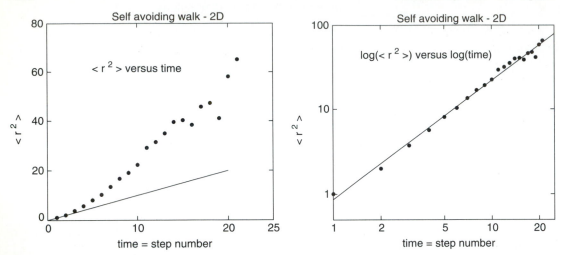

Figure 7.12: Left: results for $< r^2 >$ as a function of step number (that is, time) for a self-avoiding walk in two dimensions. Note that $< r^2 >$ increases much more rapidly here than it does for a simple random walk, which would follow the solid line. Observe also the statistical fluctuations (the fluctuations about a smooth behavior). These could be reduced by averaging the results for more walkers. Right: same results, but now plotted on log–log scales. The solid line is a least-squares fit to a function of the form $< r^2 > \sim t^{\alpha}$, with the result $\alpha \approx 1.4$. For a simple random walk, as in Figure 7.9, α would be unity.

several different values), each step is independent of the one immediately before it.[18] However, for this problem a random walk ignores an important piece of physics. The path followed by our polymer molecule must not be allowed to intersect itself. Only one segment of the polymer is allowed to occupy any particular region of space. A random walk that is subject to this constraint is called a self-avoiding walk, or SAW.

A SAW can be simulated in much the same way as an ordinary random walk. The only difference is that you must keep track of all prior steps and make sure that new steps that would revisit a previously trampled site are not allowed.[19] This has two important effects on the behavior. First, as compared with an ordinary random walk, a self-avoiding walker will, on average, get farther away from its starting point in a given number of steps, since steps that take the walker back toward the origin will be the ones that tend to be forbidden by the self-avoidance constraint. This is illustrated in Figure 7.12, which shows that for a two-dimensional SAW the mean-square distance from the starting point, $< r^2 >$, does not vary linearly with time as is the case for an ordinary random walk. We see that $< r^2 > \sim t^{1.4}$ for this SAW, so the behavior is intermediate between that of a random walk (diffusion), for which $< r^2 > \sim t$, and a free particle, for which $< r^2 > \sim t^2$.

A second interesting feature of SAWs arises in simulations. It is quite common for a walker to, so to speak, back itself into a corner. That is, a walker can find itself with no possible next step that

---

[18]Of course, in a real case these angles might not be completely independent of each other. This could be put into the simulation by adding some effective memory of previous steps, and models of this type have been studied. We will ignore this complication here and focus instead on another type of constraint.

[19]In our simulations we simply terminate a walk when no further steps consistent with the SAW constraint are possible.

satisfies the self-avoidance constraint. This can be a nuisance in simulations, since the probability of constructing a long walk that is self-avoiding decreases rapidly with the number of steps, particularly in two dimensions. This is less of a problem in three dimensions, since there are more possible steps in this case. In any event, long polymers seem to manage very well in real life. There are many variations of the SAW model, which can be found in the references.

Exercises

1. Simulate SAWs in three and four dimensions. Determine the variation of $< r^2 >$ with step number and find the value of α, where this parameter is defined through the relation $< r^2 > \sim t^\alpha$. Compare your results with those in Figure 7.12. You should find that α approaches the simple random-walk value of unity as the dimensionality is increased ($\alpha \sim 1.25$ in three dimensions and 1.15 in four dimensions). Can you explain this trend qualitatively?

7.6   Random Walks and Diffusion

We have mentioned several times that random walks are equivalent to diffusion. In this section we will explore this connection in a little more detail. We will again adopt the cream-in-your-coffee analogy in which we have a large number of molecules (cream) moving in solution (coffee). The goal is to calculate how these molecules are spatially distributed as a function of time. In our discussion of random walkers we have, up to this point, focused on the motion of individual walkers. An alternative way to describe the same physics involves the density of molecules, $\rho(x, y, z, t)$, which can be conveniently defined if the system contains a large number of molecules (walkers). The idea, known as *coarse graining*, is to consider regions of space that are big enough to contain a large number of molecules so that the density ($\equiv$ mass/volume) can be meaningfully defined. This density obeys what is known as the diffusion equation

$$\frac{\partial \rho}{\partial t} = \mathcal{D} \nabla^2 \rho \,, \tag{7.11}$$

where $\mathcal{D}$ is a parameter that will turn out to be closely related to the diffusion constant we learned about in our work on random walks. We encountered a similar differential equation in our studies of waves in Chapter 6, and the numerical approach we used there can be extended to treat the diffusion equation. For ease of notation we will assume that ρ is a function of only one spatial dimension, x, although everything we do below can readily be extended to two or three dimensions. We can then write $\rho(x, t) = \rho(i \Delta x, n \Delta t) = \rho(i, n)$, so that the first index corresponds to space and the second to time. Converting (7.11) to one dimension yields

$$\frac{\partial \rho}{\partial t} = \mathcal{D} \frac{\partial^2 \rho}{\partial x^2} \,. \tag{7.12}$$

The (hopefully familiar) finite-difference forms for these partial derivative are

$$\frac{\partial^2 \rho}{\partial x^2} \approx \frac{\rho(i + 1, n) + \rho(i - 1, n) - 2 \rho(i, n)}{(\Delta x)^2} \,, \tag{7.13}$$

and

$$\frac{\partial \rho}{\partial t} \approx \frac{\rho(i, n + 1) - \rho(i, n)}{\Delta t} \,. \tag{7.14}$$

Inserting these into the one-dimensional diffusion equation and solving for the density at time step $n+1$ in terms of ρ at step n we find

$$\rho(i, n+1) \;=\; \rho(i, n) \;+\; \frac{\mathcal{D}\,\Delta t}{(\Delta x)^2}\,[\rho(i+1, n) \;+\; \rho(i-1, n) \;-\; 2\,\rho(i, n)]\,. \qquad (7.15)$$

If we are given the initial distribution of the cream molecules, $\rho(x, t=0)$, we can use (7.15) to solve for ρ at future times. A program to implement this can be constructed along the lines we developed in Chapter 6 to deal with waves on a string, so we will leave the details to the exercises. While the programming is straightforward, there remains the choice of spatial and temporal step sizes. As you might have guessed, the numerical instabilities we encountered when solving the wave equation can also arise here. While it is not easy to provide a general analytic solution to the diffusion equation, one special case is very instructive. You can verify by substitution that the function

$$\rho(x, t) \;=\; \frac{1}{\sigma}\,\exp\left[-\frac{x^2}{2\,\sigma^2}\right], \qquad (7.16)$$

satisfies (7.12), provided that σ is *time dependent*, with $\sigma = \sqrt{2\mathcal{D}t}$. This result can be understood intuitively from Figure 7.13, which shows sketches of the density at two different times. At any particular time the spatial distribution has a gaussian form whose half-width σ is, roughly speaking, the spatial size occupied by the clump of particles. As time passes, the density maintains a gaussian form with the only change being that the width increases as $\sigma \sim \sqrt{t}$. That this is also just the root-mean-square distance traveled by an average particle can be seen as follows. At $t=0$ the clump of particles will, according to our assumptions concerning how the drop is deposited, be very small ($\sigma \sim 0$). At a later time the cream distribution will be of order σ in extent, so this must also be the distance traveled

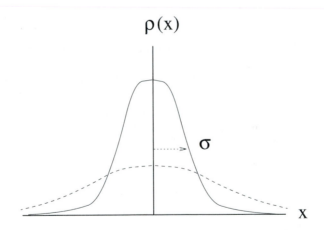

Figure 7.13: Schematic solutions of the diffusion equation at two different times. The solid curve shows the density at an early time, while the dashed curve shows it at some time later. The gaussian distribution broadens with time, but the area under the curve, which is equal to the total number of particles, does not change.

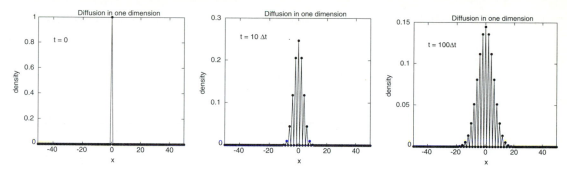

Figure 7.14: Time evolution calculated from the diffusion equation in one dimension at $t = 0$ (left), $t = 10\Delta t$ (center), and $t = 100\Delta t$ (right). The spatial step was $\Delta x = 1$ so the density was calculated only at the locations $x = 0, \pm 1, \pm 2$, etc. The lines are simply drawn to connect these points. We chose $\mathcal{D} = 1$ and $\Delta t = 0.5$ so as to satisfy the stability condition (7.17) as an equality. Note that the vertical scales are different in the different plots; the maximum value of the density decreased as t increased, so as to keep the total number of particles fixed.

by a typical diffusing cream molecule. Hence, the distance moved by a molecule as it diffuses varies as $t^{1/2}$. This behavior[20] is precisely what we found in our studies of random walkers (7.7).

This analytic result tells us that a disturbance such as a particle distribution can be expected to spread by an amount as large as $\sim \sqrt{2\mathcal{D}\Delta t}$ during each time step of a simulation. To guarantee numerical stability we must make sure that the space and time steps satisfy

$$\Delta x \geq \sqrt{2\mathcal{D}\,\Delta t}\,, \tag{7.17}$$

since smaller values of the spatial step size would not allow the distribution to spread as quickly as we know that it must. This potential instability is similar to that found in connection with waves on a string, which should not be surprising since we are dealing with a similar equation.

A numerical solution of the diffusion equation obtained using (7.15) is shown in Figure 7.14. Here we have assumed that the initial density is zero everywhere except at the origin, $x = 0$; thus, our drop of cream is all initially located in one very small region. At $t = 10\Delta t$ the density profile has broadened, as the particles have spread over the range $x \approx \pm 6$. The amount of spreading has increased further at $t = 100\Delta t$. Qualitatively this distribution has spread out an additional factor of ≈ 3 for a tenfold increase in time, which is what we expect for diffusion.

A curious feature of the results for $t > 0$ is that the density alternates between zero and nonzero values. This behavior is due to the initial density profile, which we assumed. Our initial profile had all of the density situated at a *single* grid site. This violates our usual rule-of-thumb that step sizes should always be smaller than any of the characteristic scales in the problem. Here one characteristic length scale is the spatial extent of the density profile. By allowing all of the density to be located at a single

---

[20]This result is also an example of the central-limit theorem, which we mentioned above in connection with the distribution functions associated with random processes. In the present problem many random values (steps in the diffusion/random-walk process) combine to yield a gaussian distribution. The width of this distribution is proportional to $N^{1/2}$, where N is the number of steps. Here $N \sim t$.

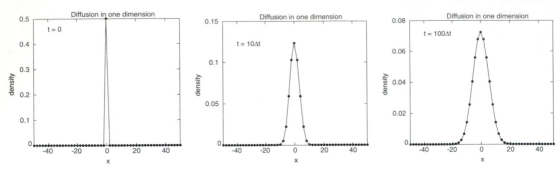

Figure 7.15: Time evolution calculated from the diffusion equation in one dimension at $t = 0$ (left), $t = 10\Delta t$ (center), and $t = 100\Delta t$ (right). Here we have averaged the values from Figure 7.14 at adjacent spatial grid sites to minimize discreteness effects.

grid site we are effectively taking the density distribution to be a singular function.[21] The price we pay for this is that the finite difference equation (7.15) produces these spurious zeros.[22]

One way to overcome this problem would be to use a smaller spatial step size so that the initial density profile is spread out over many grid sites. We will explore this approach in the exercises. Another, perhaps a bit more expedient (but equivalent) solution is to simply average the results in Figure 7.14 over adjacent grid elements. That is, we can average the results for adjacent spatial sites so as to "smooth over" the points where the density was zero. Doing this yields the results in Figure 7.15. The density profiles at $t = 10\Delta t$ and $100\Delta t$ now have the expected gaussian shapes. The amplitude of the gaussian distribution decreases and its width increases as we follow the motion to larger times. We will leave it for the reader to show that the width of the distribution, which is the scale over which the particles are spread, varies as $\sqrt{t}$. This is, of course, a defining feature of diffusion.

This numerical approach to the diffusion equation is very general and can be used just as well in two or three dimensions. We will explore the derivation of the corresponding finite difference equations [which are analogous to (7.15)] in the exercises. The stability condition becomes somewhat more restrictive on Δt as the dimensionality increases, a topic we will leave for the references. Figure 7.16 shows some results for a two-dimensional case. Here we have assumed initial conditions as in the cream-in-your-coffee problem, with all of the molecules confined to a square region surrounding the origin. The density profile then spreads with time in an approximately spherical manner. This numerical approach can also be used to study other types of problems. All that is needed is the initial density profile. The finite difference algorithm (7.15) can then be used to calculate the profile at all future times.

To make the connection between the diffusion equation and random walks even more explicit, we now consider the same cream-in-your-coffee problem using a random-walk approach. We do this by considering a large number of walkers that all start at the origin. This corresponds to the cream molecules just after they have been deposited into the coffee. To obtain the density profile at time

---

[21]This is much like a Dirac delta function or a "point" charge.

[22]This can be appreciated by evaluating $\rho(i, 1)$ by hand, using (7.15), for the initial profile in Figure 7.14. If you do this you will also see that in order to get a density of precisely zero at alternating grid sites, the spatial and temporal grid sizes must be chosen according to the stability condition, as we have done in our simulation. Other choices of the grid sizes would not necessarily lead to such exact cancellations of the density, but would still yield values that alternate in magnitude.

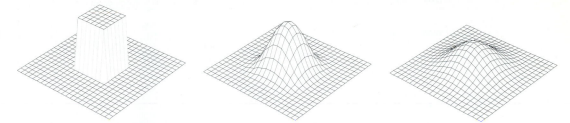

Figure 7.16:   Time evolution calculated from the diffusion equation in two dimensions. At $t = 0$ (left) all of the particles were confined to "clump" at the center of the system. The distributions at $t = 6\Delta t$ (center), and $t = 20\Delta t$ (right) are also shown. The parameters used in the calculation were $\Delta x = 1$, $\mathcal{D} = 1$, and $\Delta t = 0.25$. The region shown here covers the range $|x, y| \leq 10$.

$t = n\Delta t$, we calculate the *probability distribution* of the walkers after n steps. That is, we let every walker take n steps, each of length unity, and record their positions. A histogram of the number of walkers that end up at location x, as a function of x, is then constructed. This is the desired probability distribution, or equivalently, density profile.

Some results for the one dimensional case are shown in Figure 7.17, and at first sight they might seem a bit strange as the probability of finding a walker at the odd-numbered grid sites is zero. However, this can be understood by recognizing that if a walker that starts from the origin takes an even-number of steps, it must end up at an even numbered site. Thus, we should really average the results over adjacent grid sites, much as we did with the diffusion-equation results.[23] In any case, the random-walk results exhibit the gaussian spreading of the particle distribution that we have come to expect. Indeed, it is possible to make the analogy with the solution to the diffusion equation (7.11) exact. The general approach is to consider a large number of walkers distributed in space according to the particular initial conditions of the problem. Each walker is then allowed to move and the distribution of walkers is monitored as a function of step number, that is, time. We will employ this approach to bring out another aspect of the cream-in-your-coffee problem in Section 7.7.

---

[23]We could also start with walkers distributed over several grid sites, or let the number of steps be randomly distributed over some range.

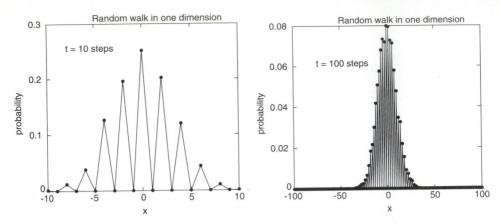

Figure 7.17: Random-walk distributions in one dimension. A large number of walkers began at the origin, and their positions after 10 (shown at left) and 100 steps (shown at right) were used to obtain the probability distribution as a function of position.

Exercises

1. Write a program to solve the finite-difference form of the diffusion equation in one dimension, (7.15). Use it to confirm that (7.16) is, indeed, a solution. To do this, begin with an initial density profile that is sharply peaked at $x = 0$, but choose the grid size such that this profile extends over at least several grid sites. Then show that at later times the density distribution satisfies (7.16).

*2. Repeat the calculation of the previous problem in either two or three dimensions (or both). Begin by deriving the finite-difference equation corresponding to (7.15), suitably generalized to the desired dimensionality. Then show that the density distribution spreads in time according to (7.16) with a half-width that grows as $t^{1/2}$.

*3. Use the program developed for the previous problem to investigate how more complicated initial-density distributions evolve with time. For example, consider an initial distribution that is a constant along the x axis and zero everywhere else. Study how this distribution spreads with time.

7.7   Diffusion, Entropy, and the Arrow of Time

We introduced the cream-in-your-coffee problem at the beginning of this chapter when we were trying to motivate an interest in random processes. Now we want to reconsider it from the point of view of nonequilibrium statistical mechanics and use it to illustrate how a system approaches equilibrium.

Our initial conditions are, again, a cup of black coffee containing a drop of cream at its center. For simplicity we consider a two-dimensional cup with an initial cream distribution as shown in Figure 7.18. The black dots, which form a square black mass at $t = 0$, are the cream molecules. For the simulation we assume that each of these molecules executes a random walk on a two-dimensional square lattice and allow multiple occupancy of a lattice site (although our results would not change qualitatively if we were to limit occupancy to only one molecule per site). At each time step we choose a molecule at random and let it take one step in its random walk. The distributions after 10^4, 10^5, and 10^6 time steps are shown in Figures 7.18 and 7.19. As expected, the cream spreads with time in a manner that appears by eye to be diffusive (we will leave quantitative verification of this claim to the exercises). We have assumed that there are walls at $x = \pm 100$ and $y = \pm 100$, so the molecules are constrained to stay in the region shown here.

These results are equivalent to our solution of the two dimensional diffusion equation in the previous section. Here we want to carry this example one step further and discuss how it is related to the second law of thermodynamics and the manner in which systems approach equilibrium. For this it is useful to consider the entropy of the system. Roughly speaking, entropy is a measure of the amount of disorder. A perfectly ordered system has zero entropy, while a disordered one has a large entropy. Furthermore, statistical physics tells us that the entropy of a closed system will either remain the same or increase with time.

Our cream-in-your-coffee simulation illustrates these ideas very nicely. Initially, all of the cream molecules are packed tightly into a small region of the cup, so the system is highly ordered and has a small value of the entropy. As time passes the molecules spread to fill the cup and their arrangement becomes more disordered. We can make this description quantitative by calculating the entropy explicitly. To do this we recall that the statistical definition of entropy S is

$$S = - \sum_i P_i \ln P_i , \tag{7.18}$$

where the sum is over all possible states of the system and P_i is the probability of finding the system in state i. To apply this definition to our problem we imagine that the system is divided into a square grid, as shown in Figure 7.20. Note that this grid is *not* related to the square lattice occupied by our walkers. It is just a convenient way of partitioning space; each of these partitions is a distinct state in

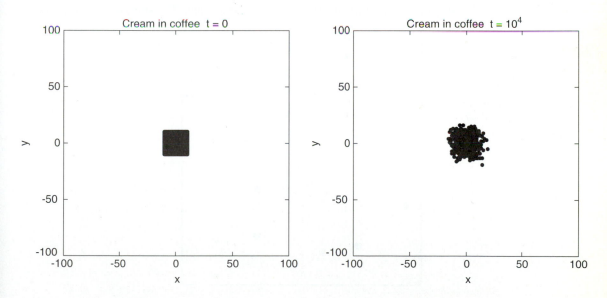

Figure 7.18:   Random-walk simulation of diffusion of cream in coffee. Left: the initial ($t = 0$) cream distribution in which all of the molecules were near the center of the cup. Right: after $t = 10^4$ time steps, only a little spreading has taken place. There were 400 molecules constrained to a 200×200 square lattice.

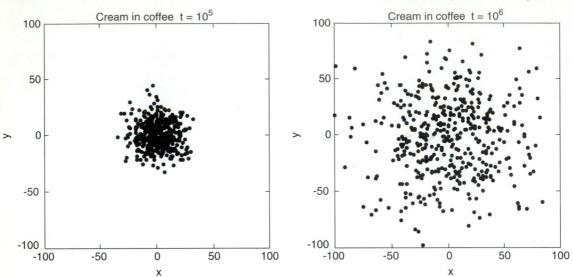

Figure 7.19: Diffusion of cream in coffee; continuation of the random-walk simulation in Figure 7.19. Left: after $t = 10^5$ time steps; right: after $t = 10^6$ time steps.

which a molecule might be found. To appreciate the meaning of (7.18) it is useful to first imagine a system containing only a single cream molecule (we'll add the others from Figures 7.18 and 7.19 in a moment). The state we label i then corresponds to the molecule being located in grid cell i, and P_i is the probability of finding the molecule in this cell at any particular time. The sum over i in (7.18) is,

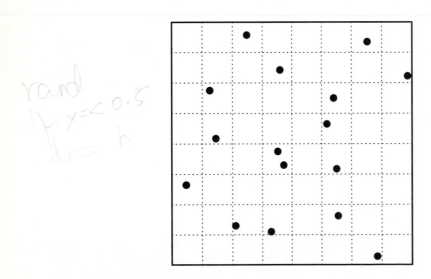

Figure 7.20: Schematic division of our coffee cup into grid cells, with a few molecules distributed throughout the cup. P_i is the probability of finding a molecule in cell i.

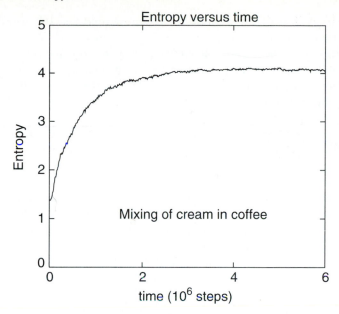

Figure 7.21: Entropy as a function of time (total number of random-walk steps) for cream mixing in coffee, calculated from the simulation that yielded the snapshots in Figures 7.18 and 7.19. The grid used to calculate the entropy had $8 \times 8 = 64$ cells.

then, a sum over all of the cells in the grid. The simulations in Figures 7.18 and 7.19 involve a large number of molecules, and we can use all of them in the computation of P_i.

We have used the molecular positions from the random-walk simulation in Figures 7.18 and 7.19 to calculate these probabilities and evaluate S, and some results are shown in Figure 7.21. The behavior is in complete accord with our intuitive definition of entropy as it applies to the cream. The system is initially in a highly ordered state, with a low value of S. As time passes, the entropy increases and eventually levels off; it approaches a constant value at long times, signaling that the system has reached equilibrium.

This illustrates how a closed system approaches equilibrium. The molecules spread to fill the available states (in this case the available space) uniformly, thereby maximizing the entropy. This tendency to maximize the entropy is not built into the microscopic equations of motion. Rather, it occurs because the system explores (or spends time in) all of the available states with equal probability. This eventually makes the probability of finding a cream molecule the same in all of the grid cells. The equilibrium condition is one in which all available states have equal probabilities.

According to the *ergodic hypothesis*, all of the available states of a system in equilibrium will be occupied with equal probabilities. This is not a result of Newton's laws or any other microscopic equations of motion. Rather, it is a *hypothesis* that plays a key role in statistical physics. While it has not been possible to derive this hypothesis from microscopic laws or principles, it has been shown to hold (rigorously) for certain systems. The difficulty with deriving the ergodic hypothesis in a completely general way can be appreciated from the snapshots of the cream in Figures 7.18 and 7.19. The picture at $t = 10^6$ shows a fairly random distribution of molecules, which contrasts greatly with the completely ordered picture at $t = 0$. If we were to follow the system beyond $t = 10^6$, we would expect to find the randomness of this distribution to either stay the same or increase; we would certainly not expect it to decrease. However, such a decrease would not violate any microscopic laws of nature. These laws leave open the possibility that a cream distribution such as the one at $t = 10^6$ might evolve with time into a perfectly ordered arrangement like that at $t = 0$. That is, the cream could "unmix" and all flow to the center of the cup. However, this is extremely unlikely and, so far as we know, has never been observed in nature.

In the present example the ergodic behavior is a result of the rules of our random walk. The fact that each step is independent of the previous steps leads the particles to explore all parts of the cup with equal probability. However, this assumption of independence is just that, an *assumption*. We know that on a microscopic level the trajectory followed by a molecule is not independent of its prior history, but could in principle be calculated (using, for example, molecular dynamics as we will discuss in Chapter 9). So how can we explain why the ergodic hypothesis is so widely applicable? The answer to this question is not completely settled, but one attractive possibility can be seen from our work on chaotic systems. There we saw that deterministic systems can behave chaotically and exhibit an extreme sensitivity to initial conditions.[24] This sensitivity leads to essentially random behavior of systems such as the pendulum, asteroids near a Kirkwood gap, etc. It may be that this essentially random behavior is responsible for the ergodic behavior observed in nature. With this in mind, it is intriguing to reconsider the billiard problem discussed in Chapter 3. That can be viewed as a (classical) model for the motion of gas molecules in a closed container and is thus very similar to our cream-in-your-coffee problem. You may recall that except for very specially shaped containers, the motion of the billiard is chaotic. Thus it would not be surprising to find that the motions of our cream molecules are also chaotic, making the system ergodic.

Exercises

1. Calculate the entropy for the cream-in-your-coffee problem, and reproduce the results in Figure 7.21.

2. Calculate S as a function of time for the cream-in-your-coffee problem for containers with different sizes. Show that the time necessary to reach equilibrium varies as the square of the size.

*3. Perform the random-walk simulation of Figures 7.18 and 7.19 and show that the size of the drop of cream increases as $t^{1/2}$ (our familiar diffusive behavior), so long as the drop is smaller than the size of the container. Show that the behavior changes when the drop has spread so much that it uniformly fills the container. The time at which the size of the drop stops increasing should be the same as the time at which the system reaches equilibrium as determined by the entropy. Hint: A convenient measure of the size of the drop of cream is the root-mean-square distance of the particles from the origin, $\sqrt{(\sum r_i^2)/N}$.

*4. Perform the random-walk simulation of spreading cream (Figures 7.18 and 7.19), and let one of the walls of the container possess a small hole so that if a cream molecule enters the hole, it leaves the container. Calculate the number of molecules in the container as a function of time. Show that this number, which is proportional to the partial pressure of the cream molecules, varies as

---

[24]They are also extremely sensitive to changes in external parameters, which would also contribute to ergodicity.

$\exp(-t/\tau)$, where τ is the effective time constant for the escape. Hint: Reasonable parameter choices are a 50×50 container lattice and a hole 10 units in length along one of the edges.

5. Carry out an analysis of the entropy for the nonlinear damped pendulum studied in Chapter 3. Consider the behavior of $\theta(t)$ and divide the possible range for θ into a number of cells (try 100). Simulate the pendulum and calculate a histogram of the number of times the pendulum angle falls into a cell as a function of θ; sample $\theta(t)$ in synchrony with the drive force, as we did in calculating the Poincaré sections. Calculate the entropy using (7.18) as a function of the driving force. You should find that S is small in the periodic regime and large when the pendulum is chaotic. What is S in the period-2 and period-4 regimes?

7.8   Cluster Growth Models

We have spent a good deal of time in this chapter exploring random walks and their connection with diffusion and the approach to equilibrium. Another interesting random process which turns out to be closely related to random walks, concerns the growth of clusters, such as snowflakes and soot particles. In this section we will examine two different models of cluster growth. The first is known as the Eden model and operates according to the following rules. Consider a two dimensional lattice of points (x, y), where x and y are both integers. These are the allowed locations for the particles that will make up the cluster. We begin by placing a seed particle at the origin $(x = 0, y = 0)$; this is our initial cluster. A cluster grows by the addition of particles to its perimeter. Our initial cluster has nearest-neighbor points on the lattice at $(\pm1, 0)$ and $(0, \pm1)$. We will refer to such unoccupied near-neighbor sites as the perimeter sites of the cluster. We next choose one of these perimeter sites at random and place a particle at the chosen location. The cluster now contains two particles and a correspondingly larger perimeter. This process is then repeated; a perimeter site is chosen at random, and a particle added at that location. We continue this process until a cluster of the desired size is obtained. This is the Eden model of cluster growth.

A typical Eden cluster is shown in Figure 7.22. While it is a little rough around the edges, it is basically a circular disc with a few holes. Note that as the cluster grows these holes tend to fill in, since they are treated on the same footing (they are equally likely to be occupied by the next particle) as the exterior perimeter sites.

The Eden model is sometimes referred to as a "cancer" model, because the clusters grow from within by expanding their borders. However, not all clusters grow in this manner. For example, snowflakes and soot particles grow by the addition of new particles that originate from outside the cluster.[25] This process is captured by a different cluster model, which is known as diffusion-limited aggregation, or DLA.

The growth rules for DLA clusters are as follows. We again start with a seed particle at the origin. We then release a particle at a randomly chosen location (x, y) that is some distance away from the seed and let it perform a random walk. If (or when) this walker lands on a perimeter site, it sticks there and becomes part of the cluster. This process is repeated with many walkers until a large cluster is grown. One way to motivate (or justify!) the choice of these growth rules is to consider how a large particle might be built up from smaller particles or molecules in a solution. If the cluster is located well away from any other objects, such as walls or other clusters, small particles will approach it from all

---

[25]More precisely, the places where new particles are added depend on processes that take place outside the cluster.

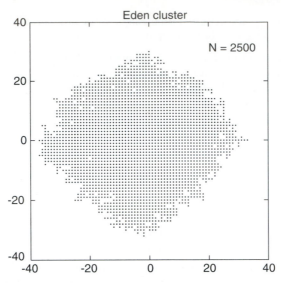

Figure 7.22:   Eden cluster containing 2500 particles. Note that there are very few "holes" inside the main body of the cluster.

directions. In addition, it seems reasonable to assume that small particles will move diffusively as they travel through the solution around the cluster. This process is captured in the DLA growth rules since, as we have already seen, diffusion is equivalent to a random walk. Of course, we can imagine situations in which these rules would not be appropriate. For example, there might be some localized source of the small particles, or perhaps a prevailing current, that would give an overall drift velocity in addition to the random walk. These are perfectly reasonable models and each could be interesting depending in part on possible connections to real systems.

A cluster grown using the DLA rules is shown in Figure 7.23 (we will consider the programming associated with generating such clusters in the exercises). Comparing our DLA cluster with the Eden cluster Figure 7.22, it is obvious that they have very different properties. The Eden cluster is, as we have already noted, essentially a solid disk with very few holes and a fairly smooth perimeter. In contrast, the DLA cluster contains many large open spaces and the perimeter is very irregular. These differences are directly connected with the growth rules. For the Eden clusters all perimeter sites, even the interior ones, are equally likely to be filled by the next particle. This tends to fill in any holes or cracks, since those were likely formed long before the outermost parts of the cluster. For DLA it is extremely unlikely that such crevices will be filled in, as the probability that a random walker will manage to navigate past the outermost parts of the cluster on its way deep into a crack is very low. A walker is much more likely to first make contact with the outer edges of the cluster.

This intuitive explanation of the difference between Eden and DLA clusters is useful, but we would like to have a quantitative measure of this difference. This brings us to consider objects that are known as *fractals*, which will be our primary topic for the remainder of this section and the next one as well. Rather than try to give a very general definition of what it means to be a fractal, we will instead introduce a few terms and concepts associated with these objects. A definition will gradually emerge as we proceed.

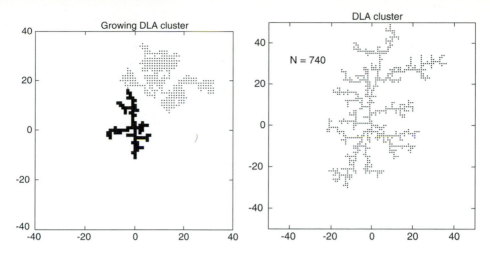

Figure 7.23: Left: growing DLA cluster. The filled squares are sites in the cluster and the dots are the lattice sites visited by a particular random walker as it approached. This walker eventually touched the perimeter at the top edge of the cluster and became attached there. Right: DLA cluster containing 740 particles.

Let us consider how we might measure the dimensionality of an object. At first this may seem like a silly exercise. Your intuition tells you that straight lines are one-dimensional objects, flat disks are two dimensional, etc. But what about a piece of spaghetti, or a string that is tangled, or a piece of crumpled paper? While your intuition probably would still feel comfortable in these cases, it is instructive to construct an *operational* definition for dimensionality. There are several ways to approach this problem. In the next section we will discuss simple curves and other objects that are close to being one dimensional. Here we will consider the problem for our Eden and DLA clusters.

Suppose we have a large disk of uniform density that lies in the x–y plane, as illustrated in Figure 7.24. If we consider the mass of the disk that is contained within a circle of radius r, it is easy to see that this is given by

$$m(r) \; = \; \sigma \, \pi \, r^2 \,, \tag{7.19}$$

where σ is the mass per unit area. The key point is that the mass scales as r^2, and this 2 is also the dimensionality of the object. If we instead had straight line or a similar type of curve, the mass would be

$$m(r) \; = \; 2 \, \lambda \, r \,, \tag{7.20}$$

where λ is the mass per unit length. The mass now scales as r^1, and 1 is again the spatial dimensionality of the object.

These observations form the basis of an operational definition that we can use to calculate the effective dimensionality of a cluster. Our definition is

$$m(r) \; \sim \; r^{d_f} \,, \tag{7.21}$$

where d_f is the effective or *fractal* dimensionality of the object. We have already seen cases that yield $d_f = 1$ (a simple line or curve), and $d_f = 2$ (a solid disk); a solid sphere would be described by $d_f = 3$. It remains for us to devise objects for which d_f is not an integer.

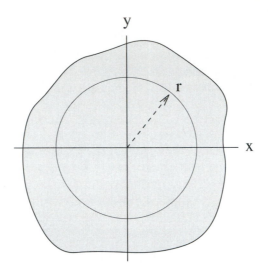

Figure 7.24:   Method for calculating the effective dimensionality of a cluster, shown as the shaded region. $m(r)$ is the mass contained within a circle of radius r.

To apply this definition to one of our clusters we need to calculate the mass inside a circle of radius r, which is centered inside the cluster. For convenience we choose the initial seed particle for the origin. Assuming that all of the particles have the same mass, we can find $m(r)$ by counting the number of particles within a distance r of the origin. Values for the mass as a function of r for our Eden and DLA clusters are shown in Figure 7.25, where we have plotted the results on logarithmic scales. Such plots are useful, since taking the logarithm of both sides of (7.21) yields

$$\log m \sim d_f \log r , \tag{7.22}$$

so the slope of a log-log plot is equal to the fractal dimensionality.

For both types of clusters the results for $\log m$ versus $\log r$ are consistent with a straight line and thus with the relation (7.22) for small r. However, the curves flatten out for large r. This is due to the finite size of the clusters. For very large measuring circles (see Figure 7.24) the entire cluster will be inside the circle, and in this case $m(r)$ will be independent of r. For the same reason, when r is only a little less than the maximum "radius" of the cluster, r_{max}, $m(r)$ will be suppressed below its value for the ideal case; that is, for an extremely large (infinite) cluster. In practice, a particular cluster can only be used to estimate $m(r)$ for distances up to about $r_{\mathrm{max}}/2$.

The solid lines in Figure 7.25 are least-squares fits of (7.22) to the results for $m(r)$ out to $r_{\mathrm{max}}/2$. The slopes of these lines are the fractal dimensionalities, and we find $d_f \approx 1.99$ for the Eden cluster and 1.65 for the DLA cluster. To within the statistical errors the Eden cluster has a dimensionality of 2. This is in accord with our intuition; the Eden cluster is essentially just a solid disk. However, the DLA cluster has a fractal dimensionality much less than 2 (and also much greater than 1). Indeed, this is why it is known as a fractal.

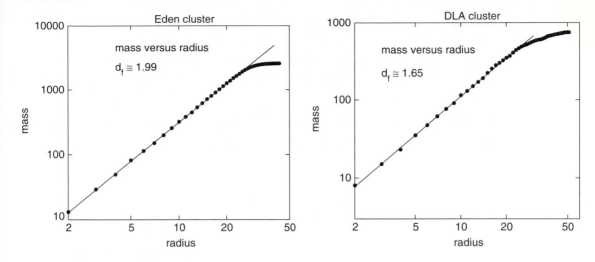

Figure 7.25: Left: plot of $\log m$ versus $\log r$ for the Eden cluster in Figure 7.22. The solid line is a least-squares fit whose slope is the fractal dimensionality, which for this cluster was $d_f \approx 1.99$; it was equal to 2 to within the statistical uncertainties. Right: plot of $\log m$ versus $\log r$ for the DLA cluster in Figure 7.23. The solid line is again a least-squares fit whose slope is the fractal dimensionality, which for this cluster was $d_f \approx 1.65$.

In order for a cluster to have an effective dimensionality d_f, which is not an integer, its mass must increase more slowly[26] than r^2. This means that it must contain holes or cracks, as we have observed in the DLA clusters. However, simply containing such open spaces is not enough. An object that has a certain, constant fraction of open space[27] would still have $d_f = 2$. In order to have $d_f < 2$, the sizes of these open spaces must *increase* with r. Evidently, DLA clusters have just this property.

Exercises

1. Write a program to generate DLA clusters and calculate their fractal dimensionality. Here are a few programming suggestions for this problem. We have already seen that random walkers can take a long time to move an appreciable distance and this can make the generation of a DLA cluster very slow if you are not careful. Initially, start new walkers a distance r_{start} away from the origin, by choosing the initial position of a walker at random on a circle of radius r_{start} (but make sure that they are on the lattice).[28] If the walker wanders too far from the cluster, say farther than $1.5 \times r_{\text{start}}$, it may never hit the cluster, so a new walker should be started. As the cluster grows, r_{start} should be increased so that the walkers don't begin too close to the cluster. Try keeping r_{start} at least 5 units larger than the maximum cluster size (that is, the point on the cluster which is

---

[26]We assume here that the cluster is grown on a planar lattice and not a three-dimensional one.

[27]Assuming it to be planar.

[28]Be sure that you pick the initial location of the walker at random from possible locations on the circle. This is most easily done by choosing an angle at random in the range 0–2π and using it to specify the starting point of the walker.

farthest from the origin). Also, when the walker is far from the cluster you can let it take steps of length 2 (to speed up the walk), then decrease the step length as it approaches the cluster.

2. Grow a DLA cluster using the algorithm described in the previous problem, but instead of letting the walkers start from points on a circle that surrounds the cluster, have all of the walkers begin at a location on the x axis. How does this affect the shape and structure of the cluster?

3. Generate a DLA structure using an initial "seed," which is the entire x axis. That is, begin with all of the sites on the x axis occupied and let the walkers begin some distance above this axis. The resulting structure is sometimes used to model the paths followed by electric discharges in a gas (that is, lightening bolts).

*4. Repeat the previous problem, but allow your random walkers to move on a *three-dimensional* lattice. You should find a value of $d_f \sim 2.5$ in this case.

5. Generate a DLA cluster using walkers that perform a biased random walk. That is, let your walkers have a higher probability for walking in one particular direction (along the $+x$ direction, for example) than in other directions. This is a biased random walk, as we have considered in an earlier exercise. Study how both d_f and the overall shape of the cluster depend on the magnitude of this drift velocity.

*6. An interesting variation on DLA is to begin with a lattice in which some fraction of sites are occupied with particles, and then let the cluster diffuse and pick up particles as it makes contact with them. Use a square lattice and place particles on sites at random with some probability ($p = 0.1$ is a good choice). Let the cluster perform a random walk and whenever a perimeter site is occupied by a particle, that particle then becomes part of the cluster. Generate clusters in this way and calculate their fractal dimensionality. You should find $d_f \sim 1.7$, which is about the same as a DLA cluster. Interestingly, d_f for this cluster-diffusion model seems to vary with p. Calculate d_f for other values of p and show that d_f becomes larger (it should approach ~ 1.95) for large values of p. This calculation was first performed by Voss (see Voss [1984]).

7.9   Fractal Dimensionalities of Curves

While DLA clusters may be nice to look at, we must still ask what it is about fractals that makes them interesting from a *physics* point of view. We will discuss this question in due course, but it is useful to first to consider another problem concerning fractal objects. It is convenient to introduce this problem using a class of regular fractals that are known as Koch curves. In contrast to the fractal clusters grown using the DLA model, Koch curves are generated by *deterministic* rules. While such regular fractals do not have a direct connection with physics, they are useful for learning more about fractals, as we will now see.

Perhaps the simplest way to define a Koch curve is through the examples in Figure 7.26, which shows a family of such curves. The first member of the family is shown at the bottom and is just a straight line of length L; we will refer to this as a Koch curve of order one. The second-order Koch curve (the second curve from the bottom) is derived from the first-order curve by replacing the straight section with four segments of length $L/3$, oriented with respect to the original (first-order section) as shown. The third-order curve is obtained from the second-order curve by replacing *each* of its straight sections by four more segments, with lengths $L/9$. The fourth and higher-order curves are obtained in an analogous manner. This procedure can be used to obtain curves of arbitrary order.

Figure 7.26:   A family of Koch curves generated at several different levels of recursion. The first-order curve is shown at the bottom, the second-order curve is the second curve up from the bottom, etc.

The Koch curves are thus defined *recursively*. A member of the series is generated from the preceding member by replacing each of its straight sections by four new segments, as described above. We can clearly generate other types of Koch curves by using different replacement rules. However, the key (and common) property of such curves is that at "infinite" order they will look the same on *all* length scales. That is, no matter what scale or magnification we use to examine such a curve, it will always have the same appearance. This is a property of fractal curves that is not found in regular, nonfractal objects. You may not think this to be very impressive; after all, it can only be a property of a regular fractal. A DLA cluster is a random fractal and will not have precisely the same appearance on all length scales. However, a DLA fractal will have significant structure on all length scales, and we have argued above that it is just this property that leads to a fractal dimensionality that is less than 2. The important point is that a DLA fractal will have the same general appearance, the same structure of open spaces and cracks, and hence the same value of d_f, on *all* length scales.

Let us now consider the effective dimensionality of a Koch curve. As in the previous section, we are after an operational definition. A procedure involving $m(r)$, such as the one we employed to compute d_f for the Eden and DLA clusters, could be used here, but we will instead introduce another approach that is a bit more natural for objects that are close to being one dimensional. Imagine that the

Koch curves are walking paths and that you are moving in steps of length L_s along one of the high order Koch curves in Figure 7.26. We define the effective length of the curve to be the number of steps, N_s, required to walk from one end to the other, multiplied by the length of each step, that is, $L_{\text{eff}} = N_s L_s$. For an ordinary curve this product is a constant,[29] which means that the length of the curve does not depend on the size of the steps you use to measure it. However, the results for a high-order Koch curve are a bit different. For a given L_s, a step along a Koch curve will pass over the fine structure present at scales smaller than L_s. As the step length is made smaller, more and more of this structure becomes apparent, causing an increase in the number of steps required. For this reason the effective length $N_s L_s$ now depends on the size of the step.

Another way to think of this is to imagine that you are examining a Koch curve through a microscope. At low magnification much of the fine structure is blurred and the curve appears as one of the low order curves in Figure 7.26. As the magnification is increased, more structure is apparent and the effective order of the curve increases. This extra visible structure will make the curve appear longer than it does at lower magnification. If the magnification is increased further, even more structure becomes visible, etc. For a fractal curve, increasing the magnification always reveals more structure and thus a longer curve.

This operational definition of length can be used to define the effective or fractal dimensionality of a curve. For an ordinary nonfractal curve the number of steps would vary as L_s^{-1}, where the factor of 1 is just the dimensionality in this case. We therefore define d_f through

$$L_{\text{eff}} \equiv N_s L_s \sim L_s^{1-d_f} . \tag{7.23}$$

For the regular Koch curves in Figure 7.26 this expression can be evaluated analytically. If the length of the first-order curve (the bottom one) is unity, then for a step of length $L_s = 1$, $N_s = 1$ steps will be required. For $L_s = 1/3$, the number of steps will be $N_s = 4$, etc., for step lengths of $1/9$, $1/27 \ldots$. Inserting this into (7.23) yields $d_f = \ln 4 / \ln 3 \approx 1.262$. Since $d_f > 1$, this confirms that the Koch curve is indeed a fractal.

For random fractals or cases where only the coordinates of the curve are known, (7.23) can be used as the basis of a numerical approach. Here we consider two cases. The first is the ordinary nonfractal curve shown in Figure 7.27; it is just a semicircle. For this example we calculated the coordinates of the curve at 1000 points and used these coordinates in a calculation of the number of steps required to traverse the entire curve. We will leave a discussion of the programming to the exercises. The number of steps required, N_s, was calculated as a function of the step length, and the value of N_s then used to obtain the effective length of the curve. The results are shown in Figure 7.27. The effective length is seen to be essentially a constant, independent of L_s, as expected for a nonfractal curve. The scatter in the results for L are due to the finite step lengths (this is also why the values fall a few percent below the exact value), the effects of which are explored in the exercises.

We have repeated this calculation for the random fractal shown in Figure 7.28. This was generated using the Koch algorithm, but instead of replacing each straight section by four simple (but shorter) segments, we have chosen the lengths and angles of these four segments at random. A program for generating such random Koch curves is given in Appendix 4. The effective length of this curve as

---

[29] Strictly speaking, it is a constant only when L_s is smaller than any of the structure in the curve. For an ordinary (nonfractal) curve it always possible to choose a suitably small value of L_s, but for fractal curves there is structure on *all* length scales, so this is not possible.

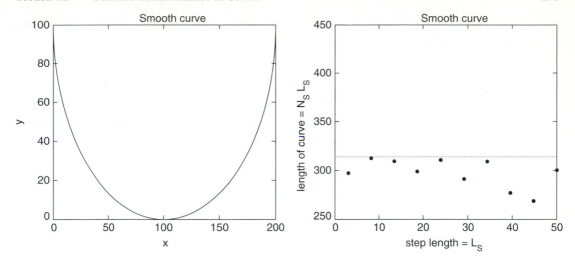

Figure 7.27:   Left: typical smooth curve. Right: length of the curve at left, calculated by "walking" along the curve, as a function of the length of the walker's steps. The dotted line shows the exact value of the length. The calculated values fall slightly below the exact result due to the manner in which the finite step size was handled (this issue is explored in the exercises).

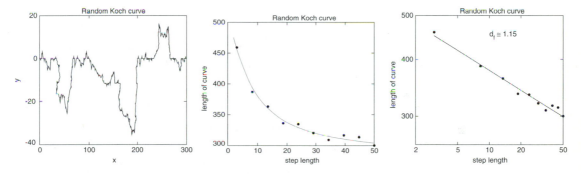

Figure 7.28:   Left: random Koch curve generated using 5 levels of recursion. Middle: length of the curve at left, calculated by walking along the curve, as a function of the length of the walker's steps. Right: same plot as the middle graph, but on log–log scales. A least-squares fit to (7.23) gives the solid line, whose slope corresponds to $d_f \approx 1.15$.

a function of step size, L_s, is also shown. It is seen that L_{eff} increases as L_s is made smaller, as expected for a fractal curve. Smaller steps allow more of the curve's structure to be discerned, yielding a longer measured length. The slope of the log-log plot of L_{eff} as a function of L_s yields the fractal dimensionality from (7.23), and we find $d_f \approx 1.15$. This is not far from the value we found above for the regular Koch curve (the difference is probably due to the effects of finite step size combined with the uncertainty associated with the least-squares fit in Figure 7.28), suggesting that randomizing the curve in this simple manner does not significantly affect d_f.

Nature contains many examples of random fractal curves. Empirically it has been found that the coastlines of most countries are fractal (see Mandelbrot [1977] for more on this), as are the shapes of many rivers. Much effort has been (and is still being) devoted to trying to understand why nature seems to prefer such fractal shapes.

Exercises

1. Use (7.23) to calculate the fractal dimensionality of various curves, including smooth curves such as the one shown in Figure 7.27, and fractals such as the one shown in Figure 7.28. A program that generates such fractals is given in Appendix 4. Programming suggestions: To implement this algorithm you must first obtain the coordinates of the curve at a large number of points; 1000 will typically be enough. To calculate d_f, start at the initial point, (x_i, y_i), and then walk down the list of points until you reach one, call it (x_1, y_1), which is a distance L_s or greater from the starting point. In general the distance from (x_i, y_i) to (x_1, y_1) will not be precisely L_s. That is, the end of the step will fall between coordinates. You can deal with this in three different ways. One way is to effectively back up the step to the previous point and thereby use a step length slightly smaller than L_s. Another is to move on to the next point and thus use a step that is slightly larger than L_s. The third option is to let the step land in the middle and use a landing spot that interpolates between the two adjacent points. Try all three in your program, and show that they lead to similar values of d_f, provided that the spacing between points is small compared to L_s. This finite step effect is the cause of the scatter and the deviations from the expected values in Figure 7.27.

2. Use the algorithm associated with Figure 7.24 to calculate the fractal dimensionality of the collection of lattice sites visited by a three-dimensional random walk. Such a walk will often revisit sites, so be sure that you do not count a visited site more than once when calculating the mass of the cluster. Also, you should repeat the calculation for a number of different walks so that you can estimate the average fractal dimensionality.

*3. Write a program to generate fractal curves recursively. In the Koch example discussed in this section we used an equilateral triangle as the basic "unit." Generate fractals with other basic units; interesting possibilities include squares, pentagons, and random multisided objects. Hint: One approach to recursive programming is to structure the algorithm schematically as follows.

```
!    x_i = initial x coordinate
!    y_i = initial y coordinate
!    x_f = final x coordinate
!    y_f = final y coordinate
!    level = number of recursive "levels"
sub show(x_i,y_i,x_f,y_f,level)
    if level <= 1 then                ! have reached the "bottom"
       plot x_i,y_i;x_f,y_f           ! just draw a line from (x_i,y_i) to (x_f,y_f)
    else
       dx = x_f - x_i                 ! compute new points to pass to show()
       dy = y_f - y_i                 ! these determine shape of fractal
       x_c = x_i + dx/2 - dy/2
       y_c = y_i + dx/2 + dy/2
       call show(x_i,y_i,x_c,y_c,level-1) ! call show() again with new coordinates
       call show(x_c,y_c,x_f,y_f,level-1) ! your language must allow recursion
    end if
end sub
```

The routine show is called with the coordinates of the beginning and ending points of the curve and the desired number of recursive "levels"; this routine serves two intertwined functions.

If the level number is 1, then show simply draws a line between the starting and ending points. If the level number is greater than 1, show calls itself but with different arguments. These arguments are new starting and ending points, which will generally be more closely spaced than the previous ones, and the way these new points are chosen will determine the pattern of the fractal. Note also that each time the show routine is called the level number is reduced by one so that the recursive scheme will eventually terminate. This particular version of show will plot a simple fractal. We suggest that you try to predict what the pattern will look like for n of 2–5 before you run the program. Random fractals can be generated by choosing the new starting and ending points randomly.

7.10   Percolation

The motion of groundwater through the soil, the strength of a porous network, and the flow of oil through porous rock, are all problems that fall under the general heading known as percolation. The most basic percolation problem is illustrated in Figures 7.29 and 7.30, where we have a square lattice of sites with each site occupied at random according to a certain probability, p. Here the occupied sites are plotted as filled squares while the unoccupied sites are left uncolored. It is useful to group the occupied sites into clusters according to the following rule. If two neighboring sites are both occupied, that is, if two filled squares have a common edge, they are considered to be part of the same cluster. Membership in a particular cluster extends to all sites that share an edge with at least one other member of the cluster. Hence, a cluster is simply a collection of interconnected sites.

For small occupation probability, such as $p = 0.2$ in Figure 7.29, nearly all of the occupied sites are isolated, so the majority of clusters are of size 1, just single sites. When p is increased to 0.4, most sites are connected to several others and the typical cluster contains 5–10 sites. At the opposite extreme, illustrated by $p = 0.8$ in Figure 7.30, it is rare to find occupied sites that are not part of a large cluster. In fact, for large p nearly all sites belong to the *same* cluster, which extends throughout the lattice. The

Figure 7.29:   Left: 40×40 square lattice of sites occupied with probability $p = 0.2$. Some typical clusters are circled. Right: same, but with $p = 0.4$.

Figure 7.30:   Left: 40×40 square lattice of sites occupied with probability $p = 0.6$; right: same but with $p = 0.8$.

most interesting structure is found for $p = 0.6$. Here many sites are members of fairly large clusters, but these clusters are often barely connected. That is, the removal of a single site would change the size of the cluster drastically. Nevertheless, these barely connected clusters seem to be the rule. If you look carefully you will find that in Figure 7.30, with $p = 0.6$, one such cluster spans the entire lattice, as it touches all four edges of the lattice. Such a cluster is said to be a spanning cluster, and a lattice that possesses such a cluster is said to "percolate."

These clusters, particularly the spanning cluster, will turn out to be central to many aspects of the behavior of a percolating system.[30] It is interesting to consider the size of typical clusters as a function of p. We have already seen that for large p we are essentially guaranteed to have a spanning cluster, while for small p the odds are that such a cluster will not occur. It turns out that the transition from one regime to the other is a sharp one. For an infinitely large lattice this transition occurs at a critical concentration, p_c, whose value depends on the lattice structure. For the two-dimensional square lattice considered here, $p_c \approx 0.593$, so the example with $p = 0.6$ is essentially right at the percolation threshold. The problem of calculating p_c is a bit different from anything we have encountered so far. Estimating the percolation threshold requires that we determine whether or not a spanning cluster exists, and the answer to this question involves a global examination of the system. The nature of the problem can be appreciated if we imagine that we start with an empty lattice and then occupy sites (chosen randomly) one at a time. We terminate the process when a spanning cluster first appears and the concentration of occupied sites at that instant is p_c. The last site to be occupied will provide a connection between two or more clusters that then combine to make up the final spanning cluster. However, simply examining this last site and its immediate surroundings will not tell us that it was the missing link in the spanning cluster. The information required to determine if a cluster spans the lattice or not is effectively distributed *throughout* the lattice.

---

[30]For example, if the occupied sites are voids in an otherwise solid rock, then the flow of a fluid (such as oil) through the rock will be controlled by the properties of the spanning cluster.

The spanning question is really a sort of pattern recognition problem, and any computer scientist will tell you that such problems can be very difficult to solve. One way to handle this problem is to simply examine the percolating system by eye, as we did in discussing the results in Figures 7.29 and 7.30; in effect, using your brain as the pattern analyzer. While this method works well in practice for lattices up to about 50×50 in size, it can become tedious. One efficient numerical algorithm for detecting spanning clusters involves labeling the sites in each cluster in the following manner.

We begin with an empty lattice and proceed to generate a percolating system by occupying sites at random. An initial site is chosen (randomly, of course); it is designated as the first cluster, that is, number 1. A second site is then chosen at random and its neighboring sites are checked to see if any of them happen to be the site that is cluster number 1. If this is so, the new site is added to cluster number 1 since by our definitions it becomes part of that cluster; if not, this new site is designated cluster number 2. A third site is then chosen at random, and its neighboring sites checked. If one of its neighbors is occupied, the new site is given that cluster number. If two or more of the sites adjacent to a newly chosen site are occupied, the new site is assigned to the adjacent cluster with the smallest number. In this case it is also necessary to *reassign* the cluster numbers of the other adjacent sites. The basic idea of this scheme is to make sure that all sites in a particular cluster are assigned the same cluster number. When a new site forms a bridge between two clusters that were previously separate, it is necessary to renumber things so that all of the sites of the combined cluster have the same number.[31]

This labeling procedure is continued as more and more sites are occupied. To check for the existence of a percolating cluster we must determine if the cluster number of any of the edge sites is found on all four edges; if so, that number corresponds to the spanning cluster. We will leave the programming of this algorithm to you and now consider some of the results that can be obtained using it.

Let us first return to the problem posed above, the calculation of p_c. Strictly speaking, p_c is smallest concentration at which a percolating cluster is first found for an *infinitely* large lattice. For the finite lattices used in a simulation the concentration at which a spanning cluster first appears will fluctuate statistically from one simulation to the next. To obtain an estimate of p_c we must average the values for many different lattices, and the results of such a calculation are shown in Figure 7.31. Here we plot the average values of p_c obtained for a square lattice as a function of L^{-1} for a series of $L \times L$ lattices. There is a small but noticeable variation of p_c with L (note that the vertical scale is greatly expanded), and by plotting our results in this manner we can more easily extrapolate to the case of an infinite lattice. The dotted line shows the result for an infinitely large lattice, $p_c = 0.593$, and while there are some statistical fluctuations in our values, they do appear to be heading to the expected target.

The percolation threshold at p_c is an example of a second-order *phase transition*. It has much in common with other types of phase transitions, such as the ferromagnetic-paramagnetic and melting transitions, which we will discuss in Chapters 8 and 9. One key feature of a second-order transition is that it is characterized by singularities in various quantities. For the percolation transition, certain cluster properties exhibit singular behavior. As an example we consider the spanning cluster at concentrations above p_c. We saw in Figure 7.30 that for large p nearly all of the occupied sites were part of the infinite cluster, but as p_c was approached, many small clusters appeared. Let us, therefore, calculate the fraction

---

[31] It is convenient, but certainly not required, to use the smaller of the two cluster numbers for the new larger cluster.

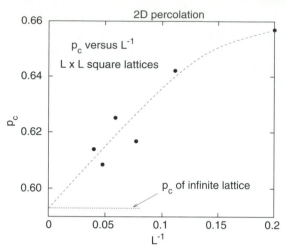

Figure 7.31:   Results for the critical concentration as a function of lattice size for $L \times L$ square lattices. For each lattice size we have averaged the results for 50 different simulations. The dotted line shows the value of p_c for an infinitely large lattice, while the dashed curve suggests a smooth extrapolation to the infinite lattice limit.

of sites F, which are in the spanning cluster as a function of p. This can be accomplished using the cluster-numbering algorithm by first generating a lattice with a given probability of occupied sites and then using the labeling scheme to determine which are in the spanning cluster. Some results for F are shown in Figure 7.32. Note that F is the number of sites that are in the spanning cluster divided by the

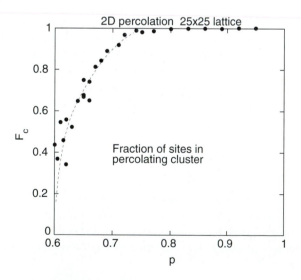

Figure 7.32:   Fraction of sites in the percolating cluster as a function of concentration for a 25×25 lattice. The dashed curve is simply a guide to the eye and is intended to illustrate the singularity at p_c.

number of occupied sites, *not* the total number of lattice sites. We see that F drops precipitously and seems to be heading to zero at p_c. It turns out that the variation of F near p_c is given by a power law

$$F = F_0 (p - p_c)^\beta , \tag{7.24}$$

where β is a number known as a *critical exponent*. The results in Figure 7.32 are not accurate enough to provide an accurate estimate for β, although they certainly suggest that F goes to zero in a singular manner; that is, $dF/dp \to \infty$ as $p \to p_c$. Careful analytic calculations (see the references) have shown that the behavior is indeed singular, and that $\beta = 5/36$ for all two dimensional lattices, such as square, triangular, and honeycomb. Singularities of this form are very common near second-order phase transitions.

While the singular behavior of F is very important, we should note another striking feature of Figure 7.32. At p_c the spanning cluster has an infinite size so as to span the system, yet, since $F \to 0$, it contains a *vanishing* fraction of the occupied sites! An object that has an infinitely large extent but has no volume, is certainly very unusual and should make you suspicious that a fractal is involved. To investigate this we have used the cluster-labeling algorithm to separate the spanning cluster from the other sites for a lattice with $p = 0.6 \approx p_c$, as shown in Figure 7.33. This spanning cluster is seen to have a very open structure, and in many places it is just barely connected. That is, the removal of only one or a very few occupied sites would destroy the connectedness of the cluster. Hence, the visual evidence also suggests that the spanning cluster is a fractal.

To get a better feeling for the structure of the spanning cluster at p_c it is useful to consider much larger lattices and to compare results for different concentrations. While this can be accomplished with the cluster labeling algorithm we have employed to this point, there is a more convenient method for directly generating clusters for a specified value of the concentration. We begin by placing a seed at the

Figure 7.33:   Plot of the spanning cluster (solid squares) and occupied sites that are not part of the spanning cluster (dots). The concentration is 0.60 and the lattice size is 25×25. Sites that contain neither squares or dots are unoccupied.

Figure 7.34: Clusters grown with $p = 0.55$ (left), $p = 0.60 \approx p_c$ (center), and $p = 0.70$ (right). Note that the plot on the left is greatly expanded as compared to the others, as this cluster contained far fewer sites.

origin. We know that for the final arrangement of occupied sites, the points adjacent to this seed will be occupied with probability p, so we make a list of these sites (in this case there are four of them) and pick at random from this list. The chosen site is then occupied with probability p. If the site is then picked to be occupied, any additional perimeter sites associated with it are added to the list of potential new sites. If the site is not chosen for occupancy, it is removed from the list since we cannot later reconsider it for occupancy without changing the effective value of p.

This process of choosing sites from the list, occupying them with probability p, updating the list, etc., is an effective method for directly generating clusters for a given value of p.[32] Some clusters grown in this way are shown in Figure 7.34, where we consider several different values of p. These plots show particular clusters for a given p, while we are really interested in typical (that is, average) clusters. To estimate the properties of a typical cluster it is necessary to perform an average over many clusters grown with the same value of p, and we will get to that in a moment. Our point is that when growing a single such cluster it is always statistically possible that we may obtain a cluster containing only a single site or a cluster that contains an infinite number of sites (assuming that p is neither 0 or 1). These possibilities, and all cluster sizes in between, are all conceivable although their probabilities will vary strongly with p.

With this proviso, the plots in Figure 7.34 show "representative" clusters. At $p = 0.55$ the cluster-growth algorithm often terminated with clusters containing 10–20 sites, or even fewer. This is what we should have expected, since we know that below p_c there will not be an infinite (spanning) cluster. For $p = 0.7$ we are above the percolation threshold, so we expect a spanning cluster to be found. This was indeed the case, as the cluster in Figure 7.34 continued to grow without bound; we stopped the simulation to obtain this snapshot. The cluster for $p = 0.7$ has a qualitative appearance very similar to that of Eden clusters, with a fairly smooth perimeter and relatively few interior holes. The cluster at $p = 0.6 \approx p_c$ has a rather different appearance. Its perimeter is much more irregular and there are many large cracks. This is reminiscent of the DLA clusters, and it should not be surprising to learn that the infinite cluster at p_c is a fractal. We will leave a study of its fractal dimensionality to the exercises, although we note that d_f for the spanning cluster at p_c is different from that of a DLA cluster.

---

[32]It is also more efficient computationally than "harvesting" clusters as we did in Figure 7.33.

The fractal nature of the percolating cluster at p_c has many interesting consequences. For example, if we are modeling the mechanical properties of a porous material and the unoccupied sites are voids in the system, the strength will be strongly dependent on the connectivity of the spanning cluster. The flow of a fluid like water or oil through such a system would also be a sensitive function of the connectivity. Another interpretation is to suppose that the occupied sites are trees in a forest. If a fire is somehow set at one edge of the forest, we can use a percolating network to study how the fire will propagate into the forest. This can be modeled by assuming that all of the trees (that is, occupied sites) on one edge of the lattice are set to burn at time $t = 0$. At the next step all of the trees adjacent to a burning tree will themselves start to burn, while the trees burning at $t = 0$ will burn out. This process is then repeated; at step t_n the previously unburned trees that are adjacent to a burning tree will start to burn, and the trees burning at t_{n-1} will burn out.

It is instructive to calculate the time it takes for a fire to burn out completely . For small p the fires burn out quickly since the clusters of connected trees are on average very small. The only trees to burn will be those near the edge where the fire is lit, and most of the forest will be spared. For large p the fire burns across the system rapidly. Since essentially all of the trees are connected in this case, the number of time steps for a fire to burn-out is $\sim L$ where L is the size of the lattice, and nearly all of the trees will be engulfed. However, for p near p_c the fractal structure of the spanning cluster forces the fire to follow a tortuous path through the system, and the fire takes many time steps to burn out completely. Some results for the fire burn-out time are shown in Figure 7.35, which shows precisely this behavior. There is a large peak in the fire lifetime at p_c, which directly reflects the fractal connectivity of the critical cluster at p_c. If we were to study this peak as a function of lattice size (a task we will leave for the exercises), we would find that the burn-out time *diverges* for an infinitely large lattice. The nature of this divergence contains important information about the fractal nature of the critical cluster, a topic we will leave for the references. Our results also imply that a forest whose concentration of trees places it below p_c has a better chance of surviving a fire than a more concentrated forest.

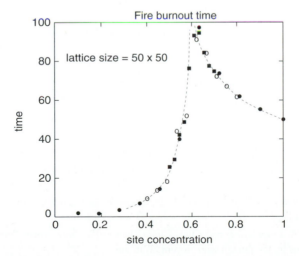

Figure 7.35:   Forest fire burn-out times for a 50×50 square lattice. The different symbols were obtained from independent simulations. All three simulations computed the average burn-out time for several forests of each size. The dashed curves are guides to the eye that suggest a singularity near $p_c \sim 0.593$.

Exercises

1. Use the cluster numbering scheme to calculate the critical concentration for percolation for a two-dimensional triangular lattice [a triangular lattice is one for which each site has 6 connected (nearest) neighbors]. Consider various lattice sizes up to 10×10 or 20×20 (whatever your computer can handle comfortably). You should find $p_c \approx 0.500$ in this case.

*2. Repeat the previous problem but use a three-dimensional simple cubic lattice. You should find $p_c \approx 0.312$. Comparing this with the value of p_c for a square lattice, we notice that for a given lattice type p_c becomes smaller as the dimensionality is increased. Give a qualitative argument to explain this trend.

3. In this section we discussed only the problem of *site* percolation, for which the lattice sites were occupied with a specified probability. We can also consider the problem of *bond* percolation, in which the links between sites are present with a probability p. Calculate the critical bond probability for percolation in a two-dimensional square lattice. Consider various lattice sizes up to 10×10 or 20×20 (whatever your computer can handle). You should find $p_c = 0.5$; can you give an argument to explain this value?

4. Consider the properties of the spanning cluster for a two dimensional square lattice at $p = p_c$. Generate such a cluster using the method discussed in connection with Figure 7.34. Use it to study diffusion by simulating a random walker that is restricted to stay on the cluster. Show that $< r^2 > \sim t^\alpha$, and calculate α (you should find a value close to 1.4 for a two-dimensional lattice). Also estimate the fractal dimensionality of the cluster. You should find a value of d_f, which is slightly smaller than 2 (the expected value is $91/48 \approx 1.90$).

5. Grow percolation clusters for $p \leq p_c$ and calculate the average cluster size, ξ. One way to estimate ξ is by calculating the average distance of particles in the cluster from the seed (the first occupied site). Show that ξ becomes very large at p_c (it actually diverges there), reflecting the infinite size of the spanning cluster.

*6. Calculate the burn-out time for $L \times L$ forests with different values of L. Show that the peak at p_c becomes larger as the forest is made bigger and try to extrapolate your results to estimate the burn-out time as a function of p for an infinite lattice. Hint: In making an extrapolation to the case $L \to \infty$ it is useful to plot things as a function of L^{-1} so that $L = \infty$ is on the graph.

References

BAKER, G. L. and J. P. GOLLUB. 1990. *Chaotic Dynamics*. Cambridge, 1990. Describes the chaotic behavior associated with several simple models. The logistic map equation has a form that is very similar to the random number generator (7.1).

BINDER, K., and D. W. HEERMANN. 1992. *Monte Carlo Simulation in Statistical Physics: An Introduction*, 2d ed. New York: Springer-Verlag.

MANDELBROT, B. B. 1977. *Fractals: Form, Chance, and Dimension*. New York: Freeman. An early and very readable book on fractals by the person who "invented" them.

MEAKIN, P. 1988. "The Growth of Fractal Aggregates and their Fractal Measure." In *Phase Transitions and Critical Phenomena* Vol. 12. C. Domb and J. L. Lebowitz, eds. Orlando: Academic Press. An extensive discussion of research on the growth of fractal clusters and their properties.

PRESS, W. H., B. P. FLANNERY, S. A. TEUKOLSKY, and W. T. VETTERLING. 1986. *Numerical Recipes*. Cambridge: Cambridge University Press. This book discusses the generation of random numbers along with numerous statistical tests.

REIF, F. 1965. *Fundamentals of Statistical and Thermal Physics*. New York: McGraw-Hill.

STAUFFER, D. 1984. *Introduction to Percolation Theory*. Bristol, PA: Taylor and Francis. 1985. A very entertaining book and an excellent introduction to the subject.

VOSS, R. F. 1984. "On 2D Percolation Clusters and on Multi-particle Fractal Aggregation." In *Kinetics of Aggregation and Gelation*, F. Family and D. P. Landau, eds. New York: Elsevier. A nice paper (and some nice pictures) illustrating how the fractal structure can depend on the growth rules.

8

Statistical Mechanics, Phase Transitions, and the Ising Model

In the early chapters of this book, all of our problems involved a small number of particles, often only one or two. It was only in Chapter 7 that we first considered many particle systems, and these led us to explore topics such as fractal clusters and percolation. The interesting behavior of multiparticle systems will be the central theme of this and the following chapter, where we consider systems in which the *interactions* between particles play a key role. In particular, we will see that systems of many interacting particles can exhibit a very important phenomenon known as a *phase transition*. Examples include the condensation of a gas into a liquid and the appearance of ferromagnetism in materials such as iron, so these transitions are quite common in nature. You should notice that both of these examples involve the concept of *temperature*, and this will lead us to consider issues in the realm of thermal and statistical physics.

In this chapter we will explore a stochastic approach in which the interaction of a system with its environment is simulated with the aid of a random number generator. This approach is known as the Monte Carlo method, and we will use it to study the Ising model of magnetism. Along the way we will review and illustrate some statistical mechanical ideas relating to phase transitions and the canonical ensemble, and observe a connection with the percolation phase transition that we studied in Chapter 7.

8.1 The Ising Model and Statistical Mechanics

Magnetism is an inherently quantum phenomena. It is interesting that Niels Bohr, one of the creators of quantum mechanics, made a seminal contribution to the field of magnetism. He showed that a classical system could never exhibit ferromagnetism. Quantum mechanics had not yet been invented when he proved this theorem, so in a sense the existence of ferromagnets such as iron is clear and compelling evidence that the world cannot be described in full by classical physics. A key ingredient in the theory

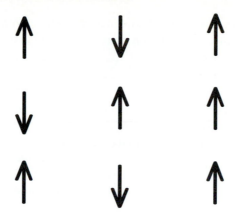

Figure 8.1:   Schematic spin model for a ferromagnet.

of magnetism is the electron's spin and the associated magnetic moment.[1] Ferromagnetism arises when a collection of such spins conspire so that all of their magnetic moments point in the same direction, yielding a total moment that is macroscopic in size.[2] A central issue in the study of ferromagnetism is to understand how the interaction between spins gives rise to this overall alignment. Since we also know that systems generally loose their magnetism at high temperatures,[3] we would also like to understand why and how the magnetic properties depend on temperature.

The model of a ferromagnet that we will consider is shown schematically in Figure 8.1. It consists of a collection of magnetic moments, which we denote by arrows and which we can think of as being atoms with spin $= \frac{1}{2}$ magnetic moments. For simplicity we assume that these spins are situated on a regular lattice. Since spin is a quantum mechanical phenomena, this is in a sense a quantum model. A fully quantum mechanical treatment of the model would require that we include all of the quantum rules for dealing with spin angular momentum, etc., in our simulations. It turns out that such a calculation would be extremely difficult, so we will not attempt it here.[4] We will instead make a few simplifications. Much work in this field has shown that despite the simplifications we are about to make, our model does capture the essential physics of magnetism.

We will assume that each spin is able to point along either $+z$ or $-z$; that is, either up or down. *No* other orientation is permitted. Hence, the ith spin in the system can have one of only two possible values, which for convenience[5] we take to be $s_i = \pm 1$. Each of these so-called Ising spins interacts with other spins in the lattice; in a ferromagnet this interaction will favor parallel alignment of pairs of spins. In a real magnetic material the interaction will be largest between spins that are nearest neighbors

---

[1]There can also be a contribution to the total magnetic moment from the orbital angular momentum, but for simplicity we will refer to the moment as if it were due solely to spin. This is not a crucial or limiting assumption, but will make our treatment (mainly the terminology), which is aimed at so-called local moment systems, a bit simpler. The more challenging problem of magnetism in a metal is too much for us to tackle here.

[2]Assuming, of course, that there are a macroscopic number of electrons, as in a typical solid.

[3]For example, iron is no longer a ferromagnet above about 1000 K.

[4]The study of quantum spin models is an active area of current research.

[5]We could instead let the values be $\pm \frac{1}{2}$, but that would only amount to a rescaling of the exchange constant in (8.1).

and fall off rapidly with increasing separation between the two spins. With this motivation, the simplest Ising model assumes an interaction only between nearest neighbors so that the energy of the system is

$$E = -J \sum_{<ij>} s_i \, s_j \,, \tag{8.1}$$

where the sum is over all pairs of nearest neighbor spins $< i, j >$, and J is known as the exchange constant, which we will assume to be positive. It is useful to imagine that the spin system is in a particular state, corresponding to a particular arrangement of the individual spins (particular values of the spin variables s_i). Equation (8.1) is then the energy of this particular state of the entire system. The energy function (8.1), together with the description of an Ising spin given above, serves to define the Ising model. It was first conceived by Wilhelm Lenz who suggested it as the Ph.D. topic for his graduate student Ernst Ising in the 1920s.

Before proceeding to a quantitative treatment of the Ising model, it is useful to first anticipate the qualitative behavior we will find and, in the process, give a quick review of statistical mechanics. According to the energy function (8.1), two neighboring spins will have an energy of interaction $-J$ if they point in the same direction and $+J$ if they are antiparallel. Since J is assumed positive, the interactions favor *parallel* alignment of neighboring spins. If each spin is parallel to its neighbors, then *every* spin in the lattice will be parallel to every other spin. Such alignment of all of the magnetic moments would lead to a nonzero magnetic moment for the system and thus yield a ferromagnet. A system that has a magnetic moment in the absence of a magnetic field is said to have a spontaneous magnetization.

While the energy of the spin system is lowest if all of the spins are parallel to one another, the disordering effect of temperature must also be considered. We will assume that our spin system is in equilibrium with a heat bath at temperature T, so that the behavior is described by the canonical ensemble. For an introductory discussion of the canonical ensemble see Reif (1965). One way to view this is that over time different spins flip back and forth, and the system will thereby "move" into different spin configurations. The behavior observed in an experimental measurement will depend on how much time the system spends in the different possible spin configurations. It is a fundamental result of statistical mechanics that for a system in equilibrium with a heat bath, the probability of finding the system in any particular state is proportional to the Boltzmann factor

$$P_\alpha \sim e^{-E_\alpha / k_B T} \,, \tag{8.2}$$

where E_α is the energy of state α (not to be confused with spin i) as calculated from (8.1), k_B is Boltzmann's constant, and P_α is the probability of finding the system in state α. Each of these states is a particular configuration of spins, which we will refer to as a *microstate* of the system. If we have a lattice containing N Ising spins, each spin can be in either of two states, so there are 2^N different possible microstates of the system as a whole. We will be most interested in systems for which N is large, so the number of microstates will be very large. This will make the problem difficult to solve, but will also lead to some interesting behavior.

From a microscopic point of view, it is the interaction of the spin system with a heat bath that causes the system to undergo transitions from one microstate to another. Individual spins flip from $+1$ to -1 or vice versa, as they gain energy from, or loose energy to, the heat bath. A macroscopic measurement of a quantity such as the total magnetic moment (which we will also refer to as the magnetization[6]) effectively averages over the many microstates that the system visits during the course of a measurement. In order to calculate the macroscopic behavior we, therefore, need to calculate the probabilities P_α of finding the system in its various microstates.

For example, the magnetic moment of a microstate M_α is the sum of the values of s_j for all of the spins in that particular state. The *measured* magnetization of the system will then be

$$M = \sum_\alpha M_\alpha P_\alpha , \qquad (8.3)$$

where $M_\alpha = \sum s_j$, with the values of the spin variables in this sum corresponding to the spin directions in microstate α. Similarly, other properties can be expressed in terms of the probabilities P_α. This should all be familiar to you from statistical mechanics and can be is reviewed by reading the references at the end of this chapter.

In the next few sections we will consider how to calculate quantities such as the magnetization and other properties of our spin system. This calculation is made difficult by the large number of microstates. We noted already that for an Ising system with N spins there will be 2^N states, and we will be interested in systems for which $N \to \infty$, so the number of states will be very large indeed.[7] Analytic approaches have proved very formidable, and only a relatively few exact results are known for these systems. This makes simulations very attractive for this problem.[8]

Before we move on to calculate the properties of our spin system, it is useful to put the model itself into perspective. In the past few paragraphs we have introduced an *extremely* simple spin model. Many other spin models have been introduced and studied. For example, we can let the spins be fixed-length vectors that are free to rotate either in a plane (the so-called XY model), or in three dimensions (the Heisenberg model).[9] It is also interesting to consider the effect of increasing the range of the interactions between spins. That is, we can let spins that are second, third, or more distant nearest neighbors interact. In addition, there is the possibility that a real spin system might have to be treated quantum mechanically, and this makes our job even more challenging. All of these models of magnetism exhibit interesting properties and have been studied extensively over the past 50 years or so. Among other things, this work has shown that the simple Ising model captures many of the essential features of the phase transition to the ferromagnetic state. This makes it ideal for studying phase transitions. Readers who want stiffer challenges can find them in the references.

8.2   Mean-Field Theory

In this section we consider a very useful *approximate* approach for calculating the properties of a spin system. We will use it to introduce and illustrate several interesting features of the phase transition, along with some useful numerical techniques. While the calculational method explored here is a useful

---

[6]Although strictly speaking the magnetization is the magnetic moment per unit volume, we can assume that our system has unit volume so that these two quantities are equal.

[7]When dealing with a sum involving such a large number of terms, it is sometimes possible to ignore many of the terms because they are small. However, it turns out that near a phase transition such a simplification does not occur. Essentially *all* of the terms are important in that case.

[8]A number of very powerful approximate analytic methods have also been developed, as described in the references. We certainly don't want to give the impression that numerical simulations are the only useful way to attack this problem.

[9]Physicists have also been led to consider spin vectors with more than three and less than one components!

qualitative tool for the study of phase transitions, its results are not quantitatively accurate, so we will revisit some of the same issues and problems when we consider another approach later in this chapter.

The magnetization is closely related to the average spin alignment $< s_i >$, where the angular brackets denote a thermal average. It is useful to think of this as a time average for a system in thermal equilibrium with a heat bath.[10] As described in Section 8.1, the interaction with the heat bath causes spins to flip from $+1$ to -1 and vice versa. A thermal average is an average with respect to the different microstates that are generated by these spin flips. For an infinitely large system the spins will all have the same average alignment. This can be seen by noticing that the spins are all equivalent in the sense that each one interacts with four nearest neighbors and (in this idealized case) each is infinitely far from any boundaries. Hence all spins must have the same *average* properties. The total magnetization at temperature T for a system of N spins will then be

$$ M = \sum_i < s_i > = N < s_i > , \tag{8.4} $$

where in the last term we can use any value of i that is convenient, since we have argued that all spins are equivalent. Thus if we can calculate $< s_i >$, we immediately have M as well. An exact computation of $< s_i >$ would require the probabilities of all possible microstates, the P_α terms in (8.2). This is a formidable task (which we will take up in the next section), so we consider here an approximate alternative known as mean-field theory.

If we add a magnetic field to the problem, the energy function becomes

$$ E = -J \sum_{<ij>} s_i s_j - \mu H \sum_i s_i , \tag{8.5} $$

where H is the magnetic field and μ is the magnetic moment associated with each spin [compare with (8.1)]. This field will tend to make the spins orient themselves parallel to H, since this lowers the energy. To obtain the mean-field approximation we first assume that our system contains just a single spin, s_i, so that the only energy involved is the field energy. A single spin has two possible states, $s_i = \pm 1$, whose energies are $E_\pm = \mp \mu H$. The probabilities of finding the "system" in these two states $P_\pm$ are given by (8.2) as

$$ P_+ = C\, e^{+\mu H / k_B T} , \tag{8.6} $$
$$ P_- = C\, e^{-\mu H / k_B T} , $$

where C is a coefficient that can be determined by requiring that the two probabilities add up to unity. This yields

$$ C = \frac{1}{e^{+\mu H / k_B T} + e^{-\mu H / k_B T}} . \tag{8.7} $$

The thermal average of s_i can then be calculated as

$$ < s_i > = \sum_{s_i = \pm 1} s_i\, P_\pm = P_+ - P_- = \tanh(\mu H / k_B T) . \tag{8.8} $$

---

[10]The problem of time averages is at the heart of the ergodic hypothesis, which we discussed in Chapter 7.

This is the exact result for the behavior of a single spin in a magnetic field. We now use it to obtain an *approximate* solution for a system of N interacting spins. The mean-field approximation is based on the *assumption* that the interaction of a spin s_i with its neighboring spins, which is what yields the first term on the right-hand side of (8.5), is equivalent to an *effective* magnetic field acting on s_i. The result for $< s_i >$ can then be calculated using (8.8), with H replaced by the effective field, H_{eff}. It remains for us to estimate H_{eff}.

The energy function (8.5) can be rewritten in the suggestive form

$$ E = - \left(J \sum_{<ij>} s_j \right) s_i - \mu H s_i , \tag{8.9} $$

which shows that the term involving J (which describes the interaction of s_i with its neighbors) has the form of a magnetic field with $\mu H_{\text{eff}} = J \sum s_j$. Now comes the approximation. We assume that the spin variables s_j in this expression for H_{eff} can be replaced by their thermal averages. Since all of the spins have the same average alignment, their thermal average values will all be the same. Denoting this by $< s >$ (since we can now drop the subscripts) and assuming that the "true" externally applied field $H = 0$, we have

$$ H_{\text{eff}} = \frac{J}{\mu} \sum < s > = \frac{z J}{\mu} < s >, \tag{8.10} $$

where z is the number of nearest neighbors. Combining this with (8.8) leads to the result

$$ < s > = \tanh(z J < s > / k_B T) . \tag{8.11} $$

This is an *implicit* relation for $< s >$, which cannot be solved analytically except in certain limits, such as when $< s >$ is small, as we will discuss in a moment. We therefore consider a numerical approach. To illustrate the nature of the problem, Figure 8.2 shows a schematic plot of the two sides of (8.11), both as functions of $< s >$. The value(s) of $< s >$, at which the two curves intersect, are the solutions we are after, since intersection is just a graphical way of expressing the equality (8.11). There is always a solution at $< s > = 0$ corresponding to the thermal average with zero magnetization. This is usually referred to as the *paramagnetic phase*. There is a second solution[11] at low temperatures where the function $\tanh(z J < s > / k_B T)$ has an initial slope that is larger than $< s >$. This solution has $< s > \neq 0$ and thus corresponds to a phase with a nonzero magnetization; this is the ferromagnetic state. Furthermore, the solution with $< s > \neq 0$ has a lower free energy[12] than the one with $< s > = 0$, so mean-field theory predicts that the system is indeed ferromagnetic at low temperatures. Our next job is to calculate this solution, that is, to find $< s >$ as a function of temperature.

One of the simplest ways to solve (8.11) is with a relaxation method. We start with an initial guess for the solution, s_0, indicated schematically by a filled circle in Figure 8.2. This is inserted into the right-hand side of (8.11) and used to compute an improved guess $s_1 = \tanh(z J s_0 / k_B T)$. At low temperatures this corresponds to moving upward in the figure, along the dotted arrow to the tanh curve. Moving to where this improved guess lies on the $< s >$ line then takes us horizontally to the next solid dot. From here we insert s_1 into the right-hand side of (8.11) to obtain s_2, etc. The process is iterated

---

[11] There are actually three solutions in this case, since if $< s > = +s_0$ is a solution, then $< s > = -s_0$ is one also.

[12] We know from statistical mechanics that the system will always assume a state with the lowest possible free energy.

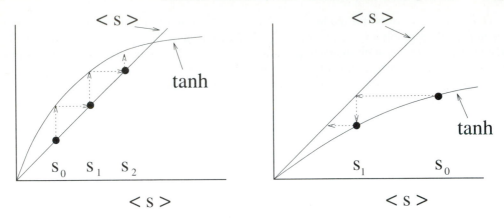

Figure 8.2:   Basis of the relaxation method for solving the mean-field equation. Left: for low temperatures the function $\tanh(zJ < s > /k_B T)$ has a larger initial slope than $< s >$. Right: at high temperatures the tanh function has a smaller initial slope.

until consecutive values of s_n differ by a sufficiently small amount, which means that we have reached the neighborhood where the two curves in Figure 8.2 intersect. Note that this procedure converges to the solution with $< s > \neq 0$ at low temperatures, and the one at $< s > = 0$ at high temperatures, as shown on the right side of Figure 8.2. This approach is in precisely the same spirit as the relaxation method we employed in our work on Laplace's equation in Chapter 5. While Figure 8.2 demonstrates that the method does indeed converge, it does not tell us how fast a solution will be reached. We will consider the speed of convergence shortly.

The mean-field solution for $< s >$ as a function of temperature obtained using the relaxation method is shown in Figure 8.3. Since the magnetization is proportional to $< s >$ there is a spontaneous magnetization $M > 0$ at low temperatures, that is, the system is ferromagnetic. At high temperatures the disordering effect of temperature dominates, and the system is paramagnetic with $M = 0$. The transition between these two phases is abrupt, occurring at what is known as the critical temperature, T_c. Mean field theory predicts that $T_c = 4$ in this case (that is, taking $J/k_B = 1$).

This is an example of a second order phase transition and has some important features in common with the percolation transition studied in Chapter 7. The spontaneous magnetization is what is known as the *order parameter* for this transition; roughly speaking, it tells what phase the system is in. Here a nonzero value of the order parameter M is found when the system is in the ferromagnetic phase, while $M = 0$ means that it is paramagnetic. The results in Figure 8.3 suggest that M vanishes in a singular manner at T_c, as the slope dM/dT becomes extremely large as $T \to T_c$. The form of this singularity can be obtained analytically using the fact that $\tanh(x) \approx x - x^3/3$ for small x. Thus, when $< s >$ is small (8.11) becomes

$$< s > \approx \frac{zJ < s >}{k_B T} - \frac{1}{3}\left(\frac{zJ < s >}{k_B T}\right)^3 , \tag{8.12}$$

which has the solutions $< s > = 0$ and

$$< s > = \sqrt{\frac{3}{T}\left(\frac{k_B T}{zJ}\right)^3}\left(\frac{zJ}{k_B} - T\right)^{1/2} \sim (T_c - T)^\beta , \tag{8.13}$$

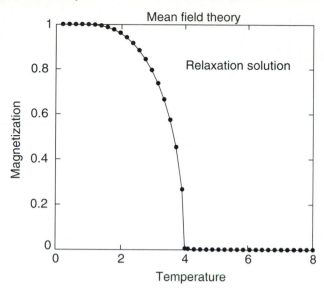

Figure 8.3:   Solution of the mean-field equation (8.11) using the relaxation method. Here we have taken $J/k_B = 1$ and $z = 4$ corresponding to the number of nearest neighbors in a square lattice.

where in the last step we have made the identification $T_c = zJ/k_B$ ($= 4$ for our choice of J, in agreement with the numerical results in Figure 8.3) and $\beta = 1/2$. The parameter β is a *critical exponent*. This behavior is analogous to what we observed near the percolation transition.[13] A second-order phase transition is characterized by power law behavior of many properties. We will describe the power law singularities associated with several quantities in the next section, where we will introduce the Monte Carlo method for calculating the behavior. It will turn out that while mean-field theory does lead to the correct power law form for $< s >$, the value of the critical exponent β predicted by mean-field theory is not correct. However, before we proceed to those issues it is worth using the mean-field approach to study the relaxation method in a little more detail.

You can see from Figure 8.2 that this method will always converge to a solution of (8.11). Near T_c the two curves $< s >$ and $\tanh(zJ < s > /k_BT)$, whose points of intersection we want to find, will have nearly the same slope. This will cause the convergence to be extremely slow, as each iteration will move only a very small distance along the $< s >$ axis. It is, therefore, useful to consider ways to speed up the convergence.

One way to accomplish this is to begin by rewriting (8.11) as

$$f(< s >) \equiv < s > - \tanh(zJ < s > /k_BT) = 0 . \tag{8.14}$$

We thus need to find the roots of the function $f(< s >)$. This is a problem that arises in many contexts, so we now consider a general approach. In Figure 8.4 we show a hypothetical function, $f(x)$. To find a root, that is, a value of x for which $f(x) = 0$, we begin with an initial guess for the solution, x_0. In order

---

[13] In that case the fraction of sites in the spanning cluster played the role of the order parameter.

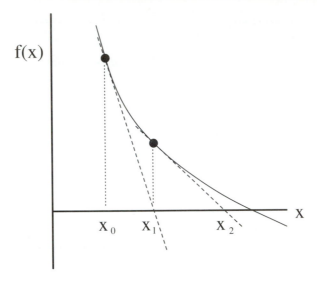

Figure 8.4: Solution of the mean-field equation using Newton's method. Starting at x_0 we extrapolate linearly, using the slope of the function at x_0 to construct the dashed line that is tangent to the curve at this point. This dashed line intersects the x axis at x_1, which becomes our new approximation for the root. The process is then repeated to obtain an improved approximation x_2.

to obtain an improved guess we evaluate the derivative of $f(x)$ at x_0 and use it to extrapolate linearly to the x axis, as indicated by the dashed line that intersects the axis at x_1. If $f(x)$ was a straight line this procedure would yield the exact solution. In most cases however, the curvature will not be zero, so x_1 may not be a sufficiently accurate approximation. However, we can repeat the process starting from x_1 to obtain a better approximation x_2, etc.

This approach is known as Newton's method and is usually superior to the relaxation algorithm since it makes use of the slope of $f(x)$. We can use it to solve the mean-field equation (8.14), and the results for M are identical to those shown in Figure 8.3 so we haven't bothered to plot them here.[14] More interesting is the number of iterations required to obtain convergence. In Figure 8.5 we compare the number of iterations required by the relaxation method with the number needed by Newton's method for our mean-field problem. As anticipated, the relaxation method converges very slowly near T_c where the number of required iterations (for a given desired accuracy) becomes very large. Newton's method requires far fewer iterations at all temperatures, especially near T_c.

Exercises

1. Solve the mean-field equation (8.11) numerically using either the relaxation approach or Newton's method. Compare the results near T_c with the analytic result (8.13).

---

[14]One important aspect of implementing Newton's method is how we evaluate the derivative of $f(x)$. In this example we evaluated this derivative numerically (using finite differences), but this is not always the best approach. If possible, it is best to compute the derivative analytically, an option we could have taken in this case. For more on this and other algorithms for finding roots we refer the reader to Press et al. (1986).

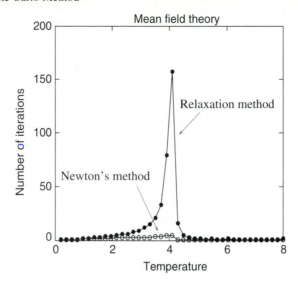

Figure 8.5: Number of iterations required to solve the mean-field equation (8.11) with a convergence criteria of $\delta < s > = 10^{-3}$, where $\delta < s >$ is the change in $< s >$ from one iteration to the next. Solid symbols: relaxation method; open symbols: Newton's method.

2. At low temperatures the tanh function in (8.11) can be expanded to yield an analytic result for $< s >$ in the limit of small T. Do this, and compare it with the numerical solution.

8.3   The Monte Carlo Method

We have already remarked that mean-field theory predicts there will be an abrupt transition between the ferromagnetic and the paramagnetic phases of the Ising model. We also noted that while the mean-field approximation is correct in predicting singular behavior [usually power laws such as (8.13)] near T_c, it generally does not yield correct values of the critical exponents. A more powerful approach is required to get a quantitatively accurate picture of the behavior, especially near a phase transition. In this section we consider one such approach, which is known as the Monte Carlo method. Rather than beginning with an abstract definition of the method, we will instead describe how it works in practice. After having gained some perspective on its operation, we will then discuss why it works.

Our goal is to simulate how a spin system interacts with its environment; in the language of statistical physics the environment is often termed a *heat bath*. We will consider the particular case of a collection of Ising spins, but the method can readily be extended to deal with more complicated situations.[15] According to statistical mechanics, the role of a heat bath is to exchange energy with the spin system and thereby bring it into equilibrium at some temperature T. As the system gains energy from, or looses energy to, the bath, spins are flipped causing the system to move to new microscopic states. Each of these microstates corresponds to a *particular* arrangement of the spins. The measured

---

[15] While our treatment here makes use of the canonical ensemble, it can also be modified to apply to the microcanonical ensemble. If you are not familiar with these statistical ensembles, see Reif (1965).

values of quantities such as the magnetization then depend on the probabilities of finding the system in its different microstates.

The Monte Carlo method uses a stochastic approach to simulate the exchange of energy between the spin system and the heat bath. We begin with the system in a particular microstate as illustrated schematically in Figure 8.1. The interaction with the bath is then modeled as follows. A spin is chosen[16] and the energy required to make it flip, E_{flip}, is calculated. For our Ising model this energy is calculated using (8.1). If E_{flip} is negative (so that the energy would be lowered by reversing the spin), the spin is flipped and the system moves into a different microstate. If E_{flip} is positive (so that the energy of the system would be increased), a decision must be made. A random number that is distributed uniformly in the range between 0 and 1 is generated and compared to the Boltzmann factor $\exp(-E_{\text{flip}}/k_B T)$. If this Boltzmann factor is larger than the random number, the spin is flipped, otherwise the spin is left undisturbed. Hence, in this case, the system may or may not move to a different microstate, depending on the value of the random number. This completes one Monte Carlo time step. Another spin is then chosen, E_{flip} is calculated, and the spin is either flipped or left unchanged according to the algorithm just described.

This procedure is repeated a large number of times, so that every spin is given many chances to flip. We can view each Monte Carlo time step as one interaction with the heat bath. The effect of this interaction varies according to the temperature, since T enters through the Boltzmann factor probability for flipping a spin. Let us now consider why this Monte Carlo algorithm correctly mimics the interaction with a heat bath. As we noted above, a chosen spin is *always* flipped when $E_{\text{flip}} < 0$, that is, when it would *lower* the energy of the system. If this were the only flipping criteria, the system would rapidly move to the state with lowest energy,[17] which for our model is a microstate with all spins parallel to each other, the ferromagnetic state. However, we must also allow for transitions to states of *higher* energy, whose probabilities should be governed by the Boltzmann factor $\exp(-E_{\text{flip}}/k_B T)$ with $E_{\text{flip}} > 0$. At low temperatures this factor is small, so the probability of flipping a spin to a higher energy state is very low. Hence, at low temperatures the system will usually be found in a microstate that is very close to the fully aligned state (the state with the lowest energy). That is, the system will be ferromagnetic, although M will not have the value corresponding to complete alignment. At high temperatures the Boltzmann factors will not be as close to zero, so the probability for flipping to a higher energy state will be quite significant. Indeed, as T becomes very large the Boltzmann exponential factor will approach 1, and this will make the spin arrangement tend toward complete randomness. This is the paramagnetic state.

These arguments show that the Monte Carlo flipping procedure gives the correct qualitative picture in both the high- and low-temperature limits. Let us now consider things quantitatively. A Monte Carlo spin flip connects two microstates; let us call their energies E_1 and E_2 and assume that $E_1 > E_2$. If the system is in state 1, the flipping rules specify the probability for flipping the selected spin during a given time step, hence the *rate* of transitions from state 1 to state 2. We will call this rate $W(1 \rightarrow 2)$ and since by assumption $E_1 > E_2$, the rules tell us that $W(1 \rightarrow 2) = 1$. Likewise, if the system is in state 2, the probability of a Monte Carlo transition to state 1 during the next time step is $W(2 \rightarrow 1) = \exp[-(E_1 - E_2)/k_B T]$, since $E_{\text{flip}} = E_1 - E_2 > 0$. When our system reaches thermal equilibrium the probability of finding it in any particular state will, on average, be independent

---

[16]The spin can be chosen either at random or by stepping systematically through the lattice.

[17]Assuming that this ground state can be reached by flipping one spin at a time. We will not worry here about possible complications associated with metastable states, although they may be important in practice, as we will see later in this chapter.

of time, so we expect that the number of transitions from state 1 to state 2 must be equal to the number of transitions in the reverse direction. The number of transitions of a particular kind is proportional to the product of the transition rate W and the probability of the system being found in the appropriate initial state. Equating the number of transitions $1 \rightarrow 2$ and $2 \rightarrow 1$ then gives

$$P_1 \, W(1 \rightarrow 2) \;=\; P_2 \, W(2 \rightarrow 1) \,, \tag{8.15}$$

where P_1 and P_2 are the probabilities of the system being found in these two microstates. Inserting our results for the W factors we find

$$\frac{P_1}{P_2} \;=\; \exp\left[-(E_1 - E_2)/k_B T\right] \,. \tag{8.16}$$

Comparing this behavior with (8.2) we see that this is precisely what is expected for a system in thermal equilibrium. The Monte Carlo algorithm thus leads to a situation in which the relative probabilities of being found in different microstates are given by the correct Boltzmann factors. Assuming that all of the microstates are accessible via the flipping rules, this procedure will indeed simulate a system in contact with a heat bath.

   This concludes our brief introduction to the Monte Carlo method. In the next two sections we will use it to study the behavior of the Ising model and investigate phase transitions in that system. However, before moving on we should make a few further comments about the method. First, while we have described how it can be used to simulate a spin system in equilibrium with a heat bath, this method is not restricted to spin systems. *Any* system can be studied in this way. All that is needed is some way of enumerating the microstates and an expression for the energy of each of these states, so that the appropriate flipping rules, that is, transition rules, can be formulated. Second, a system in equilibrium with a heat bath is described by what is known as the canonical ensemble. It is also possible to modify the flipping rules so that the Monte Carlo method simulates either the microcanonical or the grand canonical ensemble, but this is more than we want to tackle here.

8.4   The Ising Model and Second-Order Phase Transitions

We are now ready to apply the Monte Carlo method to the study of phase transitions in the Ising model. We will encounter two types of transitions, which are classified as first order and second order. Rather than try to give a completely general definition of these classifications and all that they entail, we will illustrate them by example in this and the following section.

   Our model is again a collection of Ising spins arranged on a square lattice as illustrated in Figure 8.1. The spins interact with each other and with a magnetic field according to the energy function (8.5). We begin by considering only the case with $H = 0$, leaving the behavior as a function of field to the next section. For convenience we measure energy in units of k_B and take $J = 1$, so that T is effectively unitless.

   We have already considered the mean-field solution for the spontaneous magnetization, see Figure 8.3, so our first goal will be to compare the Monte Carlo results with that prediction. The construction of a Monte Carlo program for the Ising model presents no new programming challenges, so we will not discuss it in great detail here (we will say a little more in the exercises; also, a listing of such a program is given in Appendix 4). The calculation consists of using the Monte Carlo rules described in Section 8.3 to simulate the spin system over the course of many Monte Carlo time steps.

During each step we choose a spin, calculate the energy that would be required to flip it according to (8.5), and then either flip it or leave it unchanged, depending on how the Boltzmann factor compares to a random number that is uniformly distributed in the range 0–1. In our program we use two loops to choose spins systematically by moving along successive rows of the lattice. We could also choose spins at random, but so long as many time steps are considered so that each spin has many opportunities to flip, the results do not depend on how the spins are chosen. After each complete pass through the lattice we compute the total magnetic moment $M = \sum s_i$ and total energy [according to (8.5)]. We then average M and E over many passes through the lattice to obtain the values appropriate for thermal equilibrium.

Ideally we would like to calculate the behavior of very large systems. A real magnet, such as a piece of iron, would usually contain a large number of spins (of order 10^{23}), and one of our goals is to understand the behavior of a real system. Moreover, it will turn out that the phase transitions described above occur only in the limit of very large systems. However, the computer time required for an accurate simulation will limit us to lattices that contain no more than $\sim 10^3$ spins. For such a finite system the behavior of spins at the edges can have a pronounced effect.

With a square lattice these edge spins have only three nearest-neighbor spins, or two if they are at a corner, as compared to four neighbors for the interior spins. Since it is the exchange interaction (8.1) that causes neighboring spin to tend to point in the same direction, and since the edge spins have fewer neighbors, the spins at the edges of the lattice will have less of a tendency to align with the other spins. While real systems will also have edge spins, the *fraction* of spins at the edges, as compared to the number in the interior, will be much greater for a small lattice. Hence, it is important in our simulations to minimize the effects of the edges as much as possible. One way to accomplish this is to use *periodic boundary conditions* as illustrated in Figure 8.6. In our original description of the Ising model we specified that spins interact only with their nearest neighbors. Now we assume that a spin on the edge interacts also with the spin on the *opposite* edge of the lattice, as indicated by the dotted lines that wrap around the lattice. Alternatively we could imagine that our lattice is situated on a torus so that these "edge" spins are really neighbors of each other. In either case we have, in a sense, eliminated all of the edge spins. *Every* spin now has four nearest neighbors so that all spins are in equivalent locations. The

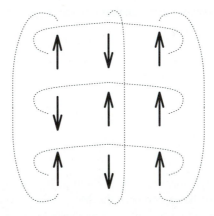

Figure 8.6:   Ising model with periodic boundary conditions. Spins that are connected by the dotted lines that wrap around the lattice are considered to be nearest neighbors and thus to interact with exchange energy J.

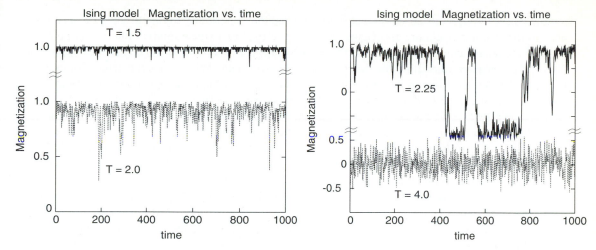

Figure 8.7:   Magnetization versus time for the Ising model on a 10×10 square lattice at several different temperatures. Note that we have normalized the magnetization so that $M = 1$ corresponds to complete alignment of all of the spins. Left: at relatively low temperatures compared to T_c, with the results for $T = 1.5$ offset upwards for clarity; right: at temperatures near and above T_c (the two results are again offset for clarity).

use of periodic boundary conditions thus allows us to largely circumvent boundary effects. However, this does *not* mean that a 5×5 lattice with periodic boundary conditions will behave in the same way as a much larger lattice. For an $L \times L$ lattice with periodic boundary conditions the distance between two spins cannot be larger than $L/\sqrt{2}$ lattice spacings, the maximum separation along a diagonal. Precisely why this is important will be discussed below.

Periodic boundary conditions are often used in Monte Carlo simulations and in many other types of calculations, but they are certainly not the only boundary conditions that we can imagine. We could instead choose *free boundary conditions* in which the spin system simply terminates at the edges, or *fixed boundary conditions* in which the spins at one edge are all constrained to point in a certain direction. For our work in this and the next section we will employ periodic boundary conditions, as these will tend to minimize the effects of finite lattice size. However, as mentioned above, this will not completely eliminate such effects. The best way to calculate the properties of a very large system is to perform simulations on a number of lattices of different sizes, and to then extrapolate to the infinite lattice limit. We will not have occasion to do this in any detail in our calculations here, but this procedure will be explored in the exercises and is described in the references.

For our simulations we begin at low temperatures where we know that the system will be in the ferromagnetic state. We, therefore, choose an initial spin configuration with all spins along the positive direction, that is, the fully aligned state, and use the Monte Carlo procedure to calculate the magnetization as a function of Monte Carlo time as the simulation proceeds. Some results for a 10×10 lattice at several temperatures are shown in Figure 8.7. Here one unit of time[18] corresponds to one

---

[18]This measure of time is solely a product of the Monte Carlo method and is not related to real time, since the Monte Carlo algorithm does not employ the microscopic equations of motion.

complete pass through the lattice, so that every spin had the opportunity to flip once during each time step. At the lowest temperature the magnetization stays very close to the saturation value corresponding to all of the spins being parallel. While the Monte Carlo rules do lead to the occasional flipping of a spin to the negative direction, the fluctuations in M are small. When the temperature is raised to $T = 2.0$, the average value of M decreases to a value corresponding to about 90 percent of the fully aligned value, since the Boltzmann factor at this temperature favors a spin flip to the higher energy state of order 10 percent of the time. Our system is still ferromagnetic, but the degree of order is reduced from its value at lower temperatures. In addition, the magnitude of the *fluctuations* increases significantly. These fluctuations are important for several reasons. First, we will see shortly how they can be used together with the *fluctuation-dissipation* relation of statistical mechanics to calculate several other thermodynamic quantities. Second and more importantly, these enhanced fluctuations signal that we are approaching a second order phase transition, also known as a *critical point*. A system at its critical point is extremely sensitive to small perturbations, as its properties change very rapidly in response to changes in temperature, magnetic field, etc. We will see that these fluctuations are intimately related to the singularities at T_c.

When we warm further to $T = 2.25$ the fluctuations become larger, as the system fluctuates between values as large as $M \sim \pm 0.8$. Hence, there are fluctuations in which the magnetic moment of the *entire* system changes direction.[19] For the Ising model on a square lattice, exact analytic calculations yield the result $T_c = 2/\ln(1 + \sqrt{2}) \approx 2.27$, so we are very close to the critical point.[20] Proceeding to higher temperatures, we find that at $T = 4$ the fluctuations decrease in magnitude and are centered around $M \sim 0$. We are now well above T_c, in the paramagnetic phase. Comparing the behavior at different temperatures we see that the fluctuations are largest near T_c. We will analyze them in more detail shortly.

From the simulations at different temperatures we can calculate the average values of M over time to obtain the magnetization as a function of T, and some results are shown in Figure 8.8. While there is some scatter in the results due to the statistical errors associated with averaging data like that in Figure 8.7, M drops precipitously to zero at a value of T, which is consistent with the exactly known value of the critical temperature as just mentioned ($T_c \approx 2.27$). The overall quality of these results could be improved in several ways. First, we could simply let the simulations run longer so that more Monte Carlo steps are employed in the averaging at each temperature. This would reduce the statistical errors at a rate roughly proportional to $N_{\text{steps}}^{-1/2}$, where N_{steps} is the number of Monte Carlo time steps used in the calculation.[21] Second, we could study the behavior of larger lattices and extrapolate to the infinite lattice limit. We will leave these tasks to the exercises.

It is interesting to compare the Monte Carlo results for M with the prediction of mean-field theory, Figure 8.3. While the two results have the same the qualitative form, mean-field theory overestimates T_c by nearly a factor of 2. In addition, the mean-field prediction for M goes to zero at T_c somewhat more gradually than we find from the Monte Carlo results. As we have already mentioned, the variation of M near T_c is determined by the critical exponent β according to

$$M \sim (T_c - T)^\beta . \tag{8.17}$$

---

[19]The probability for such complete flips decreases as the system is made larger.

[20]This exact value is much lower than the mean-field estimate that we derived earlier.

[21]This should remind you of our discussion of averaging and the central-limit theorem in Chapter 7. While this estimate of the Monte Carlo uncertainty is qualitatively correct, there are some subtleties associated with long correlation times near T_c, which we will leave to the references (Binder and Heermann [1992] and Stanley [1971]).

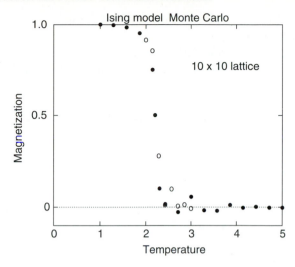

Figure 8.8: Spontaneous magnetization as a function of temperature for the Ising model on a 10×10 square lattice. The different symbols show results for two separate simulations. At each temperature M was obtained by averaging over 1000 passes through the lattice.

Mean-field theory predicts $\beta = 1/2$, while the exact (analytic) result in two dimensions is $\beta = 1/8$. The Monte Carlo results in Figure 8.8 would not yield a terribly precise value of β (we'll discuss how to do a reasonable job of this in the exercises), but they are in much better agreement with the exact value than with mean-field theory. Large scale Monte Carlo simulations (see the references) yield a value of β, which has an uncertainty of less than 1 percent, and which agrees well with the analytic result. Hence, while mean-field theory yields a reasonable qualitative picture for the behavior, the quantitative details are not correct. We will consider where mean field theory goes wrong in a moment.

So far the only property we have considered is the magnetization, but much can be learned from the examination of other quantities. In Figure 8.9 we show the variation of the energy with temperature. This was obtained from the same simulations used to calculate M; after each Monte Carlo pass through the lattice our program recorded E [calculated using (8.5)]. At low temperatures, with the spins fully aligned, every spin has an interaction energy of $-J$ with each of its four nearest neighbors. The total energy at $T = 0$ should thus be $-4NJ/2$, where N is the number of spins and the factor of 2 is inserted since we have counted each pair of spins twice. The Monte Carlo results are in good agreement with this result in the limit $T \to 0$. On the other hand, at very high temperatures the spins will be randomly oriented, so on average each spin will have two neighbors that are aligned parallel and two that are antiparallel. The thermal average of the total energy in this limit will thus be zero. While the results in Figure 8.9 are tending toward $< E > = 0$ at high temperatures,[22] they are substantially below this value even at $T = 5$, which is more than twice the critical temperature. This implies that the neighbors of any particular spin are *not* randomly oriented above T_c, even though we know through the results for M that the average alignment of the entire lattice is zero. This indicates that the orientations of neighboring spins are *correlated*, which will turn out to be very important.

---

[22]The angular brackets again denote a thermal average.

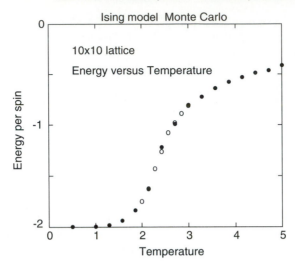

Figure 8.9: Thermal average of the energy versus temperature for the Ising model on a 10×10 square lattice. These results were obtained in the simulations used to calculate M in Figure 8.8. Note that $J = 1$ for this simulation and that we normalized $< E >$ to obtain the energy per spin, $< E > /N$. In the low-temperature (fully aligned) limit, we argued that $< E > /N$ should approach $-2J = -2$, which is in agreement with these Monte Carlo results.

These arguments allow us to understand the behavior of $< E >$ at both high and low temperatures, but the behavior near T_c is not as simple. We see from Figure 8.9 that $< E >$ exhibits an inflection point with a very large slope near T_c. In fact, for an infinitely large system the derivative $d < E > /dT$ is infinite at T_c. From thermodynamics we know that the specific heat is related to the energy by $C = d < E > /dT$, so this means that the specific heat diverges at T_c. This divergence is another of the singularities associated with the critical point. As with the magnetization, this singularity is described in general by a power law

$$C \sim \frac{1}{|T - T_c|^\alpha} , \tag{8.18}$$

where α is yet another critical exponent.[23] There are two ways to study the behavior of the specific heat using the Monte Carlo method. One is to numerically differentiate[24] the results for E. The other is to study the fluctuations of E as a function of time. When we first considered the calculation of M we noted that its value fluctuates with time and that the magnitude of these fluctuations becomes large near T_c. A convenient measure of the size of such fluctuations is the variance. For example, if we consider the energy as a function of time, we could generate time-dependent plots that are qualitatively similar

---

[23]For simplicity, and in accordance with scaling, we assume that the exponents above and below T_c are equal; that is, $\alpha = \alpha'$. We will make a similar assumption for other exponents. See Stanley (1971) for more on this point. For the Ising model in two and three dimensions, it turns out that C is divergent at T_c. However, for some other spin models $\alpha < 0$, so C is singular, but does not diverge. We should also add that for the two-dimensional Ising model $\alpha = 0$. An exponent of zero in (8.18) might seem a bit odd, but it turns out that when (8.18) is suitably generalized, an exponent value of zero corresponds to a logarithmic singularity. This is also discussed by Stanley.

[24]Differentiating such noisy "data" numerically generally leads to large uncertainties. This is studied in the exercises.

to those shown for the magnetization in Figure 8.7 (we will leave this task for the exercises). From such results we can compute the average energy as shown in Figure 8.9

$$< E > = \frac{1}{N_m} \sum_{\alpha} E_{\alpha} , \tag{8.19}$$

where the sum is over N_m microstates α generated by the Monte Carlo simulation. Likewise we can consider the variance

$$(\Delta E)^2 \equiv < E^2 > - < E >^2 , \tag{8.20}$$

where

$$< E^2 > = \frac{1}{N_m} \sum_{\alpha} E_{\alpha}^2 . \tag{8.21}$$

According to the fluctuation-dissipation theorem of statistical mechanics, the variance of the energy is related to the specific heat by

$$C = \frac{(\Delta E)^2}{k_B T^2} . \tag{8.22}$$

This shows that the singularity in the specific heat at the transition is *directly* connected with the extremely large fluctuations found near T_c. Equation (8.22) can also be used to calculate C using the Monte Carlo results for E as a function of (Monte Carlo) time.

The behavior of C estimated using (8.22) is shown in Figure 8.10. As we had anticipated, C exhibits a large peak in the vicinity of T_c. The value observed here does not diverge because the lattice has a finite size (recall that the singularities associated with a phase transition are, strictly speaking, only found in an infinite system). By studying the behavior as a function of lattice size, as we will explore in the exercises, we can show that the peak in the specific heat per spin does indeed increase in magnitude as the system is made larger.

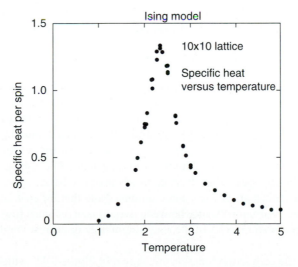

Figure 8.10: Heat capacity calculated using the fluctuation-dissipation relation for a 10×10 lattice. Here we plot the heat capacity per spin, C/N, and take $J = 1$.

The fluctuation dissipation relation applies to a number of other quantities, one of which is the susceptibility $\chi \equiv dM/dH$. This is a measure of how much magnetization is induced by the application of a magnetic field. In this case the fluctuation-dissipation theorem yields

$$\chi = \frac{(\Delta M)^2}{k_B T} , \tag{8.23}$$

where $(\Delta M)^2$ is the variance of M, which can be calculated from results such as those in Figure 8.7. It turns out that χ also diverges at the critical point and is described by a power law form similar to (8.18), but with a different critical exponent known as γ. We will explore this more in the exercises. It is interesting that the fluctuations can be used to estimate how the system would respond to a magnetic field, even though the simulation is performed in zero field. This is an intriguing aspect of the fluctuation-dissipation theorem.

When we considered the variation of the energy with temperature in Figure 8.9, we noted that the behavior of $< E >$ above T_c implies that there must be significant correlations in the relative alignment of neighboring spins. This can be pictured as follows. Above T_c the magnetization is zero so that, on average, half the spins point up, while the other half point down. The energy of interaction between neighboring spins is not strong enough to produce a common alignment of all of the spins, so if you hadn't already seen our results for the energy above T_c, you might think that the spin arrangement above T_c would be random from one spin to the next. We will now show why this is not the case.

Consider a particular spin, call it s_0, and assume that it points up. Let us examine the alignment of the four neighbors of s_0. Since $s_0 = +1$, the neighbors will have a lower energy if they also point up. Even though the temperature may be above T_c so that the average alignment over the entire system is zero, these four neighbors will still have a higher probability of being aligned parallel to s_0, as opposed to being antiparallel. The degree to which they are parallel will depend on temperature, but it will *not* be zero even above T_c. This argument can also be applied to any one of the neighbors of s_0, call it s_1. The near neighbors of s_1 will tend to be aligned with it, and since s_1 is correlated with s_0, this tendency to be aligned will "propagate" from spin to spin through their common neighbors.

This tendency to be correlated can be measured using the *correlation function*

$$f(i) = < s_0 \, s_i > , \tag{8.24}$$

where s_i is a spin that is located i lattice sites away from s_0, and the angular brackets again denote a thermal average that can be computed by averaging over the microstates generated by the Monte Carlo algorithm. The correlation function $f(i)$ is our first encounter with a length-dependent property. It can be calculated by first choosing a spin to be the "central" spin s_0, then computing the product $s_0 s_i$ for all spins a distance i from the central spin. The average of this product is then evaluated by letting each spin be the central spin and considering many Monte Carlo time steps. For a square lattice it is convenient to let i be an integer, thereby measuring distance in terms of the lattice spacing, and to calculate the correlations for spins separated along rows and columns. Note that for an $L \times L$ lattice with periodic boundary conditions, the maximum distance between two spins in the same row or column is $L/2$, since this distance must be measured in terms of the smallest number of nearest neighbor bonds that connect the two spins.

Some results for the correlation function are shown in Figure 8.11, which shows $f(i)$ at several different temperatures. At $T = 1.5$ we find that $f(i)$ is nonzero at large distances. This is because the system has a nonzero value of M, so even spins that are very far apart will tend, on average, to point in

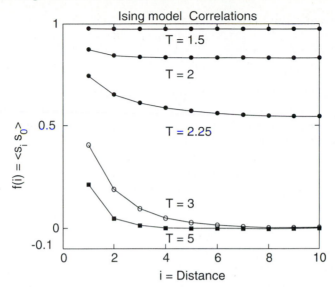

Figure 8.11:   Correlation functions calculated for a 20×20 square lattice at several temperatures. The distance between spins is measured in units of the lattice spacing, and the two spins lie in the same row or column.

the same direction. The important feature here is not the average value of $f(i)$, but rather the amount that $f(i)$ *increases* above this average value as i becomes small. At this low temperature $f(i)$ is nearly independent of separation. While the relative alignment does increase slightly at short distances, the enhancement is very small. Hence, in this case the magnitude of the correlations, which is measured by the *extra* alignment due to being in close proximity, is weak and limited to a very short range. At $T = 2$ the behavior is qualitatively similar, with only a small enhancement of the relative alignment at short distances. While this enhancement is larger than at $T = 1.5$, the spin correlations are still weak and short ranged.

The picture changes near T_c. The correlation function at $T = 2.25 \sim T_c$ differs from the low temperature behavior in two ways. First, the relative alignment at short distances is *much* larger than the value at large i. Second, the correlations are now long range as $f(i)$ approaches the $i \rightarrow \infty$ limit *very* slowly as i is increased. As the temperature is increased further to temperatures above T_c (for example, $T = 5$), the correlations become smaller in magnitude and again extend over only a few lattice spacings.

The behavior of the correlation function sheds light on the singularities found at the critical point. It turns out that away from T_c the correlations fall off exponentially with distance

$$f(i) \sim C_1 + C_2 \exp(-r_i/\xi), \tag{8.25}$$

where C_1 is a constant that is zero above T_c, r_i is the distance between the spins, and ξ is known as the correlation length. ξ gives a measure of the *range* of the correlations. As we noted from Figure 8.11, this range increases as T_c is approached. A careful calculation on a larger lattice would reveal that ξ

diverges at T_c according to the power law

$$\xi \sim \frac{1}{|T - T_c|^{\nu}} , \qquad (8.26)$$

where ν is another critical exponent. Right *at* the critical point, where $\xi = \infty$, the correlations fall off as a power law function of r. A large value of ξ means that the orientation of a single spin is felt by spins that are very far away. Since ξ diverges at T_c this range becomes effectively infinite, so that every spin is sensitive to the alignment of *every* other spin. It is this extreme sensitivity of the system at T_c that leads to the large fluctuations and the singular behavior of quantities such as the magnetization and specific heat at the critical point. These enhanced correlations are ignored by the mean-field approximation, which assumes that the relative alignment of the near neighbors is the same as the average alignment of the entire system.

Exercises

1. Calculate M for the Ising model on a square lattice and try to estimate β. You should find a value close to $1/8$. Repeat this calculation for a triangular lattice. It turns out that β is the same for all regular two dimensional lattices. However, its value does depend on the dimensionality, as studied in the next problem. Hint: There are several different ways to estimate a critical exponent from data such as Monte Carlo results. One is to perform a least-squares fit of the results to the power law expression (8.17). The slope of a plot of $\log(M)$ versus $\log(T_c - T)$ is equal to β, so you might think that a linear least-squares fit of $\log(M)$ as a function of $\log(T_c - T)$, using the procedures described in Appendix 3, would be suitable. However, there are two problems with this approach. One is that the value of T_c is usually not known ahead of time, but must also be estimated at the same time as β is determined. Second, the power law (8.17) is obeyed only near the critical point; there will be deviations as the temperature moves away from T_c, but you don't know ahead of time at what value of $(T_c - T)$ these deviations will become important. There are two ways to overcome these problems. One is to make a plot of M^{1/β^*} as a function of T. Here β^* is a *trial* value of β. By constructing such a plot with different values of β^* you can determine the value that yields a straight line as $T \to T_c$. This is the "best" estimate for β. A virtue of this approach is that it does not require that T_c be known, since it uses only the linearity of M^{1/β^*} with T and does not depend on where this line intercepts the temperature axis. A second approach is to construct plots of $\log(M)$ versus $\log(T_c - T)$ for a series of trial values of T_c. The preferred value of T_c is the one that gives a straight line as $T \to T_c$; the slope of this line then gives β. It is instructive to employ both methods to estimate β. You should find that the power law (8.17) with $\beta \approx 1/8$ is obeyed reasonably well for $2.0 < T < T_c \approx 2.27$.

2. Calculate M for the Ising model on a cubic lattice and try to estimate β (see the previous problem for some helpful hints). You should find a value close to 0.31. It is interesting that, as the dimensionality is made larger, the value of β approaches the prediction of mean-field theory. In fact, it reaches $1/2$ in four dimensions for the Ising model with nearest-neighbor interactions. This calculation is not much more difficult (conceptually) than the previous problem, but will take more computer time.

*3. Calculate χ for the Ising model on a two-dimensional square lattice using the fluctuation-dissipation relation and show that it becomes very large near T_c.

4. Obtain the specific heat as a function of temperature for a 10×10 square lattice by differentiating the energy and through the fluctuation-dissipation theorem. Show that the two methods give the same result. Which approach is more accurate (for a given amount of computer time)?

*5. The proper extrapolation to the infinite lattice limit is extremely important in a quantitative analysis of Monte Carlo results. It turns out that the manner in which this limit is approached also contains valuable information. Calculate the specific heat per spin, C/N, for $L \times L$ square lattices (pick several values of L in the range 5–40) and investigate how the maximum value (which is found at $T \approx T_c$, where T_c is the critical temperature of the infinite lattice) varies with lattice size. Show that $C_{\max}/N \sim \log L$. This behavior falls under the heading known as *finite size scaling* and is discussed by Fisher (1973).[25] Warning: The peak in the heat capacity peak becomes much sharper as L is increased, so you will need to use smaller temperature steps in locating the peak when L is large.

*6. Study the time dependence of the fluctuations of either M or E at a fixed temperature. You should find that the fluctuations not only become larger in magnitude near T_c, but also become *slower*. This happens because the regions of correlated spins have a size of $\sim \xi$, which diverges at the critical point, and larger blocks of correlated spins take longer to fluctuate (that is, reorient). Try to obtain a quantitative measure of the time scale associated with the fluctuations. This effect is known as critical slowing down.

7. Compare the behavior of M for a system with periodic boundary conditions with the results for free boundary conditions; that is, the system simply ends at the edges and the spins at the boundaries have fewer neighbors than those in the interior. The difference in behavior is largest near T_c.

8.5   First-Order Phase Transitions

In the Section 8.4 we studied the behavior of an Ising model near its critical point. This transition from the ferromagnetic state, with $M \neq 0$, to the paramagnetic state, where $M = 0$, is often referred to as a second-order phase transition.[26] This raises the obvious question: What is a first-order phase transition? First-order transitions are actually very common in nature, the freezing of water being a typical example. We can observe a first-order transition with our Ising model if we include the effect of a magnetic field. The Monte Carlo method can be used as described above, the only difference being that the energy for flipping a spin must include the energy gained or lost to the field as given in (8.5).

We now have two independent variables in the problem, T and H, so there is a larger phase diagram to explore. Let us first consider the behavior as a function of field at fixed temperature as shown in Figures 8.12 and 8.13. At $T = 1.0$ and with $H < 0$, the magnetization is large and negative. We already know that at this temperature the spins will be nearly fully aligned even without the field. Here the field serves only to determine the direction of M (since the field energy tends to align the spins with H), and this is why M changes sign abruptly when H is increased through zero. This *discontinuous*

---

[25] It turns out that this logarithmic variation with L depends on the fact that the specific heat of the two-dimensional Ising model diverges logarithmically at T_c (this also leads to a value of the specific heat exponent $\alpha = 0$, as we have already mentioned). Quantities that are characterized by nonzero exponents display a different dependence on L, as is discussed in Fisher (1973).

[26] The terms *continuous* and *higher order* are also commonly used.

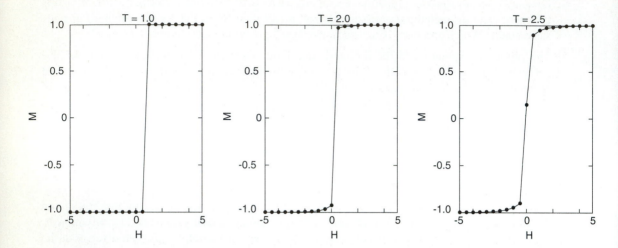

Figure 8.12: Field dependence of the magnetization for an Ising model on a 10×10 lattice at several temperatures. As in Figure 8.7, we have the normalized M so that the fully aligned state corresponds to $M = \pm 1$. These results were obtained by sweeping the field up from large negative values. Note the hysteresis near $H = 0$ when $T = 1.0$, as evidenced by the fact that M does not switch from negative to positive when the field first changes sign.

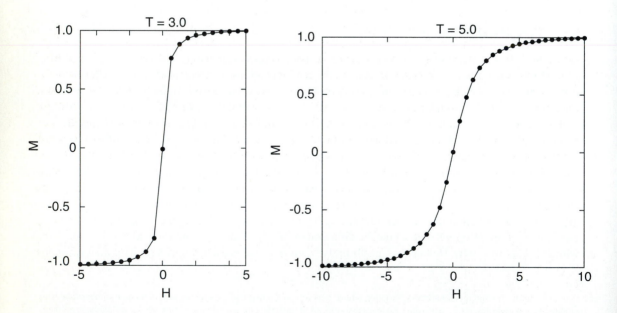

Figure 8.13: Continuation of Figure 8.12.

change of M is an indicator of a *first-order transition*.[27] This discontinuity in the magnetization involves the two states of the system that are related by a simultaneous reversal of all of the spins, $M \rightarrow -M$. When $H = 0$ these two states are equally probable, but the application of a small field will make one more likely than the other. A discontinuous jump in M as a function of field is found at all temperatures below T_c. While from energy and symmetry considerations we would expect this jump to occur at $H = 0$, it sometimes happens that there is *hysteresis* associated with the transition. This can be seen from the results at $T = 1.0$, where the jump occurred at a value of H, which was slightly but distinctly greater than zero.[28] Here the system was trapped in a metastable state ($M < 0$ with $H > 0$) over the time period of the simulation. We will have more to say about this in a moment.

Above T_c the spontaneous magnetization vanishes, so there can be no discontinuity in M as the field is swept through zero, and hence no first order phase transition. At temperatures above T_c you can go smoothly from the state with a negative magnetization, which is found when $H < 0$, to the state with a positive magnetization, with $H > 0$. The magnitude of the discontinuity found below T_c is just twice the spontaneous magnetization we calculated in the previous section. We found that this magnetization vanishes at T_c, so there is a very close connection between the first-order transition observed as a function of field and the second-order transition observed as a function of temperature. This connection can be appreciated by considering the *phase diagram* as viewed in the H–T plane.

At low temperatures the system possesses two distinct phases corresponding to $\pm M$, as denoted by the arrows in Figure 8.14. We can pass from one phase to the other by crossing the temperature axis, and as we have seen in Figure 8.12, M varies discontinuously when we do this at temperatures below T_c. This is the location of the first-order transition and yields a line in the H–T plane as shown in Figure 8.14. This line of first-order transitions ends at the critical temperature, where the spontaneous magnetization vanishes. At this temperature the difference between the two phases disappears. At and above T_c we can pass from positive to negative fields without any discontinuity in M.

From the phase diagram we see that the line of first-order transitions terminates at a critical point. This geometry is a general feature of first-order transitions. For example, in a liquid-gas system there is a very similar situation. In that case the relevant variables are pressure (replacing H), temperature, and density (replacing M), as shown schematically in Figure 8.14. The transition from a liquid to a gas is first order over a range of pressures, with a discontinuity in the density. As the pressure is increased, the magnitude of this discontinuity becomes smaller, and it vanishes at the critical point. As in a spin system, there are singularities in various properties of a liquid-gas system at T_c, and these singularities are described by power laws with critical exponents. Interestingly, the values of the critical exponents of a liquid-gas system are believed to be the *same* as those found for the Ising model.[29] This universality of the behavior suggests that the essential features of the critical behavior transcend the specific model or system. This is a very interesting subject that the reader may pursue using the sources in the references.

---

[27]This nomenclature was introduced by Ehrenfest who proposed the name *first order* for a transition in which a first derivative of the free energy (such as M) is discontinuous. Likewise, according to the Ehrenfest scheme a second-order transition is one in which a second derivative of the free energy, such as the specific heat, is discontinuous. It turns out that such behavior is actually very rare, so the term *second order* is now often used for transitions at which a second derivative of the free energy is divergent, as observed in Section 8.4.

[28]This is our first encounter with a metastable state. Such behavior is commonly found in connection with first-order transitions. We will also observe it in a rather different system in Chapter 11.

[29]Note, however, that the exponent values do depend on dimensionality, so the exponents for two-and three-dimensional Ising models are different.

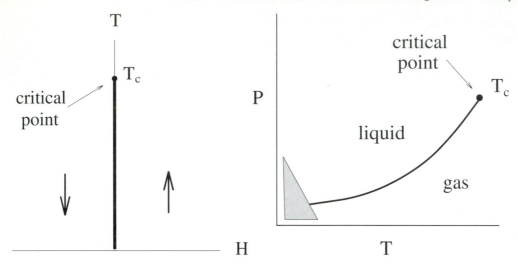

Figure 8.14: Left: phase diagram of a ferromagnet in the *H–T* plane. The heavy solid line that lies along the temperature axis denotes a first-order transition between states $\pm M$. This line ends at the critical point, T_c. Right: schematic pressure-temperature phase diagram of a liquid gas system. The thick curve is a line of first-order transitions that separates the gas and liquid phases. This line ends at the critical point. At low temperatures there will generally be a solid phase and a triple point (in the shaded region), but these are not shown.

Returning to Figure 8.14, an interesting feature of the Ising model phase diagram is that you can move from the "up" phase to the "down" phase in two very different ways. One is to cross the temperature axis and thereby experience a first-order transition. The other is to go *around* the critical point at high temperatures and thus avoid the first-order line altogether. Of course, these two options are also available in a liquid-gas system, where you can either pass through the first-order transition line or go from liquid to gas without a transition by navigating around the critical point.

Finally, we should emphasize an important difference between first- and second-order transitions. Near the critical point the fluctuations become very large in anticipation of the singular behavior that is found there. That is, the systems "knows" that something important is about to happen. However, a first-order transition occurs abruptly. There are no enhanced fluctuations or any other sort of "warning" that discontinuities are imminent.

This lack of warning is connected with the fact that the spin configurations before and after the transition are very different. At the low temperatures considered here, these two states are ones in which the spins are nearly all parallel to each other, with *M* either "up" or "down." If the system is initially in one of these states, then in order for it to undergo a transition to the other state requires that essentially *all* of the spins be flipped. The Monte Carlo flipping rules involve one spin at a time, and since at low temperatures even a single spin flip that raises the energy occurs only very rarely, the probability that a large number of spins will be able to conspire to flip together is extremely small.

This is illustrated in Figure 8.15 which shows results for *M* as a function of *H* at low temperatures. At each temperature we have started at a large negative field so that the spins were essentially all aligned in the negative direction. The field was then increased in steps. We would expect that this spin configuration would be the stable one until the field becomes positive, at which point the state with all

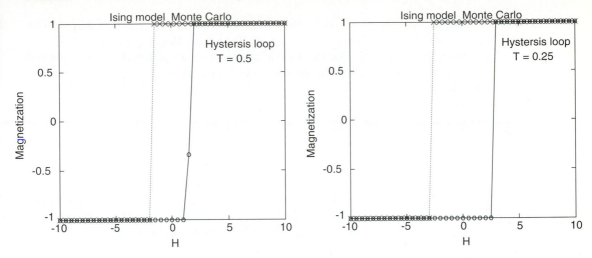

Figure 8.15: Hysteresis loops for a 10×10 Ising model calculated at temperatures well below T_c. The open circles (and solid lines) show results obtained by starting at a large negative field and increasing the field in steps, while the crosses (and dotted lines) were obtained by starting at a large positive field and decreasing the field in steps. One thousand Monte Carlo time steps (that is, one thousand complete passes throught the lattice) were spent at each field.

spins pointing in the positive direction should be the thermodynamically stable state. However, we see in Figure 8.15 that at $T = 0.5$ the system remains in the negative state until $H \sim 1.5$ before it switches to the positive state. Similarly, if we start at a large positive field, and then decrease the field in steps, we see that the system does not switch from the postive to the negative state until $H \sim -1.5$. Hence, the state of the system depends on the past history of the system, an effect known as hysteresis. This delay in switching into the thermodynamically stable state is a result of the extremely low probability for the system to make the transition. Put another way, we have here a case in which the Monte Carlo procedure did not reach equilibrium during the time scale of the simulation. Rather, the system became stuck in a nonequilibrium state. If we had waited longer at each field, this effect would be reduced and the amount of hysteresis would be smaller. However, such hysteretic behavior can often be found even if we wait for macroscopically long times. A good example of this is the behavior of a liquid near its freezing transition. In general, it is possible to cool a liquid well below the (thermodynamic) freezing temperature before it undergoes the transition to the solid phase.

It is instructive to compare the hysteresis at different temperatures. We see from Figure 8.15 that the amount of hysteresis becomes larger as the temperature is reduced. This is because the probability for a Monte Carlo spin flip varies as $\exp(-E_{\text{flip}}/k_B T)$, and hence becomes smaller as T is made smaller. This increases the likelihood that the system will become stuck in a metastable state. We will discuss metastability and related matters further in Chapter 11 when we consider the problems of protein folding and neural networks.

Exercises

1. Above T_c there is no net magnetization when $H = 0$, but applying a field induces alignment of the spins as can be seen for example at $T = 5$ in Figure 8.13. At very high temperatures the

interactions between spins have very little effect, and the field dependence is then described by approximately (8.8). Confirm this by calculating $M(H)$ at $T = 100$ (use the value $J = 1$, as we have employed throughout this chapter) and compare your results with (8.8). You should find good, though not exact, agreement. The deviations are due to the interactions between spins. Repeat your calculation at lower temperatures ($T = 30$ and 10 are good choices), and show that the deviations from (8.8), that is, the effects of the interactions, become larger as T is reduced.

*2. Calculate M as a function of field at T_c. The behavior should be described by the power law

$$M \sim H^{1/\delta} , \tag{8.27}$$

where δ is another critical exponent. Try to estimate the value of δ. In two dimensions $\delta = 15$, while in three dimensions its value is close to 5. Hint: It is difficult to get a good estimate for δ because its relatively large value (especially in two dimensions) means that M increases extremely rapidly in small fields. To overcome this it is useful to employ lattices that are larger than our standard 10×10 size. A 20×20 lattice and a field range of 0.02–0.2 are good choices, but you should try lattices of other sizes and explore the behavior for a wider field range. You may also find it necessary to average over 3000 or more Monte Carlo time steps at each field. Once you have obtained reliable results for M, you can then construct plots of M^{δ^*} as function of H for various values of δ^*. The value that gives the best straight line as $H \to 0$ then provides an estimate for δ. Alternatively, the slope of a plot of $\log M$ as a function of $\log H$ will also yield an estimate for δ.

3. Study how the hysteresis in M as a function of H at low temperatures varies as a function of the amount of time the system is given to come into equilibrium. Use a 10×10 lattice at $T = 0.25$ and calculate the hysteresis loops (as in Figure 8.15) by stepping the field in small increments ($\Delta H = 0.5$ is a good choice) and averaging over a given number of Monte Carlo time steps at each field. Observe how the amount of hysteresis depends on the amount of Monte Carlo time spent at each field.

*4. Investigate how the magnitude of the hysteresis depends on how the boundaries of the lattice are treated. Consider a 10×10 lattice at low temperatures and compare the behavior with periodic and free boundary conditions (by "free" we mean that the system simply terminates, and spins at the edges have only three near neighbors, while those at the corners have only two). You should find that there is less hysteresis in the case of free-boundary conditions. Give a qualitative argument to explain why this is so.

References

BINDER, K. and D. W. HEERMANN. 1992. *Monte Carlo Simulation in Statistical Physics*. New York: Springer-Verlag. A careful theoretical discussion of the Monte Carlo method.

FISHER, M. E. 1973. "Critical Phenomena in Films and Surfaces." *J. Vac. Sci. Technol.* **10**, 665. A very readable discussion of finite size effects near critical points.

HEERMANN, D. W. 1990. *Computer Simulation Methods in Theoretical Physics*, 2d ed. New York: Springer-Verlag. Discusses how the microcanonical ensemble can be simulated using a Monte Carlo approach.

LANDAU, D. P. and R. ALBEN. 1973. "Monte Carlo Calculations as an Aid in Teaching Statistical Mechanics." *Am. J. Phys.* **41**, 394. A nice tutorial introduction to the Monte Carlo method.

PRESS, W.H., B.P. FLANNERY, S.A. TEUKOLSKY, and W.T. VETTERLING. 1986. *Numerical Recipes.* Cambridge: Cambridge University Press. An excellent all-purpose reference on numerical methods and why they work.

REIF, F. 1965. *Fundamentals of Statistical and Thermal Physics.* New York: McGraw-Hill. Reviews statistical mechanics, including a discussion of the Maxwell-Boltzmann distributions.

STANLEY, H. E. 1971. *Introduction to Phase Transitions and Critical Phenomena.* Oxford: Clarendon Press 1971. A standard text on phase transitions and critical phenomena. Includes treatments of mean-field theory and the Ising model.

9

Molecular Dynamics

9.1   Introduction to the Method: Properties of a Dilute Gas

In this chapter we consider a mechanical approach for studying multiparticle systems. The method we describe is known as molecular dynamics, and it is in many respects complementary to the Monte Carlo method employed in Chapter 8. The Monte Carlo algorithm is very convenient for studying the *equilibrium* properties of a system that is in contact with a heat bath. However, there are many questions that cannot be addressed with such an approach. For example, suppose we are interested in how fast a system will come into equilibrium after a sudden change in the temperature. With the Monte Carlo method the dynamics is governed entirely by the Monte Carlo transition rules (for an Ising model these are the spin-flipping rules), together with the appropriate Boltzmann factors. While these rules are designed to simulate a system in thermal equilibrium, they cannot tell us how fast in real time that a system will move from one particular microstate to another, or if such a transition is even possible.

One way to deal with such questions is to directly simulate the dynamics using the microscopic equations of motion, and this is the philosophy of the molecular dynamics technique. The basic idea is similar to the cream-in-your-coffee problem of Chapter 7, but here we are going to use the appropriate equations of motion to treat the full many-body problem, rather than simulate the motion of an "average" molecule. We imagine a box containing a collection of molecules. These molecules move throughout the box as they collide with each other and with the walls of the box. To simulate this process we employ Newton's second law to calculate the positions and velocities of all of the molecules as functions of time. The kinds of questions that can be addressed with this approach include the nature of the melting transition, the rate of equilibration after a sudden addition or loss of energy, and the rate at which molecules diffuse.[1] You may recall that we spent the first part of Chapter 7 arguing that

---

[1] We will now have a way to calculate the value of the diffusion constant that we have encountered in several previous problems.

such a microscopic approach provides results that are much too detailed for many of the questions we might like to address, and that claim still stands. However, some questions *do* require such a full-blown microscopic treatment; we will now describe how to carry out such a treatment, along with some of the problems for which it is needed.

While the general simulation scheme we are going to consider in this chapter could apply to any system containing a large number of particles, including droplets in an aerosol, particles in a flame, or stars in a galaxy, molecular dynamics is, as its name implies, usually employed to study the motion of molecules. We might, therefore, worry that a *classical* approach involving Newton's second law would not be appropriate, and that we should instead aim for a fully quantum mechanical simulation. A quantum simulation would be *much* more time consuming and computationally difficult than a classical simulation, so it is fortunate that a classical treatment is justifiable for many situations of interest. That this is, in fact, the case can be seen from the following arguments. Let us consider the simulation of a collection of atoms, such as argon. All of the electrons associated with each argon atom are bound fairly tightly to their respective nuclei; the energy required[2] to promote an electron to an excited state, or to remove it entirely from an argon atom, is of order 10 electron volts (eV). This energy is much larger than the typical kinetic energy associated with the center of mass motion of an atom, which is of order 0.1 eV at room temperature. This large energy difference means that collisions between argon atoms will not involve enough energy to have an effect on the electron configuration of either atom. In particular, there is not nearly enough energy available to strip away an electron. For this reason it is a very good approximation to treat each atom as a simple structureless particle. In addition, the DeBroglie wavelength of an argon atom at room temperature is of order 10^{-7} Å. The average spacing between atoms in a solid is of order 1 Å, and we will see shortly that in typical liquids and gasses the atoms never get closer than ~ 1 Å during a collision. Hence, the atomic wavelength is much smaller than the particle separation, which again justifies a classical approach. We can, therefore, use Newton's second law to calculate the positions of the atoms as a function of time.

For simplicity (and also conservation of computer time) we will consider atoms moving in a plane.[3] For each atom i we then have the equations of motion

$$\frac{dv_{i,x}}{dt} = a_{i,x} ,$$

$$\frac{dx_i}{dt} = v_{i,x} ,$$

$$\frac{dv_{i,y}}{dt} = a_{i,y} ,$$

$$\frac{dy_i}{dt} = v_{i,y} ,$$

(9.1)

where $v_{i,x}$ and $v_{i,y}$ are the components of the velocity of the ith atom, which is located at position (x_i, y_i). The components of the acceleration of each particle, $a_{i,x}$ and $a_{i,y}$, are determined by the forces from all of the other particles in the system. To solve these equations numerically we have several choices. In nearly all of the problems we have encountered so far in this book, either the Euler

---

[2]You may recall that the binding energy of an electron in the ground state of a hydrogen atom is ~ 13.6 eV.

[3]The extension to three dimensions is straightforward.

or Euler-Cromer method has been adequate. However, in molecular dynamics we will be interested in computing the motion over a very large number of time steps, and it turns out that the numerical errors associated with Euler type methods are too big to tolerate. It is, therefore, necessary to use a slightly more complicated scheme for solving the differential equations arising from Newton's second law. The scheme we will employ here is known as the Verlet method and is introduced in Appendix 1. As usual, we discretize time in steps Δt. Letting $x_i(n)$, $v_{i,x}(n)$, and $a_{i,x}(n)$ be the x components of position, velocity, and acceleration of particle i at time-step n, their values at the next time step are given according to the Verlet method as

$$x_i(n+1) \approx 2\,x_i(n) - x_i(n-1) + a_{i,x}(n)\,(\Delta t)^2 \,, \tag{9.2}$$

$$v_{i,x}(n) \approx \frac{x_i(n+1) - x_i(n-1)}{2\,\Delta t} \,,$$

with similar equations for y_i and $v_{i,y}$. These equations are derived in Appendix 1 where it is also shown that the numerical errors associated with the Verlet method are much smaller than with the Euler method (for a comparable amount of computing time).

At first glance, (9.2) doesn't look much like our usual Euler or Euler-Cromer expressions. However, the origin of this relation for $x_i(n+1)$ can be appreciated if we recall the finite-difference approximation for a second derivative

$$\frac{d^2 x_i}{dt^2} \approx \frac{x_i(n+1) + x_i(n-1) - 2\,x_i(n)}{(\Delta t)^2} \,, \tag{9.3}$$

which we have encountered on several previous occasions. If we use the fact that $d^2 x_i/dt^2$ is the acceleration and rearrange (9.3) to solve for $x_i(n+1)$, we obtain precisely (9.2) (a more careful derivation is given in Appendix 1, where the errors associated with this approximation are also estimated). An important feature of the Verlet method is that it conserves energy very well over the course of many time steps, which is crucial if we want to perform an accurate molecular dynamics simulation. It is interesting to note that the position can be calculated directly from the acceleration; we don't really have to calculate the velocity as an intermediate step, as is necessary with the Euler method. However, we will see that the velocity contains some very useful information, so we will always compute it along with the position.

A molecular-dynamics simulation consists of solving the Verlet equations for every particle in the system. A key quantity required in this calculation is the acceleration. Each particle experiences a force from all of the other particles; this is what gives rise to collisions between the particles. To estimate the force between any two particles requires knowledge of the interaction potential, $V(r)$, where r is the separation of the particles. The calculation of $V(r)$ *does* involve quantum mechanics; it depends on what kinds of atoms are involved and the nature of the forces between them. For elements such as argon the situation is relatively simple. For large separations the interaction is due to the Van der Waals force, which is a weak attraction arising from the transient electric dipole moments of the two atoms. We don't have space to give a derivation here;[4] all we really need to know is that this potential varies as r^{-6} and is attractive. When the atoms get close together there is also a repulsive force due to the overlap of their electron clouds. The precise form of this force is hard to calculate, since it involves

---

[4] See any introductory quantum mechanics text, such as Schiff (1963).

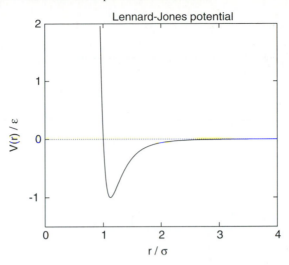

Figure 9.1:   Lennard-Jones potential.

many electrons. Common practice is to approximate it by a term that varies as r^{-12} and is repulsive. Adding this to the Van der Waals component yields what is known as the *Lennard-Jones* potential

$$V(r) = 4\epsilon \left[\left(\frac{\sigma}{r} \right)^{12} - \left(\frac{\sigma}{r} \right)^{6} \right], \qquad (9.4)$$

where ϵ and σ are constants that set the energy and distance scales associated with the interaction. This function is plotted in Figure 9.1; the associated force is the derivative $F = -\partial V / \partial r$, and is directed along the line connecting the atoms. We see from Figure 9.1 that the two atoms experience a significant attractive force when the separation is in the range $\sim (1.1\text{--}2.0)\,\sigma$. For separations larger than about 3σ the force is essentially zero, while for $r \leq 1.1\sigma$ the force is very strongly repulsive.

We will follow standard molecular-dynamics practice and use the Lennard-Jones potential in our calculations.[5] Its magnitude is set by ϵ, so it is convenient to work in units for which $\epsilon = 1$. Thus, we effectively measure all energies in terms of ϵ, which for argon is $\epsilon / k_B = 120$ K. Argon is a popular choice for molecular-dynamics simulations, since the Ar-Ar interaction is very well described by the Lennard-Jones potential. Likewise, it is convenient to set the length scale $\sigma = 1$, so that all lengths are measured in units of σ, which has a value of 3.4 Å for argon. These are often referred to in the literature as *reduced units* and are denoted by E^* and r^*, etc.; we will usually just use the symbols E and r for convenience. Finally, standard practice also sets the mass of an atom to unity, so that all masses are measured in terms of the mass of one argon atom. Since energy has units of mass times velocity squared, this leads us to measure time in units of $\sqrt{m\sigma^2/\epsilon}$ and velocity in units of $\sqrt{\epsilon/m}$, where m is the mass of an argon atom. One (reduced) unit of time for argon is $\approx 1.8 \times 10^{-12}$ s, about 2 picoseconds.

---

[5]Other potentials are sometimes used, for example, to study systems such as metals in which conduction electrons contribute significantly to the interaction.

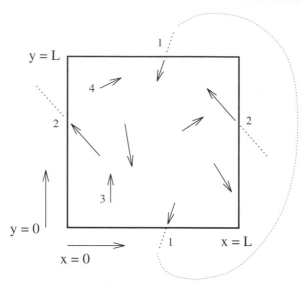

Figure 9.2: Periodic boundary conditions for a molecular dynamics simulation using an $L \times L$ box. The arrows denote atoms and their velocities.

Before we discuss the programming there is one more issue that must be addressed, namely the boundary conditions. Perhaps the most obvious way to enclose the particles is in a box[6] with hard, perfectly reflecting walls. The problem with this approach is that for presently available computers we are limited to systems containing a relatively small number of atoms. Much can be learned from calculations (like those described in this chapter) on a small machine involving a few tens of atoms, but even with a very fast computer it is difficult to deal with more than a few thousand atoms in a reasonable amount of time. In such small systems collisions with the walls would be a significant fraction of the total number of collisions, in contrast to a real system where the behavior would be dominated by collisions with other particles. Moreover, the *shape* of a small container can greatly affect how the particles are spatially arranged, which can be a serious problem if we want to study a condensed phase (a liquid or a solid). For these reasons it is common practice to use *periodic boundary conditions*. We have already encountered such boundary conditions in our Monte Carlo simulations of the Ising model, but the situation there was a little simpler since the spins did not move. Here periodic boundary conditions work as illustrated schematically in Figure 9.2, which shows a collection of atoms in a square, two-dimensional box with walls at $x = 0, L$ and $y = 0, L$. Whenever an atom encounters a wall it is transported instantly to the *opposite* side of the system. For example, the atom marked 1, which reached the wall at $y = 0$, was transported to the opposite side at $y \approx L$. Note that *only* the y coordinate was affected by this move. The x coordinate and both components of the velocity were unaffected.

One way to view periodic boundary conditions is to imagine that the box is situated on a torus. Two particles that are near opposite faces in a plot such as Figure 9.2 are then actually very close to each other. This avoids all collisions with walls (since there are no walls!), but poses a slight complication

---

[6]We need some sort of enclosure to keep the particle from traveling away and never coming back.

when we calculate the force between two particles, since this force depends on their separation. For example, particles 3 and 4 in Figure 9.2 are separated by a distance of $\approx 3L/4$ along the y direction. However, if we take advantage of the teleportation of periodic boundary conditions, their separation is only $\approx L/4$. In order for our equations of motion to be consistent, particles should only be allowed to interact once, so we must use the smaller of these two separations to calculate both the magnitude and the *direction* of the force.

We have now described the basic conceptual details associated with molecular dynamics and next consider how to construct a program. One example of such a program is given in Appendix 4; here we will describe only its main components. After setting the size of the box (i.e., torus), the number of particles, and the time step, we must pick the initial positions and velocities. These will depend on the particular problem we want to study. As an example, let us consider a fairly dilute gas. Your intuitive picture of a gas probably has the atoms arranged randomly within the box, so it is natural to choose the initial positions randomly. However, this intuitive picture does not take into account the hard-core repulsion of the potential. Even in a gas, the atoms are *not* arranged completely at random. If there is an atom at a particular location (x_1, y_1), the probability of finding a second atom within a distance σ of this position is essentially zero. To take this into account in our initialization it is convenient to give the atoms an approximately regular arrangement so as to guarantee that no two atoms are too close to each other. The program listed in Appendix 4 does this by first placing the atoms on a square lattice in which the spacing between nearest neighbors is greater than 2σ and then displacing the atoms from these locations at random by a distance $\leq \sigma/2$. This gives a somewhat random initial arrangement and keeps the atoms well separated from each other. The choice of initial velocities is not as complicated. One possibility is to give each particle a speed v_0 in a randomly chosen direction. We will consider other possibilities shortly.

After initializing the particle positions and velocities, our program uses the Verlet method to calculate the motion of each atom. In accord with (9.2) we use two-dimensional arrays `x(i,j)` and `y(i,j)` to store the x and y coordinates of particle `j`. The first index corresponds to time with `i=1` being the previous time step [corresponding to the index $n-1$ in (9.2)], `i=2` the current time step, and `i=3` the "next" time step, that is, the one that is in the process of being calculated. The acceleration components of particle `j` are `ax(j)` and `ay(j)`, and these are obtained from the Lennard-Jones potential. The components of the acceleration for particle j are obtained by simply summing the individual forces from all of the other particles in the system

$$a_{j,x} = \frac{1}{m} \sum_{k \neq j} f_{k,j} \, \cos \theta_{k,j} \,, \tag{9.5}$$

$$a_{j,y} = \frac{1}{m} \sum_{k \neq j} f_{k,j} \, \sin \theta_{k,j} \,,$$

where $f_{k,j}$ is the force of particle k on particle j (note that in our reduced units $m = 1$), and $\theta_{k,j}$ is the angle that the line between them makes with the x axis. These sums exclude terms like $f_{j,j}$, since a particle does not interact with itself. The pair forces are given by

$$f_{k,j} = -\frac{\partial V}{\partial r_{k,j}} = 24 \left(\frac{2}{r_{k,j}^{13}} - \frac{1}{r_{k,j}^{7}} \right), \tag{9.6}$$

where $r_{k,j}$ is the separation between particles k and j, and we have assumed $\sigma = \epsilon = 1$ so that we are using reduced units as mentioned above. Note that $r_{k,j}$ and the associated angle must be measured with the
"minimum" separation rule of periodic boundary conditions. For example, particles 3 and 4 in Figure 9.2
are a distance $\approx L/4$ apart (not $3L/4$). The angular factors in (9.5) can be estimated from the relative
positions of the two particles. If their separation along x is Δx, then $\cos\theta_{k,j} = \Delta x/r_{k,j}$, etc. for $\sin\theta_{k,j}$.

    At each time step it is necessary to compute the acceleration of every particle. Since each particle
interacts with every other particle, this involves the calculation of *many* pair forces $f_{k,j}$. In practice
this is the most time-consuming part of the calculation, so it is worth making this part of the program
efficient. To this end we first recall from Figure 9.1 that the interaction potential is essentially zero
for $r > 3$ (remember that this distance is measured in reduced units, so $r = 1$ corresponds to a real
separation of σ). We will, therefore, take the force to be exactly zero when $r > 3$. This is known
as "cutting off" the potential, and speeds things up since we can avoid calculating $f_{k,j}$ for most pairs
of particles.[7] Another way to speed things up is to note that $|f_{k,j}| = |f_{j,k}|$, which is required from
Newton's third law. It is, therefore, most efficient to calculate all of the $f_{k,j}$ at one time (with two nested
loops), being careful that each pair of particles is considered only once.

    After calculating the $f_{k,j}$ as just described, our program estimates the new position of particle j
using (9.2) to compute x(3,j) and y(3,j). At the same time the new velocities are also calculated.
Note that with (9.2) we use a symmetric form of the derivative to find the velocities, so when we
calculate the positions at step $n + 1$ we are then able to obtain the velocities at step n. This will be
important[8] when we consider the total energy, since we will want to calculate the kinetic and potential
energies at the *same* value of t. After obtaining the new positions we must then check to see if any
of the particles have "left" the box. If so, our program uses the periodic boundary condition rules to
teleport the particle to the opposite side of the system. To be consistent, we also teleport the previous
value of the position since this will be needed in the calculation of the velocity at the next time step.
The velocity does not need any adjustment.

    This completes one time step of the calculation. The above procedure is then repeated for as
many time steps as desired. The results can be monitored and analyzed in several ways, which we
will now describe as we consider specific simulations. Figure 9.3 shows the results for 20 particles in
a 10×10 box. It is usually not necessary to (permanently) record or display the positions after each
time step, since the particles should move little during an interval Δt; otherwise Δt was not chosen
small enough in the first place! Here we have plotted the positions sufficiently often that the individual
trajectories can be followed without confusing one particle for another. Many pair "collisions" can be
noted, although the dots plotted here never actually "touch" each other, since the hard-core repulsion of
the Lennard-Jones potential effectively prevents the particles from getting closer than about σ, which
is unity in our reduced units. We also see several cases of particles exiting one side of the box and
reappearing at the opposite side. A much better feeling for the behavior is obtained from observing the
motion in "real time" as the calculation proceeds, but unfortunately we cannot include a movie here.
This is also a very good way to find programming errors.

---

    [7]However, our program does calculate $r_{k,j}$ for every pair so that it can decide whether or not to evaluate $f_{k,j}$. We could
go a step further and not even bother to calculate $r_{k,j}$ for particles that were very widely separated at the previous time step. This
approach will speed things up even more, but the programming is a bit more complicated since we must decide how often to
check on the value of $r_{k,j}$.

    [8]There are several different variations on the Verlet algorithm, as discussed in Heermann (1990), and some of these avoid
this problem. Watch out for this when comparing our program with those of other authors.

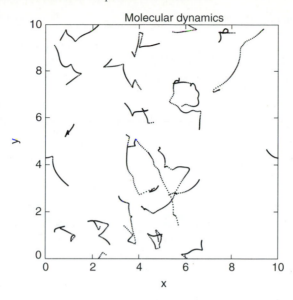

Figure 9.3: Trajectories of 20 particles in a 10×10 box with periodic boundary conditions, with initial speeds $v = 1$ in randomly chosen directions. The time step was 0.02 and the positions of the particles were plotted after every third time step.

The results in Figure 9.3 show that we can, indeed, compute the motion of a collection of particles. It remains for us to demonstrate that our simulations have anything in common with a real system. Perhaps the most fundamental issue is whether our system reaches a proper equilibrium state, and if so, how fast it comes into equilibrium. This also raises the question of how such an equilibrium state is described in terms of statistical mechanics. Since the only forces in our problem are those between particles, the total energy must be conserved, corresponding to the microcanonical ensemble of statistical mechanics. There is no external heat bath as we had in our Monte Carlo simulations. Even so, the concept of temperature can still be useful. One way to view this is to imagine a restricted "system" consisting of a small fraction of the particles, with the remaining particles then acting as a heat bath. Thus, we can still use the concept of "temperature," but unlike the case with the Monte Carlo method developed in the previous chapter, the value of T is not an explicitly given parameter. Rather, we will have to calculate T from the behavior of the system. This can be accomplished using the equipartition theorem, which states that for a classical system the average energy of each "quadratic" degree of freedom[9] is $k_B T / 2$. This theorem can be used in association with the velocity components of each particle, since the kinetic energy associated with v_x is $m v_x^2 / 2$, etc., for v_y. The assertion is that our molecular dynamics simulation will describe a system whose temperature can be computed using the equipartition theorem.

To justify this claim we next consider if and how the system in Figure 9.3 reaches an equilibrium state. We will focus on the behavior of the particle velocities, since we know that in equilibrium a

---

[9]That is, each coordinate or velocity that contributes a quadratic term to the energy.

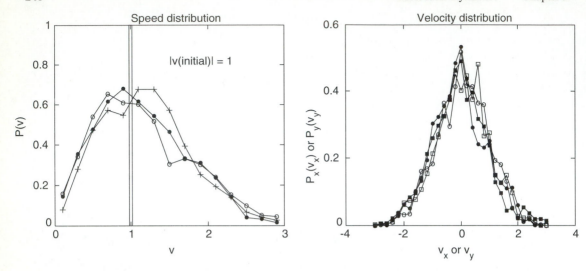

Figure 9.4: Left: speed distribution of the gas of particles in Figure 9.3 at various times. At $t = 0$ the distribution was the vertical bar at $v = 1$ (which is not drawn to scale). The other symbols correspond to averages over the reduced time intervals $t = 0$–20 (solid circles), $t = 20$–40 (open circles), and $t = 40$–60 (pluses). Right: velocity distributions obtained in a similar simulation, but using a different initialization of v_x and v_y. These velocity distributions were calculated by averaging over the intervals $t = 0$–20 and 20–40. Aside from the statistical uncertainties, these results agree with the Maxwell distribution (9.8).

classical gas is described by the Maxwell distribution. For a two-dimensional gas we have the *speed* distribution

$$P(v) \;=\; C\,\frac{v^2}{k_B T}\,\exp\left(-mv^2/2k_B T\right)\;, \qquad (9.7)$$

where $P(v)$ is the probability per unit v of finding a particle with speed v, and C is a constant that depends on the mass of the particle. The corresponding *velocity* distribution is

$$P(v_x) \;=\; \frac{C_x}{(k_B T)^{1/2}}\,\exp\left(-mv_x^2/2k_B T\right)\;, \qquad (9.8)$$

with a similar expression for $P(v_y)$. If the molecular dynamics method describes the behavior of a real gas, it should yield velocity and speed distributions that have the Maxwell forms.

In Figure 9.4 we show the speed distribution of the gas in Figure 9.3 calculated by averaging over several different time intervals as the simulation proceeded. Initially all of the particles were given a velocity whose magnitude was unity ($v = 1$ in reduced units) and whose direction was random, yielding a speed distribution as shown by the vertical bar at $v = 1$ in Figure 9.4. We then let the simulation run, and after every 10 time steps the speed distribution was recorded by dividing the v range into bins and tabulating the number of atoms whose speed was in the range corresponding to each bin. These histograms[10] were averaged over the time intervals $t = 0$–20, 20–40, and 40–60, with the results shown in Figure 9.4. We will leave it to the exercises to demonstrate in detail that in all three cases the

---

[10]Note that these distributions have been normalized so that $\int P(v)dv = 1$, etc.

speed distribution has a form that (to within the statistical fluctuations) is well described by (9.7). The conclusion is that our system did indeed come into thermal equilibrium. Moreover, once reached, this equilibrium distribution was *maintained* at future times, since apart from the statistical fluctuations due to the relatively small number of particles in the system, the distribution remained unchanged as the simulation continued.

The results in Figure 9.4 show that our system reaches the expected equilibrium distribution when started from a particular initial state. It is also interesting to consider the behavior starting from *different* initial states. We know that a real system can be started in different initial states but still reach the *same* final equilibrium state, assuming of course that the temperature, pressure, etc., are kept the same.[11] The same is true for our molecular dynamics model. This can be demonstrated using the speed distribution, as we will explore in the exercises. Here we consider this question using the *velocity* distributions $P_x(v_x)$ and $P_y(v_y)$. While these are closely related to the speed distributions just considered, they contain additional information relating to the direction of the motion. While our results for the speed distribution indicated that the magnitudes of the velocities were distributed properly for a system in thermal equilibrium, the velocity distributions can tell us if the directions are also given correctly.

We chose an initial state in which half the particles were given an initial x component of (reduced) velocity chosen randomly in the range $-1 \le v_x \le +1$ with $v_y = 0$, and the others were given $v_x = 0$ with $-1 \le v_y \le +1$. This is certainly a very peculiar situation, which is nowhere near a Maxwell distribution (9.8), so if the system manages to come into equilibrium starting from this state, we would expect that the same would be found for (most) other initial states (we'll consider some exceptional situations in the exercises). We see from the results on the right in Figure 9.4 that our gas quickly reached the expected distributions for both $P_x(v_x)$ and $P_y(v_y)$; we will leave it to the reader to verify that these distributions do indeed have the Maxwell form (9.8). This provides us with more evidence (and greater confidence) that molecular dynamics provides a way to simulate a mechanical system in thermal equilibrium.

An important quantity for a system in thermal equilibrium is the temperature. As we have already mentioned, T does not enter the simulations as an input parameter. It must instead be "measured," and the results for the speed and velocity distributions give us a way to make this measurement. To demonstrate this we show in Figure 9.5 the results for the speed distributions obtained from two separate simulations. In one case the initial velocity components were both chosen randomly in the range ± 1, while in the second this range was ± 2. Hence, on average, the atoms in the latter case had greater speeds and were, therefore, "hotter." This can be seen from the fact that the speed at which the peak occurs in $P(v)$ is shifted to higher values of v in the system that had the larger initial velocities. Comparing this with the form of the Maxwell distribution, we can see that the location of this peak is determined directly by the temperature. We could thus use the peak location in conjunction with (9.7) to measure T.

A more commonly used approach is to make use of the equipartition theorem. As mentioned above, this theorem states that for a classical system an average energy of $k_B T/2$ is associated with any degree of freedom that enters the energy quadratically. The kinetic energy of an atom in our two-dimensional system is $m(v_x^2 + v_y^2)/2$, so the equipartition theorem tells us that for a system in thermal

---

[11] Indeed, this is one of the features that makes the concept of equilibrium so useful in the first place.

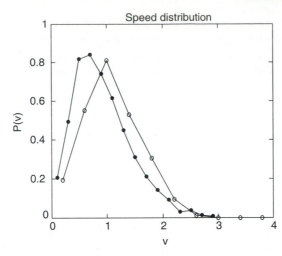

Figure 9.5: Speed distributions. Filled circles: obtained after equilibration from a state with initial velocities v_x and v_y chosen randomly in the range ± 1. Open circles: same, but with v_x and v_y chosen randomly in the range ± 2. The system thus had more energy in this case, and the peak in the speed distribution comes at a correspondingly larger value of v. These speed distributions were obtained by averaging over the interval $t = 0 - 20$.

equilibrium[12]

$$k_B \, T \; = \; < \frac{m}{2} \; (v_x^2 \; + \; v_y^2) > \, , \tag{9.9}$$

where the (reduced) temperature is measured in units of ϵ / k_B, which is ≈ 120 K for argon. Here the angular brackets can be interpreted in two ways. According to one point of view, (9.9) applies to each atom in the system, so we can obtain T by computing the *time* average of the kinetic energy of one particular atom. However, since the atoms are all equivalent, the same result can be obtained by averaging (at a particular instant in time) over the different atoms in the system.[13] In practice, the best computational accuracy will be obtained by combining the two points of view and computing the time average of the kinetic energy per atom averaged over all of the atoms. We will leave it to the exercises to compare the temperature calculated from (9.9) with the value obtained by fitting the Maxwell distribution functions directly to the results in Figures 9.4 and 9.5.

Exercises

1. Calculate the speed distributions for a dilute gas as in Figure 9.4 and compare the results quantitatively with the Maxwell distribution. This analysis also yields the temperature; compare the value you find with the result calculated directly from the equipartition theorem (9.9).

---

[12]Note that this assumes that the overall translational kinetic energy of the system as a whole is negligible. For a molecular-dynamics simulation this simply means that the center of mass velocity must be much smaller than that of a typical atom. Otherwise a system in which the atoms were all at rest relative to each other would, if the center of mass velocity were large, have a high temperature, at least according to (9.9). However, we know that this cannot be the case.

[13]This should remind you of the ergodic hypothesis.

2. Calculate the speed distributions starting from different initial states and show that if the initial kinetic energy is the same and the particles are widely separated so that the potential energy is also the same, the equilibrium distributions are the same. Hint: Choose the initial velocities so that the average values of v_x and v_y are both zero. See the next problem for a discussion of why this is important.

*3. Repeat the previous problem, but now consider how (and if) certain "peculiar" initial states approach equilibrium. Consider a dilute gas in a 10×10 box containing 20 particles. Give all of the particles an initial v_x, which is positive; you might, for example, choose v_x randomly in the range 0–1. Show that the distribution $P(v_x)$ never assumes the form (9.8), as the average value of v_x will always be positive rather than zero. Explain why this follows from conservation laws. Hint: Consider the conservation of momentum.

4. Study the diffusion of particles in a dilute system. For example, take 16 particles in a 10×10 box and calculate the mean-square displacement of an atom as a function of time. Show that the motion is indeed diffusive [that $(\Delta r)^2 \approx Dt$], and find the value of the diffusion constant. You can also study how D varies with density. The diffusion of an atom in a system containing a large number of like atoms is known as self-diffusion. Hint: Be sure to allow for the teleportation associated with the periodic boundary conditions when you calculate Δr.

5. The first molecular-dynamics simulations (see Alder and Wainwright [1959]) treated a system of hard disks. In this case the potential is zero when the separation exceeds the disk diameter and infinite for smaller separations, and collisions are assumed to be elastic. Perform a simulation for this case and compare the velocity distribution with the Maxwell form. This may remind you of the billiard problem of Chapter 3.

*6. The Lennard-Jones potential (9.4) describes a pairwise interaction between atoms and is a function only of their separation. Explain why this potential would *not* be useful for modeling a system in which the bonding between atoms is covalent. Discuss what new features the potential must have in this case. Hint: Consider the role of bond angles.

*7. Investigate the approach to equilibrium of a system containing only a few particles. We have already seen in connection with Figure 9.4 that a gas containing 20 particles will come into equilibrium, as observed using the velocity distribution. However, as an extreme case we know that this will not happen for a gas containing only a single particle, since in this case v_x and v_y will never change (assuming periodic boundary conditions). Perform simulations like those in Figure 9.4 for a system containing 2 particles. Does this system come into equilibrium in the sense of (9.7) and (9.8)? Explain why it does not. Hint: Consider how momentum is exchanged in each collision. Repeat the calculation with 3, 4, ... particles and explain your results.

8. Write a program that uses hard-wall boundary conditions. That is, when a particle hits a wall it should be specularly reflected, as in the billiard problem of Chapter 3. Show that a gas of 20 particles in a 10×10 box reaches an equilibrium state such as that shown in Figure 9.4.

*9. The behavior of the total energy of a gas as a function of temperature can reveal the importance of interactions between the atoms. This can be appreciated by calculating the energy as a function of T for several different densities (a time step of 0.01 is a good choice for all of the simulations below).
   a) Begin by calculating E, the sum of the kinetic and potential energies of all of the particles, for a system containing 16 particles in a box of size 20×20. Show that to a reasonably good

approximation E varies linearly with T, with $E \rightarrow 0$ as $T \rightarrow 0$. Explain why this should be expected for a very dilute gas. Hint: When the particles are far apart the potential energy will be negligible, so E is then approximately equal to the kinetic energy. What does the equipartition theorem then tell you about $E(T)$?

b) Increase the density by confining the same number of particles to a 5×5 box. You should now observe that E does not vanish as $T \rightarrow 0$. Explain how this is a result of the interactions between particles. This is an example of a "nonideal" gas.

10. In order to fully characterize a gas it is useful to measure (or calculate) the equation of state. For this you need to know the pressure. This can be calculated in a molecular-dynamics simulation in the following way. If the simulation employs hard-wall boundary conditions, the pressure on a wall of the container will be the force per unit area exerted by the particles that are reflected by the wall. This force can be calculated from the momentum change that the wall imparts on each particle it reflects. A simulation that uses periodic boundary conditions will not have any walls or reflections, but the same quantity can be obtained by considering the particles that "pass through" a particular boundary as part of the teleportation process associated with periodic boundary conditions. Every time a particle tries to pass through the surface at $x = +L$ (we assume an $L \times L$ box), it is transported via the periodic boundary conditions to $x = -L$. This particle carries an amount of momentum mv_x in the x direction. If there had been a hard wall at this location, the particle would have been reflected ($v_x \rightarrow -v_x$), which would have imparted a momentum $2mv_x$ to the wall (since momentum is conserved in a collision with the wall). The force on the wall is the momentum per unit time that is transferred to it by all collisions, and the pressure is the force per unit area.

Use this approach to calculate the pressure of a dilute gas as a function of temperature. Good parameter choices are 16 particles in a 10×10 box with $\Delta t = 0.02$. Calculate P and show that it varies linearly with T. Explain why this is so. Hint: Consider the equation of state for an ideal gas.

9.2   The Melting Transition

In Section 9.1 we introduced the technique of molecular dynamics and used it to investigate several properties of a dilute gas and how it approaches equilibrium. In this section we will use the same method to investigate the melting transition. Melting is a phenomenon in which the interactions between particles play a crucial role. The phases involved in melting, the liquid and solid phases, are direct results of these interactions. Hence, in order to provide a quantitative description of melting, a method that treats interparticle interactions in a realistic manner is essential. Molecular dynamics is an ideal choice.

We have already mentioned that melting is a first-order phase transition, so we expect to find an abrupt change in the system when it melts. One of our tasks will be to devise useful measures of "liquidness" and "solidness." This will turn out to be a little more difficult than you might suspect and will force us to think carefully about what is meant by the terms *liquid* and *solid*.

Let us first establish that our molecular-dynamics approach yields a system that is a solid under the appropriate conditions, namely low temperatures and high density. In order to make T as low as possible, we will start with all of the particles at rest. This does not mean that they will remain at rest, since each will move in response to forces from neighboring particles. Nevertheless, this will give us a low initial temperature. The density is also important, since we expect that for low densities, that is,

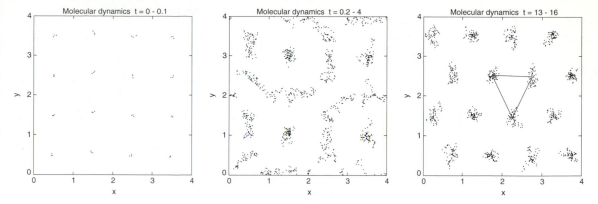

Figure 9.6: Snapshots of a system of 16 particles in a 4 × 4 box at a low temperature. The time step in the simulation was 0.005 in reduced units. These are "time-lapsed" pictures, taken over the time intervals indicated in each figure. The position was recorded after every 10 time steps. On the right we have drawn lines connecting several nearest neighbor atoms to make the triangular structure clear.

for a large average particle separation, the system will be a gas. Examining the Lennard-Jones potential in Figure 9.1 we note that the maximum attraction occurs for an interparticle spacing of approximately $1.2\sigma = 1.2$ in reduced units. Hence, we are led to choose a density of approximately 1 particle for each (reduced) unit of area.

Some results for such a dense system are shown in Figure 9.6. Here we consider 16 particles in a 4 × 4 box, with the particles initially arranged on a square lattice. However, while the particles were at first all at rest, this arrangement was not stable and they immediately began to move; Figure 9.6 shows "time-lapsed" snapshots of the system during various time intervals. The plot on the left shows snapshots taken over the first few time steps, and it is seen that the particles have moved only a little from their initial positions, as the square lattice is still apparent. However, when given some time the particles move substantial amounts, as shown in the plot in the center, which shows a superposition of snapshots taken during the period $t = 0.2$–4. Eventually an equilibrium state is reached, which is shown in the picture on the far right in Figure 9.6. While the particles are still in motion here, each moves in a region that is only $\approx \pm 0.2$ units in size. This is a crystalline solid.[14] However, we can see

---

[14]We need to choose our words carefully here, since the stability of a solid in two dimensions is a rather tricky issue. It turns out that in two dimensions, an infinitely large solid would actually be unstable. That is, an infinitely large two-dimensional crystal would not be the thermodynamically stable phase at any nonzero temperature. This has been established through exact analytic arguments, as described by Mermin (1968) (see also Nelson [1983]). Nevertheless, it appears that finite systems, such as those we study in this section, can be in a state that for nearly all practical purposes is a crystalline solid. The melting transition of an infinitely large two-dimensional system is believed to differ in some subtle ways from that of a three-dimensional solid, as discussed in the references. We will ignore these complications here, as they do not affect the points we wish to make regarding the qualitative aspects of melting. To within the accuracy and resolution of our simulations it is safe to assume, as we will below, that our two dimensional system is an ordinary solid at low temperatures and that the melting transition in two dimensions is an ordinary first-order transition.

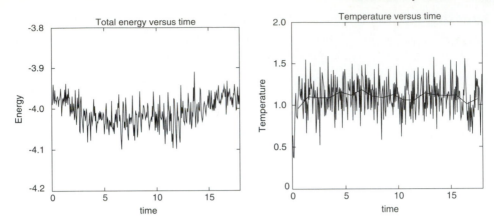

Figure 9.7: Energy and temperature as functions of time for the simulation in Figure 9.6. The solid slowly varying line on the right shows the temperature as averaged over intervals of $\Delta t = 1$.

that the arrangement of the atoms now is *not* a square lattice (as set up originally). Rather, we have a *triangular* lattice. It turns out that this structure minimizes the energy[15] for particles interacting through the Lennard-Jones potential.

Given the rather small size of our system we might worry that boundary effects could influence the crystal structure. Even though we have employed periodic boundary conditions, this does *not* eliminate the effects of the boundaries. These boundary conditions still impose a "square" shape on the system, since the periodicity conditions have that geometry. The fact that we have obtained a structure that is far from square implies that a triangular structure has a significantly lower energy than a square lattice and that the free energy barrier that separates the two phases is also not too large (this should remind you of our discussion of hysteresis in connection with the Ising model in Chapter 8). Thus, it is probably safe to conclude that in this case a triangular lattice is the most stable solid structure for the Lennard-Jones potential. It is possible to treat the periodic boundary conditions in a more general way, in which the *shape* of the effective box is allowed to vary. Such an approach is more complicated, but is required if we want to determine the most stable solid without any bias imposed by the simulation.

We mentioned earlier that the Verlet method was chosen because it conserves the energy fairly well over the course of many time steps. This claim is justified in Figure 9.7, which shows both the total energy (kinetic plus potential) and the temperature for the simulation that yielded the snapshots in Figure 9.6. Since there are no external sources of energy, E should be conserved exactly. We see that the energy remained approximately constant (the vertical scale here is greatly expanded), with fluctuations of about ± 2 percent due to numerical errors associated with the Verlet method. These errors could be made smaller by using a smaller time step, but this would require more computer time. The time step used here is suitable for our purposes, but a research calculation would probably strive to keep variations in E below 1 percent.

The plot on the right in Figure 9.7 shows the variation of the temperature for the same simulation. As in the previous section, we have calculated T using the equipartition theorem, (9.9). It is important

---

[15]Actually it minimizes the free energy, but at the low temperature considered here this is nearly equal to the energy.

to realize that this relation holds for any classical system, even one in which the interactions between particles are strong, as they are here. While the fluctuations in the energy are fairly small, the corresponding fluctuations in the temperature are much larger. They are so large, in fact, that we might worry that the concept of temperature may not be useful (or appropriate). However, the difficulty here is not with the concept of temperature, but in our calculation of the averages needed to evaluate (9.9). To estimate T we need to compute the averages of v_x^2 and v_y^2 for all of the particles. In the simulation here the number of particles was fairly small (only 16), so we shouldn't expect these averages to have a high precision. However, this problem can be circumvented by performing an additional time average of the values of T in Figure 9.7, an example of which is shown in Figure 9.7. Here we have averaged the values of T over time intervals of size $\Delta t = 1$, and the fluctuations are now much reduced. The message here is that when evaluating the averages that arise in statistical physics, the fact that there is a small number of particles must be kept in mind. Actually, while this is a concern for small-scale simulations like those we have used here to illustrate the molecular-dynamics algorithm, it would usually not be a serious problem in a research calculation, as these typically use many thousands of particles.

Now that we have obtained a system that is a solid, we must devise a method to heat it in order to observe melting. This is usually accomplished by increasing the kinetic energy "by hand." That is, we increase the velocities of all of the particles by a factor that is greater than unity. This gives them all some additional kinetic energy and through (9.9) will increase the temperature. After increasing the velocities we must then give the system a chance to come into equilibrium. The additional energy is injected as purely kinetic energy, but we know that as the system comes back into equilibrium this energy will be redistributed among the kinetic and potential energies of the particles.

As a programming note, we must be careful when rescaling the velocities since it is the positions that enter[16] the equations of motion (9.2). With the Verlet algorithm we have the position at both the current and the previous time step. A convenient way to rescale the kinetic energies is to adjust the location at the *previous* time step in the following way. Let $\vec{r}_c$ and $\vec{r}_p$ be the current and previous positions [$\vec{r}_c = (x_c, y_c)$, etc.]. If we want to increase the velocity by a factor of 2, we adjust $\vec{r}_p$ so as to make it twice as far from $\vec{r}_c$. In general, to rescale the velocity by an amount R we take

$$\vec{r}_p \;\rightarrow\; \vec{r}_c \,-\, R\,(\vec{r}_c \,-\, \vec{r}_p)\,. \qquad (9.10)$$

This is not the only way that we could rescale the velocities, but it does have one important property; it does not alter the current positions. If we had, instead, chosen to adjust $\vec{r}_c$, we would affect the current potential energy, as well. However, as long as the time step is small, either approach would be suitable. While we will usually use this rescaling procedure to increase the temperature, it can also be used to decrease the temperature, as would be needed to study freezing or condensation.

In Figure 9.8 we show snapshots of our system as it was heated in stages. The corresponding energy and temperature as functions of time are shown in Figure 9.9, where the abrupt steplike increases in E show the times when the kinetic energy was increased. At each of these points the velocities were increased by a factor of 1.5, and as expected the temperature increases along with E. The fluctuations in T also increased dramatically as the temperature was raised. In our discussion of the Monte Carlo method in Chapter 8, we saw that such fluctuations are related to quantities such as the specific heat (we will leave the exploration of this issue to the industrious reader).

---

[16]While the velocities can be calculated at each time step, for the form of the Verlet method that we have described they do not enter into determining the position at the next time step.

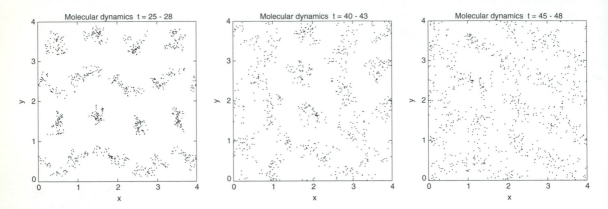

Figure 9.8: Time-lapse snapshots at several temperatures as the system considered in Figure 9.6 was heated in stages. The time intervals are given at the top of each plot, and the corresponding energy and temperature are shown in Figure 9.9.

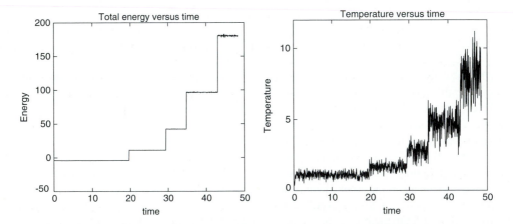

Figure 9.9: Energy and temperature as functions of time for the simulation in Figures 9.6 and 9.8. Each abrupt increase in E was produced by rescaling the velocities by a factor of 1.5.

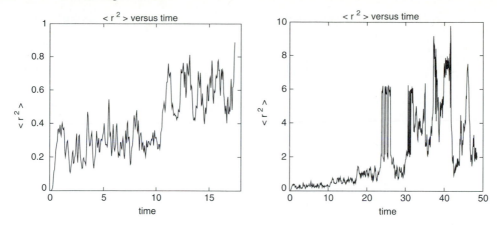

Figure 9.10: Motion of a "test" particle in the simulation of Figure 9.8. Left: behavior at early times corresponding to a temperature $T \sim 1.1$; right: variation of $< r^2 >$ as the temperature was increased in stages as shown on the right in Figure 9.9. Note that the vertical scale is very different in the two plots.

Our goal in this section is to observe the melting transition, and it is time for us to finally tackle that problem. By examining the snapshots of the system at various temperatures in Figure 9.8, we can clearly see by eye that the system became increasingly disordered as the temperature was raised. However, it not obvious (at least to the author) how to locate the melting transition from these snapshots alone. In a sense, the information in the snapshots is too "microscopic." Most of the properties that we associate with a solid are based not on the positions of individual atoms, but on thermodynamic types of variables. Unfortunately, thermodynamic variables are often the ones that are most difficult to determine accurately with molecular dynamics.

What we really need is a quantitative measure of solidness and liquidness; preferably this measure should be closely connected with the motion of individual atoms, since that is the type of information we have at our disposal. It turns out that there are several such measures that could be employed. One is to consider in detail the motion of a particular particle, which might be termed a "test particle" even though it is equivalent to all of the others in the system. To illustrate the approach, we have chosen one particle in Figure 9.8 and recorded its position as a function of time. The square of the displacement from its initial position is shown in Figure 9.10. These values were obtained from the simulation considered in Figure 9.9, so the corresponding temperatures can be read from those results. At the lowest temperature (corresponding to the earliest times) the particle quickly settled into a position a small distance away from its initial position, as the structure changed from the initial square form to a triangular lattice. Our test particle then remained nearly stationary up to $t \approx 11$. While the particle did move a little during this interval, the mean-square displacement was a small fraction of the spacing between atoms (which was ≈ 1). There was an abrupt shift in the particle's position at $t \approx 11$, but the overall displacement was still much less than the average spacing between particles and was probably due to motion of the entire lattice.[17] Overall, the behavior for $t < 11$ is that expected for a particle in a solid.

---

[17] Precisely what happened at $t \approx 11$ could be determined by examining snapshots before and after the displacement. The beauty (and power) of molecular dynamics is that we have such information in great detail.

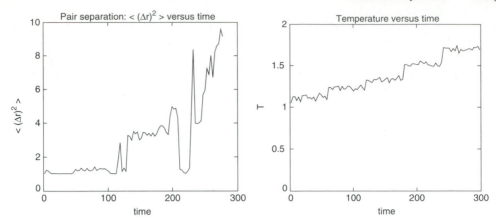

Figure 9.11:   Left: mean-square separation of a pair of atoms as a function of time while a system similar to that in Figure 9.8 was slowly heated; right: corresponding variation of the temperature. The temperature was increased by rescaling the velocities by a factor of 1.1 at $t = 60, 120, 180, \ldots$.

As the temperature was increased, the fluctuations of the particle's position became larger. During the period $t \approx 23$–26 it shifted back and forth between two fairly well-defined locations, before returning (approximately) to its original location at $t \approx 28$. It thus appears that the particle was moving between several different lattice sites, or perhaps the entire lattice was shifting in space. With either interpretation, while our test particle was certainly more mobile than it was at lower temperatures, the system was probably still a solid, since there appear to be fairly discrete "lattice positions" available to the particle. However, after the temperature increase at $t \approx 30$, the behavior changed qualitatively, as the displacement fluctuated rapidly over distances much greater than a lattice spacing and did not tend to prefer any discrete values. This suggests that the system had become a liquid.[18] These fluctuations increased further in magnitude as the system was heated again at $t \approx 35$ and 42. From the corresponding results for the temperature as a function of time in Figure 9.9 we conclude that the melting transition took place at a temperature somewhere in the range $T \sim 1.5$–2.0.

There are several other measures that we can use to discern whether the system is a solid or a liquid, several of which will be explored in the exercises. We will next consider one that involves the *relative* separation of two atoms. We monitor the square of the separation of two adjacent atoms, $(\Delta r)^2$, as a function of time, the idea being that in a solid this separation will remain (fairly) constant with time, while in a liquid it will not, since in the latter case the atoms will undergo diffusion. Some results of this kind are given in Figure 9.11, which shows $(\Delta r)^2$ as the system was slowly heated, starting again from the solid phase. The separation was initially ~ 1 (in reduced units) as the atoms were in adjacent lattice sites. This separation remained relatively constant up to about $t \approx 120$, when it increased to $(\Delta r)^2 \sim 3.5$ (recall that here we are plotting the square of the separation), but then it stayed at that value. This indicates that one of the atoms in the pair jumped to a different lattice site, but since the separation remained at a (relatively) "quantized" value, the system was still a solid. Comparing this

---

[18]Strictly speaking, from these results we really can't distinguish between a liquid and a gas. That would require a study of the phase diagram.

with the triangular lattice in Figure 9.6, we see that this separation corresponds to the separation of second nearest neighbors in our triangular lattice. [$(\Delta r)^2 \sim 3.5$ in Figure 9.11 implies a spacing of about 1.9 in reduced units.] However, at $t \approx 200$ the separation began to change rapidly and erratically with time, signaling a much enhanced motion of one or both of the atoms. This is precisely what we expect for a liquid, and we conclude that melting occurred at $T \sim 1.5$. This value is a little more accurate than that obtained from Figure 9.10, as in this simulation the system was heated more slowly.

A key feature of these results is that the melting transition was, to within the resolution of these simulations, abrupt. There were no warnings or enhanced fluctuations to indicate that the transition was imminent. This is in accord with the claim we made earlier that the melting transition is *first order*. While this has admittedly been a very rough analysis of melting, our results do show that the behavior changes dramatically as the temperature is increased. To do a better job of locating the transition would require a careful examination of other properties. We will leave this to the exercises (and also to the readers' exploration of references).

Exercises

1. Study the melting transition at different densities. You should find that the melting temperature drops as the density is reduced. For 16 particles in a box of size 4.3×4.3, you should find melting near $T = 1.0$. Toxvaerd (1978) describes a careful study of the melting curve in two dimensions.

2. In our determination of the lattice structure in Figure 9.6, we began the simulation with the particles in an ordered array. How do we know that the triangular lattice we found is really the stable-lattice type? One way to address this question is to repeat the simulation with the atoms in different initial arrangements. For example, we could begin with the atoms in a honeycomb lattice (in which all of the atoms have three nearest neighbors), or you could start with a disordered arrangement. Perform this simulation at several temperatures below the melting temperature determined from the results in Figure 9.11 (keeping the same density as in that simulation), and determine the final stable structure of the atoms.

3. Investigate melting in a three-dimensional system. First determine the structure of the solid (it should be face-centered cubic), then try to locate the melting temperature.

*4. A useful quantity for studies of structure is the pair correlation function, $g(r)$. This is the density of particles per unit distance, at a separation r from any given particle. Calculate this from a simulation like that in Figure 9.8, with 16 particles in a 4×4 box and a time step of 0.001. Take one particle as the "origin" and let r be the distance as measured from this point. Divide the r axis into bins (try ~ 40 or so, from $r = 1$ to 3 for this rather small system), and after every 10 time steps record the number of particles in each bin. After many time steps this will yield a histogram that is proportional to $g(r)$. Compare the results for $g(r)$ in the solid and liquid phases. You should find that at low temperatures (i.e., in the solid phase) the correlation function has a large peak at $r \approx 1.1$, with a slightly smaller peak at $r \approx 1.9$ and a much smaller one at $r \approx 2.8$. These correspond to the spacing of first-, second-, and third-nearest neighbors in the (triangular) lattice (Figure 9.6). The (relative) size of the first peak should decrease and its width should increase when the system melts. Give a qualitative argument to explain this. Why do you expect to find peaks in $g(r)$ even in the liquid state? Rahman (1964) gives results for $g(r)$ for a three-dimensional Lennard-Jones system.

*5. Investigate condensation from a gas. Begin with the system in a fairly dilute high-temperature phase; a system of 16 particles in a 30×30 box is a good choice. Then gradually cool the system and see if you can observe condensation. Hint: It is worth thinking carefully about how you can distinguish a liquid from a gas.

*6. Consider again the process of self-diffusion discussed in the exercises in Section 9.1. Here we are interested in using the associated diffusion constant to study melting and, in particular, to locate the melting transition. Calculate the diffusion constant for self-diffusion for a system of 16 particles in a 4×4 box as a function of temperature. Compare its value in the solid and liquid phases. Can it be used to determine when the system melts? Hint: To improve your statistical accuracy, average the diffusion constants for all of the particles; this makes sense since they are all identical and should, therefore, diffuse in the same manner. However, be sure to account for the teleportation associated with the periodic boundary conditions when calculating the mean-square displacement of an atom.

References

ALDER, B. J. and T. E. WAINWRIGHT. 1959. "Studies in Molecular Dynamics I. General Method." *J. Chem. Phys.* **31**, 459. Pioneering application of molecular dynamics to a system of hard disks.

HEERMANN, D. W. 1990. *Computer Simulation Methods in Theoretical Physics*, 2d ed. New York: Springer-Verlag. Contains a nice introduction to molecular dynamics and discusses how the method can be used to simulate a system that evolves according to the canonical ensemble.

MERMIN, N. D. 1968. "Crystalline Order in Two Dimensions." *Phys. Rev.* **176**, 250. Some intriguing exact results concerning the (non)stability of a hypothetical *infinitely* large solid.

NELSON, D. R. 1983. *Defect-mediated Phase Transitions*, in *Phase Transitions and Critical Phenomena*, vol. 7. C. Domb and J. L. Lebowitz, eds. Orlando, Fla.: Academic Press, p. 1. Contains a detailed discussion of the theory of melting in two dimensions.

RAHMAN, A. 1964. "Correlations in the Motion of Atoms in Liquid Argon." *Phys. Rev.* **136**, A405. A very readable paper describing a molecular dynamics study of pair correlations in a Lennard-Jones liquid.

REIF, F. 1965. *Fundamentals of Statistical and Thermal Physics*. New York: McGraw-Hill. Reviews statistical mechanics, including a discussion of the Maxwell-Boltzmann distributions.

SCHIFF, L. I. 1968. *Quantum Mechanics*, 3d ed. New York: McGraw-Hill. Contains a nice discussion of the origin of the Van der Waals interaction, which is a key ingredient of the Lennard-Jones potential.

TOXVAERD, S. 1978. "Melting in a Two-Dimensional Lennard-Jones System." *J. Chem. Phys.* **69**, 4750. A careful study of melting in two dimensions using molecular dynamics.

VERLET, L. 1967. "Computer 'Experiments' on Classical Fluids. I. Thermodynamical Properties of Lennard-Jones Molecules." *Phys. Rev.* **159**, 98. Description of the Verlet method and a nice description of some molecular dynamics simulations.

10

Quantum Mechanics

There are only a few problems in quantum mechanics that can be solved exactly, most notably the harmonic oscillator, a particle in a box, and the hydrogen atom. Nearly all other nontrivial quantum problems either have no known analytic solutions or can be attacked analytically only with extreme difficulty. This is why perturbation methods play such an important role in quantum theory, and also why numerical methods are an attractive alternative. Indeed, an extremely wide variety of numerical methods have been developed for dealing with quantum problems. There are far too many such methods for us to even mention all of them in this chapter. Our goal, instead, will be to describe a few of the algorithms that have been developed with quantum mechanics in mind, and use them to treat several representative problems.[1] We also hope to find some enlightening overlap with problems and techniques we have encountered in earlier chapters.

This chapter opens with a brief review of the Schrödinger equation and a few of the fundamental ingredients of quantum theory. We then consider several methods for treating time-independent problems. While we have dealt with partial differential equations in a number of previous settings, this is our first encounter with eigenvalue problems. These involve extra complications associated with boundary conditions and require some extensions of the methods we have previously employed. We also describe how Monte Carlo methods can be teamed up with the variational principle to calculate wave functions and eigenvalues. In the second half of this chapter we turn to time-dependent problems and describe two numerical approaches. One involves a direct attack using a matrix formulation, while the other employs a spectral method. The goal, as usual, be to learn how to deal with problems that are difficult or impossible to treat analytically. However, we will find it useful to apply our numerical approaches to several exactly soluble problems, as this will allow us to test the methods and also illustrate some of the key themes of quantum theory.

---

[1]It is not our intention that this chapter be a substitute for a first course in quantum mechanics, although we will review a few aspects of the theory in the next several pages.

10.1 Time-Independent Schrödinger Equation: Some Preliminaries

The time-independent Schrödinger equation for a particle in three dimensions is

$$-\frac{\hbar^2}{2m_-}\nabla^2\psi + V(\vec{r})\,\psi = E\,\psi\,, \tag{10.1}$$

where $\hbar$ is Planck's constant, m is the mass of the particle, V is the potential energy, E is the energy of the particle, and ψ is the wave function. As is well known with quantum theory, it is much easier to write this equation down than to really understand it. The key quantity here is the wave function, which has no direct classical counterpart. In the most general case, ψ is a complex function of position and $\psi(\vec{r})^*\psi(\vec{r})$ is the probability per unit volume that the particle will be found at $\vec{r}$. Here we use the usual notation in which ψ^* is the complex conjugate of ψ.

The fact that ψ can be complex will complicate our numerical treatments.[2] However, another aspect of (10.1) will turn out to be much more important in numerical attacks on this equation. This is a partial differential equation whose form is not very different from the wave equation encountered in Chapter 6, with one important exception. The energy E is *also* an unknown. A complete solution involves determining both ψ and the corresponding energy. These are also known as the eigenfunction and eigenvalue of the equation.[3] An interesting property of eigenvalue problems is that in many cases solutions exist only for certain special values of the eigenvalue, in this case E. Mathematically, this is the origin of the discrete energy levels of quantum theory. It is useful to illustrate these points with an example that can be solved analytically; we will revisit this problem shortly using a numerical approach. Consider a particle moving in free space, that is, a region in which the potential is constant. Since we are free to shift the origin of the potential energy scale, we will take $V = 0$ everywhere. For simplicity we also assume that space is one-dimensional so that $\psi = \psi(x)$ and the ∇^2 operator in (10.1) reduces to the second derivative d^2/dx^2. The Schrödinger (time-independent) equation then becomes

$$-\frac{\hbar^2}{2m}\frac{d^2\psi}{dx^2} = E\,\psi\,, \tag{10.2}$$

which has the general solution

$$\psi = A\,\exp(\imath kx)\,, \tag{10.3}$$

where $\imath \equiv \sqrt{-1}$, and A and k are constants. That this is indeed a solution to (10.2) can be verified by substitution, which yields

$$E = \frac{\hbar k^2}{2m}\,. \tag{10.4}$$

The wave function (10.3) has the form of a plane wave with wave vector $k = 2\pi/\lambda$, where λ is the wavelength of the particle. k is also closely related to the particle's momentum, p, with $p = \hbar k$.

---

[2]While the wave function may be complex, there are many cases in which its phase can be chosen so as to make ψ real. In fact, in our numerical work we will not encounter any situations that absolutely demand that ψ be complex until we deal with time-dependent problems.

[3]Equations in which an operator, such as the ∇^2 operator in (10.1), acting on a function is equal to a constant times the function are known as eigenvalue equations and arise in many other contexts. Griffiths (1995) and Schiff (1968) contain introductions to this topic.

In this particular problem there is a solution to the Schrödinger equation for any value of k, and thus all nonnegative values of E are allowed. We do not have quantized energy levels in this example (at least not yet). The constant A is not determined directly by the Schrödinger equation. Our solution satisfies the wave equation (10.2) for any value of A, a fact we should have expected since the equation is linear. Constants such as A, which set the overall magnitude of the wave function, are determined by the physical interpretation of ψ and its relation to the probability density. We already noted that the probability of finding the particle in a particular region of space is proportional to $\psi^*\psi$. For our one-dimensional case $\psi(x)^*\psi(x)dx$ is the probability of finding the particle within a region of length dx in the neighborhood of x. Since we are considering the behavior of a single particle, this probability must satisfy the normalization condition

$$\int \psi^*\psi \, dx \; = \; 1 \, . \tag{10.5}$$

In words, the total probability for finding the particle someplace must be unity. This condition can generally be used to set the overall magnitude of the wave function. However, applying it to our plane wave yields a minor difficulty. For the wave function (10.3) we have $\psi^*\psi = A^2$, so that $\int \psi^*\psi dx = A^2 \int dx$. If our particle is allowed to roam freely over an infinitely large region, we must make A infinitely small in order to preserve normalization.

It is convenient to deal with this situation by assuming that the particle is confined to a box that extends from $x = -L$ to $x = +L$. The plane wave (10.3) must then fit in this box. The corresponding potential is now $V = 0$ inside the box and very large outside, as sketched in Figure 10.1. Since $V(x)$ is a discontinuous function of position, it is simplest to solve for ψ separately in the regions $|x| \leq L$ (inside the box) and $|x| > L$ (outside the box). Inside we have $V = 0$, so ψ in this region is still given by (10.3). If we assume that the potential outside is $V = \infty$ and that the energy of the particle is not infinite, then the only way we can satisfy the Schrödinger equation in the outside region is if $\psi_{outside} = 0$. This implies that $d^2\psi_{outside}/dx^2 = 0$ also, so both sides of (10.2) are zero. Physically this

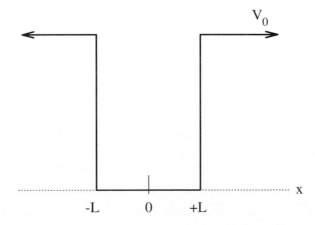

Figure 10.1: Potential energy for a particle in a box. The potential is $V = 0$ inside the box (i.e., for $|x| \leq L$) and V_0 outside. If $V_0 = \infty$, then the box is said to have "hard" walls, while if V_0 is finite, the walls are "soft."

result should not be surprising. A particle with a finite energy will have no chance of being found in a region where $V = \infty$, so the probability amplitude ψ must vanish.

To complete our solution we make use of one more constraint on ψ; it must be a continuous function[4] of x. Since ψ vanishes for $x > \pm L$, the solution for ψ inside the box must vanish at $x = \pm L$. This constraint can be satisfied by noting again that the Schrödinger equation is linear, so the sum of two solutions is also solution. We can, therefore, construct wave functions of the form

$$
\begin{aligned}
\psi_+ &= \tfrac{A}{2}\left[\exp(\imath k_+ x) + \exp(-\imath k_+ x)\right] = A\,\cos(k_+ x)\,, \\
\psi_- &= \tfrac{A}{2}\left[(\exp(\imath k_- x) - \exp(-\imath k_- x)\right] = A\,\sin(k_- x)\,.
\end{aligned}
\tag{10.6}
$$

These are just standing waves, similar to what is found with a vibrating string. The condition $\psi(\pm L) = 0$ requires that

$$
k_+ = \frac{\pi}{2L}\,,\ \frac{3\pi}{2L}\,,\ \cdots = \frac{(2n-1)\pi}{2L}
\tag{10.7}
$$

$$
k_- = \frac{\pi}{L}\,,\ \frac{2\pi}{L}\,,\ \cdots = \frac{n\pi}{L}\,.
\tag{10.8}
$$

This constraint on k means that we now have discrete energy levels. Only certain special values of the wave vector are allowed. These values are those yielding standing waves that satisfy the boundary conditions on ψ at the walls of the box, as shown in Figure 10.2. Quantization of k also implies quantization of the energy since $E = \hbar^2 k^2 / 2m$. Constraints such as these boundary conditions generally lead to quantized levels. We will find that they play a major role in constructing numerical solutions to the Schrödinger equation.

It is interesting to notice that the wave functions (10.6) all have a definite parity; they are either even $\psi(+x) = \psi(-x)$, or odd $\psi(+x) = -\psi(-x)$, with respect x. This property can be traced to the potential energy. Whenever the potential is an even function of x, the wave functions can always be written so as to have a definite parity. This will prove useful in developing a numerical approach in the next section. Note also that the wave functions (10.6) can be properly normalized without coefficients that are infinitely small. The normalization condition (10.5) can be used to determine the value of A for these functions, yielding $A = L^{-1/2}$.

Two other features of the wave functions (10.6) will turn out to be very useful later in this chapter. The forms of these functions may remind you of the sines and cosines encountered in connection with Fourier transforms in Chapter 6 and Appendix 2. It is thus not surprising that these wave functions form an complete set of orthogonal functions over the interval $|x| \leq L$. The term orthogonal means that $\int \psi_1^* \psi_2 dx = 0$, unless ψ_1 and ψ_2 refer to the same eigenstate. The term complete set means that any function[5] in this interval that vanishes at $x = \pm L$ can be written as a sum of these wave functions with suitably chosen coefficients. The orthogonality property makes this expansion, that is, the set of coefficients, unique. Such a collection of functions is usually referred to as a basis set. The

---

[4]This condition is required to make quantities such as the momentum physically well behaved.

[5]We will not worry about pathological functions here.

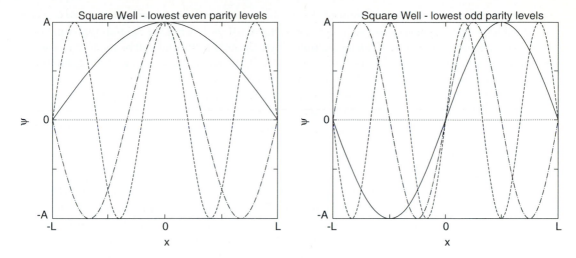

Figure 10.2:   Wave functions for the lowest six eigenstates for a particle in a box. These are the standing waves in (10.6). The figure on the left shows the cosinelike (even parity) standing waves, while the sinelike (odd parity) wave functions are shown at right. In each case the solid curve is the lowest energy state (of that parity). Note that $A = L^{-1/2}$ is required for the wave functions to be properly normalized.

similarity to Fourier transforms, in which the basis set is also composed of sines and cosines, should be evident. However, the basis set need not be this simple, as we will see in an example later in this chapter.

10.2   One Dimension: Shooting and Matching Methods

We next consider how we can solve numerically the time-independent Schrödinger equation in one dimension, using methods similar to those we have previously developed in connection with ordinary differential equations. We begin with the particle-in-a-box problem, as this will allow us to compare with the analytic solution obtained above. We will then consider several problems for which analytic solutions are not available.

The Schrödinger equation in one dimension (10.2) is very similar in form to the equations of motion we encountered in connection with projectiles in Chapter 2. In those cases we had a differential equation involving the position, x, as a function of time. Starting with initial values for x and dx/dt we were able to numerically integrate forward in time to obtain $x(t)$. Now we have a differential equation for ψ as a function of x and we want to use a similar approach. To do this we need the values of ψ and $d\psi/dx$ at some location so that we can begin the integration. These "initial conditions" for the wave function and its derivative are analogous to the initial conditions in a projectile problem. For a projectile these conditions are determined by how the object is struck or thrown, etc. The initial conditions for a wave function are obtained in a somewhat different manner.

When the potential is symmetric, as it is for our particle in a box, we can use the symmetry to our advantage. We noted earlier that if $V(x)$ is an even function of x, the wave functions can be written as purely even or purely odd functions of x. That is, the wave function must satisfy either $\psi(+x) = \psi(-x)$, or $\psi(+x) = -\psi(-x)$. Indeed, we have already observed this symmetry in the analytic solutions for the infinite square well, Figure 10.2. An even parity solution has $d\psi/dx = 0$ at $x = 0$, and it is safe to assume (as we will see shortly) that $\psi(0) \neq 0$. Since the Schrödinger equation is linear, we also know that a solution can be multiplied by a constant factor and still be a solution. We are, therefore, free to *provisionally* choose $\psi(0) = 1$ as an initial value for integration of the Schrödinger equation. When we are finished and have a numerical solution of the equation in hand, we can then normalize that result by a constant factor so as to satisfy the probability constraint $\int \psi^* \psi\, dx = 1$ and thereby obtain a physically acceptable wave function.

The same approach can be used to obtain an odd-parity solution. Since in this case $\psi(x) = -\psi(-x)$, we must have $\psi(0) = 0$ and $d\psi/dx \neq 0$ at $x = 0$. We are again free to pick the scale of ψ, as long as we normalize it at the completion of the calculation, so we can use $\psi(0) = 0$ and $d\psi/dx = 1$ as initial conditions.

By exploiting the symmetry we have thus obtained values for ψ and $d\psi/dx$ at $x = 0$. These are the initial conditions for our integration. The next step is to rewrite (10.2) in finite-difference form. In most of our previous examples we have written such second-order differential equations as two separate first-order equations. Here, since we aren't interested in the derivative $d\psi/dx$, we will take a slightly different approach (which may remind you of the Verlet method). As usual, we discretize space in steps of size Δx and write $\psi_n \equiv \psi(n\Delta x)$. The second derivative in (10.2) can be written in the usual finite-difference form

$$\frac{d^2\psi}{dx^2} \approx \frac{\psi_{n+1} + \psi_{n-1} - 2\psi_n}{(\Delta x)^2}, \tag{10.9}$$

which is similar to the expression we encountered in connection with the wave equation in Chapter 6. Inserting this into (10.2) we have

$$-\frac{\hbar^2}{2m}\frac{d^2\psi}{dx^2} \approx -\frac{\hbar^2}{2m}\left[\frac{\psi_{n+1} + \psi_{n-1} - 2\psi_n}{(\Delta x)^2}\right] \approx (E - V_n)\psi_n, \tag{10.10}$$

where we have written $V_n = V(n\Delta x)$ and have used the $\approx$ signs to emphasize that this is only an approximation to the original differential equation. This can be rearranged to obtain ψ_{n+1} in terms of ψ_n and ψ_{n-1}. For convenience we will, henceforth, use units in which $\hbar = 1$ and $m = 1$, which leads to

$$\psi_{n+1} = 2\psi_n - \psi_{n-1} - 2(\Delta x)^2 (E - V_n)\psi_n. \tag{10.11}$$

Let us first consider the even-parity solutions. We have already argued that we can take $\psi(0) = 1$, so we will first apply (10.11) at $n = 0$ (i.e., $x = 0$). Since we also have $d\psi/dx = 0$ at $x = 0$, we take $\psi_{-1} = 1$ as well, so we can use (10.11) to calculate $\psi_{n+1} = \psi_1$. We then move on and use ψ_0 and ψ_1 to obtain ψ_2. The process can be repeated to find ψ_n for all values of n that are of interest.

This procedure is similar to the way we dealt with projectile motion. However, now we have a complication that we didn't have with baseballs. From the analytic solution for a particle in a box we saw that with hard walls ($V_0 = +\infty$) the wave function must vanish at the walls. This means that we have a boundary condition that ψ must satisfy at $x = \pm L$. In terms of projectiles this is analogous to requiring that the baseball land at a precise location. This will only happen if the initial velocity of the ball has a particular value.[6] Likewise, we will see that for our wave function the conditions at $x = \pm L$ will be satisfied only for certain values of the energy.

---

[6]Or perhaps a value chosen from a discrete set of possibilities.

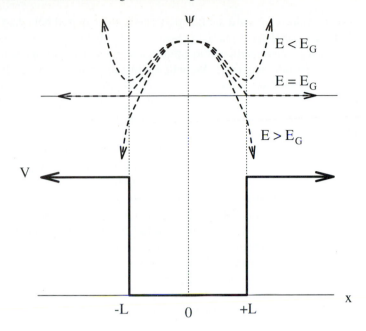

Figure 10.3: Schematic results for ψ calculated from (10.11) for several values of E. Top: behavior for the even-parity solution with E near the ground-state energy, E_G. Bottom: corresponding potential energy. The potential outside the box ($|x| > L$) is assumed to be very large.

It is useful at this point to consider, in a qualitative sense, the behavior of ψ_n obtained by iterating (10.11) with different values of E. Schematic results for three different values of the energy near the ground-state value E_G (you should recall that the ground state is an even-parity solution) are shown in Figure 10.3. We already know E_G from the analytic results. For the units we have chosen here ($\hbar = 1$, $m = 1$, and a box with $L = 1$), the ground state has an energy[7] of $E_G = \pi^2/8 = 1.2337\ldots$. If we were to use (10.11) to calculate ψ for a value of E that is smaller than this, we would find that ψ is greater than zero when we reach $x = L$ and then diverges to $+\infty$ at larger x, so the boundary condition is *not* satisfied. This is illustrated by the top curve in Figure 10.3. While this function is a solution of (10.2), it cannot be normalized and thus cannot be made to yield a physically acceptable probability density. It is, therefore, not an allowed wave function for our particle. On the other hand, if we were to perform this calculation with a value of E that is slightly larger than E_G, we would find that ψ drops too quickly with x, so that it is negative when we reach $x = L$ and diverges to $-\infty$ at larger x, as illustrated in Figure 10.3. Only if E has *precisely* the value E_G will the wave function reach zero at precisely $x = L$ and remain zero at larger values of x. This wave function is normalizable and is the ground state ψ for our particle in a box.

This approach for solving a differential equation that has boundary conditions that must be satisfied at *both* ends of an interval is known as the shooting method. The method is analogous to trying to throw a baseball or shoot a cannon shell so as to hit a specified target. Only for certain special

---
[7]This can be verified from the results for k_+ (10.7) in the previous section.

conditions, in this case the value of E, will the function satisfy the required boundary conditions (that is, will the ball land at the desired spot). In the present case the boundary conditions[8] are such that the wave function must vanish at two particular locations ($x = \pm L$). This was a result of choosing the potential outside the box to be infinitely large. We will see in a moment how to handle cases in which the potential energy varies more slowly with position, such as a box with "soft" walls or a harmonic oscillator.

Let us next consider how to construct a program that implements this approach. The basic plan is to use (10.11) to calculate $\psi(x)$ for different values of the energy, and choose the result that comes closest to satisfying the boundary conditions at the walls of the box. This procedure will yield *both* the wave function and the corresponding energy. We will actually design our program to search systematically for the proper value of E and thereby approach the correct value very closely. The subroutine listed below uses the shooting method to integrate starting from $x = 0$ (we again assume $L = 1$), beginning with $\psi_{-1} = \psi_0 = 1$ corresponding to an even-parity solution.[9] After initializing variables such as the spatial step size $\Delta x =$dx and the initial estimate for the energy E, the subroutine calculate is called. This routine integrates from i=0 (which corresponds to $x = 0$) to larger values of i, stopping when the wave function psi begins to diverge. At this point the loop is exited and the results for psi displayed (the display routine is given with the rest of the program in Appendix 4). From Figure 10.3 we know as that, assuming E was not precisely equal to one of the eigenvalues, the value of the energy should now be adjusted either up or down depending on which direction psi last diverged. Our routine adds an amount de to E, giving a new estimate for the energy, and the integration is repeated. Let us suppose that E has just been increased (de > 0). If in the next trial psi diverges in the *same* direction as in the previous case, this means that we did not change the energy enough. The routine would then increase E again and repeat the integration. However, if psi now diverges in the opposite direction, that means we have changed E by too much and have *overshot* the correct value of the energy. The calculate routine then cuts the value of de in half, changes its *sign*, and adds it to E, so that we now proceed back toward the solution. We thus hunt down the correct value of the energy with ever-decreasing values of |de|.

---

[8]Because of the symmetry, we, in effect, have boundary conditions at $x = 0$ and $x = L$.

[9]We will leave it to the exercises to modify this routine to deal with the odd-parity solutions.

```
! psi() = wave function, dx = spatial grid size, Vmax is potential outside box
! energy is current best guess for E, de is amount E is changed in hunting
! for a solution
sub calculate(psi(),dx,Vmax,energy,de)
    declare def potential      ! potential energy function
    psi(0) = 1                 ! search for an even-parity solution
    psi(-1) = 1
    last_diverge = 0           ! use to keep track of direction of last divergence
                               ! loop as we zero in on the proper value of E
    print "Energy (hit any key to go to the next trial energy)"
    do
        print energy
        for i = 0 to size(psi)-1      ! integrate from x=0 to 1
            psi(i+1) = 2 * psi(i) - psi(i-1)
                - 2 * (energy - potential(i*dx,Vmax))* dx^2*psi(i)
            if abs(psi(i+1)) > 2 then exit for   ! psi is diverging so stop now
        next i
        call display(psi,i,dx)            ! display this estimate for psi
        get key z                         ! wait for a key stroke before continuing
        if chr$(z) = "q" then exit do     ! exit if the current solution is
                                          ! close enough
        if psi(i+1) > 0 then              ! keep track of which way psi diverges
            diverge = +1                  ! so can change de if necessary
        else
            diverge = -1
        end if
        if diverge * last_diverge < 0 then de = -de / 2
        energy = energy + de              ! choose a new value of energy and repeat
        last_diverge = diverge
    loop
end sub
def potential(x,V)         ! the potential is 0 inside the box and V outside
    if abs(x) <= 1 then    ! walls are at x = +1 and -1
        potential = 0
    else
        potential = V
    end if
end def
```

In the `calculate` routine it is convenient to employ a user-defined function[10] for $V(x)$. This function is called `potential` and its listing is also shown. Using a custom function in this way makes `calculate` easier to read and understand and also makes it simpler to modify the program to deal with other potential functions.

Some results from this program are shown in Figure 10.4 where we plot ψ calculated for several values of E near the exact value for the lowest energy level, $E_G = 1.2337\ldots$. Here we have taken $V = 0$ inside the box and $V = V_0 = 1000$ outside. This behavior is just like the schematic illustrations in Figure 10.3, with ψ diverging to either $+\infty$ or $-\infty$, depending on whether E is above or below the energy that best satisfies the boundary conditions. As the search routine approached this value, the boundary condition $\psi(L) = 0$ was satisfied with increasing precision and the divergence of ψ was pushed to larger and larger values of x. The last value of E considered here was 1.1790; decreasing it

---

[10]By this we mean a function that is constructed by the user as opposed to being built into the language (or its libraries).

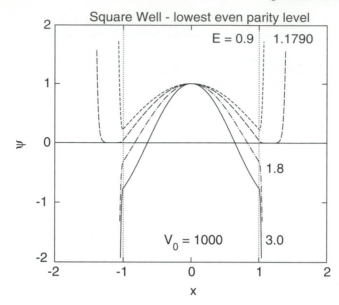

Figure 10.4: Trial ground-state wave functions calculated for a box, that is, a square well, with the shooting method for several values of the energy. The potential was $V = 0$ inside the box ($|x| \leq 1$) and $V = 1000$ outside. The dotted lines show the positions of the walls of the box. The spatial step size was $\Delta x = 0.01$. The calculation assumed $\psi(0) = 1$, so the wave functions are not normalized.

by only 0.0001 caused ψ to diverge to $-\infty$. Hence, these two values of E closely bracket the "best" numerical value. You may notice that this is a few percent lower than the exact value for a box with infinitely hard walls. We will see in a moment that this difference is due (largely) to the value used for V outside the box. The exact value for E_G quoted above assumes $V_0 = +\infty$, while the calculation here used $V_0 = 1000$.

This procedure can be employed to find the other even-parity levels by beginning the search at higher values of E. Finally, we should point out that the wave functions given in Figure 10.4 are not properly normalized. To do this would require that ψ be rescaled by a constant factor so as to satisfy (10.5). Note that this rescaling should be done using the wave function for $|x| \leq L$ from Figure 10.4 (that is, the diverging part outside the box should not be included). We will leave this task to the reader.

Next we consider the calculation of the odd-parity levels. We will leave this job mainly to the exercises, although we will show a few results here. As we have already mentioned, the odd-parity wave functions are the solutions to (10.2) for which $\psi(+x) = -\psi(-x)$. Applying this condition at $x = 0$ requires that $\psi(0) = 0$. Since, as we have argued above, the overall magnitude of ψ at this stage is arbitrary,[11] we take $d\psi/dx = 1$ at $x = 0$. Hence, the `calculate` routine can again be used to obtain $\psi(x)$ by integration, the only difference being that we must employ the initial values `psi(-1)=-dx` and `psi(0)=0`. The rest of the calculation proceeds as before, as our routine hunts down the value of

---

[11] We can once again adjust the magnitude of $\psi(x)$ at the end of the calculation so as to satisfy the normalization condition $\int \psi^* \psi \, dx = 1$.

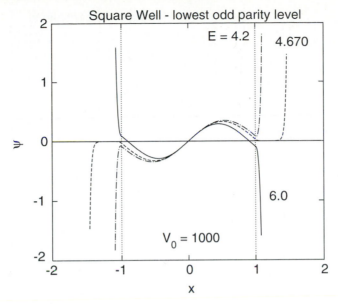

Figure 10.5: Trial wave functions for a square well with $V_0 = 1000$. All of the parameters are the same as in Figure 10.4, except that here we consider the lowest odd-parity level.

E that best satisfies the boundary conditions at $x = \pm L$. Some results for several different values of E are shown in Figure 10.5; the value we find for the energy of the lowest odd-parity level is ≈ 4.670, which is about 5 percent below the exact value for a box with infinitely high walls ($\pi^2/2 = 4.934 \ldots$). As with the ground-state energy, this difference is due mainly to the fact that the potential outside the box is not infinitely large.

If you were to examine Figures 10.4 and 10.5 with very high resolution, you would notice that while the wave function at the walls of the box is small, it is not quite zero, even for the best values of E. You may recall that we obtained the boundary condition $\psi = 0$ at the walls of the box under the assumption that the potential is infinite outside the box. Actually, in our computations we have used a slightly different criteria for choosing the best wave function. This criteria involved the divergence of the wave function at large x and is a more general approach since it can be applied to a wide variety of potentials (as we will see in a moment). For a box with infinitely hard walls, that is, if the potential outside the box is truly infinite, this divergence criteria is equivalent to the boundary condition that ψ vanish at the edges of the box. However, for a box with soft walls the wave function will be small, but nonzero, in the region beyond the walls. This is a well-known result of quantum theory, which is not found in classical physics.

According to classical theory, a particle cannot venture into a region where V is larger than its total energy. This would require that the classical kinetic energy be negative, which is not allowed. However, quantum theory places no such restriction on the particle. There is a small, but nonzero, chance of finding the particle *anywhere* in space so long as the potential energy is not infinite. This leads to a variety of interesting and important effects such as tunneling, which we will explore shortly. For the particle in a box problem it means that ψ need not go completely to zero at the walls of the box.

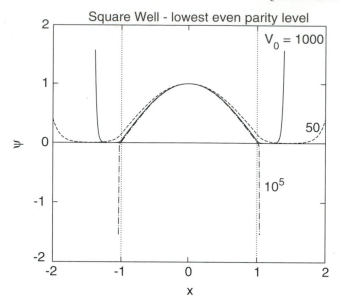

Figure 10.6: Ground-state wave function (unnormalized) calculated using the shooting method for a square well with different values of the potential outside the box, V_0. The walls of the box are at $x = \pm 1$. The ground-state energies here are 1.019, 1.179, and 1.221 for $V_0 = 50$, 10^3, and 10^5. The spatial step size was $\Delta x = 0.01$.

It turns out that when $V > E$ the wave function decays exponentially with distance as we go farther and farther outside the box. This decay becomes more rapid as $V_{\text{outside}} \equiv V_0$ is made larger, as illustrated in Figure 10.6. Here we show the wave function for the lowest energy level with different values of V_0. In all three cases E is within ± 0.0001 of the ground-state energy for that particular value of V_0. We see that the magnitude of ψ at the wall increases as V_0 is reduced. In addition, the rate at which ψ diverges as $|x|$ is increased beyond the walls (at $x = \pm 1$) also increases greatly as V_0 is made larger. We will explore this behavior further in the exercises and in some other examples below.

The shooting method is a convenient way to deal with boundary-value problems in one dimension. However, it is limited to situations in which values of ψ and $d\psi/dx$ at some initial location can somehow be determined. In our particle-in-a-box problem the symmetry of the potential was essential for obtaining ψ and its derivative at the center of the box. In situations involving a nonsymmetric potential, the wave functions will not have a definite parity; thus we cannot obtain initial values of ψ and $d\psi/dx$ from symmetry arguments. In such cases a different approach that relies on the continuity of ψ can be employed. Consider the nonsymmetric potential shown schematically in Figure 10.7. This has a form much like the Lennard-Jones potential we encountered in our molecular dynamics work in Chapter 9 and is similar to what we might find for a system involving two atoms, with one located at $x = 0$.[12] Note, however, that in this example we restrict things to one dimension, so we are not yet treating the

---

[12]For simplicity we can imagine that the atom at $x = 0$ is much more massive than the other so that it can be taken as fixed in space, and we need worry only about the wave function of the light atom.

full three-dimensional Schrödinger equation. We expect, on physical grounds, to find a bound state in which the atom has a large probability of being found near the minimum of the potential. The wave function for this state will vanish at both large and small x and be significantly different from zero only in the region where V is large in magnitude and negative.

Let us, therefore, consider calculating ψ using (10.11), with integrations beginning in the regions where ψ is very small (i.e., at large x and small x) and proceeding toward the middle. That is, we now perform two integrations. One starts from a point on the far left in Figure 10.7, at the point $x = x_L$. At this location we set $\psi = 0$ and give the derivative $d\psi/dx$ a very small value. We then use (10.11) to obtain ψ at $x_L + \Delta x$, $x_L + 2\Delta x$, etc., and thus determine ψ at ever-increasing values of x. We call this function ψ_L, since it is obtained by integrating in from the left-most region. This procedure is then repeated starting from a point $x = x_R$, far to the right in Figure 10.7. At this location we set $\psi = 0$ and give $d\psi/dx$ a small value, in preparation for the application of (10.11). We then integrate toward smaller values of x, and obtain a function we call ψ_R. The plan is to combine the functions ψ_L and ψ_R to obtain the wave function over the entire range.

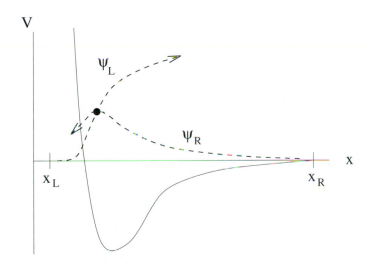

Figure 10.7:   Schematic illustration of the matching method for solving the Schrödinger equation. The solid curve shows the potential, while the dashed curves show (hypothetical) wave functions calculated using (10.11), starting the integration from the left (ψ_L) and from the right (ψ_R). In this case the two trial functions do not match smoothly, and thus cannot be combined to give an acceptable solution of the Schrödinger equation.

The correct wave function must be a smooth, continuous function. That is, ψ and its derivative must both be continuous.[13] This means that if a combination of our two functions ψ_L and ψ_R is to form an acceptable wave function, they must intersect somewhere (so that the wave function is continuous), and they must have the same slope at the intersection point (so that $d\psi/dx$ is continuous). We can always arrange for ψ_L and ψ_R to intersect since, as has already been noted several times, we can scale the calculated ψ by a constant factor and still obtain a solution to the Schrödinger equation. It is usually convenient and numerically advisable, to pick a location somewhere near the minimum of the potential as the matching point since the wave function will be large there, and then scale either ψ_L or ψ_R or both so that their values are equal at that point.[14] This still leaves us with the requirement that the derivatives be equal at the matching point. The only remaining adjustable parameter in the computation is the energy. For most values of E we would generally find the situation depicted in Figure 10.7, where the derivatives $d\psi_L/dx$ and $d\psi_R/dx$ do *not* match. However, it is usually possible to adjust the value of E so as to make these derivatives match. When this occurs, the combination of ψ_L and ψ_R gives the wave function, and the associated value of E is the energy of the level.

This approach is often called the matching method, for obvious reasons. It can be implemented numerically by modifying the `calculate` routine we developed for the shooting algorithm. A search routine can again be used to obtain an ever more accurate match of the derivatives $d\psi_L/dx$ and $d\psi_R/dx$, and thus better and better estimates for the wave function and energy. We will leave this task for the exercises.

Figure 10.8 shows some results for the one-dimensional Lennard-Jones problem[15]

$$V(x) = 4\epsilon \left[\left(\frac{\sigma}{x} \right)^{12} - \left(\frac{\sigma}{x} \right)^{6} \right]. \tag{10.12}$$

Here we plot results for two values of E. In each case we have normalized both ψ_L and ψ_R to unity at the matching point $x_{\text{match}} = 1.4$. For the case on the left there was a sizable discontinuity in $d\psi/dx$ at the matching point, so this solution is not satisfactory. After letting the search routine iterate several times, we obtain the result on the right, where ψ_L and ψ_R join much more smoothly. By starting the search at other values of E we can obtain the wave functions for other energy levels. We will, as usual, leave this for the exercises.

While we introduced the matching strategy for dealing with nonsymmetric potentials, it is not limited to such cases. An interesting example is a square well containing a small potential barrier inside the well, shown schematically in Figure 10.9. This particular potential is actually symmetric, so we could use the shooting method here, starting from $x = 0$. However, there are many interesting variations on this problem; for example, we could move the small barrier off center or make the potential of the barrier vary with x. Such asymmeric potentials require the matching approach.

Before we construct the wave functions for the potential in Figure 10.9, it is worthwhile to anticipate some of the physics of the problem. This potential consists of two square wells, one to the left and one to the right of the barrier. If the barrier is large (very high or very wide or both), the two wells are effectively uncoupled, since the wave function in one will not penetrate far enough into the barrier to reach into the other well (compare with Figure 10.6). The wave functions in each well will, therefore, be unaffected by the presence of the other, and the solutions will be those we have already

---

[13]This assumes that the potential is a smooth function.

[14]This is equivalent to scaling the derivatives at x_L and x_R so as to make $\psi_L = \psi_R$ at the matching point.

[15]You may recall that this is the potential we used in our molecular-dynamics calculations in Chapter 9.

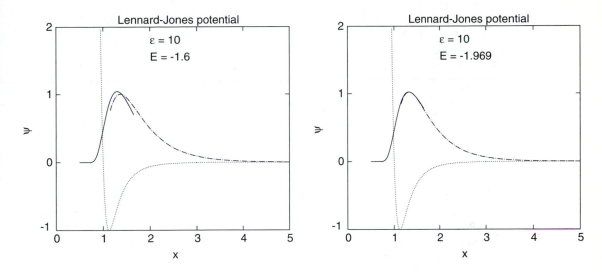

Figure 10.8: Solution for the ground state of the Lennard-Jones potential [(10.12) with $\epsilon = 10$ and $\sigma = 1$] constructed using the matching method. The integrations were started at $x_L = 0.5$ (on the left) and $x_R = 5$ (on the right) with $\Delta x = 0.01$. The two trial functions are shown by the solid (ψ_L) and dot-dashed (ψ_R) curves, and the potential is shown by the dotted curve (the scales for ψ and $V(x)$ are not the same). Left: for $E = -1.6$ the derivatives of ψ_L and ψ_R are not equal at the matching point ($x = 1.4$). Right: for $E = -1.969$ the derivatives match fairly well, so this is an acceptable approximation for the wave function. Note that this wave function is not normalized.

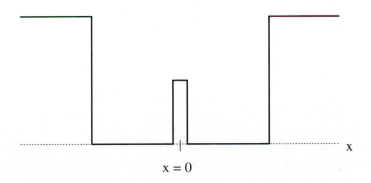

Figure 10.9: Two potential wells separated by a narrow "tunnel" barrier.

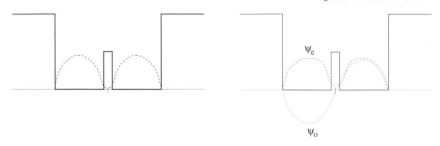

Figure 10.10: Left: the dashed curves showing the approximate unperturbed wave functions in the two nearby potential wells; right: wave functions (very schematic!) after we allow for mixing of the unperturbed wave functions.

encountered in our work on the particle-in-a-box problem. The ground-state wave function for this case is shown schematically on the left side of Figure 10.10.

If, on the other hand, the barrier separating the two wells is not large, the unperturbed wave function from one side will be able to penetrate through to the other before it decays to a negligibly small value. Actually, the unperturbed wave functions from both wells will decay as they penetrate the barrier from opposite sides. These two wave functions must meet continuously in the center, just as we saw with ψ_L and ψ_R in the Lennard-Jones problem (Figure 10.8). This leads to what is usually referred to as *mixing* of the two, initial, unperturbed wave functions. If we denote the unperturbed wave functions as ψ_1 and ψ_2, then to a first approximation they will combine to form wave functions for the entire two-well system as either $\psi_e \sim \psi_1 + \psi_2$, or $\psi_o \sim \psi_1 - \psi_2$. That is, they can form either an even (ψ_e) or odd (ψ_o) combination.[16] These are sketched on the right side of Figure 10.10. Note that the wave functions we have sketched are derived (approximately) from the initial unperturbed wave functions in the two separate wells. Similar combinations are formed from the unperturbed, excited-state wave functions.

The two wave functions ψ_e and ψ_o will have energies close to that of the initial unperturbed states. According to perturbation theory, the mixing of two such states leads to a small splitting of the energy levels, with the even level (ψ_e) being pushed to a lower energy and the odd level pushed higher. This can be illustrated nicely using the solutions obtained from the matching algorithm. The ground state has even parity and is considered in Figure 10.11. On the left we show the behavior for a value of E that is too low, and we see that ψ_L and ψ_R do not match smoothly. In the middle case E is slightly too large, although the derivatives of ψ_L and ψ_R match fairly well on the scale shown here. On the right we show results for a value of E that yields a slightly better match. It is interesting that even here the wave function is not quite symmetric; you can see this from the fact that the amplitudes of the two maxima are not quite the same. This is a result of the numerical errors that arise when integrating through a classically forbidden region (the tunnel barrier), as the solutions tend to be divergent in such regions (compare again with Figure 10.6). In this particular problem we could have obtained a better result by employing the shooting method, as this would preserve the symmetry inherent in the problem. However, using the matching method in this case gives a good impression of the strengths and weaknesses of that algorithm.

---

[16]The precise parity of the solutions in this case can be traced to the symmetry of the potential. When the potential is not symmetric the solutions will not have a definite parity, but there will still be two wave functions constructed (approximately) as the sum and difference of the two unperturbed wave functions.

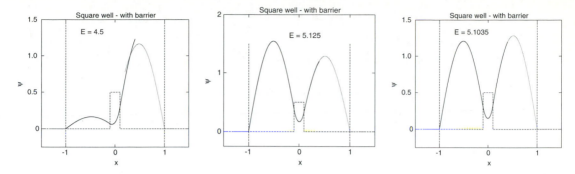

Figure 10.11:   Results for ψ_L and ψ_R calculated with the matching method for the potential in Figure 10.9, for several values of E. The integrations were started at $x = \pm 1.3$, the step size was $\Delta x = 5 \times 10^{-4}$, and the matching was done at $x_{\text{match}} = 0.3$. The parameters associated with the potential were $V = 0$ inside each well, $V = 10^5$ for $|x| > 1$, and $V = 100$ for $|x| \leq 0.1$. The vertical dashed lines indicate the edges of the potential wells. Note that the scale for ψ varies from plot to plot.

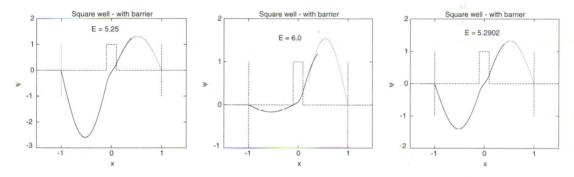

Figure 10.12:   Results for ψ_L and ψ_R calculated with the matching method for the tunnel potential in Figure 10.9. Here we have used several values of E that are near the energy of the lowest odd-parity level. The other parameters were the same as in Figure 10.11.

The numerical difficulties associated with integrating through a classically forbidden region (where $V > E$) bring up a related issue. In all of our applications of the matching method we have started the integrations in such forbidden regions and integrated toward the regions where $V < E$, that is, the regions where we expect the wave function to be large. In principle we could have started at a location where $V < E$, and integrated toward the classically forbidden regions. However, the numerical problems and divergences are usually more severe in the latter case. As a general rule it is best to integrate away from classically forbidden regions, toward regions where ψ is large.

Figure 10.12 shows results for slightly higher values of E. The left and middle plots show behavior for values of E that are too low and too high and thus provide poor matches. The plot on the right shows a good match, and the wave function is seen to have odd parity, as expected from the discussion given above.

The shooting and matching methods described in this section are well suited for the time-independent Schrödinger equation in one dimension and similar types of boundary-value problems. We

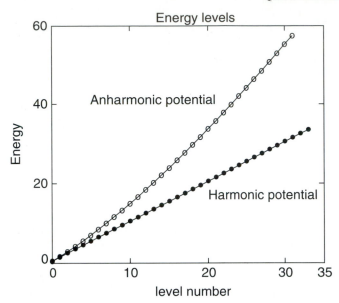

Figure 10.13: Lowest few energy levels for a harmonic oscillator ($V = Kx^2/2$ with $K = 1$) and an anharmonic oscillator [$V = (k_1 x^2 + k_2 x^4)/2$, with $k_1 = 1$ and $k_2 = 0.1$]. In both cases we have used our usual choice of units, for which $\hbar = m = 1$. Note that for the harmonic case the energy varies linearly with level number (which agrees with the well-known, analytic solution). For the anharmonic case the corresponding energies are shifted to progressively higher values. For the higher levels the wave function has more of its "weight" at larger values of x (classically speaking, the vibration amplitude is higher) where the potential is larger due to the anharmonic term, and this pushes the energy higher than in the harmonic case.

have only been able to consider a few examples here; the exercises explore these and several other cases in more detail.

Exercises

1. Use the shooting method to obtain the lowest six energy levels for a square well. This will require that you write a program that can deal with both even- and odd-parity solutions. Examine how the energy varies with level number and test your values against the exact results (10.7) and (10.8). Compare the wave functions (make sure that they are properly normalized!) with the exact solution (10.6). It is also instructive to examine the behavior as a function of the spatial step size Δx. Study how the value of the ground-state energy varies with the choice of step size; try $\Delta x = 0.05, 0.01$, and 0.005, for a box with walls at $x = \pm 1$.

2. Use the matching method to calculate the wave functions and energies of the first few energy levels of the harmonic oscillator potential $V = Kx^2/2$. Show that the levels are evenly spaced in energy and compare with the exact result $E = (n + \frac{1}{2})\hbar\omega$, where n is an integer $(0, 1, 2, \ldots)$ and $\omega = \sqrt{K/m}$ (see Figure 10.13). It is also worthwhile to compare the wave functions with the exact results.

3. Use either the shooting or matching method to calculate the energy levels for the potential $V = x^n$ for different values of n. As n becomes very large this approximates an infinite square well.

4. Calculate the first few energy levels and the associated wave functions for a potential of the form $V = (k_1 x^2 + k_2 x^4)/2$. For small x the first (k_1) term dominates, and the behavior is close to that found for the harmonic oscillator, while for large x the second (k_2) term dominates and the behavior is *anharmonic*. Some typical results for the energy levels in this case are given in Figure 10.13.

5. Use the shooting method to study how the wave function for a particle-in-a-box depends on the magnitude of the potential outside the box V_0. Examine the variation of ψ beyond the walls of the box and show that it decays exponentially with distance in this region. Study the decay length as a function of V_0 and compare the results for different energy levels. As the energy of the level approaches V_0 the decay length should become larger.

*6. Use the matching method to obtain the wave functions for the first few states above the ground level for the one-dimensional Lennard-Jones potential. Compare the variation of the energy with level number with the results shown for the harmonic and anharmonic potentials in Figure 10.13. Depending on the number of levels you wish to consider, you may have to make the value of ϵ in (10.12) larger than the value used in Figure 10.8. A deeper potential well possesses more bound states.

*7. Many three-dimensional quantum mechanics problems can be reduced effectively to one- or two-dimensional problems. For example, the hydrogen atom is three dimensional as it involves the wave function of an electron as a function of position relative to a (fixed) proton. However, the spherical symmetry makes it possible to write the wave function in the form

$$\psi(r, \theta, \phi) = f(r) \, Y(\theta, \phi) \,, \qquad (10.13)$$

where r is the (radial) distance between the proton and the electron, and θ and ϕ are the usual spherical coordinates [see Griffiths (1995) and Schiff (1968) for discussions of (10.13) and the derivation of (10.14)]. Here $f(r)$ is a function of r only, and all of the angular dependence is contained in the function $Y(\theta, \phi)$. As you may know, these angular functions turn out to be the spherical harmonics. In this problem we will be concerned with the radial function, $f(r)$. When the form (10.13) is inserted into the three-dimensional Schrödinger equation we obtain a differential equation for $f(r)$. It is common practice, at this point, to deal instead with the related function $g(r) \equiv rf(r)$, which satisfies the equation

$$\frac{d^2 g}{dr^2} = \left(2[V(r) - E] + \frac{\ell(\ell + 1)}{r^2} \right) g \,, \qquad (10.14)$$

where $V(r) = -1/r$ is the Coulomb potential[17] and ℓ is an integer associated with the angular momentum of the electron that arises from the solution for $Y(\theta, \phi)$. Employ the shooting method to solve (10.14) for $g(r)$ starting your integration at $r = 0$, with the initial value $g(0) = 0$. Consider the cases $\ell = 0$ and $\ell = 1$ and compare your results with the analytic solution for the

---

[17]More precisely, this is the electric potential multiplied by the charge of the electron. We use units in which this charge is -1.

hydrogen atom. Hint: In the units used here the energies of the bound states should be given by $-1/2n^2$, where n is an integer.

10.3   A Variational Approach

The methods developed in Section 10.2 can handle most one-dimensional quantum mechanics problems. However, life is more difficult in two or three dimensions for the following reason. As we have already seen, ψ must, in general, satisfy certain boundary conditions. In one dimension these usually concern the value of ψ at two locations; typically at the two extremes of a region. In higher dimensions we must worry about the value of the wave function on a *surface*, which could be a circle in two dimensions or a sphere in three dimensions. In some cases the potential may have enough symmetry that the problem can be reduced to a differential equation involving only one variable. For example, we have seen in the exercises in Section 10.2 that with the hydrogen atom we can separate the radial and angular dependences of ψ and thereby reduce the radial dependence to a one-dimensional problem. In such cases the matching or shooting method can then be used. Many textbook problems are like this, for the simple reason that more complicated cases can almost never be solved analytically!

Shooting and matching methods are not well suited for satisfying boundary conditions at more than one point and, therefore, cannot (easily) be used in two or three dimensions. A very general method for dealing with these cases is to write the Schrödinger equation in the form of a matrix eigenvalue problem. While such an approach is computationally very difficult to carry through, it is useful for illustrating several important points.

Consider a two-dimensional problem and assume that, as usual, we break up space into a lattice of points, with $\psi(m, n)$ being the value of the wave function at location (m, n) on the lattice. The boundary conditions then specify the value of ψ on the boundary. For example, ψ might vanish on the edges of the system; if the system is rectangular, we would have $\psi(0, n) = \psi(M, n) = \psi(m, 0) = \psi(m, N) = 0$, where the lattice runs from $m = 0$ to M and $n = 0$ to N. The Schrödinger equation (10.1) then has the form

$$-\frac{\hbar^2}{2m}\nabla^2\psi + V(\vec{r})\,\psi = -\frac{\hbar^2}{2m}\left[\frac{\partial^2\psi}{\partial x^2} + \frac{\partial^2\psi}{\partial y^2}\right] + V(\vec{r})\,\psi \tag{10.15}$$

$$\approx -\frac{\hbar^2}{2m}\left[\frac{\psi(m+1,n) + \psi(m-1,n) - 2\psi(m,n)}{(\Delta x)^2} + \frac{\psi(m,n+1) + \psi(m,n-1) - 2\psi(m,n)}{(\Delta y)^2}\right]$$

$$+ V(m,n)\,\psi(m,n)$$

$$\approx E\,\psi(m,n)\,,$$

where the last several lines give the wave equation in finite-difference form. This is a system of algebraic equations for $\psi(m, n)$; there are (of order) $M \times N$ unknown values of $\psi(m, n)$ and the same number of equations. These equations can be written in matrix form as[18]

$$\begin{pmatrix} 4 - V(0,0) - E & -1 & 0 & \dots \\ -1 & 4 - V(0,1) - E & -1 & \dots \\ & \dots & \dots & \dots \end{pmatrix} \begin{pmatrix} \psi(0,0) \\ \psi(0,1) \\ \dots \end{pmatrix} = \begin{pmatrix} 0 \\ 0 \\ \dots \end{pmatrix}. \qquad (10.16)$$

If we define a column vector $\vec{\psi}$ whose elements are $\psi(m,n)$, and a square matrix $\mathcal{M}(E)$ whose elements are shown as the left-most matrix in (10.16), this can be written as

$$\mathcal{M}(E)\,\vec{\psi} \;=\; \vec{0}\,, \qquad (10.17)$$

where $\vec{0}$ is a column vector whose elements are all zero. This is a standard matrix eigenvalue problem. Here we have indicated explicitly the fact that the matrix $\mathcal{M}(E)$ is a function of E. In general there will be MN values of E for which this equation has a nontrivial solution.[19] Formally, these eigenvalues are the roots of the algebraic equation

$$\det[\mathcal{M}(E)] \;=\; 0\,, \qquad (10.18)$$

where det denotes the determinant of the matrix. Each eigenvalue is associated with an eigenvector, which is the wave function for that particular energy level.

This matrix approach is completely general and can be very useful, especially in formal arguments. However, it is often not helpful in numerical work for the following reasons. First, the matrix $\mathcal{M}$ can easily be very large. For example, if there are 50 grid elements along both m and n in a two-dimensional problem, you have a 2500×2500 matrix to deal with. In three dimensions the matrix would be $125{,}000 \times 125{,}000$. Second, the numerical problem of finding the eigenvalues and eigenvectors of a matrix is not an easy one. Eigenvalue problems arise in many applications, so efficient programs for carrying out these computations can be found in all serious packages of mathematical routines. Nevertheless, computing the eigenvalues and eigenvectors of such large matrices is usually a formidable task, which can require large amounts of computer time. Because of these problems, we will not pursue this computational line farther here.[20]

The difficulties with a "direct" matrix approach to eigenvalue problems have motivated the development of a number of alternative schemes. We do not have space to discuss all of them here; the interested reader can explore some of them through the references. In this section we will introduce one of these schemes to give an example of how the Schrödinger equation can be attacked. The method we now describe involves a Monte Carlo approach, similar to that described in Chapter 8, coupled with the variational principle.

The variational principle of quantum mechanics can be expressed as follows. Let φ be a "trial" wave function. We imagine that we are searching for the ground-state solution to the Schrödinger

---

[18] Here we have taken the liberty to set $\Delta x = \Delta y$ and to absorb factors such as these into V and E. The points we wish to make here depend on the general *form* of these equations, so we will avoid the notational distractions associated with specifying all of the factors precisely.

[19] A trivial solution is one for which all of the $\psi(m,n)$ are zero. Note also that because of the boundary conditions on $\vec{\psi}$, the number of solutions may be less than MN.

[20] However, it can be quite useful for quantum problems in which, for some reason, the size of the $\vec{\psi}$ vector is not too large. Cases of this kind arise, for example, in magnetic problems in which the number of spin (or angular momentum) states is often of order 10 or less.

equation for a particular problem and that φ is a proposed wave function, or perhaps our best numerical guess for the true wave function. We can calculate the "energy" corresponding to this trial function

$$E^* \equiv \frac{\int \varphi^* \mathcal{H} \varphi \, d\vec{r}}{\int \varphi^* \varphi \, d\vec{r}} , \tag{10.19}$$

where the integrations are over all space and $\mathcal{H}$ is the Hamiltonian operator

$$\mathcal{H} \equiv -\frac{\hbar^2}{2m}\nabla^2 + V(\vec{r}) . \tag{10.20}$$

Note that we have given this effective energy the symbol E^* to emphasize the fact that since φ is not necessarily a solution of (10.20) (it was only a "proposed" wave function), E^* is not necessarily the energy of a true eigenstate.

According to the variational principle, the true ground-state energy is *always* less than or equal to E^*. In fact, the only time they are equal is when the trial wave function is precisely the true ground-state wave function. For *all* other functions φ the effective energy E^* will be higher than the ground-state energy. This principle allows us to recast the problem of solving the Schrödinger equation as a minimization problem. The goal is to find the function φ which minimizes E^*. There are several ways to implement this strategy, corresponding to different ways of searching through the space of all possible wave functions. The approach we describe below is very general, yet also somewhat crude. After seeing how it works, we will explore improved ways of constructing φ and performing the search procedure, some of which will be explored in the exercises.

To be specific we consider again the problem of finding the ground state of the one-dimensional Lennard-Jones potential. We dealt with this problem earlier with the matching method, so we already have a solution with which to compare it. To implement a minimization strategy we must first choose an initial trial wave function, which we will call φ^0. As usual, we discretize space into bins Δx in size and let φ_n^0 be the value of the initial trial function at $x = n\Delta x$. We also restrict the domain[21] of our function to the range $x = 0.7 - 5$ (in reduced units), since we know on physical grounds that the ground state will be one in which the particle is localized near the minimum in the potential, $x_{\min} \sim 1.1$. Hence, our bins run from $n = 0$ corresponding to $x = 0.7$, up to $n = N$ corresponding to $x = 5$. We choose an extremely simple initial trial function: $\varphi_n^0 = $ constant for $1 \leq x \leq 4$ and zero outside this range, as shown in Figure 10.14. The constant is determined by requiring that our function satisfy the normalization condition $\int \varphi^* \varphi \, dx = 1$. This is certainly a poor approximation to the true ground-state wave function, so if the method can succeed with this choice of φ^0 it can probably be successful with any choice!

The only remaining part of the algorithm that must be specified is the procedure for how to use φ^0 (or any other trial function) to obtain an improved trial function. We will employ a Monte Carlo approach, which operates as follows. First, we pick one of the bins along x at random by choosing an integer in the range 0–N; we will call this bin *ntest*. Second, we construct a provisional function by changing the value of the trial function at that location, φ_{ntest}^0, by an amount chosen randomly in the range $\pm d\varphi$. Third, we calculate E^* for this provisional function. If it is lower than the corresponding value for φ^0, the provisional function must be "closer" to the true wave function, and we use it as the

---

[21]We will take $\sigma = 1$ and $\epsilon = 10$ in (10.12), so that the potential is the same as that considered in Figure 10.8.

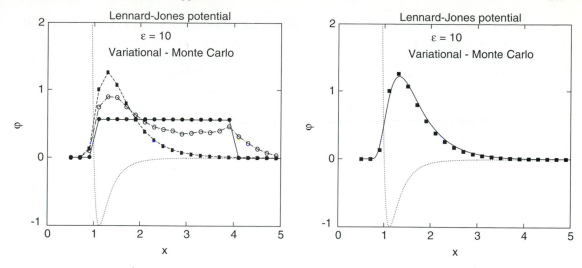

Figure 10.14:   Left: trial wave functions, φ, during the course of a variational–Monte Carlo calculation for the Lennard-Jones problem. The filled circles show the initial trial function, φ^0, the open circles show the trial function after 10^3 attempted Monte Carlo moves (i.e., changes in the wave function), and the squares show it after 10^4 attempted moves. E^* for these trial wave functions was 0.11, -1.43, and -2.18, respectively. Right: comparison of the final variational wave function with the results of the matching method (Figure 10.8). The filled squares here are the best trial functions from the plot on the left. Note that both of these wave functions have been properly normalized and that the potential (the dotted curves) is not shown to scale.

new trial function. If E^* for the provisional function is higher than the value for φ^0, we discard the provisional function and keep φ^0 as the trial function.[22]

We will leave the construction of a variational–Monte Carlo program to the exercises (a full listing of such a program is given in Appendix 4). All of the key ingredients of such a program have been described above. We will mention only one programming subtlety here. You must decide at the outset whether or not the trial functions are to be properly normalized (and if so, when to do it). This arises when evaluating E^*, since if φ is normalized the denominator in (10.19) is unity and thus need not be computed. For this reason it is convenient to always normalize φ. However, if you perform this normalization after each tentative Monte Carlo modification of the trial function, you must make sure that you can return to the previous trial function if the Monte Carlo modification is rejected.

As the Monte Carlo process is repeated many times, both the trial function and the corresponding value of E^* should converge to those of the true ground state. Some results for the trial function for the Lennard-Jones problem at various stages of the calculation are shown on the left in Figure 10.14. After a relatively small number of Monte Carlo iterations (10^3 in Figure 10.14) φ exhibits fluctuations that arise because this function was constructed from a small collection of random changes. However, after a large number of Monte Carlo adjustments φ becomes a smooth function of x, as we would expect for the true wave function. The final trial function shown here had an energy $E^* = -2.18$, which agrees

---

[22]Unlike the Monte Carlo method employed in Chapter 8, this algorithm does not involve a temperature parameter to enable changes that increase the energy.

with the value found with the matching method (Figure 10.8) to within about 10 percent. The trial function itself also agrees well with the wave function calculated with the matching method, as shown on the right in Figure 10.14. There are some slight differences and we will show in the exercises that they are due to the finite grid size used in describing the variational functions.

The variational–Monte Carlo method can thus deal effectively with one dimensional situations such as the Lennard-Jones problem. However, its real strength is that it can be applied with very little additional effort to treat two- and three-dimensional cases. To illustrate this we now consider a particle confined by a two-dimensional harmonic potential. The Schrödinger equation in this case is (10.1) with the potential

$$V(x, y) = \frac{1}{2} k_x x^2 + \frac{1}{2} k_y y^2 , \qquad (10.21)$$

where k_x and k_y are related to the curvatures of the potential in the x and y directions. The astute reader will notice that this problem can be separated into two independent one-dimensional harmonic oscillators, one along x and one along y, which can be solved analytically. We will use this exact solution to evaluate the usefulness of the variational–Monte Carlo method. Several problems for which there are no known exact analytic solutions will be considered in the exercises.

To implement the variational approach for the two-dimensional oscillator we discretize space along the x and y directions into segments of length Δx and Δy, and write our trial functions as $\varphi(m, n)$, with $x = m\Delta x$, and $y = n\Delta x$ (for convenience we take $\Delta y = \Delta x$). We also restrict x and y to the range $-N\Delta x \le x \le N\Delta x$ and $-N\Delta x \le y \le N\Delta x$, so that we have $(2N+1)^2$ bins altogether. For this calculation we again pick an extremely simple initial trial wave function, $\varphi^0 =$ constant for all points in the region $|x| \le 1.6$ and $|y| \le 1.6$, and zero otherwise. This trial function is shown in Figure 10.15.

The Monte Carlo algorithm can then be implemented as in our previous example. During each Monte Carlo step a grid location (mtest, ntest) is chosen at random, and a provisional function obtained by changing the initial trial function φ^0(mtest, ntest) by a small amount chosen randomly from the range $\pm d\varphi$. If E^* for this provisional function is lower than that of φ^0, then the provisional function becomes the new trial wave function. If E^* is higher, we keep φ^0 as the trial function. Some results are given in Figure 10.15, where on the left we show the trial function as the calculation proceeds. The final trial function has a roughly gaussian shape, which may be familiar to you from the analytic solution of the harmonic oscillator. Figure 10.15 also shows the behavior of E^* during the calculation. It is a monotonically decreasing function, as required by the Monte Carlo procedure. After many Monte Carlo time steps it approaches a constant, which signals the convergence of the algorithm.

A plot of the final trial wave function as a function of both x and y is shown in Figure 10.16. The wave function falls off more slowly in the x direction than along y, since in this example we have chosen $k_x < k_y$. This means that the "spring constant" for vibrations along x was softer than the one along y, so the effective amplitude of vibration was larger along x. The value of E^* for this trial function is ~ 4.79, which differs from the exact value $4.743\ldots$ by about 1 percent. We will see in the exercises that this small difference is due to the finite grid size.

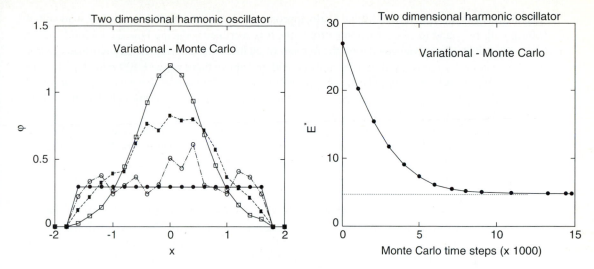

Figure 10.15: Left: trial wave functions plotted as $\varphi(x, 0)$ as a function of x, at various stages in the variational–Monte Carlo procedure. The filled circles show the initial trial function, and the open circles, filled squares, and open squares show φ after 2000, 5000, and 15,000 Monte Carlo time steps. Right: variation of E^* as the calculation proceeds. The potential energy was (10.21) with $k_x = 10$ and $k_y = 40$, the maximum values of $|x|$ and $|y|$ were 2.0 (so that $\varphi = 0$ outside this region), and the grid size was $\Delta x = \Delta y = 0.2$.

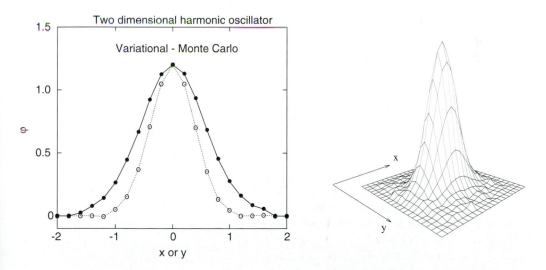

Figure 10.16: Left: plot of $\varphi(x, 0)$ as a function of x (filled circles) and $\varphi(0, y)$ as a function of y (open circles) for the final trial wave function from Figure 10.15. Right: three-dimensional plot of the wave function.

While the specific variational–Monte Carlo approach we have described here is fairly well suited for dealing with two- and three-dimensional problems, it is worth considering how the method can be improved. One difficulty is connected with the number of elements of the trial wave function $\varphi_{m,n}$. For the two-dimensional harmonic oscillator example considered above there were ~ 400 grid elements. In order for the Monte Carlo strategy to be successful, it is necessary for each of these $\varphi_{m,n}$ to be adjusted many times, and if the number of grid elements is large, this can require a long computation. This difficulty can be dealt with in several ways.

First, it pays to make a good choice of the initial trial function, as then an accurate estimate for the true wave function can be reached with fewer Monte Carlo iterations. Here "good" means that φ^0 should have a form close to the true ground-state wave function. We didn't attempt to do this in our calculations here, but it is usually possible to make an informed choice for φ^0. In the exercises we will explore how this can speed up convergence.

Second, in our oscillator example we chose the ranges of x and y to be large enough that the boundaries were far from the region where the wave function was nonzero. This was by design, since ideally the boundary condition $\varphi = 0$ should be applied at $x, y = \pm\infty$. However, this means that there will be many grid elements where φ is extremely small and it would be nice to arrange for the Monte Carlo algorithm to spend less time updating $\varphi(m, n)$ in these regions, since they are not as important as the regions where the wave function is large. This can be accomplished by modifying the way the test locations for the Monte Carlo changes are chosen. In our discussion above we chose the grid element to be considered in the variational procedure, mtest and ntest, at random from the *entire* allowed range of m and n. It would be better to choose the test point with a probability proportional to the value of φ at that point, since then the points where φ is largest would get the most attention from the algorithm. To do this requires that we be able to generate random numbers with a specified distribution. This is a problem that was discussed in Chapter 7, where we considered two ways to generate random numbers with a nonuniform distribution. In the problem we are now considering the rejection method is most useful since we do not have an analytic expression for the desired probability function. We have already considered the method in Chapter 7, so we will not go into much detail here. A subroutine that generates mtest and ntest with a probability proportional to $\varphi(m, n)$ is listed below.

```
! psi is the current trial wave function - psi(m,n) is also the probability
! of choosing the point (m,n) when generating random points in the
! region inside the square running from -max to max in the x-y plane
! arrays nx() and ny() contain the generated values of the coordinates m and n
! we generate n_attempts pairs of points
sub calc_nxy(psi(,),max,nx(),ny(),n_attempts)
   psi_max = psi(0,0)          ! assume that the largest value of the trial
   for i = 1 to n_attempts     ! function is at the origin - use this value
      do                       ! later for normalization
         x = int((max+1)*2*(rnd-0.5))
         y = int((max+1)*2*(rnd-0.5))
         if rnd < psi(x,y)/psi_max then exit do  ! here is where the rejection
      loop                                       ! method is used
      nx(i) = x                ! the probability for choosing the point
      ny(i) = y                ! (x,y) is proportional to psi(x,y)/psi(0,0)
   next i
end sub
```

This routine generates the values of mtest and ntest as follows. The current trial function is contained in the array psi(), and this is used (after the appropriate normalization) as the probability distribution for choosing a point (m,n). The rnd random number generator is first used to generate points that are uniformly distributed over the entire allowed region of the plane, in this case -max<m<+max, etc., for n. These values, which are contained in the variables x and y, are distributed *uniformly* due to the nature of the rnd generator. Given these uniformly distributed points we then *accept* points with a probability proportional to psi(m,n). This procedure again makes use of rnd, and it yields a distribution that is governed by psi, as desired. The routine calc_mn can readily be used in our variational–Monte Carlo calculations. In fact, we already used it in our work on the two-dimensional harmonic oscillator! In the exercises we will consider how much it speeds up the calculation as compared with simply choosing mtest and ntest uniformly.[23]

A third useful modification of the variational–Monte Carlo method involves the manner in which we represent the trial functions. So far we have taken a direct, but in some ways crude, approach by simply storing the value of φ at each grid site separately. A different strategy, which is in the spirit of a Fourier decomposition, would be to write the trial function as a sum of *basis* functions.[24] For example, with the harmonic oscillator we might choose the basis set to be gaussian-like functions with different widths. The important point is that these functions be orthogonal so that an arbitrary trial function can be written uniquely in a form such as

$$\varphi(x, y) = \sum_k a_k \, b_k(x, y) \, , \tag{10.22}$$

where $b_k(x, y)$ are the basis functions and the coefficients a_k specify the overlap between the trial wave function φ and the different basis functions. The variational procedure then involves adjusting the values of these coefficients so as to minimize the effective energy E^*. This can again be accomplished using a Monte Carlo approach.

Exercises

1. Write a program to implement the variational–Monte Carlo approach and apply it to the two-dimensional harmonic oscillator. Study how the choice of initial trial wave function affects the number of Monte Carlo steps required to obtain a "good" wave function. Here the "goodness" of a wave function can be judged from E^*. Compare the results for the very crude φ^0 considered in the text with that found for a gaussian function. Other things to study include the influence of grid size on φ and E^* and the speed of convergence with and without a biased choice of the test points. Hint: Convergence can be determined by requiring that the change in E^* per iteration be less than some specified value. However, since some Monte Carlo iterations will not alter φ (and hence not change E^*), the convergence test cannot be performed after every iteration. Rather, you should make the test after every 10 or 100 iterations. A plot of E^* as a function of Monte Carlo time is also useful in testing for convergence.

---

[23] In most cases it is advisable to initially choose mtest and ntest from a uniform distribution. This prevents errors (i.e., zeros) in the initial trial wave function from unduly restricting the form of later trial functions. After the trial function begins to resemble the true wave function, you can then switch to choosing from a biased distribution and thereby speed up the final convergence of the Monte Carlo algorithm.

[24] We will encounter such basis functions in detail later in this chapter.

2. Employ the variational–Monte Carlo approach to obtain the ground-state wave function and energy for the one-dimensional square well. Compare your results with those obtained in Section 10.2 with the shooting method.

*3. Perform a variational–Monte Carlo calculation using an approach based on expressing the trial wave functions as functions with the form (10.22). Use the potential of your choice (it might be best to start with a simple square well).

4. Use the variational–Monte Carlo method to find the ground-state wave function for a particle in a box in three dimensions. Compare the results for boxes with different wall potentials.

5. Employ the variational–Monte Carlo method to calculate the ground-state energy and wave function of the anharmonic oscillator whose potential is given by $V(x) = x^4$.

**6. The variational theorem as stated at the beginning of this section concerns the ground-state energy and wave function. That is why all of the problems in this section have (so far) been concerned with the ground state. However, the method can also be used to deal with the excited states in the following way. The wave functions of the ground and excited states form a complete orthogonal set of basis functions. If the variational function φ is orthogonal to the ground-state wave function, then the final result of a variation calculation will be the wave function of the first excited state and E^* will be the energy of this state. While this may sound simple in principle, a difficulty in practice is that even though φ^0 may be constructed so as to be orthogonal to the ground state, the Monte Carlo changes may spoil this orthogonality.

Investigate this problem by using the variational–Monte Carlo method to estimate the first excited state of a particle in a square well. The challenging part of the problem is to ensure in some manner that after each Monte Carlo modification of φ, this function is still orthogonal to the ground-state wave function.

10.4   Time-Dependent Schrödinger Equation: Direct Solutions

In the past few sections we have explored several approaches for solving the *time-independent* Schrödinger equation. We have seen how to calculate the wave functions of the ground and excited states for different potentials in one, two, and three dimensions. However, to appreciate some of the most interesting aspects of quantum mechanics it is necessary to consider the time dependence of the wave function. This will be our aim in the remainder of this chapter. Our first goal is to treat problems such as wave-packet propagation in free space, reflection from a potential step, and tunneling through a barrier.

The time-dependent Schrödinger equation has the form

$$ -\frac{\hbar^2}{2m}\nabla^2\psi + V(\vec{r})\,\psi = \iota\hbar\,\frac{\partial\psi}{\partial t}, \tag{10.23} $$

where t is the time and again $\iota \equiv \sqrt{-1}$. Dealing with this problem in three dimensions is a formidable computational problem, so we consider the (numerically) simpler case of one dimension. We then have

$$ -\frac{\hbar^2}{2m}\frac{\partial^2\psi}{\partial x^2} + V(x)\,\psi = \iota\hbar\,\frac{\partial\psi}{\partial t}, \tag{10.24} $$

where now ψ is a function of x and t. We will explore two ways of dealing with this problem. One is a spectral method, much like the one we employed in connection with waves on a string in Chapter 6;

we will describe that approach in the next section. Here we consider a somewhat more direct attack, which is related to the matrix formulation that was encountered in the previous section.

It is instructive to rewrite (10.24) in the form

$$\imath \hbar \, \frac{\partial \psi}{\partial t} \;=\; \mathcal{H} \, \psi \,, \tag{10.25}$$

where the Hamiltonian operator is defined by

$$\mathcal{H} \;\equiv\; -\frac{\hbar^2}{2m} \frac{\partial^2}{\partial x^2} \;+\; V(x) \,. \tag{10.26}$$

While (10.25) has the appearance of a simple first-order differential equation involving the time dependence of ψ, things are complicated by the fact that $\mathcal{H}$ is an operator rather than a number. Ignoring that fact for a moment, (10.25) has the formal solution

$$\psi(x, t) \;=\; \exp(-\imath \, t \, \mathcal{H}/\hbar) \, \psi(x, 0) \,, \tag{10.27}$$

where $\psi(x, 0)$ is the wave function at $t = 0$. Thus, if we know $\psi(x, 0)$, we can *formally* calculate the behavior at all future times using (10.27). However, this formal solution is not as useful as we might hope because of the operator $\mathcal{H}$ in the exponent. To be clear on what it means mathematically to have an operator expression of this kind, it is useful to rewrite (10.27) using the Taylor expansion of the exponential factor

$$\exp(-\imath \, t \, \mathcal{H}/\hbar) \, \psi \;=\; \left(1 - \frac{\imath \, t}{\hbar} \mathcal{H} - \frac{t^2}{2 \hbar^2} \mathcal{H}^2 \, \dots \right) \psi \,, \tag{10.28}$$

where $\mathcal{H}^n$ means that the operator $\mathcal{H}$ is applied n times in succession. The problem comes when we have to evaluate terms such as $\mathcal{H}^2 \psi$. Recalling the definition of $\mathcal{H}$, we see that such a term expands to give

$$\mathcal{H}^2 \, \psi \;=\; \mathcal{H} \, \mathcal{H} \, \psi \;=\; \left[-\frac{\hbar^2}{2m} \frac{\partial^2}{\partial x^2} + V(x) \right] \left[-\frac{\hbar^2}{2m} \frac{\partial^2}{\partial x^2} + V(x) \right] \psi \,. \tag{10.29}$$

Difficulties now arise from the fact that the two terms that make up $\mathcal{H}$ do not commute; that is, the order of operation is important. We cannot simply switch the order with which we apply the derivative term in $\mathcal{H}$ (the kinetic energy piece) and the potential energy part (which, in general, depends on position). This is what makes dealing with the time-dependent Schrödinger equation more complicated than dealing with a simple first-order differential equation such as those discussed in Chapter 1.

While (10.27) is a perfectly fine formal solution, it is not of much practical use since the expansion (10.28) involves a very large (infinite) number of terms. However, this formal solution does suggest a way to proceed numerically. Let us consider applying the formal solution over a very small time interval. Indeed, let us discretize time in steps Δt; using (10.27) we obtain

$$\psi(x, t + \Delta t) \;=\; \exp(-\imath \, \Delta t \, \mathcal{H}/\hbar) \, \psi(x, t) \,. \tag{10.30}$$

But, you might ask, how can this be a useful approach in view of the difficulties with the expansion (10.28)? The reason we could have some optimism with regard to (10.30) is that a small value of Δt

will make the higher-order terms in the expansion (10.28) small. Let us assume for now that these terms can be made small enough that we can stop at the term linear in $\mathcal{H}$, which yields[25]

$$\psi(x, t + \Delta t) \approx (1 - \imath\,\Delta t\,\mathcal{H}/\hbar)\,\psi(x, t) = \left[1 + \frac{\imath\,\Delta t}{2}\frac{\partial^2}{\partial x^2} - \imath\,\Delta t\,V(x)\right]\psi(x, t)\,, \quad (10.31)$$

where in the last step we have assumed $\hbar = 1$ and that the mass of the particle is also unity. We have now gotten rid of the troublesome powers of $\mathcal{H}$, and things look like they might be easily manageable. Unfortunately, looks can be deceiving, as we will now describe.

Given (10.31), a natural way to proceed is to discretize space into units of size Δx and write the wave function as $\psi(m, n) \equiv \psi(m\Delta x, n\Delta t)$. Expressing the second partial derivative in the usual finite-difference form, (10.31) becomes

$$\psi(m, n + 1) \approx \psi(m, n) + \frac{\imath\,\Delta t}{2}\left[\frac{\psi(m + 1, n) + \psi(m - 1, n) - 2\,\psi(m, n)}{(\Delta x)^2}\right] \quad (10.32)$$
$$- \imath\,\Delta t\,V(m)\,\psi(m, n)\,.$$

Hence, given $\psi(m, n)$ it appears that we can readily calculate $\psi(m, n + 1)$, the wave function at the next time step. However, this approach contains two flaws. The first is that it is numerically unstable. It turns out that the effect of small round-off or other errors (due, for example, to the higher-order terms we have neglected) grows rapidly with time, essentially because of the exponential factor in (10.30) from which this finite-difference equation was derived. Amazingly, this numerical instability can be cured by rewriting (10.30) so as to, in a sense, propagate *backward* in time[26]

$$\psi(x, t) = \exp(+\imath\,\Delta t\,\mathcal{H}/\hbar)\,\psi(x, t + \Delta t)\,, \quad (10.33)$$

which leads to the finite-difference equation

$$\psi(m, n) \approx \psi(m, n + 1) \qquad\qquad\qquad\qquad\qquad\qquad (10.34)$$
$$- \frac{\imath\,\Delta t}{2}\left[\frac{\psi(m + 1, n + 1) + \psi(m - 1, n + 1) - 2\,\psi(m, n + 1)}{(\Delta x)^2}\right]$$
$$+ \imath\,\Delta t\,V(m)\,\psi(m, n + 1)\,.$$

We will not go into the details of precisely why the scheme (10.34) is stable, but leave that for interested readers to explore using the references. From a purely numerical point of view this approach is not as convenient as (10.32), since it is an *implicit* equation for $\psi(m, n + 1)$. Our goal is still to calculate ψ at the next time step, but $\psi(m, n + 1)$ now appears on the right in (10.34) and this cannot be rearranged to solve simply for $\psi(m, n + 1)$ in terms of the wave function at the previous time step. Hence, we cannot just step through the values of m and use (10.34) to calculate the wave function at the next time step. We must instead solve a system of algebraic equations, and this amounts to a matrix formulation as described earlier in this chapter.

---

[25]This could also be obtained by expressing (10.25) in finite-difference form, but we will have further use for (10.30) moment.

[26]Note that we are using the notation $\psi(x, t)$ and $\psi(m, n)$ to represent the same function. The choice of which is more convenient depends on whether we are considering the differential equation form (which involves x and t) or the finite-difference form (which involves m and n).

However, even this price is not enough to pay. While (10.34) is numerically stable, it shares an important flaw with (10.32) [we warned you that (10.32) has two flaws, so you should have been waiting for another one!], which concerns a fundamental property of quantum mechanics. We have already seen that the wave function must be properly normalized. In one dimension this means that $\int \psi^* \psi \, dx$ must equal unity at all times. It is a property of the Schrödinger equation, known as unitarity, that if a wave function satisfies the normalization condition at one particular value of t, then it satisfies this condition at *all* times. It is important that numerical solutions of the Schrödinger equation preserve unitarity, since the total probability for finding a particle somewhere in space must always be unity. It turns out that neither (10.32) or (10.34) are unitary, and for this reason we must devise a different strategy.

An approach that does satisfy unitarity involves writing the exponential factor in (10.30) in what is known as the Cayley form

$$\exp(-\imath \, \Delta t \, \mathcal{H}/\hbar) \approx \frac{1 - \imath \, \Delta t \, \mathcal{H}/2\hbar}{1 + \imath \, \Delta t \, \mathcal{H}/2\hbar} \,. \tag{10.35}$$

We will leave it to the reader to show that to lowest order in $\mathcal{H}$ (in a Taylor expansion), this is equal to both $1 - \imath \, \Delta t \, \mathcal{H}$ and $(1 + \imath \, \Delta t \, \mathcal{H})^{-1}$, which are the key factors in (10.31) and (10.33). However, these three ways of approximating the exponential factor $\exp(-\imath \, \Delta t \, \mathcal{H})$ are *not* equivalent with regard to maintaining unitarity, as can be seen in the following way. Using (10.35) to propagate our wave function forward in time we have

$$\psi(x, t + \Delta t) \approx \frac{1 - \imath \, \Delta t \, \mathcal{H}/2\hbar}{1 + \imath \, \Delta t \, \mathcal{H}/2\hbar} \psi(x, t) \,. \tag{10.36}$$

Unitarity requires that $\int \psi^*(x, t + \Delta t)\psi(x, t + \Delta t)dx = 1$. From (10.36) we find

$$
\begin{aligned}
\int \psi^*(x, t + \Delta t)\psi(x, t + \Delta t) \, dx &= \int \left[\frac{1 + \imath \, \Delta t \, \mathcal{H}/2\hbar}{1 - \imath \, \Delta t \, \mathcal{H}/2\hbar} \right] \psi^*(x, t) \\
&\quad \left[\frac{1 - \imath \, \Delta t \, \mathcal{H}/2\hbar}{1 + \imath \, \Delta t \, \mathcal{H}/2\hbar} \right] \psi(x, t) \, dx \\
&= \int \psi^*(x, t)\psi(x, t) \, dx \,.
\end{aligned}
\tag{10.37}
$$

This result can be derived by expressing ψ as an expansion in terms of eigenfunctions [as in (10.22)], together with Taylor expansions to move all of the terms involving $\mathcal{H}$ out of the denominators. A little algebra together with the orthogonality property of a basis set of eigenfunctions then leads to the final equality in (10.37). The moral is that unitarity is maintained if we use (10.36). This will be the basis for our numerical approach.

From (10.36) we first obtain

$$\left[1 + \frac{\imath \, \Delta t \, \mathcal{H}}{2\hbar} \right] \psi(x, t + \Delta t) = \left[1 - \frac{\imath \, \Delta t \, \mathcal{H}}{2\hbar} \right] \psi(x, t) \,. \tag{10.38}$$

Replacing $\mathcal{H}$ by (10.26), converting everything to finite-difference form, and rearranging a few terms then yields

$$\psi(m + 1, n + 1) + [2\imath\lambda - 2(\Delta x)^2 V(m) - 2] \, \psi(m, n + 1) + \psi(m - 1, n + 1) \tag{10.39}$$
$$= -\psi(m + 1, n) + [2\imath\lambda + 2(\Delta x)^2 V(m) + 2] \, \psi(m, n) - \psi(m - 1, n) \,,$$

where for notational convenience we define $\lambda \equiv 2(\Delta x)^2/\Delta t$. The system of equations (10.39) has a form that is different from anything we have encountered in previous chapters. Most importantly, they cannot be rewritten so as to express $\psi(m, n+1)$ solely in terms of $\psi(m, n)$. Hence, we cannot simply loop through the values of m and compute each $\psi(m, n+1)$ in a straightforward manner. Instead, we have an *implicit* numerical problem, which means that the value of $\psi(m, n+1)$ for a particular value of m depends on $\psi(m', n+1)$, where $m' \neq m$. That is, we have a set of algebraic equations (which can again be cast as a matrix problem) that must be solved to obtain the wave function at the next time step.

As noted earlier in this chapter, many eigenvalue problems can be expressed in matrix form, with the solution then requiring that a matrix be diagonalized or inverted. In the present case we must invert the matrix whose coefficients can be read from (10.39). The bad news is that this will be a *large* matrix. In the particular problems we will consider below, the number of grid elements along x is typically 1000, so the associated matrix is 1000×1000 in size. This is a formidable computational problem, especially when we realize that such a matrix must be inverted for *each* time step! Fortunately, there is some good news: Most of the elements of this matrix are zero. If we examine (10.39) we see that the equation for $\psi(m, n+1)$ involves just $\psi(m \pm 1, n+1)$, and no other values of ψ [except for itself, $\psi(m, n+1)$]. Thus, each row of our matrix has only three nonzero elements.[27] Since one of these is on the diagonal and the other two are just one space away, this matrix is *tridiagonal*. Such matrices arise often in numerical work, since as in the present case the effectively "local" nature of the underlying differential equation gives rise naturally to this matrix structure.

As you might expect, the large number of the zeros in the matrix can be used to our advantage. We now describe an algorithm for solving (10.39), which is known as the Crank-Nicholson method. The particular approach discussed below follows the paper by Goldberg, Schey, and Schwartz (1967).[28] We begin by defining a shorthand for the right-hand side of (10.39)

$$\Omega(m, n) \equiv -\psi(m+1, n) + [2\iota\lambda + 2(\Delta x)^2 V(m) + 2]\psi(m, n) - \psi(m-1, n), \qquad (10.40)$$

so that (10.39) can be written as

$$\psi(m+1, n+1) + [2\iota\lambda - 2(\Delta x)^2 V(m) - 2]\psi(m, n+1) + \psi(m-1, n+1) = \Omega(m, n). \quad (10.41)$$

Numerically it would be extremely convenient if we could write $\psi(m+1, n+1)$ as a function of just $\psi(m, n+1)$, as this would be easier than having to deal with an entire system of equations.[29] That is, we would like to be able to write

$$\psi(m+1, n+1) = e(m, n)\,\psi(m, n+1) + f(m, n), \qquad (10.42)$$

so that we can calculate $\psi(m+1, n+1)$ directly from $\psi(m, n+1)$. At this point you might object (strongly!) that since we began with an implicit expression for $\psi(m, n+1)$, how can a form as simple

---

[27] The astute reader will also notice that the rows of the matrix that pertain to the two ends of the system will contain only two nonzero elements. We will make use of this fact shortly.

[28] Be careful when comparing our equations with those of Goldberg, Schey, and Schwartz. We use units with $\hbar = 1$ and $m = 1$, while they take $\hbar = 1$ and $m = 1/2$, so there are some extra factors of 2 in various places!

[29] What we would *really* like is to be able to write $\psi(m, n+1)$ as a simple function of $\psi(m, n)$, so that we could simply update the wave function at each grid site using just the value at that site from the previous time step. Alas, that is not possible, so we will settle for (10.42).

as (10.42) exist? The answer is that the e and f factors must be determined "carefully." We will see that these factors are themselves functions of the various $\psi(m, n)$ and $\psi(m, n+1)$, so (10.42) is still an implicit relation for the wave function. However, its general form suggests that if the wave function at a particular site m is known, the wave function at an adjacent site $m + 1$ can be readily calculated. It will turn out that our algorithm will work its way along the system in just this manner.

If we insert (10.42) into (10.41) and do a little arithmetic, we find that e and f must be given by

$$e(m, n) = 2 + 2(\Delta x)^2 V(m) - 2\iota\lambda - \frac{1}{e(m-1, n)} \qquad (10.43)$$

$$f(m, n) = \Omega(m, n) + \frac{f(m-1, n)}{e(m-1, n)} .$$

Hence, as we anticipated, the e and f factors themselves are defined implicitly.

At this point you may be doubting that we really gained anything by rewriting things in this way. Actually, we are now finished with the preliminaries and are ready to lay out the algorithm. We imagine that our particle is confined to some region of space so that the spatial index runs from $m = 0$ to M and impose the boundary conditions $\psi(0, n) = 0$ and $\psi(M, n) = 0$. The expressions for e and f in (10.43) apply only in the interior of the system. From the boundary condition for the wave function at $m = 0$, together with (10.40) and (10.42), we find that at this end of the system

$$e(1, n) = 2 + 2(\Delta x)^2 V(1) - 2\iota\lambda \qquad (10.44)$$

$$f(1, n) = \Omega(1, n) .$$

For the first time step, $n = 0$, the factors $\Omega(1, 0)$, $e(1, 0)$, and $f(1, 0)$ can all be calculated explicitly from the initial wave function $\psi(m, 0)$, which is assumed given as an initial condition (we'll discuss how to choose the initial wave function in a moment, when we consider our first example). Once we have the values of $e(1, 0)$ and $f(1, 0)$, we can use (10.43) to obtain $e(2, 0)$ and $f(2, 0)$, etc., for all m along the system. Hence, we traverse the system from $m = 0$ to $m = M$, to calculate $e(m, 0)$ and $f(m, 0)$ for all m.

We used the boundary condition for ψ at $m = 0$ to obtain (10.44). We now make use of the boundary condition at the other end where $m = M$. We first rearrange (10.42)

$$\psi(m, n+1) = \frac{\psi(m+1, n+1) - f(m, n)}{e(m, n)} . \qquad (10.45)$$

At the end of the system $m = M$ the wave function again vanishes, so we have

$$\psi(M-1, n+1) = \frac{\psi(M, n+1) - f(M-1, n)}{e(M-1, n)} = -\frac{f(M-1, n)}{e(M-1, n)} , \qquad (10.46)$$

since $\psi(M, n) = 0$ for all n. We can thus use (10.46) to obtain $\psi(M-1, 0)$, that is, the value of the new wave function one spatial unit in from the "right" boundary. We then use (10.45) to compute the wave function at $m = M - 2$, $M - 3$, etc., as we traverse the system backward, from large to small m.

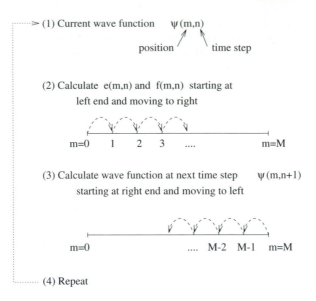

Figure 10.17:   Schematic description of the Crank-Nicholson algorithm.

The algorithm may be summarized as follows (see also the schematic description in Figure 10.17).

1. We begin with an initial wave function $\psi(m, 0)$. Exactly how this is chosen depends on the problem, as we will see when we consider some examples below.

2. The system is traversed from small m to large m, and the functions $e(m, 0)$ and $f(m, 0)$ are calculated using (10.44) initially and (10.43) thereafter.

3. The system is traversed from large m to small m, and $\psi(m, 1)$ is calculated using (10.46) initially and (10.45) thereafter. This completes one iteration and yields the wave function at $n = 1$ ($t = \Delta t$).

4. Steps (2) and (3) are repeated[30] to obtain ψ as a function of time ($n \geq 1$).

Implementing this procedure in a program mainly involves some bookkeeping with regard to (10.43) and (10.45). The only really new programming challenge is that the quantities Ω, e, f, and ψ are in general *complex*, and this complicates the arithmetic somewhat.[31] Some languages contain complex data types and can thus take care of this automatically, but this is unfortunately not the case in *True Basic*. However, it is not hard to deal with complex quantities by hand, and a program that does this is listed in Appendix 4. The approach we take there is to employ two-dimensional arrays for all of the complex functions introduced above. For example, we define an $(M + 1) \times 2$ array psi(m,k) to hold the value of the wave function at $x = m\Delta x$; the real part is kept in the array element with k=1, while k=2

---

[30]Note that while $f(m, n)$ depends on $\Omega(m, n)$ and hence varies with n (i.e., time), the factors $e(m, n)$ do not vary with n, so they need be calculated only once.

[31]Unlike the time-independent problems considered in the previous sections, for most time-dependent problems we cannot avoid a complex wave function.

holds the imaginary part. We deal with Ω, e, and f in a similar manner. The arithmetic in (10.43) and (10.45) then requires that the real and imaginary parts of these variables be combined appropriately. We urge you to write your own program to implement this procedure, and use the program in Appendix 4 only as a guide.

We now consider a few examples of the time-dependent behavior of ψ as calculated using the algorithm described above. The primary initial condition in these calculations is the initial wave function. In all of the examples considered below we assume a gaussian form for ψ at $t = 0$, so that our initial wave packet has the form

$$\psi(x, t = 0) = C \exp[-(x - x_0)^2/\sigma^2] , \tag{10.47}$$

where the center of the packet is at x_0, its width is σ, and the factor C is chosen to satisfy the normalization condition on ψ. A plot of such a wave packet is shown by the solid curve in Figure 10.18. This wave function is not stable with time; we see from Figure 10.18 that it broadens as t increases.

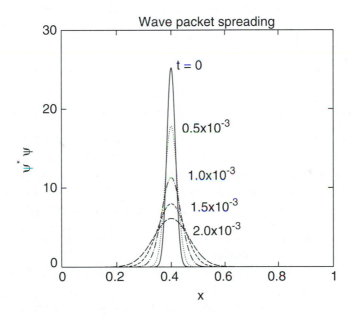

Figure 10.18: Time-dependent behavior of a gaussian wave packet. The initial wave packet ($t = 0$) is given by (10.47) with $x_0 = 0.4$ and $\sigma^2 = 1 \times 10^{-3}$. The wave function at later times (the time values are given in the figure) is seen to spread out in space. For this calculation we used $\Delta x = 0.0005$ with the boundary condition $\psi = 0$ applied at $x = 0$ and $x = 1$. We also took $\Delta t = 5 \times 10^{-7}$ so that $\lambda = 1$.

Since our algorithm maintains unitarity[32] a broader wave function must have a lower value at the peak, as also seen in Figure 10.18.

The physics responsible for this wave-packet spreading can be understood by recalling that we are dealing with an equation much like the wave equation considered in Chapter 6. The gaussian wave packet (10.47) can be decomposed into (i.e., written as) a sum of plane waves of the form e^{ikx}. These plane waves are essentially just Fourier components[33] whose amplitudes are chosen so that they add up to give the gaussian packet (10.47) at $t = 0$. However, each component is a wave that travels along the system. These waves have different wave vectors, k, and thus different velocities. In addition, half of them travel in the $+x$ direction and half along $-x$. The motion of the components causes the wave packet to spread with time. This can also be interpreted using the Heisenberg uncertainty principle, according to which $\delta x \, \delta p \geq \hbar/2$, where δx and δp are the widths of the wave packet in terms of space and momentum. Since the momentum $p = \hbar k$, the uncertainty relation tells us that confining the particle to an initial wave packet of width δx (which in Figure 10.18 is ~ 0.05) *requires* an uncertainty in k, that is, a corresponding spread in the values of k, and this makes the packet spread out with time.

The simple packet (10.47) includes components with both positive and negative wave vectors in equal amounts. This makes it a stationary packet in the sense that the average position $\overline{x} \equiv \int \psi^* x \psi \, dx$ does not change with time. This is not the case for the packet

$$\psi(x, t = 0) \;=\; C \, \exp[-(x - x_0)^2/\sigma^2] \, \exp[\imath \, k_0 \, x] \,, \tag{10.48}$$

which is just our original gaussian function multiplied by a plane wave with wave vector k_0. This wave function, which is now complex, can also be written as the sum of components with a range of k values, but with the range now centered around k_0. As a result this packet travels with an average velocity $v_0 = \hbar k_0/m$. It is interesting to compare it with the stationary wave functions considered above. While we only show $\psi^* \psi$ in Figure 10.18, you can see from (10.47) that at $t = 0$ this is also just the square of the real part of ψ and that the imaginary part is zero. Our propagating packet is a little more complicated, as can be seen from Figure 10.19. While $\psi^* \psi$ has the same simple gaussian shape, the real and imaginary parts of ψ oscillate rapidly. This oscillation is due to the factor $\exp(\imath k_0 x)$ in (10.48).

The results of our propagation program when applied to this packet, are shown in Figure 10.20. Here the packet in Figure 10.19 was allowed to move in a region with $V = 0$. That is, we had a freely moving particle. We will leave it to the exercises to show that this motion has the expected velocity. You should notice that the height of the propagating packet decreased as it moved. This is due to the wave-packet spreading we noted in connection with the stationary packet in Figure 10.18. The uncertainty relation tells us that *all* such packets will spread with time. If we had chosen a larger value of k_0, the velocity of the packet would be larger, and since the rate of spreading would be the same, the packet would better maintain its amplitude for a given distance traveled. We will investigate this in the exercises.

We can use this propagating wave packet to study a wide variety of problems involving reflection, transmission, and tunneling. The programming is essentially identical to that required to treat motion in a flat ($V = 0$) potential region. The only difference is that we must employ the appropriate potential

---

[32] It is a good idea to periodically check that $\int \psi^* \psi \, dx = 1$, as this provides a strong test that your program does not contain any subtle bugs. The wave functions shown in Figure 10.18 and in later figures all satisfy this test.

[33] Just as the sines and cosine standing waves are the Fourier components for waves on a string.

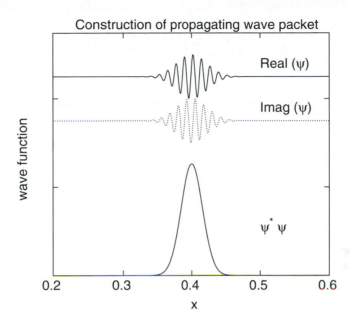

Figure 10.19: Composition of a propagating wave packet. For this packet we took $k_0 = 500$, $x_0 = 0.4$, and $\sigma^2 = 0.001$.

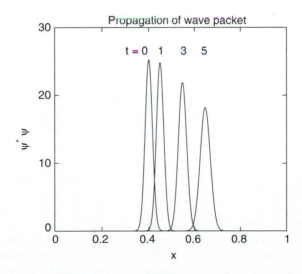

Figure 10.20: Wave packet (10.48) from Figure 10.19 propagating in a region with $V = 0$. The time values given in the figure are to be multiplied by $\times 10^{-4}$. We used $\Delta x = 0.0005$ and $\Delta t = 5 \times 10^{-7}$ in the calculation.

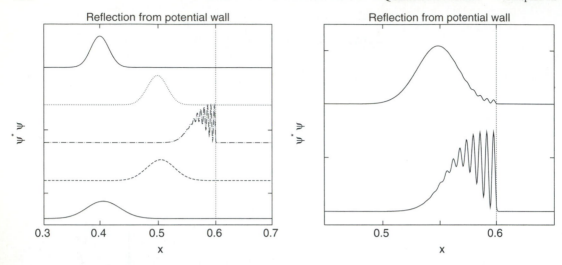

Figure 10.21: Wave packet reflecting from a wall, which is indicated by the vertical dotted lines. The wave-packet parameters were the same as those used in Figure 10.20. The potential was $V = 0$ on the left ($x < 0.6$) and $V = 1 \times 10^6$ on the right ($x \geq 0.6$). Left: plots of $\psi^*\psi$ at various times, with time increasing as we move down the sequence. The particle initially traveled from left to right, was reflected from the wall, and then traveled toward the left. Note that the wave packet at the bottom was significantly broader than the initial packet, due to the spreading effects discussed above. Right: expanded plot of two views recorded as the wave was "striking" the wall.

function $V(x)$ in the calculation. We first consider an encounter with a potential wall; that is, we let our wave packet begin in a region with $V = 0$ and propagate toward a region where V is very large. Figure 10.21 shows the behavior with a wall located at $x = 0.6$. The potential for $x \geq 0.6$ was 1×10^6. This was much greater than the average energy of the wave packet, $E_{\text{packet}} = \hbar k_0^2/2m$, which in this case was 1.25×10^5. Hence, the particle did not have enough energy to classically propagate into the region $x \geq 0.6$ and was instead completely reflected.

In some respects the reflection process resembles the behavior of a wave pulse on a string when it encounters the end of the string. However, the details in the quantum case are somewhat different as can be seen from the detailed plots on the right in Figure 10.21. The rapid oscillations of $\psi^*\psi$ are especially striking and are often not appreciated from the usual analytic treatments of the reflection process.

Another interesting case is a potential cliff. We again consider a wave packet that, as in Figure 10.21, was incident from a region in which $V = 0$. Now, however, the potential *dropped* to $V = -10^6$ when $x \geq 0.6$. From Figure 10.22 we see that while some of the packet was transmitted, a comparable amount was also reflected. That is, there was a nonzero probability for the particle to be reflected from the cliff! This is a nice illustration of the wave nature of quantum mechanics, since such behavior would never be found in classical mechanics. In a sense we could conclude that a quantum world would be a safer place to live, since it would be harder to fall off a quantum cliff than a classical one.

As a final example in this section we consider a wave packet incident on a barrier. Here the potential was $V_0 = 1.25 \times 10^5$ in the region $0.6 \leq x \leq 0.7$, with $V = 0$ to the left and right of the

Reflection from potential cliff

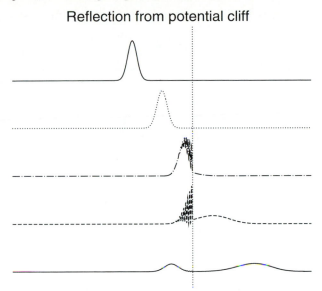

Figure 10.22:   Wave packet incident on a cliff whose position is indicated by the vertical dotted line. The wave-packet parameters were the same as those used in Figure 10.21. The potential was $V = 0$ on the left ($x < 0.6$) and $V = -1 \times 10^6$ on the right ($x \geq 0.6$). These are plots of $\psi^*\psi$ at various times, with time increasing as we move down the graph. The particle initially traveled from left to right. After the encounter with the cliff, a small packet continued to the right, while another packet was reflected and traveled to the left. Note that the transmitted packet has a higher speed than the reflected one, since in this region the kinetic energy is higher (due to the lower potential energy).

barrier. We chose this value of V_0 since it was equal to the "average" kinetic energy for this wave packet, $\hbar^2 k_0^2/2m$. We see from Figure 10.23 that the incident packet was mainly reflected. If we had plotted the results on a greatly expanded scale, you would observe that a small amount was also transmitted. In addition, on the time scale considered here a small amount of the packet "remained behind" in the barrier region. The velocity in this region is essentially zero, since the average kinetic energy is $\hbar^2 k_0^2/2m - V = 0$, so it takes a long time for a wave packet in this region to escape.

The general approach to the time-dependent Schrödinger equation, which we have described in this section, can be applied to a very wide variety of problems. Further examples will be explored in the exercises.

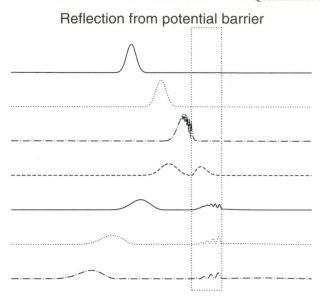

Figure 10.23: Wave packet partially reflecting from a potential barrier (indicated by the dotted lines) with $V = 1.25 \times 10^5$. The other parameters were the same as used in Figure 10.21. The packet initially traveled from left to right (top). Part of the packet was reflected and traveled away to the left, while a very small part (which is barely visible on the scale used here) was transmitted and proceeded to the right.

Exercises

1. Study the motion of a propagating wave packet in free space as in Figure 10.20 and show quantitatively that it does, indeed, move with a velocity of $\hbar k_0/m$. Compare the behavior with different values of k_0. You should find that as k_0 is made larger, our algorithm requires smaller spatial and time steps to avoid substantial numerical errors. These errors are not significant for the values of Δx and Δt we have used in the calculations in this section, but this would not have been the case if we had employed somewhat larger values of k_0.

2. Study how the rate of wave-packet spreading as observed in Figure 10.18 varies with the width of the initial packet. Compare this spreading quantitatively with the Heisenberg uncertainty relation. Do this by calculating the width of the wave packet as a function of time.

3. Observe the propagation of a wave packet in a region in which the potential increases linearly with position. Study the reflection of the wave packet in this case.

*4. Study reflection and transmission from a barrier for which the potential is greater than the kinetic energy of the incident wave packet. The probability for the particle to tunnel through such a barrier decreases rapidly as the potential is increased. In order to have a significant transmission probability you will have to make the barrier thinner than in Figure 10.23. Hint: Good parameter choices are $k_0 = 700$, $\Delta t = 5 \times 10^{-7}$, and $\Delta x = 5 \times 10^{-4}$. Let the height of the potential barrier be $V_0 = 2 \times k_0^2$ with a width of 0.05. You should also explore the behavior for other values of both V_0 and the width of the barrier.

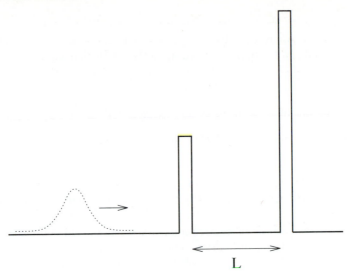

Figure 10.24:   Schematic illustration of a wave packet (dotted curve) incident on a region containing two potential barriers. $V = 0$ on the left, on the right, and between the barriers. The barrier heights are greater than the kinetic energy of the particle.

*5. Compute the scattering of a wave packet from the potential well shown in Figure 10.24. Try to observe effects associated with the bound states in the well. Hint: Start with the wave-packet parameters given in the previous problem. Assuming that the particle is incident from the left, take the height of the left-most barrier to be $4k_0^2$ and give it a width of 0.05. Give the right-most barrier the same width and a much larger height, and let the two barriers be separated by $L = 1$ (or less). You should find that the penetration of the wave function into the potential well depends on the value of k_0 and that this penetration is greatest when the energy of the particle matches the energy of one of the approximate bound states of the well.

10.5   Spectral Methods

The time-dependent Schrödinger equation can also be treated with spectral methods, much like the approach we developed in our dealings with waves on a string. These methods make use of the formal time dependence of the wave function in (10.27), together with the fact that *any* initial wave function can be written in terms of the eigenstates of the associated time-*in*dependent problem. That is, if the functions φ_n are the solutions of the time-independent Schrödinger equation for the particular potential of interest, any wave packet ψ can be written as

$$\psi = \sum_n a_n \, \varphi_n \,, \tag{10.49}$$

where the a_n are complex constants. Note that here the label n is used to refer to different eigenstates, that is, energy levels; it does *not* correspond to space or time. This is analogous to the Fourier expansions of arbitrary functions, which are discussed in Chapter 6 and Appendix 2. The eigenfunctions φ_n form a complete set in the sense that *any* function can be written in the form (10.49).

The time dependence of the basis functions follows from (10.27). Since φ_n is an eigenfunction, we know that $\mathcal{H}\varphi_n = E_n\varphi_n$, where E_n is the energy of state n. If our initial wave function happened to be $\psi(t=0) = \varphi_n$, it would evolve in time according to (10.27), which leads to

$$\psi(t) = \exp(-\imath t E_n/\hbar)\,\varphi_n . \tag{10.50}$$

For a wave packet composed of a sum of basis states such as (10.49) the same arguments give

$$\psi(t) = \sum_n a_n \exp(-\imath t E_n/\hbar)\,\varphi_n . \tag{10.51}$$

Thus, if we can construct the expansion of the initial wave function in terms of the basis states, that is, if we can determine the coefficients a_n in (10.49), we can use (10.51) to compute the wave function at all future times.

This approach is very much like the spectral method we employed in Chapter 6. There we wrote the displacement of a string in terms of Fourier components. Since the time dependence of the Fourier components for waves on a string has a very simple form (purely sinusoidal), this allowed us to compute the time dependence of a wave packet on a string. Here we take similar advantage of the simple form (10.50) for the time dependence of a basis function. Evaluating (10.51) involves only some arithmetic with complex numbers; there are no algebraic or differential equations to solve.

To illustrate this approach we consider a one-dimensional harmonic oscillator. The first step is to determine the basis functions, φ_n. In this case these are the solutions to the time-independent Schrödinger equation, (10.2), with $V = Kx^2/2$. We considered this problem numerically in the exercises in Section 10.2. The exact solution is, of course, also known (the wave functions can be expressed as the product of a gaussian and a Hermite polynomial), as discussed in Griffiths (1995) and Schiff (1968). However, since we want to show how the spectral approach works in the general case, we will calculate the basis functions numerically, using the shooting method. In principle, if we want the expansion (10.49) to represent our wave packet exactly, we need an *infinite* number of basis functions in the expansion. Of course, this is not possible in a numerical treatment; in the calculations below we will use 32 basis functions and find that this is sufficient for the particular problems we'll be considering. We will discuss how to estimate the necessary number of basis states in the exercises.

With the basis functions in hand, the next step is to calculate the expansion coefficients in (10.49). To do this we take advantage of the fact that the functions φ_n form an orthogonal set. That is $\int \varphi_m^* \varphi_n\,dx$ is zero if $m \neq n$ and unity if $m = n$. Hence we can write

$$\int \varphi_m^*\,\psi_i\,dx = \int \left[\varphi_m^*\left(\sum_n a_n\varphi_n\right)\right]dx = a_m , \tag{10.52}$$

where ψ_i is our initial wave packet. Calculation of the expansion coefficients thus requires integration of the product of each basis function with the initial wave function. Since these functions are known only at the grid locations, this integration is actually just a simple sum.

The results of this calculation for a gaussian initial wave packet (10.47) are shown in Figure 10.25. That is, we first used (10.52) to calculate the coefficients a_k, and then computed the variation of the wave function with time using (10.51). We see from Figure 10.25, that this wave packet changed very little with time. How can this be? It just so happens that we have picked an initial wave packet that is extremely close to the ground-state wave function, of the harmonic oscillator. The ground-state solution

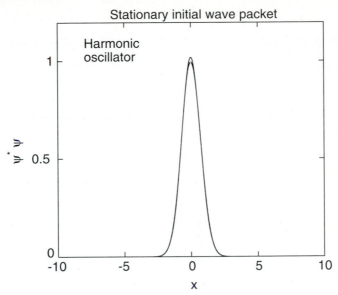

Figure 10.25: Time evolution of a stationary wave packet with an initial width $\sigma = 1$ [see (10.47)]. The potential was $V = Kx^2/2$ with $K = 1$. We have plotted the wave packet at $t = 0, 0.5, 1$, and 2, but the results overlap almost completely and are thus hard to distinguish.

corresponds classically to a particle sitting at the bottom of the potential well ($x = 0$), and this is what we find in Figure 10.25.

An example that exhibits more "action" is shown in Figure 10.26, where we consider a narrower initial wave packet. The functional form of ψ_i is again (10.47) but here we have chosen $\sigma = 0.5$. This is considerably narrower than the ground-state wave function, so we are now far from being in an eigenstate, and the result is a substantial time dependence. Our packet was initially centered at $x = 0$, and it remained so as time advanced. However, the width grew considerably from $t = 0$ to 1.5, providing another example of the uncertainty principle. The initial packet effectively contained components with wave vectors different from zero, and these components oscillated (harmonically) in the potential well. The initial symmetry was maintained, so the wave packet was always centered at $x = 0$, but the width varied with time. In fact, the width oscillated with time, as can be seen from the results plotted on the right in Figure 10.26.

It is also interesting to consider the effect of displacing the initial wave packet from $x = 0$, and this is shown in Figure 10.27. The initial wave packet was again given by (10.47), but here we took $x_0 = 2$ so that our packet was displaced from the center of the potential well. Classically this corresponds to giving the oscillator an initial displacement. We see that our particle oscillated back and forth in the well, precisely as expected for a simple harmonic oscillator.

Here the shape and width of the packet change very little with time, as we have chosen the value of σ that we have already shown to give an essentially time-independent width. We can, therefore, follow the position of the particle by simply plotting the location of the maximum of $\psi^*\psi$ as a function of time, and this is shown on the right in Figure 10.27. We find a simple cosine like oscillation, as

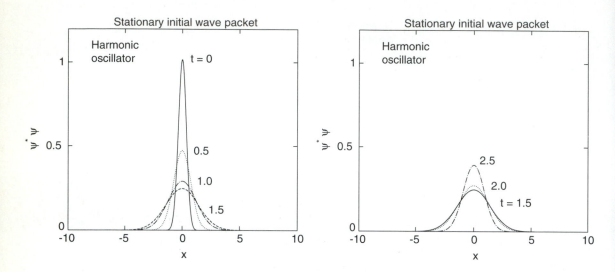

Figure 10.26: Time evolution of a wave packet with an initial width $\sigma = 0.5$. Left: $t = 0, 0.5, 1.0,$ and 1.5. Right: $t = 1.5, 2.0,$ and 2.5. The potential was the same as in Figure 10.25. Note that the packet initially broadened, but from $t = 1.5$ to 2.5 it became narrower with time.

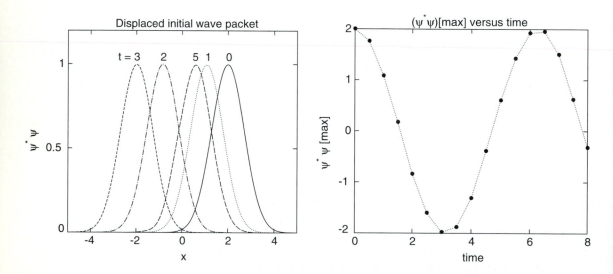

Figure 10.27: Left: time evolution of a wave packet with an initial width of $\sigma = 1$, and an initial displacement of $x_0 = 2$ [in (10.47)]. Right: location of the maximum in $\psi^* \psi$ as a function of time. From a "classical" viewpoint this corresponds to plotting the position of the particle as a function of time. The result is simple harmonic motion.

expected for a simple harmonic oscillator. We will leave it to the exercises to show that the period of these oscillations has the expected value (it does).

We have illustrated the spectral approach with a problem for which the basis states could have been calculated analytically (although we chose to calculate them numerically). However, this method can be used for problems in which little headway can be made analytically. To demonstrate this we consider the behavior of an anharmonic oscillator. We take the potential to be

$$V(x) \; = \; \frac{k_1}{2} x^2 \; + \; \frac{k_2}{2} x^4 \, . \tag{10.53}$$

For small x the potential is nearly harmonic, while for large x the quartic part dominates. We have already considered this problem in an earlier exercise, where we used (or suggested that the reader use) the shooting method to calculate the eigenfunctions. Given these basis functions we can use (10.52) to calculate the expansion coefficients for any desired initial wave packet. The time dependence of the basis functions, which follows from the energy eigenvalues, then leads to the time dependence of the complete wave packet.

Results for a stationary initial wave packet, with $\sigma = 0.5$, are shown in Figure 10.28. This is the same wave packet considered for the harmonic oscillator potential in Figure 10.26. However, the results are very different due to the change in the potential, as we now consider in more detail. While the wave packet remained centered at $x = 0$, its width oscillated with time in a manner reminiscent of the purely harmonic case. However, here the *shape* of the wave packet also changed with time. This was due to the anharmonicity of the potential. For a purely harmonic system the period of oscillation is independent of the amplitude, but this is not true for an anharmonic oscillator. For a potential proportional to x^4 the

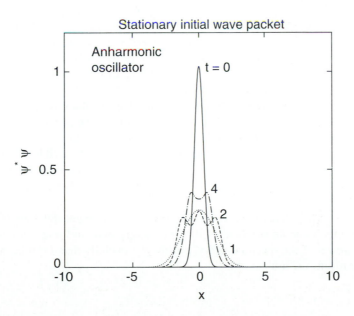

Figure 10.28: Time evolution of a wave packet in an anharmonic potential well, with an initial width $\sigma = 0.5$. The potential was given by (10.53) with $k_1 = 1$ and $k_2 = 0.1$. The lowest 32 basis states were used in the calculation.

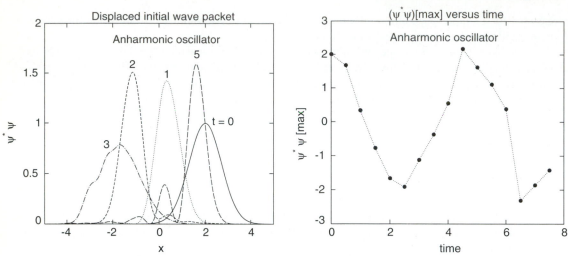

Figure 10.29: Time evolution of a wave packet with an initial width $\sigma = 1$ and an initial displacement of $x_0 = 2$, in an anharmonic potential well. The other parameters are the same as in Figure 10.28.

period *decreases* as the amplitude is increased (see Figure 10.13). This can be understood in terms of the increasing steepness of the potential at large x. As compared with the harmonic case, this confines the particle to a smaller region of space, thereby decreasing the period.

This dependence of the period on amplitude affects the wave packet in the following way. We have already noted that our gaussian packet, or indeed any other packet, can be thought of as a sum of basis functions with different effective wave vectors; that is, with different velocities, with some of the components moving to the right and others to the left. For the harmonic case the components oscillated with precisely the *same* period, and this preserved the shape of the initial wave packet. However, for the anharmonic case the components have different periods, and this causes them to get out of step with each other as time passes. One result is a distortion of the shape of the wave packet.

This anharmonicity can also be seen in the behavior of a wave packet that is initially displaced from $x = 0$. An example is shown in Figure 10.29 where we plot the time evolution of a packet that was initially centered at $x = 2$. The particle oscillated back and forth in the well but the shape of the packet varied considerably, in contrast to the behavior in the purely harmonic case (Figure 10.27). The time dependence of the location of the maximum in $\psi^*\psi$ also deviated substantially from a purely cosine form.

The relatively simple behavior of a harmonic oscillator is not, in general, found for other potentials. The contrasting results for an anharmonic oscillator illustrate some of these features. These examples also highlight the power of the spectral method and show especially that it can be applied to problems for which analytic results are not possible.

Exercises

1. Consider the harmonic oscillator and calculate the evolution of a wave packet that is initially at $x = 0$ and has a wave vector $k = 0.5$ [see (10.48)]. Show that it oscillates, and compare its period with that found when the wave packet is given an initial displacement, but no initial velocity.

*2. Perform a spectral calculation for a harmonic oscillator, and investigate how the results depend on the number of basis states that are used. Contrast the results with 8 and 16 basis functions with the results shown for 32 basis states in Figure 10.27. As a general rule, the basis functions vary more rapidly with position as their energy is increased. These functions must vary at least as rapidly as the initial wave function (if not more so), if they are to be able to accurately represent the time dependence. To see this, perform a calculation with a fixed number of basis states and compare the results for different initial displacements of the wave packet (as in Figure 10.27).

3. Calculate the (classical) oscillation period for the harmonic oscillator considered in Figure 10.27 and show that it agrees with the observed behavior.

References

BOLEMON, J. S. 1972. "Computer Solutions to a Realistic 'One Dimensional' Schrödinger Equation." *Am. J. of Phys.* **40**, 1511. Describes the shooting method and gives some examples.

DEVRIES P. L. 1994. *A First Course in Computational Physics*. New York: John Wiley & Sons. Contains a nice discussion of the so-called split-operator approach for solving the time-dependent Schrödinger equation.

GALBRAITH I., Y. S. CHING, and E. ABRAHAM. 1984. "Two-Dimensional Time-Dependent Quantum-Mechanical Scattering Event." *Am. J. of Phys.* **52**, 60. Describes how to extend the time-dependent calculations to more than one dimension.

GOLDBERG, A., H. M. SCHEY, and J. L. SCHWARTZ. 1967. "Computer-Generated Motion Pictures of One-Dimensional Quantum-Mechanical Transmission and Reflection Phenomena." *Am. J. of Phys.* **35**, 177. A very nice description of a "direct" method for solving the time-dependent Schrödinger equation in one dimension, with many nice pictures.

GRIFFITHS, D. J. 1995. *Introduction to Quantum Mechanics*. Upper Saddle River: Prentice Hall. A good introduction to the subject.

SCHIFF, L. I. 1968. *Quantum Mechanics*, 3d ed. New York: McGraw-Hill. A very useful and complete reference, which is more advanced than the book by Griffiths. Contains derivations of the analytic results discussed in this chapter, along with other useful discussions of subjects such as the variational theorem.

There are *many* numerical methods for attacking the Schrödinger equation that we did not have space to describe or even mention in this chapter. The following papers describe a few of these approaches.

LEE, M. A., and K. E. SCHMIDT. 1992. "Green's Function Monte Carlo." *Computers in Physics* **6**, 192.

REYNOLDS, P. J., J. TOBOCHNIK, and H. GOULD. 1990. "Diffusion Quantum Monte Carlo." *Computers in Physics* November/December, p. 662.

TOBOCHNIK, J., G. BATROUNI, and H. GOULD. 1992. "Quantum Monte Carlo on a Lattice." *Computers in Physics* **6**, 673.

TOBOCHNIK, J., H. GOULD, and K. MULDER. 1990. "An Introduction to Quantum Monte Carlo." *Computers in Physics* July/August, p. 431.

11

Interdisciplinary Topics

This is a book about physics. We have considered a wide range of problems in the past 10 chapters, and most readers would probably agree that they are all physics problems. However, the boundary between different disciplines is not always clear-cut. For example, you might claim that the Lorenz model belongs to atmospheric science, or that percolation, since it can be used to discuss the properties of porous materials, is really a geoscience problem. Arguments over such matters are generally not very useful, but they do illustrate that the lines between disciplines are not sharply defined. Indeed, the ideas developed in one area can often lead to important breakthroughs when applied to other fields. In this chapter we will consider three cases in which it appears that such cross-fertilization has, or may, prove extremely fruitful. The topics we now discuss are active areas of research, so even the tentative conclusions we will draw may change considerably in the next few years. Nevertheless, the computational methods we employ, which are extensions of approaches we have encountered earlier in this book, have already led to useful new insights.

The first problem in this chapter is from biology and concerns protein structure. Proteins are long flexible molecules that can fold into many different shapes. The problem is to understand the folding process so that we can predict the folded structure of a newly encountered protein and thereby learn how to design molecules with a desired shape. The second example is from geoscience and concerns earthquakes and a possible connection with phase transitions. The third problem deals with the brain and some proposals concerning the way (human) memory might work. We will see that all of these problems are closely related in a computational sense to topics we have touched on in this book. These problems will also give us a chance to illustrate further both the process and philosophy of model building in theoretical physics.

11.1 Protein Folding

A polymer is constructed by linking together a collection of short molecular segments. Many biological molecules are constructed in this way, including DNA (and its relatives) and proteins. You have

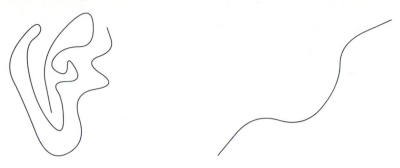

Figure 11.1:   Schematic protein in a folded (left) and unfolded state (right).

probably heard much about the wonders of DNA and the double helix, etc. Here we will focus, instead, on proteins. These are key participants in a very wide variety of biological processes. They are involved in energy storage and conversion, handle communication between cells, are important structural components in several parts of the body including tendons and bones, and are catalysts in many biochemical reactions.[1]

Proteins are built from amino acids, which are relatively short molecules containing 10s of atoms. Nature uses only 20 different amino acids to construct *all* of the known proteins. These 20 monomers (another term we will use for amino acids in this context) are very similar to each other and thus form a fairly homogeneous set of building blocks. A typical protein is made up of a few hundred amino acids linked together end-to-end, although the overall length of a protein can vary greatly. The shortest proteins contain only on the order of 50 monomers, while the longest are comprised of several thousand. A *particular* protein is composed of a *particular* sequence of amino acids. This sequence is known as the primary structure of the protein. It is believed that all of the properties and functions of a protein are uniquely determined by its primary structure.

Proteins can be viewed as chains in which the links are the amino acids. It turns out that the connections between these links are somewhat flexible. In a living cell proteins exist in a solution that is mostly water, and this makes it possible for the chain to assume different shapes. Possible shapes include the two shown schematically in Figure 11.1. In one case the protein is folded into a compact "glob," while in the other it is unfolded with an end-to-end length that is close to the maximum possible. The shapes of real proteins are generally more complicated than these two very simple illustrations. For example, some proteins form helical sublengths that then fold into sheets or globs. Our point here is only that a long chain molecule with flexible connections between monomers has the possibility of taking on *many* different shapes. Which shape is preferred will depend on temperature and the chemicals present in solution. The structure of a protein when it is in its biologically active state is known as the tertiary structure, and this is generally some sort of folded state. The biological functions of a protein are a result of its tertiary structure, since this determines what other molecules a protein can bind to, the kinds of spaces it can fit into, etc. Hence, if we want to understand how a protein works,

---

[1]We hope the reader will understand that this section has been written by a physicist. Our goal is to emphasize the aspects of proteins that are important for understanding the physics of the protein-folding problem.

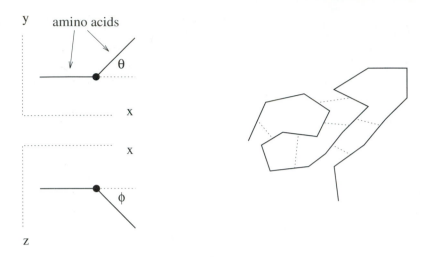

Figure 11.2: Left: angle between two amino acids when viewed in a projection in the x–y plane (top) and x–z plane (bottom). For simplicity each amino acid is drawn simply as a solid straight line (the side chains are not shown), and the covalent bond between them is represented by the filled circular dot. Right: schematic protein in a folded state. The dotted lines indicate interactions between parts of the chain that are not connected by strong covalent bonds.

we must understand its tertiary structure. In addition, if we want to *design* a new protein with a specific (presumably beneficial) property, we must be able to *predict* the tertiary structure from knowledge of the primary structure.

While the chemical bonds between adjacent amino acids in a protein chain are not completely rigid, they are also not completely flexible. The relative orientation of two adjacent amino acids in a chain are determined by the covalent chemical bond between the two and can typically assume several different values. This is illustrated in Figure 11.2, which shows a hypothetical pair of monomers that are bonded so as to have a relative angle of θ in the x–y plane and ϕ in the x–z plane. In most cases the chemical bond permits either or both of these angles to be reversed (that is, $\theta \rightarrow -\theta$) without affecting the bonding energy, yielding four possible choices for the relative orientation of the two amino acids. When we combine this with four more choices when the next monomer is added to the chain, etc., for a long chain, we can see that there are a *large* number of different tertiary structures that have the same energy as far as the direct, covalent bonds between the amino acids are concerned. While this picture is a bit simplified[2] it does illustrate (correctly!) the origin of a protein's flexibility and why it can assume many different particular shapes. If we assume four different relative orientations for each link in a chain of N amino acids, there will be $\sim 4^N$ different possible structures (ignoring self-avoidance constraints). For $N = 300$ this yields $\sim 10^{180}$ distinct tertiary structures, all arising from a single primary structure.

---

[2]The energetically allowed orientations between all possible pairs of the 20 amino acids have been determined from experiments, and the interested reader can learn about this by reviewing the references. This information could be added to the model we develop here, but would make things more complicated than necessary for our purposes.

Even though a particular protein can take on a large number of possible structures, the molecule "knows" which particular tertiary structure is the proper one. Otherwise it could not carry out its intended biological functions. Under certain conditions a protein can be induced to unfold, that is, be made to assume the stretched-out shape shown on the right side of Figure 11.1. For example, this can often be accomplished by adding the appropriate chemicals to its solution. Such an unfolded structure might also be found when a protein is synthesized initially. Experiments have shown that if an unfolded protein is put back into its biologically "natural" environment, it will fold back into its original structure. This is remarkable for two reasons. First, the protein manages to find *precisely* the proper final structure, even though there are an astronomical number of possible alternatives.[3] Second, the *time* it takes for the protein to refold is typically of the order of seconds. You might have thought that the protein would sample a significant fraction of its $\sim 4^N$ possible states on its way to a final folded structure. It was first pointed out by Levinthal that even if a protein spends only on the order of 10^{-13} s in each of these intermediate states,[4] the folding process would still take longer than the age of the universe! This conundrum is known as Levinthal's paradox.

Since proteins are, in fact, able to fold rapidly into their proper tertiary structure, it would appear that a protein is somehow able to locate the correct structure without searching through all of the possibilities. Precisely how it accomplishes this feat and how it "knows" what the proper tertiary structure should be, is not understood. This is the protein-folding problem.

In order to construct a sensible model of the folding process, we need to consider the different forces and energies in the problem. The largest energy scale is that of the direct covalent bond between adjacent amino acids. This is by far the strongest bonding in the protein, but since different tertiary structures have the same collection of covalent bonds, this energy does not play any role in *differentiating* between different folded (or unfolded) structures. This differentiation is the result of several other, much weaker forces. One of these is the Van der Waals force between amino acids that are not covalently bonded. We have encountered this force in our work with molecular dynamics, where we saw that it is attractive at moderate to long distances and falls off rapidly with separation. While it will tend to bring the monomers together, it will only be important when they are not too far apart. There will also be hydrogen bonds between nearby amino acids; these will lead to attractive forces and thus appear to prefer a folded state for the protein. The Van der Waals and hydrogen bond forces are shown schematically by the dotted lines in Figure 11.2. In addition, we must consider the effect of the water molecules and other chemicals in solution. It turns out that water is attracted to some amino acids and repelled from others. Monomers that are strongly attracted to water molecules will prefer an unfolded structure, since this would allow them to be close to more water molecules. Hence, there will be a competition between the various forces, as some prefer a folded state while others favor an unfolded structure.

The relative importance of these forces will be a complicated function of the particular amino acids in the protein chain and how they are arranged. Obtaining a quantitative understanding of the forces is itself an extremely formidable problem and is certainly more than we want to tackle here.

---

[3]That the protein has actually assumed its original structure is demonstrated by the fact that its biological properties are the same as before it was unfolded.

[4]This corresponds roughly to one period of a molecular vibration and is the time scale on which an atom or molecule is able to move a distance of one atomic spacing.

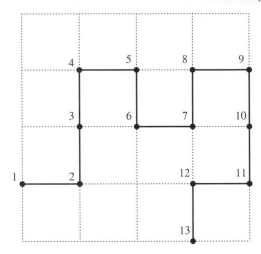

Figure 11.3:   Lattice model for a protein. The filled circles represent amino acids and the solid lines are covalent bonds between them.

While a great deal is known about these matters, this remains an area of much research. The key point for us is that folding is a *competition* between forces. Moreover, these forces are all relatively weak; they turn out to have a magnitude of order $k_B T$ (where T is room temperature) per protein. Hence, we have a very delicate interplay between these forces and the disordering effect of temperature.

This has been an extremely brief introduction to proteins, and we have obviously omitted a lot of interesting points. Nevertheless, we have described all of the key features that are needed to construct a model for the folding process. This will be an *extremely* simple model, and in some ways it will have only a faint resemblance to a real protein. Our goal is to understand how a protein folds and what factors affect the folding process. We begin with a simple model that we believe contains the essential physics. Only after understanding the behavior of this model could we have any hope in attacking a more realistic situation. We don't offer these words as an apology; rather, this is the philosophy that underlies model building in theoretical physics.

We will consider a model protein that sits on a two-dimensional lattice as shown in Figure 11.3. We assume a particular primary structure, that is, a sequence of N amino acids, which we denote as $A(1)$, $A(2)$, ..., $A(N)$. These are just numbers in the range 1–20 (with no rule against repetitions) corresponding to the 20 different amino acids. Each link in this chain of amino acids is assumed to be located on a site of the lattice, with adjacent, covalently bonded links situated on nearest-neighbor sites.[5] In order to mimic the attractive forces between amino acids that are not covalently bonded, we assume that there is an energy $J_{i,j}$ associated with two amino acids that are nearest neighbors, but that are not covalently bonded, that is, *not* adjacent in the chain. $J_{i,j}$ thus represents the combined energies of the Van der Waals and hydrogen bonds, as well as the effects of bonding to water molecules. This energy

---

[5]In comparing Figures 11.2 and 11.3 you may notice a slight change in our graphical notation. In Figure 11.2 the filled circles denote the connections between amino acids, while in our lattice model, Figure 11.3, the lattice sites denote the amino acids themselves, with the connections effectively lying on the bonds between these sites. The two descriptions are equivalent, as both describe a chain with flexible links.

will depend on the specific amino acids that are involved, so i and j are the indices of the two monomers, $i = A(n)$ and $j = A(m)$, where the nth and mth amino acids are situated on nearest-neighbor lattice sites. For example, in the model protein in Figure 11.3, amino acids 3 and 6 are nearest neighbors and are not adjacent members of the chain (that is, not directly connected by a covalent bond), so in our model they have an energy of attraction $J_{3,6}$. If two amino acids are not nearest neighbors, such as monomers 2 and 6, the energy of attraction is taken to be zero.

The energy of our model protein is then

$$E = \sum_{<m,n>} \delta_{m,n} \, J_{A(m),A(n)} \,, \tag{11.1}$$

where the sum is over all pairs of proteins $< m, n >$ in the chain. $\delta_{m,n} = 1$ if amino acids m and n are nearest neighbors that are *not* connected by direct covalent bonds and is zero otherwise. Which pairs of amino acids are noncovalently bonded nearest neighbors will depend on the tertiary structure of the protein, so this energy will be a function of the structure. The protein is assumed to be in thermal equilibrium with a heat bath, which is just the solution it is dissolved in, so we can use the rules of statistical mechanics to calculate its properties. The problem is thus analogous to the Ising model we studied in Chapter 8, and we will again use the Monte Carlo method in our simulations. We next describe the simulation procedure and make a few comments on the programming.

The first step in the simulation is to choose a primary structure. If there are N links in the protein chain, we need to specify the values of $A(1)$, $A(2)$, ..., $A(N)$. In the simulations described below we first generated a hypothetical protein by chosing a sequence of N integers at random from the range 1–20, corresponding to the 20 different possible amino acids. This was then the primary structure of our model protein, and it was held fixed during the course of a particular simulation. The interaction energies $J_{i,j}$ must next be specified. Since there are 20 different possible amino acids [values of $A(m)$], $J_{i,j}$ can be thought of as a 20×20 matrix. In principle, the elements of this matrix could be determined from a quantum mechanical calculation of the Van der Waals forces, hydrogen bonding, etc., but this very formidable task is currently too difficult to tackle in a quantitative way.[6] We will, therefore, take the convenient approach of assuming that the $J_{i,j}$ vary randomly within some specified range.[7] We hope that the important features of the simulation will not depend strongly on how the $J_{i,j}$ are chosen, but that is something we will only know after we have done some work. The final ingredient required for our simulation is the initial tertiary structure. In the calculations shown below we took this to be a completely straight chain. We might instead let it be a self-avoiding walk; we will leave such a study to the interested reader.

After choosing the initial conditions and values, the Monte Carlo method can be employed as follows. A link in the chain is selected at random by choosing a random integer in the range 1 to N. Let the lattice coordinates of this amino acid be (x_0, y_0). Since we are using a square lattice, this site has four nearest neighbors, and one of these neighbors is next chosen at random; we label it (x_n, y_n).

---

[6]In a sense, we have already conceded this by constraining the amino acids to lie on a two-dimensional lattice.

[7]An even simpler choice would be to take them all to have a constant value, but since proteins have a structure that appears to be fairly "disordered," it seems reasonable to put some randomness into the model. As described in the references, the approach we use here is taken in most current simulations of protein structure. Another interesting possibility would be to set the $J_{i,j}$ randomly to ±1; we will explore this in the exercises.

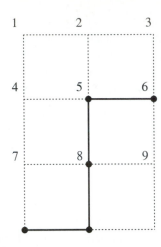 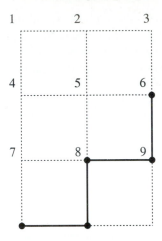

Figure 11.4: Left: hypothetical initial structure of a portion of a protein chain; right: new structure obtained by moving the amino acid initially at lattice site 5 to site 9. Based on the portion of the lattice shown here, these two tertiary structures would have the same energy. However, portions of the chain beyond the right edges of these pictures could cause them to have different energies.

If this neighboring site is not occupied by another amino acid, we then check to see if the monomer at (x_0, y_0) could move to (x_n, y_n) without breaking a covalent bond. This is illustrated in Figure 11.4, which shows a portion of a hypothetical initial structure on the left. Suppose that the amino acid at site 5 is chosen as (x_0, y_0). Site 9 is a nearest neighbor, and the amino acid at site 5 could be moved to this location without breaking (stretching or compressing) either of the bonds to adjacent sites, so this would be an "allowed" move. Site 4 is also a nearest neighbor to site 5, but moving the amino acid to this location would stretch the bonds connecting it to sites 6 and 8, so such a move is prevented by the large energy associated with these covalent bonds. After finding that a move of the amino acid from site 5 to site 9 is permitted by the covalent bond constraints, the Monte Carlo approach is then used to determine if such a move is actually made. The energy of the chain in both its original structure (on the left in Figure 11.4), and in the potential new structure (on the right) is calculated from (11.1). This yields the energy required to make the move, ΔE_{move}. If this energy is negative so that the move would lead to a state with lower energy, the monomer is moved and the structure changes. If ΔE_{move} is positive so that the move would cost energy, the monomer is moved only if the Boltzmann factor $\exp(-\Delta E_{\text{move}}/k_B T)$ is greater than a random number in the range 0–1. Hence, moves that increase the energy are made with a probability given by the Boltzmann factor. This algorithm is analogous to the Monte Carlo rules for simulating a spin system as described in Chapter 8.

   The simulation consists of repeating this procedure a large number of times. Sometimes it results in a new structure, while other times the structure is left unchanged. After each attempted move the system spends one Monte Carlo time step in the resulting state, whether the move is made or not. This (conceptually) is an essential part of computing the thermal averages of the energy and other properties. After a large number of time steps the protein should reach thermal equilibrium with the heat bath. We can then determine its properties by averaging over the state of the protein during the course of many

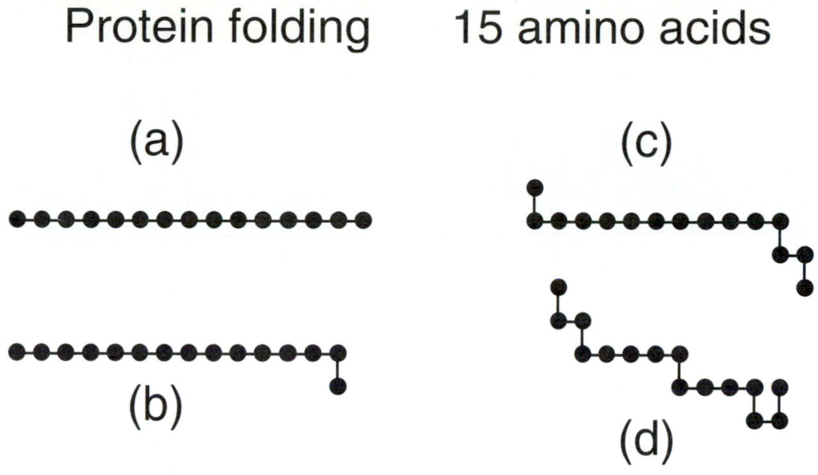

Protein folding   15 amino acids

(a)

(c)

(b)

(d)

Figure 11.5: Snapshots of a model protein at different stages of a simulation. The chain contained 15 amino acids and $T = 10$. The pictures show (a) the initial structure, (b) the structure after 25 Monte Carlo time steps, (c) 249 time steps, and (d) 996 time steps. The interaction energies $J_{i,j}$ were distributed uniformly in the range -4 to -2.

subsequent Monte Carlo steps. In the language used in Chapter 8, each Monte Carlo step leaves the protein in a particular microstate corresponding to a particular tertiary structure. Properties such as the energy or length of the chain are then obtained by performing an average over many such microstates.

Some snapshots of a protein during a typical simulation are shown in Figure 11.5. The protein was initially in a completely straight state, as shown in Figure 11.5(a). In this state only the ends of the chain can move without violating the covalent bonding constraints, so most of the randomly generated potential moves are rejected. Here it took 25 Monte Carlo time steps before a move involving an end site was accepted, and this led to the structure in Figure 11.5(b). After 249 time steps the structure in Figure 11.5(c) was obtained, and after 996 Monte Carlo steps the protein had taken on the structure in Figure 11.5(d). In many cases, the moves are between two states with the same energies. For example, the structures shown in parts (a), (b), and (c) of Figure 11.5 all have the same energies, as none are folded in such a way as to have two noncovalently bonded monomers on nearest-neighbor sites. However, the structure in Figure 11.5(d) does have a different energy. The Monte Carlo rules for acceptance or rejection of a potential move have no difficulty in dealing with two states that are degenerate in energy.

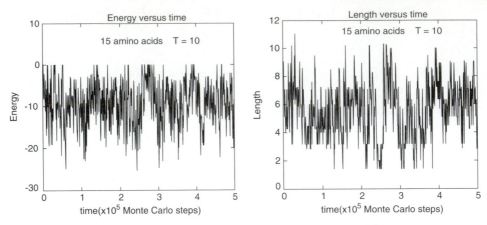

Figure 11.6: Energy (left) and end-to-end length (right) as functions of time for a protein chain with 15 amino acids. The temperature was $T = 10$ and the $J_{i,j}$ were chosen as in Figure 11.5.

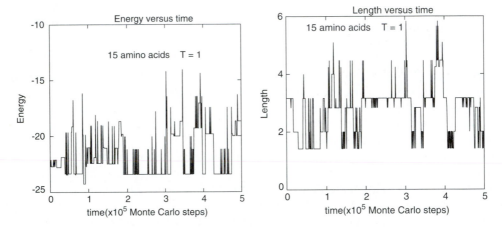

Figure 11.7: Energy (left) and end-to-end length (right) as functions of time for a protein chain with 15 amino acids. The temperature was $T = 1$. This is the same chain as considered in Figure 11.6. Note the different vertical scales as compared with Figure 11.6.

The energy as calculated from (11.1) and the end-to-end length of this chain of 15 amino acids are shown in Figure 11.6 as functions of time. Here time is measured in units of Monte Carlo time steps and the temperature was $T = 10$ (for simplicity we measure energy in units of k_B, so that temperature and the $J_{i,j}$ are effectively unitless). The smallest end-to-end length was ~ 1.4, corresponding to ends located on sites diagonally opposite one another; this is the closest the ends of a chain with an even number of links can get. The largest length was 11, corresponding to nearly the maximum separation. The protein structure thus fluctuated considerably, as it spent a good deal of time in a fairly unfolded state. The energy measured during the same simulation also fluctuated greatly.

As the temperature was lowered, the magnitude of the fluctuations became smaller (Figure 11.7). At $T = 1$ the length fluctuated between about 1.4 and 6, so the protein was now in a more compact

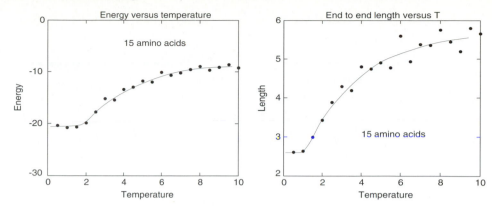

Figure 11.8:   Average energy (left) and end-to-end length (right) as functions of temperature for a protein chain with 15 amino acids. This is the same model protein as considered in Figure 11.6. The temperature was swept down in stages from $T = 10$. The "scatter" in these results (and in the results shown in the next two figures) arises from the Monte Carlo statistical fluctuations. They could be reduced by averaging over a larger number of Monte Carlo time steps.

state. The fluctuations in the energy were also smaller and occurred over much longer time scales. The protein now spent most, but certainly not all, of its time in states with the lowest energies.

The thermal averages of the energy and length as functions of temperature are shown in Figure 11.8, and we see that each of these quantities changed continuously from their values in the unfolded state at high temperatures to those of the folded state at low T. While both the energy and the length varied smoothly with temperature, most of the changes occurred between $T = 5$ and $T = 2$, with very little additional change as the temperature was lowered further. These variations should remind you of the behavior of the order parameter for the Ising ferromagnet considered in Chapter 8 in the vicinity of its second-order transition. Thus, in qualitative terms our model protein exhibits a transition in the neighborhood of $T \sim 2$, although this transition is certainly not abrupt. A true, sharp phase transition can only occur in an infinitely large system, and our protein is not infinite in extent. However, since real proteins can be *much* larger than our 15 monomer chain, it would not be surprising to find a much sharper transition in a real chain.

We can investigate this possibility by studying the behavior of longer chains, and some simulations for chains with 30 and 100 amino acids are shown in Figures 11.9 and 11.10. We again see that both E and the length decreased rapidly in the neighborhood of $T = 2$, and the results do seem to suggest that this pseudotransition to a compact structure is sharper in the longer chains. This would be in accord with the behavior of real proteins, as experiments show that they fold or unfold abruptly as conditions such as temperature or the nature of their solution[8] is changed.

In all of the simulations described so far we have started at a high temperature where fluctuations in the structure were relatively large. The temperature was then reduced in steps, and results at different temperatures obtained. In order to learn more about the specific folded structure obtained at low temperatures and to address Levinthal's paradox, it is useful to consider simulations that begin with the protein in a completely unfolded state at a low temperature. Some results of this kind are given in

---

[8]In our model this would correspond to changing the interaction energies $J_{i,j}$.

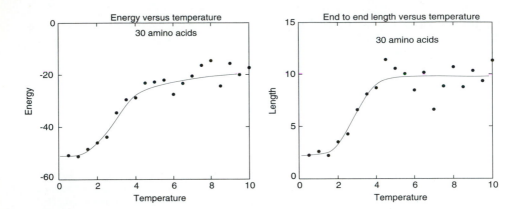

Figure 11.9: Average energy (left) and end-to-end length (right) as functions of temperature for a protein chain with 30 amino acids. The energies $J_{i,j}$ were randomly distributed in the range -4 to -2. The values at each temperature were obtained by averaging over 5×10^5 Monte Carlo time steps. The temperature was swept down in stages from $T = 10$.

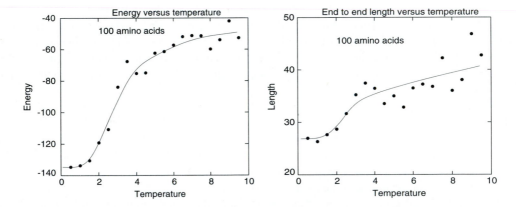

Figure 11.10: Average energy (left) and end-to-end length (right) as functions of temperature for a protein chain with 100 amino acids. The energies $J_{i,j}$ were randomly distributed in the range -4 to -2. The values at each temperature were obtained by averaging over 5×10^5 Monte Carlo time steps. The temperature was swept down in stages from $T = 10$.

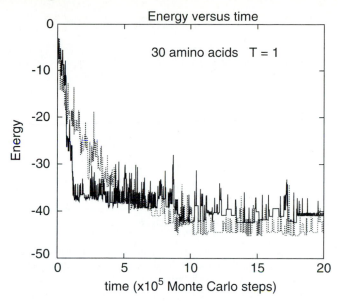

Figure 11.11:   Energy versus time for a chain with 30 amino acids at $T = 1$. The two curves show results for separate simulations with the *same* chain. In each case the chain was completely unfolded at $t = 0$. The interaction strength $J_{i,j}$ was distributed uniformly in the range -4 to -2.

Figure 11.11, which shows two independent simulations for the *same* model protein; that is, the same sequence of amino acids (primary structure) and the same interaction energies, $J_{i,j}$. The temperature used here is low in the sense that it is below the range where the energy and length changed in our previous simulations, Figures 11.8–11.10. In both cases the energy initially dropped with time as the protein folded into a fairly compact state, but the detailed variation of E was very different in the two cases. In one case, the solid curve in Figure 11.11, E dropped quite rapidly until $t \sim 1 \times 10^5$, continued to decrease slowly up to $t \sim 10 \times 10^5$, and was on average constant at longer times. In the other simulation E dropped more slowly at early times, but continued this slow decrease up to $t \sim 10 \times 10^5$. There are two important features of these results. One is that even at long times ($t > 10 \times 10^5$) the energy continued to fluctuate substantially. This implies that even though the chain had found a fairly stable structure, there were still fluctuations involving minor movements of a few amino acids. Second, the energies of the stable structures found in the two cases were significantly different. This protein found two *different* tertiary structures.

Our model protein thus does *not* behave like a real protein, as it does not fold reproducibly into the same tertiary structure. In a sense, our protein has fallen prey to Levinthal's paradox. It was not able to locate the "best" (or even the same) structure during repeated attempts at folding. In at least one of these two cases it was caught in a structure that was not the ideal one. Such nonoptimal structures are known as *metastable states*.

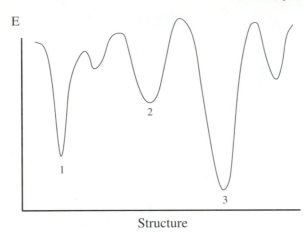

Figure 11.12: Schematic energy landscape. Different points along the horizontal axis correspond to different tertiary structures. The structures labeled 1 and 2 are metastable, while structure 3 has the lowest energy and is, therefore, the stable one at low temperatures.

The problem of trapping in a metastable state is actually a very common one in nature. The difficulty can be appreciated from Figure 11.12, which shows a schematic energy landscape for a protein. Here the vertical axis is energy while the horizontal axis corresponds to the structure of the protein. Of course, this structure is much too complicated to be described with a single coordinate, so if we wanted to be completely realistic we would have to plot the energy as a function of many variables, such as the positions of all of the amino acids. A high-dimensional plot of this kind would be difficult to project onto two dimensions and probably wouldn't be very useful anyway. The key point is that the energy of a protein is a complicated function of its tertiary structure. E will be lower for some structures than for others, and there will, in general, be many structures that are metastable, such as the ones labeled 1 and 2 in Figure 11.12. This means that all nearby structures that can be found by small movements of only a few monomers have higher energies.

The optimal tertiary structure of a protein will presumably be the one that minimizes the energy.[9] However, if it finds itself in a metastable state, the protein may, if the temperature is low, have a very difficult time escaping, since all nearby structures have higher energies. This is a second aspect of Levinthal's paradox. A protein must locate the lowest energy state without becoming trapped in a metastable state.

One way this might be accomplished is suggested by the Monte Carlo algorithm. Recall that the Monte Carlo rules for our protein simulation first generate a potential new state (that is, tertiary structure), and calculate how much energy it would cost, ΔE_{move}, to change to that state. If $\Delta E_{\text{move}} < 0$ so that the new state has a lower energy, this transition is always made. In the energy landscape picture this corresponds to moving downhill. On the other hand, if $\Delta E_{\text{move}} \geq 0$, the transition is made with probability $\exp(-\Delta E_{\text{move}}/k_B T)$. The Monte Carlo procedure thus allows the system to move uphill to higher energy states, although the probability of such a move decreases as ΔE_{move} becomes larger and

---

[9]Since a protein is in thermal equilibrium at some temperature T, there will always be fluctuations away from the equilibrium state. If a protein is to be biologically active, it must spend most of its time in its optimal structure. Ignoring these fluctuations amounts to assuming that the protein is always in the state with the lowest energy.

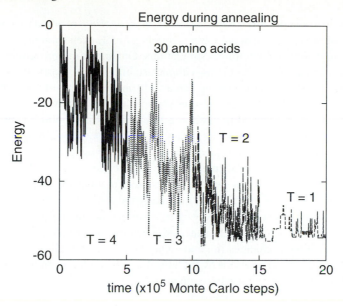

Figure 11.13: Annealing simulation. The chain of 30 amino acids considered in Figure 11.11 was simulated starting at $T = 4$ at time $t = 0$. The temperature was then reduced in stages after every 5×10^5 Monte Carlo time steps to $T = 3, 2$, and 1 as indicated.

as T is made smaller. Nevertheless, this makes it possible for a system to escape from a metastable state. The time it takes to escape will depend on both the depth of the metastable potential well and on temperature, but as long as T is not zero there will be some chance of escape.[10]

These ideas can be applied to our protein problem by beginning the simulation at a temperature that is high enough that the system does not become trapped in any of the metastable potential wells. The system is thus able to explore a large number of different structures. The temperature is then slowly lowered, and while the protein will continue to fluctuate between different structures, it will spend increasing amounts of time in those states with the lowest energies. When the final, low temperature is reached, the protein will be trapped in some state, but the hope is that it will have sampled many other states and thereby managed to choose the optimal structure.

The usefulness of this approach can be studied by slowly sweeping the temperature downward in a simulation. Some results of such a calculation are shown in Figure 11.13. Here we studied the model protein that became stuck in metastable states in the simulations of Figure 11.11. We started at $T = 4$, which we have already seen to be high enough that the fluctuations are large. The temperature was then reduced in stages to $T = 3$ after 5×10^5 Monte Carlo steps, $T = 2$ after 1×10^6 steps, and finally to $T = 1$ after 1.5×10^6 steps. The final temperature was thus the *same* as that employed in Figure 11.11.

---

[10]Here you might object to our use of the Monte Carlo method to address dynamical questions. In Chapter 8 we noted that the Monte Carlo transition rules are designed to lead to a collection of microstates with the correct equilibrium statistics, but that these rules do not correspond to the correct dynamical equations. While the same is true here, the fact that the Monte Carlo algorithm leads to the correct Boltzmann probabilities for finding a system in any particular microstates enables us to use this method for dealing with questions of metastability and the *relative* amounts of time spent in different states.

This gradual reduction of temperature, which is known as *annealing*, resulted in a protein structure that was better in terms of the energy than any obtained in Fig 11.11, even though those computations at a fixed low temperature involved much longer simulations. Our annealing procedure was thus successful in avoiding, at least to some extent, problems with metastability in this particular case.

While these results show that annealing can avoid some of the problems with metastability, this procedure is not guaranteed. There is always some chance that the chain will end up in the wrong state; we will consider this and some related issues in the exercises. At this point it is worthwhile to discuss what our simulations have taught us, and what they haven't, about the folding of real proteins. First, our model does exhibit a transition to a folded structure when the temperature is made sufficiently low. This agrees with the behavior observed in experiments. Second, the model does not avoid the trap associated with Levinthal's paradox. In general, our model protein is not able to avoid being trapped in a metastable state. However, this trapping can be greatly reduced by the procedure of annealing. The implications for real proteins is not completely clear,[11] but one interesting scenario is the following. It is possible that a real protein is effectively annealed when the environmental conditions are changed. For example, the imposition of changes in temperature or chemical conditions will always take some time, which is modeled in our calculations by the annealing procedure in connection with Figure 11.13. This sort of annealing may allow a protein to, on average, avoid falling into metastable states. Such a solution may only need to be successful *on average*, as nature may be able to tolerate the small number of proteins that would end up in metastable, and presumably biologically inert, states.

While annealing may help proteins avoid becoming trapped in metastable states, this alone would not resolve Levinthal's paradox. Our simulations imply that relatively short chains are able to explore a sufficiently large number of structures so as to locate the proper final state. But, we have already argued that the number of potential states of a real protein is *much* larger than for our small models. Even if annealing enables a real chain to avoid metastable states, this will not be a satisfactory solution unless the folding process can occur rapidly. To address this problem we must explore the nature of the energy surface in Figure 11.12, and consider the specific path a protein might follow in locating its proper structure. A solution to Levinthal's paradox would then involve showing that the length of this path does not grow unbearably long for a real protein.

Yet another (related) possibility is that proteins do *not* actually avoid Levinthal's paradox at all. As we have seen, there are a great many possible proteins, that is, primary structures; nature has chosen to make use of only a relatively few of these possibilities. It is conceivable that the ones nature has chosen are those whose energy surfaces allow them to efficiently avoid metastable states on their way to a unique tertiary structure. If so, Levinthal's paradox would be intimately connected with the evolutionary development of proteins. There has been much recent work on these issues, and the interested reader can learn about this work by exploring the references.

The correct solutions to the protein-folding problem and Levinthal's paradox are not yet known. Nevertheless, our simple simulations of protein folding have demonstrated how ideas developed with physics in mind can be very helpful in dealing with a problem that lies in the territory between physics and biology. As is often the case, our model raises as many questions as it answers (or more). Some might say that this is the sign of a good model!

---

[11] Don't expect too much; this is not yet a "solved" problem!

Exercises

1. Simulate the folding transition in three dimensions by allowing the protein to sit on a simple cubic lattice. Compare the results with the behavior in two dimensions. Of particular interest is the width of the pseudotransition from the unfolded to folded state.

2. Study the importance of the way in which the interaction energies $J_{i,j}$ are distributed. One possibility is to compare the behavior of a chain in which all of the $J_{i,j}$ are the same, with that of a chain in which $J_{i,j}$ has the same magnitude, but with randomly varying signs (i.e., $J_{i,j} = \pm 1$) This would mimic the fact that some amino acids are attracted to water molecules, while others are repelled. The time it takes to reach equilibrium and the nature of the metastable states at low temperature are of special interest.

3. In our estimates of the length of a protein, we have used the end-to-end distance. This very simple (to calculate) measure may not tell the whole story. For example, a protein could contain a single fold or have a form like a "ball of string," and have the same end-to-end length. Investigate the behavior of the mean-square size calculated in the following way. Let $\vec{r}_{cm}$ be the location of the center of mass of the protein. One measure of the size of the chain is the quantity $\Delta \equiv < |\vec{r}_i - \vec{r}_{cm}|^2 >$ where $\vec{r}_i$ is the position of the ith amino acid and the angular brackets denote an average over all pieces of the chain. Calculate Δ as a function of temperature and compare its behavior to that of the end-to-end distance.

**4. Perform a simulation of protein folding and examine the variation of the energy as a function of (Monte Carlo) time. Use this, and any other approaches you can devise, to reconstruct part of the energy landscape, as sketched in Figure 11.12. Can you say anything about the number of wells as a function of their depth? How does this distribution change as the protein chain is made longer?

*5. Investigate the problem of metastability of protein folding by comparing the structure obtained by two or more separate simulations of the same model protein. Consider a chain with 30 amino acids, and let it find two or more metastable states by letting it fold at $T = 1$, as in Figure 11.11. Then compare the actual structures of the different folded states. Are the structures similar or very different? Can you estimate the size of the energy barriers that separate the different metastable states?

11.2   Earthquakes and Self-Organized Criticality

Earthquakes often have a large and dramatic impact, which makes them a topic of continuing interest. Earth's crust contains numerous fault lines that separate large pieces of material called *plates*. Each of these plates is fairly sturdy, but the connections across a fault line are relatively weak. Over time the crust deforms, exerting forces on the plates and leading to a gradual build up of potential energy. This energy is released by the sudden movement of one plate relative to an adjacent one. Such an event is an earthquake. While this general picture of earthquakes is well established, there are many questions that are not settled. For example, we would like to know how to predict when earthquakes will occur and how large the next quake associated with a particular fault line will be.

Geoscientists have been involved in modeling earthquakes for many years. In this section we follow their lead and model two adjacent pieces of Earth's crust as masses that are able to slip past each other in response to a steadily increasing force. Such a mechanical model involves Newton's second law, which gives a small excuse for considering this to be a physics problem. However, there is another feature of earthquakes that makes them of interest to physicists. It has been proposed that earthquakes may have some important features in common with the second order phase transition we observed in connection with the Ising model in Chapter 8. In order to understand this connection we need to introduce the so-called Gutenberg-Richter law, which can be stated as follows. The size of an earthquake is often measured using the Richter scale, which is commonly referenced by the popular press. This is a *logarithmic* scale involving the *magnitude* of an earthquake. The amount that one of Earth's plates shifts relative to another during an earthquake is proportional to the moment of the event, M. This quantity is also proportional to the energy released by the event. The magnitude of the quake, $\mathcal{M}$, is equal to the logarithm of the moment, so an earthquake with a magnitude of 7 on the Richter scale is much more powerful than an event whose magnitude is 6.

A logarithmic scale is convenient because earthquakes come in an extremely wide range of sizes. Fortunately, the number of large quakes is much smaller than the number of little ones. This "preference" for small events is well-documented from observations and also follows a logarithmic form. This is known as the Gutenberg-Richter law and can be stated mathematically as

$$P(\mathcal{M}) \;=\; A\,M^{-b} \;=\; A\,e^{-b\mathcal{M}}\,. \tag{11.2}$$

Here $\mathcal{M} \equiv \ln M$ is the magnitude of an event,[12] $P(\mathcal{M})$ is the probability (per unit $\mathcal{M}$) of having a quake of a given magnitude, A is a constant, and b is a factor that lies somewhere in the range 0.8–1.5. The use of the term law in connection with (11.2) is perhaps a bit too strong, as it is really just an empirical rule that has been found to describe the distribution of earthquake magnitudes observed for many different fault lines. Surprisingly, there is no fundamental understanding of why earthquakes (or Earth itself?) follow this rule. In particular, why doesn't $P(\mathcal{M})$ vary as $e^{+\mathcal{M}}$, or even $\mathcal{M}^{-\pi}$?

The Gutenberg-Richter law is also interesting for what it implies about the amount of energy released in a typical event. Since the energy released is proportional to M, the average energy of an event is just the integral of M over the distribution (11.2)

$$E_{\text{average}} \;=\; \int_0^\infty E\,A\,e^{-b\mathcal{M}}\,d\mathcal{M} \;\sim\; \int_0^\infty M\,e^{-b\mathcal{M}}\,d\mathcal{M}\,. \tag{11.3}$$

Since $M \sim e^{\mathcal{M}}$ (and given the observed range of b) this integral *diverges*! Fortunately it appears that such "average" earthquakes don't happen very often.[13] More seriously, power law distributions such as (11.2) which have awkward (or infinite) averages, are quite rare in nature. Perhaps the best-documented and understood case in which such distributions occur is near a second-order phase transition. You may recall that in our studies of the Ising model in Chapter 8 we noted that many quantities exhibit power law singularities at a critical point. For example, the correlation length associated with fluctuations of the magnetization is infinitely large when $T = T_c$. This analogy has suggested to some researchers (see Bak and Tang [1989]) that Earth is effectively located at a critical point as far as earthquakes are concerned. The fact that there is a sort of earthquake phase transition for a certain value of Earth's density and temperature, etc., might seem unlikely, but it is at least plausible. However, it would be even

---

[12] We could choose to use either natural or base-10 logarithms. Here we follow the convention employed in Carlson and Langer (1989a and 1989b) and Carlson (1991).

[13] This strongly suggests that the Gutenberg-Richter law must break down at large $\mathcal{M}$.

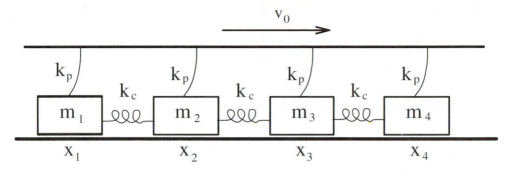

Figure 11.14: Model of two plates separated by a fault line at which an earthquake can occur. Imagine this to be a top view of Earth's surface, with the fault line running between the blocks and the bottom plate.

more surprising to find that Earth just happens to have a temperature and density that place it very near this transition. The interesting speculation is that some feature of this phenomena *automatically* causes Earth to be located at the transition. This scheme is known as *self-organized criticality*. The relevance of this concept to any real systems is not universally accepted, but this discussion does emphasize the striking nature of power law distributions such as (11.2). It has also prompted many researchers to try to account for such distributions in terms of (semi)realistic models, and that is the subject of this section.

The model we consider is copied from one proposed by Burridge and Knopoff (1967), and discussed by Carlson and Langer (1989a and 1989b); it is shown in Figure 11.14. We imagine that two of Earth's plates are moving slowly relative to one another. One of the plates is the bottom surface (the lower, thick horizontal line) in Figure 11.14, while the other plate is the top surface. Caught between them is a portion of the crust modeled by a collection of blocks. For simplicity we will assume that the blocks are arranged in a line, but we can also consider a two-dimensional array (we will explore this possibility in the exercises). The blocks are connected to each other by a force that is modeled as springs, with force constants k_c. The blocks are also connected to the top plate via "leaf" springs,[14] k_p. The only other force in the problem is a frictional force between the blocks and the bottom plate, which we will describe in detail shortly.

The top plate in Figure 11.14 is assumed to move to the right with a constant velocity v_0. Thus, through the leaf springs it exerts an ever-increasing force on the blocks. When this force is small, the frictional force from the bottom plate will prevent the blocks from moving, and energy will build up in the potential energy of the leaf springs. Eventually the force from these springs will overcome the frictional force, and one or more blocks will move suddenly. This is an earthquake. Since the blocks are connected to each other by the springs k_c, the motion of one block can cause other blocks to move as well. If this motion spreads to involve many blocks, one slip will lead to a large quake.

An important ingredient in the model is the frictional force between a block and the bottom surface. We refer to this force as friction because it is assumed to exhibit the general features we all learn in our elementary mechanics courses. When a block is stationary relative to the bottom plate the force is static friction, while if it is moving we are dealing with kinetic friction. Furthermore, we are

---

[14]While most springs have a helical form, leaf springs are a single strip of material. They resist bending (that is, "spring" back) much like a stem or leaf would if they were bent and then released.

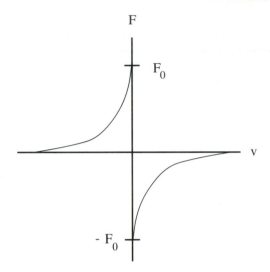

Figure 11.15: Schematic of the frictional force between a block and the bottom plate as a function of the velocity of the block.

taught that the maximum force of static friction is greater than the force of kinetic friction. This is sometimes referred to as a stick-slip force, since once an object begins to move, the frictional force becomes smaller, resulting in a sudden increase in the velocity. Figure 11.15 shows the general form we will use for the frictional force. It always opposes the relative motion of the block and the surface, and is largest when the velocity of a block relative to the bottom plate, v, vanishes. We will follow previous work on this model (see Carlson and Langer [1989a and 1989b]), and assume that the magnitude of this frictional force decreases with increasing $|v|$. Unfortunately, there is no fundamental understanding of such frictional forces (in contrast, for example, to the Van der Waals force), so it is hard to put this important feature of the model on a solid basis. We can, however, investigate how the form of this force affects the properties of the model, and we will return to this point below.

Before we consider in detail how to calculate the behavior of the model, it is worthwhile to make a few comments with regard to model building. Our goal in studying this model is *not* to reproduce the detailed behavior of Earth near any particular fault line. Instead, our aim is to determine what properties a system must have to exhibit a power law distribution of earthquake sizes (11.2). We have already encountered systems with simple harmonic forces similar to the spring forces in Figure 11.14.[15] The only unusual feature of the model we are considering here is the frictional force, so we expect that this must be the key for obtaining power law behavior. Confirming this suspicion, or showing it to be false, will be our initial concern. If we do find power law behavior, then we can conclude that we have (perhaps) captured the essential physics of the problem. If power law behavior is not found, we will be forced to continue our search to identify the key ingredient responsible for (11.2). This could require that we consider other functional forms for the frictional force, or that we generalize the model in other ways.

---

[15] We saw in Chapter 3 that this force leads to simple harmonic motion. The interesting chaotic behavior was found only when we considered deviations from a purely harmonic force.

This is the motivation behind model building in theoretical physics. The goal is not simply to construct a simulation that reproduces nature,[16] but rather to identify the essential physics responsible for the interesting behavior. This process can, of course, be iterated as we attempt to bring a model ever closer to reality.

Now let us return to our earthquake model and consider the forces in a little more detail. The model consists of N blocks whose positions are x_i where i ranges from 1 to N (see Figure 11.14), and for simplicity we assume that all have the same mass, m. The force between two adjacent blocks is due to the spring that connects them. The force from a spring is given by Hooke's law, and has the form $F = -k\Delta x$, where k is the force constant and Δx is the amount that the spring is stretched or compressed relative to its relaxed state. It is convenient to measure each x_i with respect to the equilibrium position of block i. Hence, $x_i = 0$ if a block is at its equilibrium location. The force on block i from its neighboring blocks is then

$$F_b = -k_c (x_i - x_{i+1}) - k_c (x_i - x_{i-1}) . \tag{11.4}$$

Finally, we note that our system will have "free" ends. The blocks at each end will be connected to only one other block.[17]

The force of the leaf spring on block i has a similar form, $F = -k_p(x_i - x_{\text{leaf}})$. We assume that at $t = 0$ the leaf springs are all unstretched, so that initially $x_{\text{leaf}} = 0$ for each block. The horizontal bar moves with velocity v_0, so x_{leaf} increases with time according to $x_{\text{leaf}} = v_0 t$. The force of the leaf spring on block i is then

$$F_l = -k_p (x_i - x_{\text{leaf}}) = -k_p (x_i - v_0 t) . \tag{11.5}$$

The only remaining force is that due to friction with the bottom plate. We will assume that it has the form shown in Figure 11.15. When the velocity of a block is zero the frictional force will take on whatever value is necessary to keep the block at rest. That is, the frictional force will oppose the other forces on the block so that the sum of all of the forces (friction included) vanishes. However, the static frictional force is limited to a maximum magnitude of F_0, so if the sum of the other forces exceeds this level, the block will experience a nonzero force and begin to move. If the block is moving we are then dealing with kinetic friction, which we will assume is given by

$$F_f = -\frac{F_0 \, \text{sign}(v_i)}{1 + |v_i/v_f|} , \tag{11.6}$$

where v_f is a parameter that determines the velocity dependence of the force. When $v_i = v_f$, the frictional force drops to half of its $v_i = 0$ value. The factor $\text{sign}(v_i)$ ensures that F_f always opposes the motion.

---

[16] In such a case we could say that the *computer* understands the problem; we want to understand it, too.

[17] We will leave the study of the effects of periodic boundary conditions to the interested reader. In this problem periodic boundary conditions seem unphysical. In particular, we might imagine that some earthquakes start at the end of a fault and propagate inward. Such behavior would not be possible if the model employed periodic boundary conditions.

Using springs to model the interactions between blocks and between a block and the opposite side of the fault line may seem a bit contrived, but it is actually on firm mathematical footing for the following reason. The energy of interaction between two blocks will, in general, be a function of the separation between the blocks; let us call this function $U(\Delta x)$, where $\Delta x \equiv x_{i+1} - x_i$. Assuming that $U(\Delta x)$ is a well-behaved function, we can perform a Taylor expansion

$$U(\Delta x) = U(0) + (\Delta x) U' + \frac{(\Delta x)^2}{2} U'' + \dots, \tag{11.7}$$

where U' is the first derivative of U evaluated at $\Delta x = 0$, etc. The corresponding force is $F = -dU/d(\Delta x)$

$$F(\Delta x) = -U' - (\Delta x) U'' - \dots . \tag{11.8}$$

By definition, this force vanishes when the blocks are at their equilibrium spacing, so U' must be zero. For small Δx we thus have $F \approx -(\Delta x)U''$, which is just Hooke's law with $k = U''$. Hence, the form of Hooke's law is a natural result for a force that arises from a well-behaved (Taylor expandable) potential energy function. This is one reason why springs are a popular ingredient in the models devised by physicists. They are, in fact, a very natural and general way to describe an interaction.

On the other hand, the basis of the frictional force (11.6) is not nearly as firm. As we have already noted, there is no fundamental understanding of friction. The best we can do is assume a simple form such as (11.6) and study the kind of behavior it yields. We will return to this point later.

Putting all of these forces together with Newton's second law yields an equation of motion for each block

$$m_i \frac{d^2 x_i}{dt^2} = k_c (x_{i+1} + x_{i-1} - 2x_i) + k_p (v_0 t - x_i) + F_f . \tag{11.9}$$

This can be written as two first-order differential equations,

$$\frac{dx_i}{dt} = v_i , \tag{11.10}$$

$$m_i \frac{dv_i}{dt} = k_c (x_{i+1} + x_{i-1} - 2x_i) + k_p (v_0 t - x_i) + F_f , \tag{11.11}$$

and this system of equations can be solved using the Euler method. As usual, we discretize time into steps Δt. At every time step we use the velocity of each block to estimate its position at the next step. We also calculate the force on each block and use it to obtain the velocity at the next time step. Note that the forces are functions of the current positions, so to be consistent with respect to the spirit of the Euler method we must calculate the forces on *all* of the blocks before updating the positions and velocities.[18]

---

[18] Updating in a different order could easily yield the Euler-Cromer method. For this problem the Euler and Euler-Cromer methods are both acceptable algorithms.

The programming is similar to what we have encountered in several previous cases, including the projectile and pendulum problems. For a system of N blocks we have to keep track of N different positions along with the corresponding velocities. The only really new feature is the frictional force. In order to model this force properly there are several different cases that must be considered.

1. The block is not moving at time-step n, and the sum of the forces from the block springs and the leaf spring is smaller (in magnitude) than F_0. The static frictional force will then adjust itself to precisely cancel the other forces. Since the total force will thus be zero, the velocity at time step $n + 1$ will also be zero.

2. The block is not moving at step n, and the sum of the forces from the block springs and the leaf spring is greater than F_0. The frictional force will have a magnitude of F_0, and oppose the sum of the other forces. The total force will not be zero and the velocity at the next time step will be nonzero.

3. The block is moving at step n. We calculate the velocity for time step $n + 1$ using the (kinetic) frictional force (11.6), along with the forces from the block and leaf springs. If this new velocity has the same sign as the velocity at step n, everything is fine and the calculation proceeds in the usual way. However, if the new velocity would be *opposite* to the previous velocity, this means that the frictional force is sufficiently large that it will "capture" the block; that is, bring it to rest. In this case the velocity at time step $n + 1$ must be set to zero.

This description of the frictional force is actually much longer than the number of lines needed to implement it in a program. However, it does show that a force that is a discontinuous function generally requires some extra care.

We are now ready to consider the behavior of our earthquake model. It contains 5 parameters, k_p, k_c, m, F_0, and v_0. Some of these can be effectively removed by the appropriate choice of units, but there will still be a large number of parameter choices to explore. In most of the simulations below we will use the following values: $m = 1$, $k_p = 40$, $k_c = 250$, $F_0 = 50$, and $v_0 = 0.01$. These values appear to give fairly typical behavior; other parameter values will be considered in the exercises (see also Carlson and Langer [1989a and 1989b] and Carlson [1991]).

In addition to these parameters we must specify the initial conditions. For simplicity we will always assume that the initial velocity of each block is zero, but this still leaves us with the choice of initial positions. One choice is to begin with the blocks all located in their equilibrium positions. In this case the forces on all of the blocks from both types of springs is zero at $t = 0$. Such a perfectly ordered start is not very realistic, but is useful for illustrating a few important points. Some results for this case are shown in Figure 11.16, where we plot the position and velocity of a particular block as functions of time. This simulation involved 25 blocks, but since the initial conditions were uniform, the behavior of every block was the same as that shown here. That is, they all moved together, and the

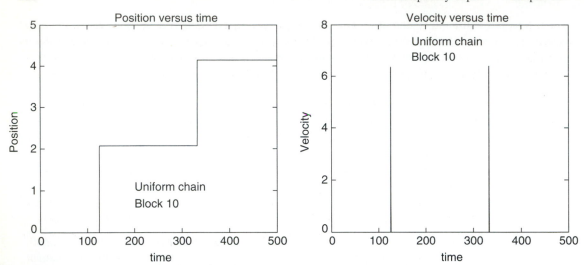

Figure 11.16: Behavior of block 10 in a 25-block system, with a completely ordered start. Left: position of block 10 as a function of time; right: velocity of the same block. The velocity was zero except for the two very narrow spikes at $t \sim 120$ and ~ 330.

springs k_c were never stretched or compressed. We see from Figure 11.16 that the block remained at $x = 0$ until $t \sim 120$. During this time the opposite side of the fault was moving steadily at speed v_0 and the force from the leaf spring gradually increased. This force was not able to overcome friction until $t = 120$, at which point the *entire* system of blocks began to move. The blocks moved approximately 2 units before the frictional force brought them to a halt. The process then repeated. The force from the leaf springs grew until it overcame friction at $t \sim 330$, and the blocks all moved again, etc. The corresponding velocity is also shown. It was zero until the blocks moved, at which point it exhibited a large but very narrow peak. Of course, this is just the derivative of the position as a function of time.

The two displacements in Figure 11.16 correspond to an abrupt motion of the system of blocks. These are earthquakes. The quakes found with an ordered start are very special, since the blocks all move together and the events occur at regularly spaced intervals.[19] This will change when we start the blocks with random initial positions. However, before we do that it is useful to compare the behavior in Figure 11.16 with some simple, analytic results. Because of the special initial conditions, the block springs k_c were never stretched or compressed. We thus need consider only a single block moving in response to the leaf spring and the force of friction. Initially, the force from the leaf spring was $k_p(v_0 t - x) = k_p v_0 t$, since $x = 0$ was the initial condition. The block will not move until this exceeds

---

[19]We only showed two quakes here, but if we had shown the behavior for longer times you would have seen that the quakes do indeed repeat at regular intervals.

F_0, which occurs at $t = F_0/(k_p v_0)$. For the parameters used in here this yields $t = 120$, in good agreement with Figure 11.16. The block should then move until the frictional force (11.6) is equal to the force from the leaf spring. We will leave it to the exercises to check that the displacements in the two events in Figure 11.16 agree with the expected value. The peaks in the velocity can be estimated in a similar way.

The results in Figure 11.16 are useful since they allow us to check our program against analytic results. This behavior also brings out an important programming issue. The earthquakes occur over a very short time compared to the interval between quakes. The duration of a quake is too small to resolve on the scale in Figure 11.16, but is of order 0.5 time units. This implies that the time step in our simulation must be a small fraction of this to avoid significant numerical errors. Our usual practice is to use a time step that is 1 percent of the characteristic time scale of the problem, which would thus be ~ 0.005. The time between quakes is on the order of 100 time units, so this would lead to $\sim 2 \times 10^4$ time steps between events. A simulation using a large number of blocks would thus take a lot of computer time. Moreover, there would be nothing happening for the vast majority of this time.

There are two ways to deal with this problem: use a fast computer and just be patient, or use *two* different time steps according to the following strategy.[20] During the times when no blocks are moving we use a (relatively) large time step. The only motion during these periods involves the top plate, and since it moves with a constant velocity, the use of a large time step does not introduce any errors. A small time step (~ 0.005 in the above example) is used during the times when the blocks are moving. This strategy is straightforward, except that we need to have a systematic way to switch back and forth between time steps. One convenient way to make these switches is as follows. When the blocks are not moving, the larger time step is used to calculate the new velocities. If the velocity of *any* block is nonzero at the next time step, an earthquake is imminent. We then "back up" to the previous time step and continue the calculation with the smaller value of the time step until after the upcoming quake is finished. When the velocities of all of the blocks are again zero, the time step is set back to the larger value and the calculation proceeds. The results in Figure 11.16 were obtained with this algorithm, using a large time step of 0.03 and a small time step of 0.003. We will leave it to the exercises to check that these values are sufficiently small that the numerical errors were negligible.

A simulation with an initially ordered configuration is not very realistic, since we don't expect Earth's crust to ever be perfectly uniform. The behavior is quite different when the blocks are given a disordered initial configuration. If we displace them initially from their equilibrium positions by

---

[20]The use of two (or more) time steps is often referred to as an "adaptive" step-size procedure. The example we describe here is a very simple one, but does illustrate the basic idea. Such an approach is useful in simulations involving functions or behaviors that have significant structure limited to small regions of time or space.

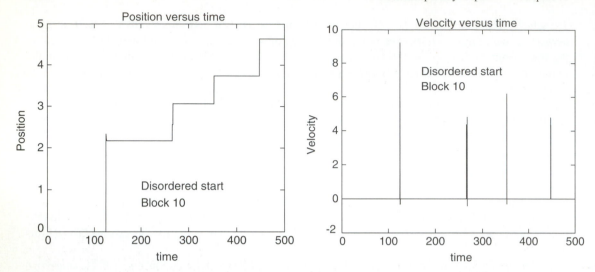

Figure 11.17: Behavior of block 10 in a 25-block system. Each block was given a random initial displacement from its equilibrium position. This displacement was in the range −0.001 to +0.001. Left: position of block 10 as a function of time; right: velocity of the same block.

random amounts in the range ±0.001, we find the results shown in Figure 11.17. Here we show only four quakes and it is seen that they had different magnitudes, that is, different total displacements. In addition, the time until the next quake varied from event to event.

It is intriguing that such a small initial displacement (only 0.1 percent of the spacing between blocks) is able to produce such dramatically different behavior. It turns out that the behavior found in Figure 11.16, with a perfectly ordered start, is *unstable* with respect to any initial displacements from equilibrium, no matter how small. That is, the behavior is extremely sensitive to small deviations from a perfectly ordered start. This should remind you of chaotic systems and their extreme sensitivity to initial conditions; this is our first indication that this earthquake model is not a "simple" mechanical system.

So far we have examined the behavior by following the motion of a single block. However, since we expect that there can be earthquakes that do not involve all of the blocks, it is useful to view the same behavior using the perspective plots in Figures 11.18 and 11.19, which show the behavior of the entire system. With an ordered start all blocks move together, as we had anticipated. In contrast, with a disordered start the quakes are much less organized. There are numerous events in a time interval that would contain only one or two quakes for the case of an ordered start. Some of these events involve many blocks, while in others only a few blocks are in motion. We thus have a distribution of earthquake sizes.

One of our primary goals is to try to understand the origin of the Gutenberg-Richter law, and to do this we need to add one more feature to the simulation. As we mentioned earlier, the magnitude of an earthquake is the natural logarithm of the earthquake moment. The moment M is proportional to the total displacement, which can be found by summing (integrating) $v_i \, \Delta t$ for each block over the course

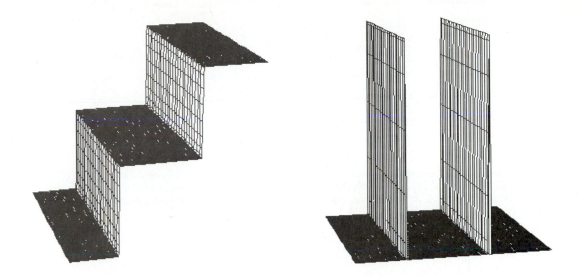

Figure 11.18: Behavior of the entire system for the simulation with an ordered initial configuration, Figure 11.16. Time goes from left to right, block number from front to back, and the vertical axis is position (left figure) or velocity (right figure). The time span here is $t = 0$ to 500, the same as that covered in Figure 11.16.

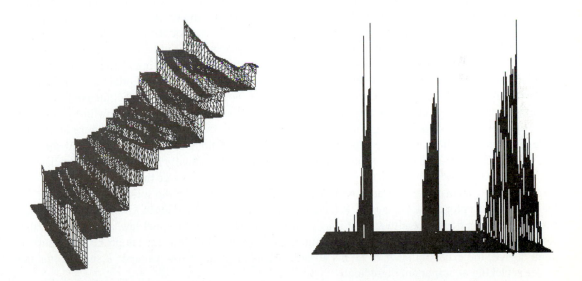

Figure 11.19: Results for the simulation of Figure 11.17 in which the blocks were in an initially disordered configuration. Time goes from left to right, block number from front to back, and the vertical axis is position (left figure) or velocity (right figure). The time span covered in the position plot is $t = 0$ to 1000, but for purposes of clarity the velocity plot shows a smaller range, $t = 300$ to ~ 500.

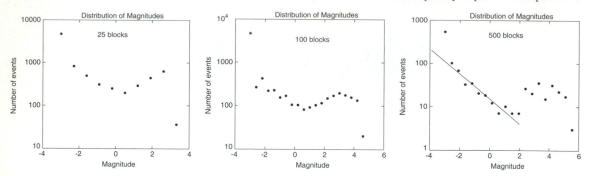

Figure 11.20: Earthquake distributions for systems of various sizes. These histograms were obtained from a collection of approximately 7000 events for the 25- and 100-block systems and 3000 events for the 500-block simulation. The vertical axis is the number of events per histogram bin and is thus proportional to the probability density of events.

of the event. The moment of an event is thus

$$M = \sum_{n=\text{time}} \left(\sum_{i=\text{blocks}} v_i \Delta t \right), \qquad (11.12)$$

where the sums are over all blocks i and over the time steps n for which the velocities are not all zero. The magnitude of the event is then $\mathcal{M} \equiv \ln M$. After accumulating the results for a large number of events we can obtain the distribution $P(\mathcal{M})$ by dividing the $\mathcal{M}$ axis into bins and counting the number of events that fall into each bin. Results for $P(\mathcal{M})$ are shown in Figure 11.20, where the figure on the left shows the distribution for the system of 25 blocks we have considered in all cases to this point. On this semilogarithmic plot the Gutenberg-Richter law (11.2) is a straight line with slope $-b \log_{10}(e) \approx -0.43b$. The results from the simulation are certainly not a simple straight line. However, a 25-block system intuitively seems to be a bit too small to be a good model for an entire fault line. We might imagine that such a small number of blocks would artificially restrict the possible event magnitudes and perhaps affect the number of large earthquakes. It is, therefore, worthwhile to consider larger systems, and results for simulations with 100 and 500 blocks are also shown in Figure 11.20. All three simulations exhibit the same type of deviation from the Gutenberg-Richter law, as all show an excess number of large events.[21] It is interesting to note that there is actually a regime of intermediate $\mathcal{M}$ where $P(\mathcal{M})$ does vary approximately linearly with $\mathcal{M}$. For example, over the range $\mathcal{M} \sim -2$ to $+2$ the 500-block system exhibits an approximate power law, as indicated by the solid line in Figure 11.20. This line is just a plot of the Gutenberg-Richter law (11.2) with $b \approx 0.7$. Hence, over this rather limited range, the system does appear to at least roughly follow the Gutenberg-Richter law, although the value of b is a little lower than that exhibited by nature. While our simulations thus approximate nature to some degree, the excess number of events at large $\mathcal{M}$ and the rather low value of b suggest that the model is lacking an important ingredient.

---

[21] There is also an excess number of events at very low $\mathcal{M}$ in the lowest bin of the distribution, but this is less troubling than the problem at high $\mathcal{M}$, for the following reason. There will be a minimum earthquake size corresponding to the motion of a single block for one time step, and this will result in a pile-up of events of some minimum size. The difficulty is thus with the numerical approach and is not an intrinsic property of the model.

The simulations we have described above have been only partially successful in explaining the Gutenberg-Richter law. However, we have been able to show that this simple mechanical model is capable of exhibiting power law behavior over at least a limited range. To some small extent this lends support to the proposals concerning self-organized criticality mentioned at the beginning of this section. As for the relevance to real earthquakes, it has been suggested that the Gutenberg-Richter law may actually fail at large $\mathcal{M}$, so perhaps part of our problem is with the law itself, rather than the model.[22] Of course, it is also possible that the problem lies with the model. You will recall our philosophy of model building, according to which we strive to construct the simplest model that contains the essential physics of the phenomena of interest. It is certainly conceivable that our simple model has omitted some key element(s). Possibilities include the following: (1) The dimensionality of the fault system; a two-dimensional array of masses might be more appropriate than the one-dimensional arrangement considered above. Here the second spatial dimension would correspond to depth beneath Earth's surface. (2) We have assumed uniform values of m, k_c, and k_p. For a real fault the analogous parameters will not be constants, but vary with position. (3) The frictional law (11.6) has no fundamental basis. We could certainly imagine other plausible possibilities. These are just a few of the ways in which the model could be modified, and we will leave such studies to the exercises. While we have not been able to answer all of the questions concerning earthquakes posed at the beginning of this section, these simulations do shed some light on the problem, and serve to illustrate the model-building process in theoretical physics.

Exercises

1. Consider the simulation in Figure 11.16 in which 25 blocks were given a perfectly ordered arrangement at the start. Continue this simulation to longer times and show that the earthquakes occur at regularly spaced intervals (as we claimed above).

2. Perform a simulation with 25 blocks, allowing for some randomness in either the masses (let m_i vary from 0.5 to 2.0) or in the spring constants (either k_c or k_p). Compare your results for the distribution of earthquake magnitudes with the results in Figure 11.20. The objective is to see if adding some disorder can lead to better agreement with the Gutenberg-Richter law or reduce the excess number of events at high $\mathcal{M}$, or both.

3. Assume that the blocks are all initially in their equilibrium positions and obtain analytic estimates for the time between quakes, the displacement of a block during a quake, and the maximum velocity during a quake. Compare these estimates with the results in Figure 11.16.

**4. Explore the properties of a two-dimensional earthquake model. A calculation of this kind is described in the references.

---

[22]This is a difficult issue to resolve, since the number of large quakes is (fortunately) small, making it hard to get a good estimate of $P(\mathcal{M})$ at large $\mathcal{M}$.

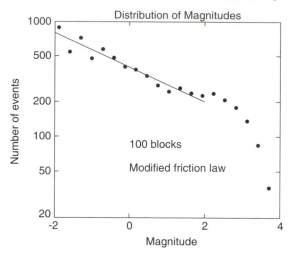

Figure 11.21: Earthquake distribution for a system of 100 blocks and the friction law described in Exercise 5. The straight line corresponds to the Gutenberg-Richter law (11.2) with $b \sim 0.35$.

*5. Investigate how the distribution of earthquake magnitudes depends on the form chosen for the frictional force. As an example, consider the case $F_f = F_0$ when $v = 0$ (static friction) and $F_f = -\text{sign}(v)F_0/2$ for $v \neq 0$ (kinetic friction). You should find (see Figure 11.21) that with this friction law there is no longer an excess of events at large $\mathcal{M}$, so the results are more realistic than that obtained with the frictional force (11.6). However, the slope for small $\mathcal{M}$ now corresponds to a value of b that is much smaller than 1, so the model still seems to lack an important ingredient. Study the behavior with other forms for the frictional force and try to determine one that gives a power law with a larger value of b.

11.3   Neural Networks and the Brain

The Ising model consists of a large number of very simple units, that is, spins, which are connected together in a very simple manner. By "connected" we mean that the orientation of any given spin, s_i, is influenced by the direction of other spins through the interaction energy $J s_i s_j$. The behavior of an isolated spin, as outlined in our discussions leading up to mean-field theory, was unremarkable. Things only became *really* interesting when we considered the behavior of a large number of spins and allowed them to interact. In that case we found that under the appropriate conditions some remarkable things could occur, including the singular behavior associated with a phase transition. In this section we will explore a rather different system, which shares some of these features.

The human brain consists of an extremely large number ($\sim 10^{12}$) of basic units called neurons, each of which is connected to many other neurons in a relatively simple manner. A biologically complete discussion of neurons and how they function is a long story. Here we will give only a brief description of those features that seem to be most relevant to a physicist's understanding of the brain.

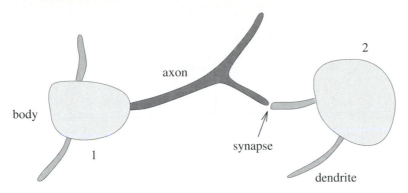

Figure 11.22:   Schematic of two connected neurons.

A schematic picture of two neurons is given in Figure 11.22. Each neuron has a body (called a soma), along with dendrites and an axon.[23] The size scale depends on the type of neuron, but the body is typically of order 10 μm across. Neurons are electrically active and communicate with other neurons through electrical signals carried by the dendrites and axons. The dendrites serve as the input lines of a neuron, while the axons are output lines. The axon of one neuron is "connected" to the dendrite of another via a synapse, through which is transmitted the electrical output signal of one neuron to the input of the other.

The axon of the hypothetical neuron (number 1) on the left in Figure 11.22 connects to a dendrite of neuron number 2 via the synapse, as indicated. A very important feature is that an axon is generally split into many branches, and thereby connects to many other neurons. Correspondingly, each neuron generally has many dendrites and thus accepts inputs from many other neurons. When we say *many*, the number we have in mind is typically $\sim 10^4$. The neurons are thus highly interconnected.

Neurons communicate using electrical pulses carried by the axons and dendrites. These pulses are typically of order 10^{-3} s in duration and 5×10^{-2} V in magnitude. A neuron emits these pulses (this is called firing) in a roughly periodic manner, with the period being a function of the input signals experienced by the neuron at that moment. If the inputs are very active, that is if there are many pulses being received through the dendrites, the neuron will fire often. On the other hand, if its inputs are not active, the neuron will fire at a much lower rate. The picture is actually a bit more complicated than this. The interface where an axon and a dendrite meet (the synapse) may be either excitory or inhibitory. In the former case a high firing rate of the sending neuron will favor a high firing rate of the receiving neuron. With an inhibitory synapse, a high input firing rate will tend to cause a low firing rate of the receiving neuron.

The firing rate of a particular neuron is a function of all of its inputs. To a very rough approximation, this rate is determined by the sum of all inputs that come into a neuron through excitory synapses minus

---

[23]There are other parts as well, but keep in mind that we are giving only a simplified description here.

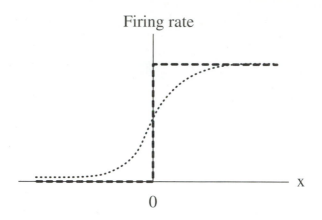

Firing rate

X

0

Figure 11.23:   Firing rate function. The dotted curve is closer to that found in real neurons. The dashed curve is the step function used in our modeling.

the total of the inputs that enter through inhibitory synapses.[24] The firing rate, R, can thus be written as

$$R = f\left(\sum v_i\right),\tag{11.13}$$

where v_i is the input signal from dendrite i (which may be either positive or negative). Experiments show that the firing function f is significantly nonlinear, as shown schematically in Figure 11.23. Because of this nonlinearity, a neuron is often modeled as a sort of on/off device.

A neural network is composed of a very large number of neurons whose basic properties we have just described. Such a network, that is, a brain, is perhaps the most remarkable object in nature, as it is responsible for the intelligence of living organisms.[25] The problem of understanding how a brain functions is of great concern to biologists, psychologists, computer scientists, and (believe it or not) physicists. It is useful to state this problem in the following way. The brain consists of a very large number of neurons that are highly interconnected. The connections are not limited to neighboring neurons, but can extend to neurons in remote areas of the brain. The state of a neuron can be described by its firing rate, which is a function of the firing rates of all of the neurons that have inputs to the neuron in question. The connectivity of the network and the strength of the connections vary from brain to brain. They vary from individual to individual (even within the same species, although there are many common features), and with time for a given individual. On a very coarse scale, brains seem to possess a significant degree of randomness, yet we know that they are capable of very precise behavior, such as logical reasoning and memory. Understanding how such an arrangement of neurons can actually function as a brain is a key problem.

---

[24]The synapses also vary in strength, so some signals contribute more strongly to this sum than others. We will ignore this slight complication here, although it will be included in the model we construct below.

[25]Some people (the author included) believe that a brain is a neural network (essentially no more and no less), while others believe that a real brain contains some physics that is not contained in such a network. Arguments over this point have filled many books (but not this one). In any case, the majority of people on both sides of the argument would probably agree that neural networks are a major component of biological brains, and this is enough to make them worth studying.

In this section we will consider how a neural network can function as a memory. Many aspects of biological memories[26] are not understood. For example, it is not yet known how information is stored (and forgotten) or how it is recalled. However, some ideas from physics have contributed greatly to recent progress in this area, and the answers to these questions may not be far away. Rather than try to give a logical or historical derivation (or justification) of the model of memory that we will study, it is simpler to just plunge ahead, and that is what we will now do. A little bit of the history of this model will be given at the end of this section.

We will model a neuron as a simple Ising spin. As we saw in Chapter 8, such a spin has two possible states, up and down. We will, therefore, assume that a neuron also has only two possible states, firing or not firing. This will, among other things, mean that we will approximate the firing function by a step function (the dashed curve in Figure 11.23), which has only two possible values. These two values will correspond to the two possible states of an Ising spin, $s = \pm 1$. The value of s_i corresponds to the current firing rate of neuron i. By convention we take $s_i = +1$ to correspond to a firing rate of 1, and $s_i = -1$ to 0 firing rate.[27] By associating the firing rate with the value of the spin we have glossed over the time dependence of the synaptic signals. At first sight this might seem to be a rather drastic approximation, but there are good reasons for believing that the timing of synaptic pulses does not play an important role in real neural networks. First, it is known from experiments that the firing times of different neurons are *generally* not correlated. That is, the brain does not appear to operate like a conventional computer in which all neuronal firing occurs in synchrony with a master clock. Second, the interneuronal signals travel at a speed of ~ 1 m/s, so the propagation delay (which is different for each pair of connected neurons) makes a significant contribution to the pulse arrival times. For these reasons it is generally argued that the *timing* of the pulses does not play an essential role.[28] Rather, the average arrival *rate* seems to be an essential feature, and this can be modeled with simple Ising spin variables.

In the Ising model studied in Chapter 8, the effect of a spin on its neighbors was through the exchange energy, and for our neural network we can model the effect of one neuron on another in a similar way. We will assume that our spins (that is neurons; we will use the two terms interchangeably) experience an exchange interaction, but now we will permit an interaction between *every* pair of spins. This is necessary in order to mimic the highly interconnected nature of a real neural net, which is believed to be crucial for its operation. We will find it very useful to consider the effective energy of our neural network/spin system, which can be written as

$$ E = - \sum_{i,j} J_{i,j}\, s_i\, s_j \,, \tag{11.14} $$

where the $J_{i,j}$ are related to the strengths of the synaptic connections, as we will describe shortly. The sum here is over all pairs of spins i and j in the network. The exchange, or more properly the synaptic, energies $J_{i,j}$ describe the influence of neuron i on the firing rate of neuron j. One way to view (11.14) is as follows. The sum of the synaptic inputs to neuron i will be $\sum_j J_{i,j} s_j$, and this will determine the

---

[26] As compared to computer memories.

[27] We could have chosen the pseudospin values to be $+1$ and 0 so as to correspond directly with the firing rate. For the way we have chosen to write the energy this would contribute a constant term to E and would not affect the behavior of the model.

[28] While this seems to be the current conventional wisdom, it has recently been suggested that correlated firing times are essential for understanding certain types of computations carried out by the brain. While the verdict has not yet been reached on this issue, it seems safe to conclude that much (if not all) of the brain's operation, including the memory functions we consider in this section, does not depend on precise timing of neuronal firing.

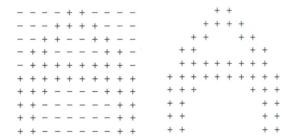

Figure 11.24: Left: a 10×10 lattice of spins with a particular configuration of $+$ and $-$ spins; right: the same lattice but with the spins for which $s = -1$ replaced by blanks. This network holds (i.e., displays) the letter A.

firing rate, that is, the *direction* of spin i. If this input is negative, then according to our model it will be energetically preferred for neuron i to have a firing rate that is also negative, $s_i = -1$. If the synaptic input is positive, $s_i = +1$ will be favored. This is precisely analogous to an Ising spin model since as we saw in Chapter 8, each Ising spin prefers to point in the direction of the effective field established by the exchange energy due to its neighboring spins. Hence, our neural network can be described by the energy function (11.14), in close correspondence with the behavior of an Ising magnet. Individual neurons will prefer to fire at rates determined by the effective fields established by the interactions with other neurons, and this will make the network prefer states that minimize this energy.

As implied by Figure 11.22, the connections in a real neural network are *not* symmetric. The connection of the axon from neuron i to a dendrite of neuron j is completely separate from the connection between the axon of neuron j and a dendrite of neuron i. Indeed, there may be a connection in only one direction. The biological importance of this asymmetry in $J_{i,j}$ is not known. For now we will assume that the connections are symmetric, as this will allow us to make use of some ideas and results from statistical mechanics. The more realistic asymmetric case will be explored in the exercises.

The energy function (11.14) enables us to model our neural net as an Ising model, which can be simulated using the Monte Carlo method. However, we have not yet specified how the exchange energies should be chosen, or even how our lattice of spins can function as a memory. A useful memory must be able to store, recall, and display patterns, so let us consider how these operations can be implemented. The display operation is the easiest and is illustrated in Figure 11.24. On the left we show a lattice of spins with a particular spin configuration. This configuration was chosen so that it stores the letter A, which is seen more clearly on the right, where we show the same lattice, but with the spins for which $s = -1$ replaced by blanks. In this way the spins can be used as pixels to display whatever character or other type of pattern is desired.

In order for our memory to recall a pattern, we require that the spin directions change with time in such a way that the spin configuration eventually ends up in the desired state. For example, if we want to recall the letter A, we want the system to take on the configuration in Figure 11.24. The recall process thus involves first giving the spins a configuration, then allowing the spin arrangement to evolve with time until the system settles into a new, and we hope stable, configuration. This time evolution is accomplished using an algorithm similar to the Monte Carlo method employed in Chapter 8. Starting from some particular configuration of the entire network, a spin is chosen and the energy required to flip it, ΔE_{flip}, is calculated using (11.14). If ΔE_{flip} is negative, that is, if flipping the spin would lower the

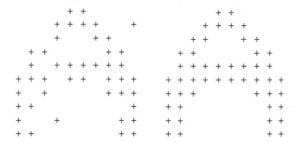

Figure 11.25: Left: spin arrangement close to the letter A, but with a few spins flipped to the wrong state; right: spin configuration after one Monte Carlo pass through the lattice.

energy, the spin is reversed. If $\Delta E_{\text{flip}} \geq 0$, the spin is left unchanged. This is precisely the Monte Carlo flipping rule employed in our work on the Ising model, with the assumption that the effective temperature is zero. We will have more to say about temperature and what it means in this problem a little later. For now, the important point is that the Monte Carlo rules ensure that the system will always evolve in time to states with the same or lower energy. If conditions are right, the memory will end up in a state in which the spins cease changing with time. This state corresponds to the pattern that is recalled by our memory.

The Monte Carlo rules, together with the energy function, determine how the spin system changes with time, and it is instructive to observe this directly in a simulation. Here, and with all of the other simulations below, we have used a 10×10 lattice of spins. For the moment we will not worry about how the interaction energies $J_{i,j}$ are determined. While their values are central to the behavior, it is simplest to postpone a discussion of how to calculate them until later. We are thus "given" a neural network, which in our specific case is a lattice of 100 spins interacting according to a certain collection of interactions $J_{i,j}$. We have, of course, chosen these interactions to yield some interesting behavior! On the left side of Figure 11.25 we show our lattice in a state that is close to the pattern for the letter A that we considered earlier. Even though a few of the spins are in the wrong state, that is, have been flipped with respect to Figure 11.24, it should be clear to your (human) brain that this pattern represents the letter A. We started a simulation with the lattice in this configuration, and after one pass through the lattice we obtained the state shown on the right side of Figure 11.25. Subsequent Monte Carlo sweeps through the lattice we produced no further changes. The system thus found the ideal letter A, and recalled it. The memory worked as it should.

An important feature of human brains is that they are able to generalize in a reasonable manner. For example, you can usually recognize a letter even if it is shown to *you* in *a* **different** TYPE face or $\mathcal{STYLE}$. There is some property of A-ness that you are able to recognize, and all patterns that fall into this class will cause you to recall the same fundamental letter A. Our model exhibits similar behavior. The left side of Figure 11.26 shows the letter A in outline form. When we initialized our lattice of spins with this pattern, one Monte Carlo sweep through the lattice yielded the ideal letter A shown on the right. At least with this simple test of A-ness, the model responded correctly.[29]

A similar test is shown in Figure 11.27, where the left side shows a damaged version of the ideal A. Here we have flipped 20 percent of the spins at random, and the resulting pattern only faintly

---

[29] We will leave the more challenging problems of a letter that is rotated or rescaled in size to the inquisitive reader.

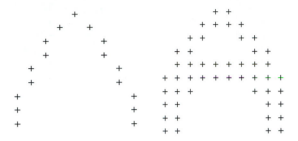

Figure 11.26: Left: spin arrangement that shows the letter *A*, but with a different pattern (that is, font) than used previously; right: spin configuration after one Monte Carlo pass through the lattice.

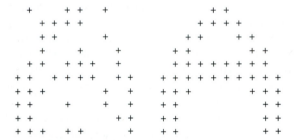

Figure 11.27: Left: spin arrangement that shows the letter *A*, but with 20 percent of the spins flipped at random; right: spin configuration after one Monte Carlo pass through the lattice.

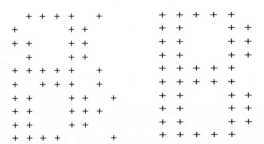

Figure 11.28: Left: spin arrangement which shows the letter *B*, but with 10 percent of the spins flipped at random; right: spin configuration after one Monte Carlo pass through the lattice.

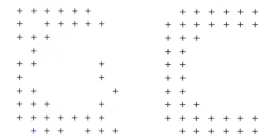

Figure 11.29: Left: spin arrangement that shows the letter C, but with 10 percent of the spins flipped at random; right: spin configuration after one Monte Carlo pass through the lattice.

resembled the ideal one. Nevertheless, after one Monte Carlo sweep through the lattice, the ideal pattern was recovered.

At this point you might suspect that we are playing a joke, as our model memory seems to recognize *every* pattern as the letter A. To demonstrate that this is not the case, we show in Figures 11.28 and 11.29 the results obtained when the lattice was initially given a configuration that resembled the letters B and C, respectively. In each case the initial patterns were barely recognizable, but after one sweep through the lattice the ideal patterns were recovered. Our model memory was thus able to recognize several different letters.

Observing the model in operation raises several important points and a few questions. First, the model is seen to operate as a *content addressable* memory. This is in contrast to the type of memory we are familiar with in connection with a conventional computer. In the case of a computer memory, a piece of information, such as the value of a particular variable, is given a *name* or address. In order to recall the value of the variable, the address must be presented to the memory, which is then able to retrieve the desired value. However, with a content addressable memory, information is retrieved by giving a rough description of the information itself. For example, the value of π could be retrieved by giving only the first few digits. This is a very important property of human brains. As another example, we might want to recall a friend's face given only a vague recollection of the shape of her chin and her hair style. In addition, such a memory should be able to recognize her face even if she cuts her hair or dyes it green. Human brains are able to handle such tasks, which are difficult for the more conventional computer-style memories.

Second, we have seen that our memory can generalize in a reasonable manner. When presented with a pattern that is similar but not identical to one that it "knows," the memory is able to choose the correct response in a reasonable way. This behavior can be understood in terms of the energy landscape of the spin system. The energy of the network depends on the specific spin configuration, that is, memory pattern, at that time. Since the interactions $J_{i,j}$ (which we promise to explain shortly) have widely varying magnitudes and signs, this energy function will depend in a complicated way on the spin configuration. Schematically it will resemble the landscape shown in Figure 11.30. Each stored pattern, the letters A, B, and C in the example we have just considered, corresponds to minima in the energy. The Monte Carlo procedure guarantees that given an initial spin configuration, that is, some initial pattern, the system will evolve into a pattern with the same or, most likely, lower energy.

In general, the pattern presented to the network will not be one of the stored patterns, so the system will initially be situated on one of the slopes in the energy landscape. The Monte Carlo flipping

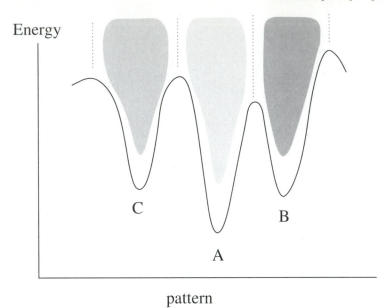

Energy

C

A

B

pattern

Figure 11.30:   Schematic energy landscape. The vertical axis is energy as calculated from (11.14), while the horizontal axis corresponds to the spin configuration. The basins of attraction of several stored patterns are indicated by the shaded areas.

rules then take it to the bottom of the nearest valley, and it thus ends up "recalling" the stored pattern associated with that minima. But what do we mean when we say that an initial pattern is close to a stored pattern? There are two ways to answer this question. In terms of the energy landscape there will be a *basin of attraction* in the neighborhood of each minima. If the network is within the basin corresponding to a particular minima, the associated stored pattern is the one that it will eventually locate. Topologically, these basins are the "valleys" surrounding each minima in Figure 11.30.

A quantitative answer to this question requires that we be a little more specific concerning the horizontal axis in Figure 11.30. A useful measure of the distance between two patterns is

$$\Delta_{m,n} \ = \ \frac{1}{N} \sum_i [s_i(m) - s_i(n)]^2 \ , \tag{11.15}$$

where m and n denote two different patterns, $s_i(m)$ is the configuration of spin i in pattern m, and N is the total number of spins. This is usually referred to as the *Hamming distance* between the two states of the system. Two patterns that are separated by a large Hamming distance will usually flow to different final stored patterns, while if the separation is small, there is a much better chance that they will flow to the same final state. For example, the letters C and O have many features in common, and will thus be closer in pattern space than are the letters A and V. Our memory will generally do a better job if the stored patterns are as different as possible.

While the Hamming distance is a quantitative measure of how similar two patterns are, it is difficult to be more precise in predicting how a particular network will respond to patterns that differ only slightly. This difficulty can again be traced to the energy landscape. Two patterns might be extremely similar, but if they happen to fall on opposite sides of an energy maxima they will flow to different final states.

The interaction energies $J_{i,j}$ are, as we have noted several times, key elements in our model memory. We are now ready to discuss how they should be chosen so as to yield a useful memory. We again let $s_i(m)$ denote the configuration of spin i in pattern m, and assume that we want our network to have this configuration as one of its stored patterns. That means that the $J_{i,j}$ must be chosen so as to make the energy a minima for this spin configuration. While there is no unique solution for this problem, a popular and very convenient choice is

$$J_{i,j} \;=\; s_i(m)\, s_j(m) \;, \tag{11.16}$$

which is often associated with the names of Hebb and Cooper, two important researchers in this area.[30] We can see that this choice for $J_{i,j}$ will make $s_i(m)$ an energetically stable pattern as follows. Inserting (11.16) into (11.14) yields

$$E(m) \;=\; -\sum_{i,j} J_{i,j} s_i\, s_j \;=\; -\sum_{i,j} s_j(m)\, s_i(m)\, s_i\, s_j \;. \tag{11.17}$$

If the network is in pattern m, we will have $s_i = s_i(m)$ and $s_j = s_j(m)$, so each term in this sum will be unity, making the energy large and negative. On the other hand, a random pattern (we will be more precise about this in a moment) will, on average, have half of its spins flipped with respect to $s_i(m)$, so roughly half of the terms in (11.17) will be positive and half negative, leading to $E \sim 0$. Thus, our desired pattern will have a much lower energy than a random pattern. Furthermore, the energy of our stored pattern will correspond to a stable minima of the landscape, since flipping any one spin from the pattern value $s_i(m)$ will increase E.

The prescription (11.16) tells us how to store a single pattern, but a useful memory must be able to store many patterns. In that case we choose the $J_{i,j}$ according to

$$J_{i,j} \;=\; \frac{1}{M} \sum_m s_i(m)\, s_j(m) \;, \tag{11.18}$$

where the index m refers to the stored patterns, and there are a total of M such patterns (we will see in a moment that there is a limit on the total number of patterns that can be stored). The arguments we just gave can be used to show that the energy associated with each stored pattern will be much lower than the energies of a random pattern. In addition, *if* the stored patterns are sufficiently different from one another, they will each correspond to distinct, well-separated minima in the energy landscape. This is how the values of $J_{i,j}$ were chosen in the calculations described above. We used the letters A, B, and C as our stored patterns, and calculated the energies $J_{i,j}$ using (11.18).

We have now completed the description of our neural network memory model. The key features are:

- An Ising spin is used to model the on/off behavior of a neuron. The firing rate of a neuron is assumed to have only two possible states, corresponding to the spin values $s = \pm 1$.

---

[30]Their work is described by Hertz, Krogh, and Palmer (1991).

- The connections between the spins $J_{i,j}$ are not limited to nearest neighbors, but link all pairs of spins in the network.

- Given a collection of patterns that we want to store, the $J_{i,j}$ are calculated according to (11.18).

- The network operates as a content addressable memory. The lattice of neurons (that is, spins) is initialized with a configuration that resembles the pattern we want to recall. The Monte Carlo rules for $T = 0$ are then used, and the system evolves to a pattern that is at a minima in the energy landscape. This is the pattern that is "recalled" by the network.

The programming of this procedure is similar to the Monte Carlo routines described in Chapter 8, so we will leave the details to the exercises. However, we will give a few tips later in this section.

The modeling of neural networks is a vast industry, and we have been able to touch on only a very small piece of it here. A brief discussion of several other aspects of this field and some historical notes are given at the end of this section. However, before finishing we want to touch on a few issues associated with the choice of $J_{i,j}$ and the desired stored memories. Our network contains N spins, and since each pair is connected, there are $\sim N^2$ different values of the interaction energies $J_{i,j}$. We have described a procedure for storing a collection of patterns, and it should be clear that this information is stored *in* the $J_{i,j}$. This brings up several questions. (1) How many different patterns can be stored? (2) Can we add the concept of "learning" to the model, so as to bring it closer to the operation of a biological memory? (3) What happens if the $J_{i,j}$ are damaged in some way? We know that real memories can function even if some of the neurons die. Is our model able to function in the presence of such damage?

Each pattern involves the configuration of N spins and there are $\sim N^2$ different $J_{i,j}$, so the maximum amount of information that can be stored is of order $\sim N^2/N = N$ different patterns.[31] However, it turns out that the maximum number of stored patterns is much less than this for several reasons. First, if two desired stored patterns happen to be close to each other (in terms of their Hamming distance), they can interfere with one another. This may make one of the patterns unstable, or cause it to be recalled in a distorted (imperfect) form. This problem can be minimized by choosing the stored patterns to be orthogonal to one another to the fullest extent possible. Here orthogonal means that $\sum_i s_i(m)s_i(n) \sim 0$ if $m \neq n$. In our simple example involving letters such orthogonality was not under our control, as it was determined by the shapes of the letters. While we can often preprocess the patterns to make them orthogonal before encoding them in the network, this may not always be convenient in cases such as, for example, the storage of arbitrary optical images.

The use of orthogonal stored patterns can increase the storage capacity somewhat, but it turns out that there is a more fundmental limit. As we use more and more patterns in the calculation of $J_{i,j}$, the nature of the energy landscape changes. Increasing the number of stored patterns means that more and more local minima must be crowded together, and this also affects the depth of each minima. It has been found that if the number of stored patterns exceeds $\sim 0.13N$, the landscape changes dramatically. In this case all of the stored patterns become unstable, and the system ceases to function as a memory. This abrupt change is actually a type of phase transition and has much in common with a system known

---

[31] This simple argument ignores the fact that the spins are binary objects, while the $J_{i,j}$ are real numbers, so this may be an underestimate of the capacity of the network.

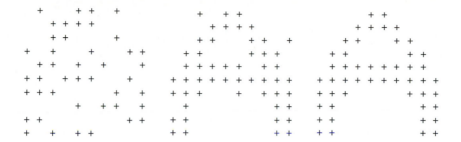

Figure 11.31: Operation with 80 percent of the $J_{i,j}$ set to zero. Left: initial pattern; middle: spin configuration after one Monte Carlo sweep through the lattice; right: configuration after two sweeps.

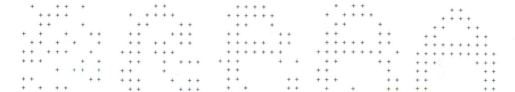

Figure 11.32: Operation with 90 percent of the $J_{i,j}$ set to zero. Left to right: initial pattern and spin configurations after one, two, five, and nine Monte Carlo sweeps through the lattice.

as a *spin glass*. This is a type of spin system in which the interactions are randomly distributed and which have been studied extensively by physicists over the past 20 years.[32] We do not have time here to say anything about spin glasses or how they are related to neural networks, other than to note that this is a very nice example of how ideas developed for one problem (spin glasses) can be profitably applied to a rather different area.

We next consider the effects of damage on the operation of our model memory. Since the information is stored in the interactions $J_{i,j}$, it is these connection values that will be damaged. We start with the $J_{i,j}$, calculated using (11.18), and the three stored patterns, A, B, and C. We then "damage" these values by randomly setting the elements of the $J_{i,j}$ matrix to zero with probability p_{damage}. Some results for $p_{damage} = 0.8$ are shown in Figure 11.31, where the initial pattern was an A, which itself has been altered from the stored pattern with probability 0.3. We recall that with the ideal $J_{i,j}$, our memory immediately found the correct stored pattern; that is, it took only one Monte Carlo pass through the lattice to obtain the stored pattern, which was then stable for all future times. With $p_{damage} = 0.8$ and after one Monte Carlo time step (one complete pass through the lattice), the system was closer to the stored pattern, but there were still some spins pointing in the wrong direction. However, after two time steps the system reached the correct, and perfect, final pattern.

The corresponding result with $p_{damage} = 0.9$ is shown in Figure 11.32. In this case it took nine Monte Carlo time steps to reach a stable pattern, but the system did eventually come to the correct

---

[32] In fact, spin glasses were studied long before it was appreciated that they had anything in common with neural networks. It turns out that spin glasses are typical of random systems with energy landscapes given by functions such as (11.14). The protein-folding problem falls into this class, as well.

Figure 11.33: Operation with 95 percent of the $J_{i,j}$ set to zero. Left to right: initial pattern and spin configurations after three, four, five, and ten Monte Carlo sweeps through the lattice. In this case our memory did not recall the letter A.

final state. However, if the $J_{i,j}$ are damaged much further the network fails, as illustrated in Figure 11.33. Here, with $p_{\text{damage}} = 0.95$, the system was unable to find the correct pattern. Instead, it ended up in a state unlike any of the stored patterns.

These simulations show that our model memory continues to function, even when severely damaged. It thus has an important feature in common with human brains. Indeed, it is amazing that the memory works so well, even with 90 percent of the connections removed. The level of damage that can be tolerated depends on the number of stored patterns. In this example, with only three stored patterns in a system of 100 neurons, we were well below the ideal theoretical limit of ~ 13 patterns. If the number of stored patterns had been closer to this limit, the level of damage that could have been be tolerated would have been smaller. Nevertheless, neural network memories can continue to function well even when significantly damaged. Intuitively, this can be understood in terms of their redundancy. With a network that contains the theoretical limit of $\sim 0.13N$ patterns, ~ 87 percent of its information content is effectively redundant. A network's operation may not be adversely affected if some of this redundant information is lost.

One aspect of neural networks that we haven't really touched on is learning. The problem is extremely important for two reasons. First, if our goal is to model a real (biological) brain, learning must be accounted for. Second, neural networks of the type described here are being considered for a number of applications, such as image processing and handwriting recognition. These applications require that the network be able to incorporate new patterns, and in some cases forget old ones. The development of learning algorithms is an active area of research, and a number of alternative ways for calculating the $J_{i,j}$ have been proposed. One of the simplest learning procedures is based on (11.18). Consider a working network that contains several stored patterns. A new pattern can be learned by adding a small contribution to the interactions

$$J_{i,j}(\text{new}) = \beta \, J_{i,j}(\text{old}) + \alpha \, s_i(p)s_j(p) , \qquad (11.19)$$

where $s_i(p)$ is the new pattern, α is a parameter that controls how fast the learning should occur, and the value of β can be adjusted to allow for the fading of old memories. This learning algorithm has also been proposed on biological grounds. If a real network is presented with a pattern $s_i(p)$, it is believed that the synapses can adjust their strengths with time so as to make the pattern a stable configuration of the network. That is, the strengths and signs of a synapse adjust so that they are "consistent" with the states of the neurons that are involved. We will explore the behavior of this and several related learning procedures in the exercises.

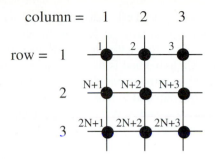

column =   1   2   3

row = 1

2

3

Figure 11.34:   Numbering scheme. N is the number of spins in one row.

Programming Notes

The simulation of a neural network memory involves the following steps.

1. The desired stored patterns must be chosen. For the example calculations described above these were just letters laid out on a 10×10 grid, but you could use any other patterns including other characters or pictures.[33] You could also use a larger array of spins. This would allow more detail in the patterns and enable the system to store more patterns, but at the cost of additional memory requirements (memory in your program).

2. A natural way to store the spin values is to use a two-dimensional array spin(m,n) where the indices m and n specify the row and column where the spin is located. This storage scheme is convenient for displaying the stored pattern. However, we also have to store the interaction energies $J_{i,j}$. Here the indices i and j do *not* refer to rows and columns. You will recall that our model allows an interaction between each pair of spins. Hence, $J_{i,j}$ is the strength of the interaction between the ith and jth spins in the lattice, where i and j refer to a particular numbering scheme. One possible scheme is illustrated in Figure 11.34. The spins in the first row (m=1) are numbered $i = 1, 2, \ldots, N$, those in the second row (m=2) have the numbers $i = N + 1, N + 2, \ldots, 2N$, and so on up to the final spin, which is number $i = N^2$. Given the row and column numbers, m and n, the spin number is

$$i = N(m - 1) + n. \tag{11.20}$$

Note that this mapping can be inverted, that is, given i we can uniquely determine m and n, although we will not need to do this in our simulations.

The stored patterns can be described using the labeling scheme in terms of spin number i, with $s_i(p)$ denoting the value of the i-th spin for the p-th stored pattern. These in turn are used to calculate the interaction energies $J_{i,j}$ according to (11.18). Storage of the interaction energies requires a two dimensional array of size $N^2 \times N^2$. Thus, a 10×10 array of spins requires $\sim 10^4$ interaction energies.[34]

---

[33] Black-and-white pictures would be simplest. We will leave gray scale or color images to the industrious reader.

[34] An alternative scheme for storing the $J_{i,j}$ would be to use a four-dimensional array J(m1,n1,m2,n2) to store the interaction energy for spin(m1,n1) and spin(m2,n2). This makes the bookkeeping simpler than the scheme involving (11.20), but some computer languages do not permit four-dimensional arrays. In addition, the method (11.20) for encoding two numbers into one in an invertible manner can be useful in other situations.

3. After the interaction energies have been calculated, the memory is ready for operation. The spins are given values corresponding to a particular pattern. In our examples this was a character that was similar, though not identical, to a letter in the alphabet, but it could be a picture or other type of image. The Monte Carlo method is then used to calculate the spin directions at future times. The method is very similar to the one used to simulate the Ising model in Chapter 8. A spin is selected and the energy required to make it flip, E_{flip} is calculated from (11.18). If E_{flip} is negative, that is, if the energy would be reduced by flipping the spin, then the spin is reversed. If $E_{\text{flip}} \geq 0$, the spin is left unchanged. These flipping rules correspond to a system in thermal equilibrium with a heat bath at zero temperature. In this case the Monte Carlo procedure takes the system to the nearest energy minima, in the spirit of the energy landscape in Figure 11.30.

4. The Monte Carlo procedure is used repeatedly, giving every spin a chance to flip. The spins can be chosen at random, or they can be selected by systematically moving through each row and column of the lattice. The two choices both work well. The most important thing is that *each* spin be given at least one chance to flip, so the systematic approach is often preferred. The Monte Carlo procedure is used until the state of the spin system becomes stable, indicating the pattern that is recalled by the memory. A network will usually find the desired pattern after only one or two Monte Carlo passes through the lattice, as the system will quickly locate the nearest energy minima. However, the behavior can sometimes be more complicated. If the number of stored patterns is close to the theoretical limit, or if two of the stored patterns are similar (have a small Hamming separation), the memory recall may not be ideal. The system may then recall a pattern that is different from any of the stored patterns (often an approximate mixture), or the network might never locate a time independent state. In the latter case it may switch back and forth in time between two or more patterns; such behavior is known as a limit cycle. In human terms we might think of this as corresponding to confusion!

Historical Notes

The field of neural networks is much too vast for us to be able to give a complete description in this section. A good historical discussion of the field is given in Hertz, Krogh, and Palmer (1991) which is listed in the references. In 1943 McCulloch and Pitts recognized that a network of simple neurons was capable of universal computation. This means that such a network could, in principle, perform any calculation that could be carried out with the most general computer imaginable.[35] This attracted a good deal of interest from researchers interested in modeling the brain.

One of the first specific network models was proposed by Rosenblatt, who introduced a model known as the perceptron. This is a network composed of layers of neurons, that is, spins, with neurons in each layer receiving connections only from neurons within the same layer and from the preceding layer. These are often referred to as *feedforward networks*, since information flows from one layer to the next and never interacts back with earlier layers. Many related network schemes were devised and studied, both from a physics perspective (in work by Cragg and Temperley, and Little, for example) and from the viewpoint of artificial intelligence. Hebb introduced the learning rule mentioned above, and it was proven that *if* a particular network was capable of computing a certain function, this learning rule would yield the appropriate interaction energies.

---

[35] More precisely, such a network can calculate any computable function in the sense of a general purpose Turing machine.

Unfortunately, some of the simplest perceptron networks are not capable of universal computation. This point was emphasized by Minsky and Papert in a very influential book that caused many workers, especially those interested in artificial intelligence, to abandon the field. Nevertheless, work on neural networks continued (albeit at a reduced level), and gradually it came back into fashion. In particular, the work of Hopfield stimulated enormous interest in the physics community. The network model we have studied in this section is often referred to as a Hopfield net and is distinguished by full connectivity (every spin is coupled to every other spin; it does not have a layered structure as in some models). In addition, the connections are often chosen to be symmetric ($J_{i,j} = J_{j,i}$) as this makes the model closely analogous to a spin model for which the theoretical machinery of statistical mechanics can be most readily applied.

Neural networks are now of very great interest to scientists from a number of different fields. They are studied as models of real (biological) brains and are used to gain insights to processes such as learning and memory. Neural networks are also attracting much interest in the computer science community, as they seem capable of massively parallel processing and could provide an efficient means for solving certain computationally very difficult problems, such as those connected with image processing. Artificial intelligence researchers are also studying neural networks, since they seem capable of generalization and association, two phenomena that have proved difficult to capture with conventional computational approaches.

In this section we have been able to give only a very brief description of one particular neural network model and have illustrated its behavior with a few simple examples. Our emphasis has been on the most important and unique features of neural networks and how these are related to the physics that we have encountered earlier in this book.

Exercises

1. Write programs to perform all of the calculations described in this section.

2. Investigate what happens when a network is overloaded with too many stored patterns. Do this by adding additional letters of the alphabet to the patterns stored by a 10×10 neural network. You should find that after storing about the first five letters in the alphabet, some of the patterns are no longer stable. However, the theoretical upper limit on the number of stable stored patterns is $\sim 0.13N^2$, which is 13 for a 10×10 network. Explain why you are not able to successfully store this many letters.

3. In the previous problem we found that the maximum number of stable stored patterns may be less than the theoretical upper limit of $\sim 0.13N^2$ for an $N \times N$ network. Using a 10×10 network, try to devise 10 patterns that can all be stored simultaneously. Hint: It is best if the patterns are as different from each other as possible (see our discussion of the importance of orthogonality).

4. The learning rule (11.18) yields values of $J_{i,j}$ that vary widely in magnitude. Investigate the effect of restricting $J_{i,j}$ to the values ± 1. Do this by first calculating the Hebb/Cooper interaction strengths $J_{i,j}$(Hebb) using (11.18), then determine the final value using $J_{i,j} = \text{sign}[J_{i,j}(\text{Hebb})]$. Compare the performance of this network with the one we studied above. Of particular interest is the maximum number of stored patterns and the sensitivity to damage. You should find that this network works nearly as well as one in which the $J_{i,j}$ are continuous variables. This result is important for those who are interested in making neural network integrated circuits. It is much

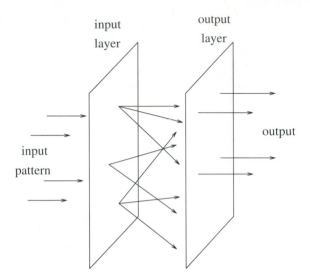

Figure 11.35: Schematic two-layer perceptron. Each layer contains a network of neurons, and the arrows between planes denote interations. There are also interactions within each layer that are not shown.

easier to design such circuits with only two different interaction strengths than to arrange for the interactions to vary continuously.

*5. A two-layer perceptron can be useful for classifying patterns. The structure of such a network is shown in Figure 11.35. The spins/neurons in the input layer are given a configuration corresponding to a pattern to be identified and locked rigidly in place. The Monte Carlo algorithm is then used to enable the spins in the output layer to reach the lowest energy state. The energy has the form (11.14), but the $J_{i,j}$ are now asymmetric; the direction of a spin i in the input layer can affect the direction of spin j in the output layer, but not vice versa. The interactions may be calculated with an expression similar to (11.18)

$$J_{i,j} \;=\; \frac{1}{M} \sum_m s_i(m)\, s_j(n) \;, \tag{11.21}$$

where m refers to the input pattern and n now refers to the desired output pattern. Implement such a network and use it to classify patterns. For example, choose the $J_{i,j}$ so that several different patterns are recognized as the letter A, several others as the letter B, etc.

*6. Throughout this section we have used the Monte Carlo procedure appropriate for a system at zero temperature. As discussed in connection with Figure 11.30, this algorithm takes the system to the nearest accessible energy minima. A drawback with this method is that a deeper minima will not be located unless it is directly "downhill" from the initial pattern. One way to avoid this problem is to use the Monte Carlo method with $T > 0$. In this case we accept spin flips with positive flipping energy with a probability $\exp(-E_{\text{flip}}/T)$, as discussed in Chapter 8. If the effective temperature is comparable to the energy barrier separating a metastable pattern from a more stable one, the Monte Carlo algorithm will enable the system to spend more time near the stable pattern. If the temperature is then slowly reduced, the network can sometimes locate the more stable pattern. Implement this procedure and study its performance. You should find that if T is too small, the network will be trapped in undesired states, as before. On the other hand, if T is too large, the system will quickly move far from the initial pattern and the final state will *not* resemble the initial one. This is not the way a memory should function. The best performance is obtained with an intermediate value of T, which is just large enough that the system can overcome the smallest energy barriers. This approach is similar to the annealing procedure we employed in our studies of protein folding.

*7. Investigate the behavior of the learning algorithm (11.19). Use a 20×20 network and begin with the $J_{i,j}$ chosen according to (11.16) so as to store the letter A. Then add more patterns to the memory using (11.19) and the stored patterns of your choice. Study the behavior for different values of the parameters α and β.

References

The topics discussed in this chapter are close to the frontiers of current research, which can make it difficult to find introductory references. The history of each topic can be traced back many years, but we don't have space here to list all of the relevant articles. We have instead listed some that we consider particularly readable and important. The interested reader can use these articles to gain access to other papers in each area. We hope that those authors we have not referenced will forgive us for omitting their articles from these lists!

Protein Folding

CALLENDER, R., R. GILMANSHIN, B. DYER, and W. WOODRUFF. 1994. "Protein Physics." *Physics World* August, p. 41. A general introduction to proteins and the folding problem. Aimed at physicists.

CREIGHTON, T. E., Ed. 1992. *Protein Folding*. New York: W. H. Freeman & Co. An introduction to proteins and the folding process.

DILL, K. A., K. M. FIEBIG, and H. S. CHAN. 1993. "Cooperativity in Protein-Folding Kinetics." *Proc. Natl. Sci. USA* **90**, 1942.

KIRKPATRICK, S., C. D. GELATT, JR., and M. P. VECCHI. 1983. "Optimization by Simulated Annealing." *Science* **220**, 671. An important paper that pointed out the wide applicability of the Monte Carlo annealing process we employed in our studies of protein folding. This simulated annealing procedure has proved extremely useful in problems ranging from the behavior of random spin systems to the design of integrated circuits.

O'TOOLE, E. M., and A. Z. PANAGIOTOPOULOS. 1992. "Monte Carlo Simulation of Folding Transitions of Simple Model Proteins Using a Chain Growth Algorithm." *J. Chem. Phys.* **97**, 8644.

ŠALI, A., E. SHAKHNOVICH, and M. KARPLUS. 1994. "How Does a Protein Fold?" *Nature* **369**, 248.

SHAKHNOVICH, E., G. FARZTDINOV, A. M. GUTIN, and M. KARPLUS. 1991. "Protein Folding Bottlenecks: A Lattice Monte Carlo Simulation." *Phys. Rev. Lett.* **67**, 1665. Our protein model was inspired by the one studied by these authors.

Earthquakes

BAK, P., and C. TANG. 1989. "Earthquakes as a Self-Organized Critical Phenomenon." *J. Geophys. Res.* **94**, 15635. A discussion of self-organized criticality from the people who invented the term. A rather different model of earthquakes is described in this paper.

BURRIDGE, R., and L. KNOPOFF. 1967. "Model and Theoretical Seismicity." *Bull. Seismol. Soc. Am.* **57**, 341.

CARLSON, J. M. 1991. "Two-Dimensional Model of a Fault." *Phys. Rev.* A **44**, 6226.

CARLSON, J. M., and J. S. LANGER. 1989a. "Properties of Earthquakes Generated by Fault Dynamics." *Phys. Rev. Lett.* **62**, 2632. Our simulations follow closely the work described in this paper, which also references earlier work on similar models.

CARLSON, J. M., and J. S. LANGER. 1989b. "Mechanical Model of an Earthquake Fault." *Phys. Rev.* A **40**, 6470.

GUTENBERG, B., and C. F. RICHTER. 1956. "Earthquake Magnitude, Intensity, Energy, and Acceleration." *Bull. Seismol. Soc. Am.* **46**, 105.

GUTENBERG, B. and C. F. RICHTER. 1956. "Magnitude and Energy of Earthquakes." *Ann. Geofis.* **9**, 1.

Neural Networks

HERTZ, J., A. S. KROGH, and R. G. PALMER. 1991. *Introduction to the Theory of Neural Computation.* New York: Addison-Wesley. A good introduction to neural networks from a physics perspective.

HOPFIELD, J. J. 1982. "Neural Networks and Physical Systems with Emergent Collective Computational Abilities." *Proc. Natl. Acad. Sci. USA* **79**, 2554. A key paper that helped revive interest in neural networks among physicists. Our model is based on the calculations described in this paper.

KINZEL, W. 1985. "Learning and Pattern Recognition in Spin Glass Models." *Z. Phys.* B **60**, 205. The calculations in this chapter are similar in many respects to those described in this paper.

Appendix 1

Ordinary Differential Equations

Many of the problems encountered in physics involve ordinary differential equations for which some initial values are specified. For example, the motion of a projectile is described by second-order differential equations that involve the position as a function of time. There are several ways to attack such problems numerically, and in this appendix we discuss and compare some popular methods. Our goal here is to understand the algorithms well enough that we can actually *use* them and also have some appreciation for their strengths and weaknesses. We begin with the workhorse algorithm for this book, the Euler method (and its relatives), and then describe the Runge-Kutta and Verlet methods.

A1.1 Euler Method and Some Relatives

The Euler method was introduced in Chapter 1, but it is useful to review it again here in preparation for our discussion of other methods later in this appendix. We imagine a problem in which the quantity we are interested in is y, and we are given the derivative $dy/dt \equiv f(t)$ along with some initial condition, say $y = y_0$ when $t = 0$. Our goal is to obtain an estimate, and we hope it is a good one, for y at other values of t. We assume, as usual, that time is a discrete variable so that $t = i\Delta t$ for integers $i = 0$, 1, 2, etc., with time step Δt. The value of our function at time step i is then y_i. We next express the derivative in finite difference form

$$\frac{dy}{dt} \approx \frac{y_{i+1} - y_i}{\Delta t} \approx f(t_i) . \tag{A1.1}$$

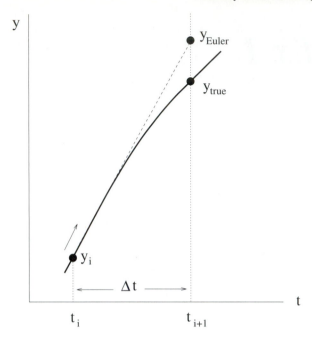

Figure A1.1: Geometrical interpretation of the Euler method. The solid curve is the actual function $y(t)$. The arrow indicates the slope of the function at t_i, and y_{Euler} is the value obtained by extrapolating linearly across the interval to t_{i+1}. This extrapolation misses the true value by an amount proportional to the curvature (that is, the second derivative) of $y(t)$.

We emphasize that this is an *approximation* for the derivative; we will consider the errors associated with it shortly. Rearranging we obtain

$$y_{i+1} \;=\; y_i \;+\; f(t_i)\,\Delta t \;. \tag{A1.2}$$

Thus, if we know y at time step i, we can estimate its value at the next time step $i+1$, and so on for as many time steps as we desire. This is the Euler method.

Figure A1.1 gives a geometric description of how the Euler method works. The derivative $f(t_i)$ is the slope of the function $y(t)$ at time step i. This slope is used to estimate the value of y at the next time step, $i+1$, assuming that y varies *linearly* over this interval. The function $y(t)$ drawn in Figure A1.1 has some curvature, however, which means that the Euler estimate will be in error by an amount proportional to the product of the second derivative of y and $(\Delta t)^2$. The size of this error can be reduced simply by making Δt smaller, so the Euler method is useful in many cases.

In the example just discussed we assumed that the first derivative was known. However, in many cases encountered in physics it is the second derivative that can be calculated. For example, if y is the position of an object, then Newton's second law tells us that the second derivative d^2y/dt^2 is equal to the force on the object divided by the mass. Let us, therefore, consider how the Euler method can be applied in this situation. We begin by defining a new variable $v \equiv dy/dt$ so that we can convert the problem into one involving two first-order differential equations

$$\frac{dy}{dt} = v \tag{A1.3}$$

$$\frac{dv}{dt} = f_2 ,$$

where $f_2(y, t)$ is our second derivative function.[1] To apply the Euler method we write each of these first derivatives in finite difference form. Proceeding as we did in the case above yields

$$y_{i+1} = y_i + v_i \, \Delta t \tag{A1.4}$$

$$v_{i+1} = v_i + f_2(y_i, t_i) \, \Delta t .$$

Geometrically this has the same description as in Figure A1.1. The derivatives evaluated at (y_i, t_i) are used to make linear extrapolations to obtain estimates of v_{i+1} and y_{i+1}.

To see the Euler method in action we now apply it to a simulation of simple harmonic motion. The equation of motion for this problem is (see Chapter 3)

$$\frac{d^2 y}{dt^2} = -A \, y , \tag{A1.5}$$

where A is a constant; hence $f_2 = -Ay$. A program that implements the Euler algorithm for this problem is outlined below. It consists of our usual three subroutines, `initialize`, `calculate`, and `display`. The job of `initialize` is to set the initial values of the variables y, v, and t [see (A1.4)], and also take care of A and the time step Δt. `display` simply plots the results. We will leave it for the reader to write these two routines. Here we concentrate on `calculate`. This subroutine uses the Euler method to solve (A1.5) and the results for y and t are stored in the arrays `y()` and `t()`. We also calculate the total energy of the oscillator, which, in this case, is given by

$$E = \frac{1}{2} v^2 + \frac{1}{2} A \, y^2 , \tag{A1.6}$$

the first term being the kinetic energy (we take the mass to be unity), while the second term is the potential energy. Note that we do not store $v = dy/dt$ in an array since we don't plan to use it later.

```
! main program for simple harmonic motion
! N. Giordano    10-1-94
program simple_harmonic
    option nolet
    library "sglib*","sgfunc*"
    dim t(5000),y(5000),energy(5000)
    call initialize(t,y,v,energy,A,dt)
    call calculate(t,y,v,energy,A,dt)
    call display(t,y,energy)
end
```

---

[1] It is also possible for f_2 to depend on v. For simplicity we will assume that this is not the case, but the results that follow could easily be generalized to handle this situation.

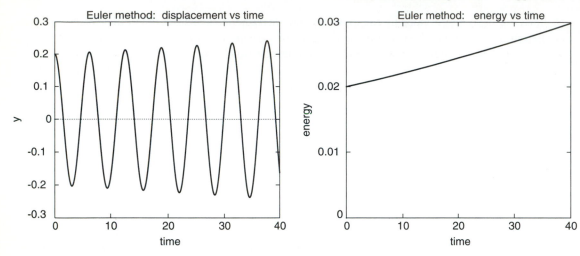

Figure A1.2:   Simulation of a simple harmonic oscillator using the Euler method. Left: displacement, y, versus time; right: total energy as a function of time. The time step was $\Delta t = 0.01$, $A = 1$, and the initial conditions were $y = 0.2$ and $v = 0$.

```
! simulation of simple harmonic motion using the Euler method
! t()   contains time
! y()   contains the variable y
! v  = angular velocity
! A  = restoring force parameter
! dt = time step
! energy  total energy
sub calculate(t(),y(),v,energy(),A,dt)
   v_old = v
   j = 1
   for i = 1 to 4000
      v_new = v_old - A * y(i) * dt          ! Euler method for v
      y(i+1) = y(i) + v_old * dt             ! Euler method for y
      t(i+1) = t(i) + dt
      energy(i+1) = v_new^2 / 2 + A * y(i+1)^2 / 2    ! kinetic + potential
      v_old = v_new                                  ! energies
   next i
   mat redim t(i), y(i), energy(i)   ! resize arrays in preparation for plotting
end sub                    ! note that i = 4001 on exiting loop
```

   Some results for the simulation are shown in Figure A1.2. Our system does indeed oscillate, but the amplitude of the oscillation grows with time, as does the energy. This is clearly *not* the kind of behavior we expect for a simple harmonic oscillator described by (A1.5). Since there is no energy being injected into our system, the total energy *should* remain constant, but this is not what our simulation yields. The problem lies with the Euler algorithm. While the method provides us with a very simple and reasonably accurate solution, it is only an approximation. The error terms we noted above in connection with (A1.1) are not zero. It turns out that for this particular problem these error terms effectively add a small amount to the energy each time step. In some cases the errors introduced by the Euler method are negligible. For example, in the problems considered in Chapters 1 and 2 the Euler method was perfectly adequate. However, in oscillatory problems the errors introduced by the Euler method generally tend to accumulate, with results like those shown in Figure A1.2. For this reason we did not use this method to treat the oscillatory problems in Chapters 3 and 4.

However, this defect of the Euler method can *sometimes* be cured with a simple modification. We have seen that the Euler method uses y_i and v_i, the estimates for y and v at time step i, to calculate the estimates at the next time step $i + 1$. A slight change in this procedure yields the Euler-Cromer method, which we described in Chapter 3. With this method we use y_i and v_i to estimate v_{i+1}, but then use y_i and v_{i+1} to estimate y_{i+1}. We could justify this by arguing that since v_{i+1} is available, why not use it! In fact, a careful analysis (see Cromer [1981]) shows that for oscillatory problems this algorithm actually *conserves energy* over each complete oscillation. This makes it a good choice for problems such as simple harmonic motion.

The Euler-Cromer method is discussed in Chapter 3 in the context of this and similar problems, so we will not consider it any further here. However, we want to caution that while the Euler-Cromer method is preferable to the Euler algorithm for oscillatory problems, the overall accuracy of the two methods for other types of problems is usually comparable. In particular, while the Euler-Cromer method conserves the total energy in oscillatory problems, this is not necessarily the case in other situations. If you need a more accurate method, it is best to use one of the schemes described next.

A1.2   Runge-Kutta Methods

The major difficulty with the Euler method, as was emphasized in connection with Figure A1.1, is that only information from the beginning of the interval is used to extrapolate to the value at the other side. While this approach is able to take the slope of the function (i.e., the first derivative) into consideration, the curvature is completely unaccounted for. In this and the next section we describe two methods that include the effect of this curvature.

Reflecting on Figure A1.1, it is clear that the average slope of our function is more closely approximated by the slope at the *center* of the interval.[2] Runge-Kutta methods use this observation to construct a better extrapolation across the interval. There is actually an entire family of Runge-Kutta methods, the simplest of which is the second-order algorithm illustrated in

---

[2]The mean-value theorem of differential calculus tells us that the average slope is equal to the instantaneous slope *somewhere* inside the interval. Common sense tells us that for most functions the middle will be a good choice.

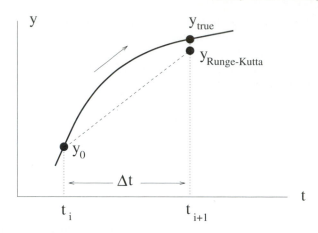

Figure A1.3:   Geometrical interpretation of the second-order Runge-Kutta method. The slope at the middle of the interval is first estimated; this is indicated by the arrow. This slope is then used to extrapolate across the interval.

Figure A1.3. To see how this algorithm works we consider the case of a single first-order differential equation, $dy/dt = f(y, t)$. Given y_i and t_i, the values at time step i, our goal is again to extrapolate across the interval to estimate the values at step $i + 1$. In order to carry out this extrapolation, the Runge-Kutta scheme first estimates where the center of the interval is located. The value of t at the center is, of course, just $t_i + \Delta t/2$, but the corresponding value of y is not as easy to find. This is accomplished using the Euler method. The Runge-Kutta algorithm then evaluates the slope of the function at this *approximate* midpoint of the interval and uses this slope to extrapolate all the way across.

The corresponding equations are

$$
\begin{aligned}
k_1 &= f(y_i, t_i)\,\Delta t \\
k_2 &= f(y_i + k_1/2, t_i + \Delta t/2)\,\Delta t \\
y_{i+1} &= y_i + k_2 \, .
\end{aligned}
\tag{A1.7}
$$

In words, $y_i + k_1/2$ is the Euler estimate for y at the center of the interval and $k_2/\Delta t$ is the slope at the center. The error in this estimate for y_{i+1} is proportional to $(\Delta t)^3$, in contrast to the Euler method for which it is on the order of $(\Delta t)^2$. Hence, in this sense the Runge-Kutta scheme is inherently more accurate than the Euler method.

Other Runge-Kutta schemes use the same basic idea as (A1.7), but essentially divide the interval into more pieces so as to reduce the extrapolation error. The higher-order methods have smaller error terms, but the derivative function must be evaluated more often for each time step.

The Runge-Kutta method is a very popular one among experts, and is a good choice when the Euler method is not satisfactory. To see how the Runge-Kutta approach works with a second-order differential equation, we again consider the simple harmonic oscillator problem, (A1.5). The

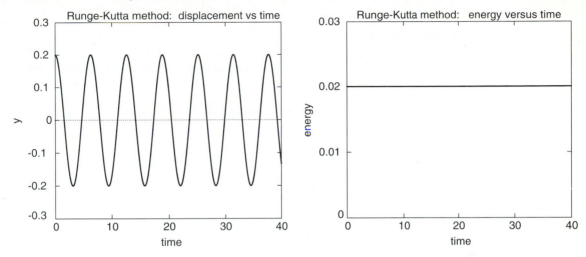

Figure A1.4: Simulation of a simple harmonic oscillator using the Runge-Kutta method (A1.8). Left: displacement, y, versus time; right: total energy as a function of time. The time step was $\Delta t = 0.01$, $A = 1$, and the initial conditions were $y = 0.2$ and $v = 0$.

second-order Runge-Kutta equations in this case are

$$
\begin{aligned}
k_1 &= v_i \, \Delta t \\
k_2 &= f_2(y_i, t_i)\Delta t \\
k_3 &= (v_i + k_2/2)\, \Delta t \\
k_4 &= f_2(y_i + k_1/2, t_i + \Delta t/2)\, \Delta t \\
y_{i+1} &= y_i + k_3 \\
v_{i+1} &= v_i + k_4 \, ,
\end{aligned}
\tag{A1.8}
$$

where the function f_2 for the oscillator problem is again just $f_2 = -Ay$. A subroutine that calculates the displacement and energy of our oscillator using (A1.8) is listed below. This routine is a direct replacement for the subroutine of the same name that appeared in the Euler program listed in Section A1.1. Here the variables y_half and v_half are the estimates for the location of the center of the interval.

```
sub calculate(t(),y(),v,energy(),A,dt) ! use the Runge-Kutta method
   for i = 1 to 4000
      y_half = y(i) + v * dt / 2      ! find approximate values of y and v
      v_half = v - A * y(i) * dt / 2  ! at the midpoint of the interval
      y(i+1) = y(i) + v_half * dt      ! now estimate y and v at other side
      v = v - A * y_half * dt          ! of the interval
      t(i+1) = t(i) + dt
      energy(i+1) = v^2 / 2 + A * y(i+1)^2 / 2   ! calculate total energy
   next i
   mat redim t(i), y(i), energy(i)          ! resize arrays for plotting
end sub
```

The results obtained using this routine are shown in Figure A1.4. The oscillations are seen to be quite stable, that is, their amplitude remains constant with time. This is in sharp contrast to the results obtained with the Euler method (Figure A1.2) for the same problem. The energy is also seen to be constant to within the resolution of this plot.

The Runge-Kutta algorithm is a very convenient and accurate method, which is not difficult to program. It could be used in place of the Euler or Euler-Cromer methods in any of the problems dealt with in this book.

A1.3   Verlet Method

You may have noticed that the Runge-Kutta method treats the extrapolation across the interval in a somewhat "unsymmetrical" manner. This can be traced back to the finite-difference form we used for the first derivative (A1.1), which can be thought of as a forward-looking derivative. A more symmetric approach can lead to smaller numerical errors. This is the basis of the Verlet method.[3] Consider the Taylor expansion of the function $y(t)$

$$y(t_i + \Delta t) \ = \ y(t_i) + \frac{dy}{dt} \Delta t \ + \ \frac{1}{2} \frac{d^2 y}{dt^2} (\Delta t)^2 \ + \ \frac{1}{6} \frac{d^3 y}{dt^3} (\Delta t)^3 \ + \cdots \qquad (A1.9)$$

$$y(t_i - \Delta t) \ = \ y(t_i) - \frac{dy}{dt} \Delta t \ + \ \frac{1}{2} \frac{d^2 y}{dt^2} (\Delta t)^2 \ - \ \frac{1}{6} \frac{d^3 y}{dt^3} (\Delta t)^3 \ + \cdots$$

As usual, we anticipate that t will be a discrete variable with time step Δt, so that $y(t_i + \Delta t) = y_{i+1}$ and $y(t_i - \Delta t) = y_{i-1}$. We also give the Taylor expansion for extrapolating *backward* in time. Of course, the forward and backward expansions are quite similar, the only difference being in the signs of the odd-order terms. Now if we add these two equations, *all* of the odd-order terms cancel exactly. We can thereby derive y_{i+1} in terms of y_i and y_{i-1} as

$$y_{i+1} \ = \ 2\, y_i \ - \ y_{i-1} \ + \ \frac{d^2 y}{dt^2} (\Delta t)^2 \ + \cdots , \qquad (A1.10)$$

where the lowest-order correction term is of order $(\Delta t)^4$. This approach is interesting for several reasons. First, the error terms are one order of Δt smaller than with the second-order Runge-Kutta method. Second, it avoids calculation of $v = dy/dt$ altogether. A minor drawback is that it requires knowledge of y_{i-1} and is thus not self starting. That is, even if the initial conditions specify y_1 and v_1, the Verlet algorithm requires that y_2 be calculated with some other method; the Euler or Runge-Kutta methods are common choices.

A subroutine that employs the Verlet method for our simple harmonic oscillator is listed below. This subroutine can be used in place of the corresponding routine in the Euler program given earlier in

---

[3]The introduction of this method to physicists seems to have been the result of a paper by Verlet, which described its application to molecular dynamics. Texts on numerical methods might refer to algorithms of this type as *centered-difference methods*.

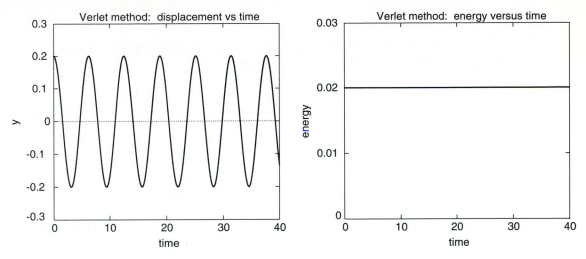

Figure A1.5:   Simulation of a simple harmonic oscillator using the Verlet method. Left: displacement, y, versus time; right: total energy as a function of time. The time step was $\Delta t = 0.01$, $A = 1$, and the initial conditions were $y = 0.2$ and $v = 0$.

this chapter. Note that we have used the Euler method to get things started (to calculate y(2)) and that in order to calculate the energy we require the value of v, which we estimate via $v_i \approx (y_{i+1} - y_{i-1})/2dt$.

```
! simple harmonic motion using the Verlet method
sub calculate(t(),y(),v,energy(),A,dt)
   y(2) = y(1) + v * dt        ! use Euler method to get things started
   for i = 2 to 4000
       y(i+1) = 2 * y(i) - y(i-1) - A * y(i) * dt^2    ! Verlet estimate for y
       t(i+1) = t(i) + dt
       v = (y(i+1) - y(i-1)) / (2 * dt)        ! calculate v
       energy(i) = v^2 / 2 + A * y(i)^2 / 2        ! estimate total energy
   next i
   mat redim t(i-1), y(i-1), energy(i-1)          ! resize arrays for plotting
end sub                               ! stop one short since v is known only
                                      ! up to this time step
```

The results from this subroutine are plotted in Figure A1.5. The Verlet method does an excellent job for this problem, as the energy remains constant to very high accuracy.

In this appendix we have considered several different methods for dealing with ordinary differential equations for which initial conditions are specified and have estimated the numerical errors associated with each. It is tempting to use these errors to classify one method as "superior" or "inferior" to another. However, such a classification is not really appropriate. Each method has its strengths and weaknesses with regard to the types of problems that it can and cannot handle well. For example, the Euler method works well for simple projectile problems, so there is no need to consider the (slightly) more complicated Runge-Kutta and Verlet methods in this case. Our point is only that even the simplest Euler method is appropriate in many cases. The optimum algorithm for a problem depends upon the problem. This issue is discussed at length by Press et al (1986), where you can also find a careful discussion of other algorithms.

Exercises

1. Write a program to simulate planetary motion using the Runge-Kutta method and compare its performance with the Euler-Cromer program in Chapter 4.

2. Repeat the previous exercise using the Verlet method.

References

CROMER, A. 1981. "Stable Solutions using the Euler Approximation." *Am. J. Phys.* **49**, 455. Discusses the Euler-Cromer method and shows analytically that it conserves energy for oscillatory problems.

PRESS, W. H., B. P. FLANNERY, S. A. TEUKOLSKY, and W. T. VETTERLING. 1986. *Numerical Recipes*. Cambridge: Cambridge University Press. Chapter 15 gives a detailed and very readable discussion of methods for dealing with ordinary differential equations.

VERLET, L. 1967. "Computer Experiments on Classical Fluids. I. Thermodynamical Properties of Lennard-Jones Molecules." *Phys. Rev.* **159**, 98. Description of the Verlet method and its application to molecular dynamics simulations.

Appendix 2

The Fourier Transform

The Fourier transform is a subject that is usually reserved for advanced undergraduate mathematics courses and often doesn't sneak into the physics curriculum until somewhat late in the game. This is unfortunate, since the basic ideas are not difficult to grasp, and it is a very useful tool in many problems. Our goal in this appendix is to give a general introduction to the Fourier transform so as to provide a basis for the ideas and techniques we need for the problems discussed in this book.

A2.1 Theoretical Background

On the left of Figure A2.1 we show a hypothetical signal. It is simply a function that describes how some quantity varies with time. This quantity might be the intensity of a sound wave, the displacement of a particular part of a vibrating string, or the voltage at some point in an electronic circuit. To the eye, this particular signal appears to have an oscillatory character. Thus it should not come as a shock to learn that it was constructed by adding the five individual sine waves shown on the right in Figure A2.1. This signal $y(t)$ can thus be written as

$$y(t) = \sum_{j=1}^{5} y_j \sin(2\pi f_j t + \phi_j) , \tag{A2.1}$$

where y_j is the amplitude, f_j the frequency, and ϕ_j the phase of the jth sine wave component.

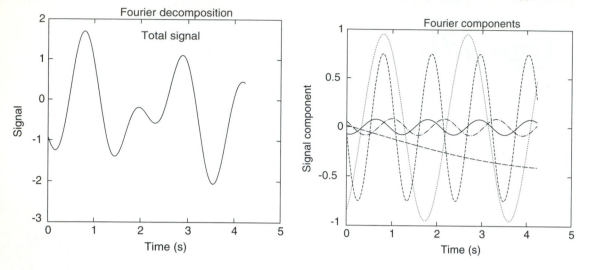

Figure A2.1: Left: hypothetical signal; right: individual sine waves whose sum yields the signal at left.

The total signal in Figure A2.1 is a very simple one, so it is probably not surprising that it can be "decomposed" into a collection of sine waves. However, it was shown by Joseph Fourier nearly 200 years ago that virtually *any* signal can be written in this way.[1] That is, *any* function, $y(t)$, can be written as a sum of sine waves. Most signals will be more complicated than the one in Figure A2.1, so the sum may involve a large (perhaps infinite) number of sine waves, but just the guarantee that such a sum exists can be extremely helpful. It is convenient to express (A2.1) as an integral over frequency, which is usually written in the form

$$y(t) = \int_{-\infty}^{\infty} Y(f)\, e^{-2\pi \iota f t}\, df \,, \tag{A2.2}$$

where $\iota = \sqrt{-1}$. The operation in (A2.2) is known as a Fourier transform. The factor $e^{-2\pi \iota f t}$ in this expression is just the sum $[\cos(2\pi f t) - \iota \sin(2\pi f t)]$. Hence, in the most general case the Fourier transform function $Y(f)$ will be complex.

While (A2.2) may have a formidable appearance, it is really just a sum of sines of cosines. It is common to refer to $y(t)$ as a function in the time domain and to its transform $Y(f)$ as existing in the frequency domain.[2] We move between these parallel universes with the Fourier transform. The so-called forward transform (A2.2) takes functions in one direction while the inverse transform,

$$Y(f) = \int_{-\infty}^{\infty} y(t)\, e^{2\pi \iota f t}\, dt \,, \tag{A2.3}$$

---

[1] Strictly speaking, this claim does not apply to extremely pathological signals. We will leave a discussion of such functions to the mathematicians (and sources in the references).

[2] It can also be useful to consider the Fourier transform of a function that is a function of space. In such cases the variables become space (that is, distance) and wave vector.

takes functions in the opposite direction. Thus, our signal can be described equally well by either function, $y(t)$ or $Y(f)$.

While functions can be written in the form (A2.2), it remains to be seen why we would want to do this in the first place. As an example, let us assume that we are dealing with an electronically recorded sound signal. The fact that it can be written as a Fourier sum means that it can be viewed as (or decomposed into) a sum of "pure" tones (or sinusoids). The frequencies of these tones are the only frequencies present in the original signal, and the Fourier transform $Y(f)$ gives a direct measure of the frequencies that are present. Most sound signals are composed of many such frequencies. In some cases these components may be harmonically related, but things can also be more complicated. In any event, the Fourier transform gives a convenient way to view a signal in the frequency domain, and we will find it useful on many occasions.

Now assume that we have used the Fourier transform to separate the components of a particular signal. What can we do with these besides perform a spectral analysis? Suppose you want to play this sound signal through the speakers in your high-fidelity system. In order to determine how the speakers will respond to this signal, we can first calculate how they would respond to each Fourier component *as if* that component was the *only* signal applied to the speakers. In many physical systems of interest, the total response is just the sum of the individual responses to each component. This approach, which relies on the linearity of the system (in this case the speakers), is intimately linked to the principle of superposition and can be used in a wide variety of problems, including waves on a string (Chapter 6), quantum mechanics (Chapter 10), and heat flow (which is the problem Fourier first treated with this method).

The next issue to consider is how to actually compute a Fourier transform. That is, given the function $y(t)$, how *in practice* do we determine $Y(f)$?

A2.2   The Fast Fourier Transform (FFT)

Suppose that a signal is specified analytically; that is, you are given the functional form of $y(t)$. The Fourier transform $Y(f)$ could then be calculated by simply performing the integral (A2.3). Of course, this may not be easy, which is why many mathematics texts have been written on the topic. However, in numerical work we are almost never given the analytic form of the signal, but instead have knowledge of its amplitude at certain discrete values of t. It is often the case that the values of $y(t)$ are known (or given) at evenly spaced intervals. For example, in our simulations of the pendulum we calculated the angular position at times $t_j = j \Delta t$, where j was an integer and Δt was the time step. In such situations it is useful to define the discrete Fourier transform [compare with (A2.2) and (A2.3)]

$$y_j = \frac{1}{N} \sum_{k=0}^{N-1} Y_k \, e^{-2\pi i j k/N} \qquad (A2.4)$$

$$Y_k = \sum_{j=0}^{N-1} y_j \, e^{2\pi i j k/N} .$$

Here we follow the usual convention and let the indices on y and Y run from 0 to $N-1$, where N is the number of data points. Again we can think of our data in the time domain where we have the values

y_j, or the frequency domain with Y_j. These are two equivalent ways of describing the *same* collection of data points.

It is important to note that the time step does not enter directly into the discrete transform (A2.4). This disappearance is possible because the signal values y_j were obtained at points equally spaced in time. Hence, the corresponding time values are fully specified by the index j and the time step Δt. It turns out that the frequency associated with each Y_j is $f_j = j/N\Delta t$. However, there are some subtleties here that we will come to in due course.

Returning to (A2.4), if we have N data points, that is, N values y_j, then there are N values of Y_j. That is, we have N pieces of information either way. However, this is not quite the whole story. Both the signal y_j and its transform Y_j in (A2.4) are, in general, *complex* numbers. Of course, most physical signals can be expressed as real numbers and in such cases the y_j are real. However, even here the Y_j can be complex. This can be understood in the following way. The exponential factors in (A2.4) are just a shorthand for the sum $[\cos(2\pi jk/N) \mp \iota \sin(2\pi jk/N)]$. The imaginary factor then causes Y_j to be complex. The real and imaginary parts of Y_j correspond to what are known as the cosine and sine transforms.

Since the Y_k are complex, it appears that we have $2N$ pieces of information in the frequency domain. If the y_k are real, we have only N pieces of information in the time domain. But if these are describing the same function, they must contain the same amount of information. The resolution of this apparent paradox is that the Y_j are then not all independent. We will have more to say about such issues in a moment.

Now we want to return to the question of the frequencies associated with each Y_j. We just noted that $f_j = j/N\Delta t$. Since the values of Y_j with $j \geq N/2$ will turn out to be redundant, the highest frequency Fourier component is $Y_{N/2-1}$. The special frequency $1/2\Delta t$ is known as the Nyquist frequency and plays a very important role. If a signal is measured at time intervals spaced by Δt, then the spectral components that can be recovered with a Fourier transform are those with frequencies below $f_{\text{Nyquist}} \equiv 1/2\Delta t$. If our signal were a simple sine wave at the Nyquist frequency, then we would be sampling it only twice during each period of oscillation. The amazing thing is that sampling *only* twice each period is sufficient to capture this Fourier component. This result is known as the sampling theorem. We will illustrate this and other properties of the discrete Fourier transform below. In particular, we will consider what happens if our signal contains components at frequencies above the Nyquist frequency.

The discrete Fourier transform (A2.4) is just a sum of exponential terms, so it *appears* to be very amenable to numerical evaluation. However, straightforward evaluation of the sums in (A2.4) is computationally very expensive. Each term involves the computation of the exponential factor, which must then be multiplied by y_j and added to the running total. Each sum has N terms and there are N data points, so the total number of operations is of order N^2. This is bad. It turns out that even with a very fast computer, this brute force approach would take a prohibitively long time for typical values[3] of N. For this reason a conventional numerical approach to evaluating discrete Fourier transforms is not practical.

While the simplest approach to evaluating (A2.4) would require of order N^2 operations, this does not mean that *all* approaches must involve the same number of operations. The exponential terms in (A2.4) are multiples of one another, and this makes it possible to "reuse" many of the terms in the sum. In fact, it is possible to evaluate the discrete transform with only of order $N \log N$ operations. This can

---

[3] $N \sim 10^6$ is not uncommon in many applications.

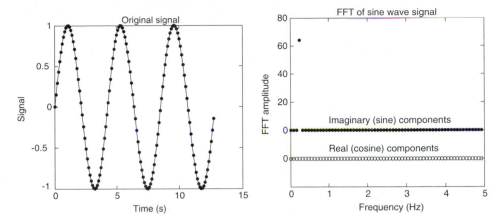

Figure A2.2:   Left: pure sine wave signal, that is, $y(t) = \sin(2\pi f t)$. These 128 points are the values of the signal that were Fourier analyzed. Right: FFT of this signal. The real (cosine) and imaginary (sine) parts of the transfrom are shown seperately. We have plotted them as discrete points to emphasize that the number of Fourier amplitudes yielded by FFT is equal to the number of original data points. Hence we have 64 cosine and 64 sine components. Only one of the points in the transform is nonzero.

be a major time reduction for large transforms, and the savings are substantial even for $N \sim 1000$, a value we will find useful for the problems in this book. There are several specific algorithms of this kind, and they are known as *the fast Fourier transform* or *FFT*. The existence of the FFT has made many important calculations feasible, and it is used in technologies such as X-ray tomography. The FFT algorithm is sufficiently complicated that we will not give a full explanation here (see the references). However, in Appendix 4 we give the listing of a Fourier analysis program that employs the FFT.

To get a feeling for how Fourier analysis works in practice, we now consider a few examples. Perhaps the simplest possible signal is a pure sine wave, such as the one shown in Figure A2.2. The period here is approximately 4.3 s and has been chosen so that the total recorded signal is precisely three complete periods.[4] Note also that the 128 signal values used in the analysis[5] are the points plotted in Figure A2.2. The FFT of this signal is shown on the right in Figure A2.2. The results are 128 Fourier amplitudes, half of which are the amplitudes of the component sine waves and half of which are the cosine amplitudes. We see that all of these are zero, *except one*, the one corresponding to the sine wave we started with. Hence, the FFT tells us that our signal is composed of a single Fourier component corresponding to a sine wave with a frequency of ≈ 0.23 Hz.

---

[4]While not absolutely necessary, we will employ the units of seconds (s) and (hertz) Hz in the following discussion, as an aid in appreciating the connection between the time and frequency domains.

[5]It turns out that the algorithm that actually evaluates the FFT requires that the number of data points it receives be a power of 2. See the discussion of our FFT program for more on this.

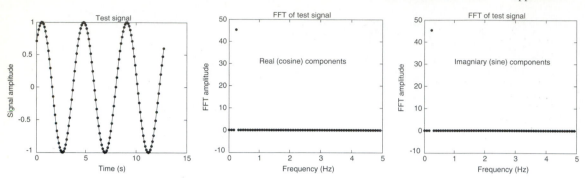

Figure A2.3: Left: test signal that is just a sine wave that is phase shifted by $\pi/4$. The dots are, again, the data points that were used in the FFT; center and right: FFT of this test signal.

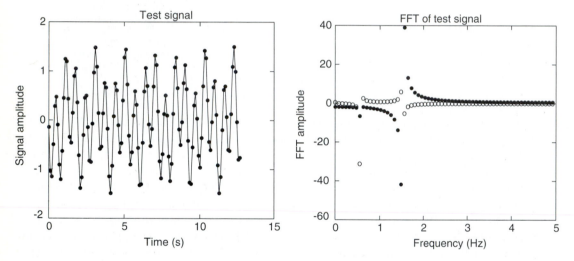

Figure A2.4: Left: test signal which is the sum of two sine waves with different frequencies, amplitudes, and phases; right: FFT of this test signal. The filled circles show the real (cosine) components, while the open circles are the imaginary (sine) amplitudes.

Next we consider essentially the same signal, but now we shift it along the time axis by adding a phase factor of $\pi/4$. That is, our signal is the function $y(t) = \sin(2\pi f t + \pi/4)$ shown in Figure A2.3. It is again sampled 128 times at intervals $\Delta t = 0.1$ s. The FFT is now slightly more complicated, with one nonzero Fourier sine component and one nonzero cosine component. These correspond to writing the signal as the sum of a sine and cosine, that is, $\sin(2\pi f t + \pi/4) = [\sin(2\pi f t) + \cos(2\pi f t)]/\sqrt{2}$. This is precisely what we find in the FFT result and shows why an FFT often yields nonzero sine and cosine components at each frequency. They are both needed if we are to be able to describe a signal with an arbitrary phase [recall the phase factors in (A2.1)].

The very simple FFT results we have observed in our first two examples are due, in part, to the fact that we have chosen the period of the signal to precisely match the total sampling time. That is, we have sampled three *complete* periods. If the sampling time does not match the frequencies of the Fourier components, the FFT has a slightly more complicated appearance. In Figure A2.4 we

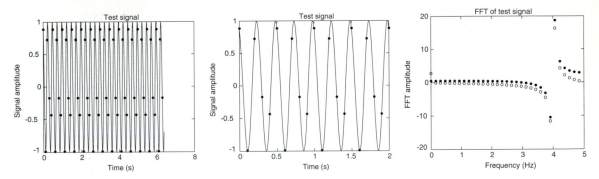

Figure A2.5: Left: test signal that is a single sine wave. The curve is what the signal would look like if it were sampled at a very large number of points, while the solid symbols show the 64 data points that were analyzed in the FFT. Center: an expanded view of the signal; right: FFT of this signal. The filled circles are the real (cosine) components, while the open circles are the imaginary (sine) components.

consider a hypothetical signal that consists of two sine waves of different frequencies, neither of which is commensurate with the sampling time. The FFT shows large components at two frequencies that match the frequencies of the sine waves used to construct the original signal. However, we also find Fourier amplitudes that are small but nonzero over a range of frequencies. This can be understood if we recall that the frequencies of the discrete transform are $f_j = j/N\Delta t$, where j runs from 0 to $N/2 - 1$. If a frequency contained in the signal does not coincide with one of these discrete frequencies, the FFT is forced to represent the signal as a sum of components over a range of f_j. However, it is important to note that such a representation will still give a *perfect* description of the original data values.

We have already mentioned the sampling theorem, which says essentially that the FFT will give us a perfect description of the Fourier components as long as the frequencies of these components are below the Nyquist frequency, $1/2\Delta t$. But what happens if this condition is not satisfied? In Figure A2.5 we show a pure sine wave signal that varies rapidly with time. The frequency here was 4 Hz, and the filled circles show the signal values used in the calculation. The FFT obtained using these 64 data points is also shown and exhibits a sizable component at 4 Hz, as expected. Note that the Nyquist frequency in this case was 5 Hz, so the sampling theorem says that we should, indeed, be able to successfully handle this signal.

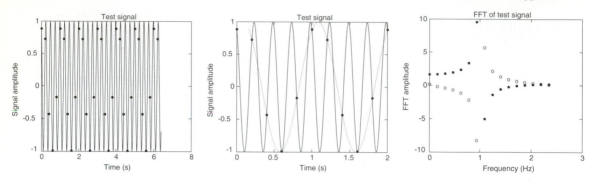

Figure A2.6: Left: test signal that is a single sine wave. The solid curve is what the signal would look like if it were sampled at a very large number of points, while the solid symbols show the 32 data points that were analyzed in the FFT. Center: an expanded view of the signal. The dotted curve shows a second sine wave, which has a much lower frequency (1 Hz) and which is seen to also pass through all of the data points. Right: FFT. The filled circles are the real (cosine) components, while the open circles are the imaginary (sine) components.

Figure A2.6 shows what happens when the signal is sampled with a different value of Δt. Here we used $\Delta t = 0.2$ s (N is now 32, so there are half as many Fourier components), which gives a Nyquist frequency of 2.5 Hz. This is lower than our signal frequency so we expect trouble, and we do indeed find it. The FFT now exhibits a peak at 1 Hz, far from the signal frequency of 4 Hz.

The location of this peak comes about in the following way. The frequency of the sine wave was greater than the Nyquist frequency, which means that there were fewer than two sampled points per period. In this situation the sampled points, y_k, can be described with equal precision by either of *two* different sine waves, one at the "true" frequency and one at a frequency that is *below* the Nyquist frequency. Here the "true" frequency was 4 Hz. The frequency of the other sine wave, which passes through these points, can be calculated by "reflecting" the true frequency about f_{Nyquist}. In this problem $f_{\text{true}} - f_{\text{Nyquist}} = 4 - 2.5 = 1.5$ Hz. The reflected frequency is then 1.5 Hz below the Nyquist frequency, that is, at 1 Hz, and this is where we find a peak in the FFT.

We must be careful here when referring to the "true" frequency. When samples are recorded only at intervals of $\Delta t = 0.2$ s, these two sine waves (one at 4 and one at 1 Hz) yield precisely the same signal. This is illustrated in the center part of Figure A2.6, which shows that a sine wave with a frequency of 1 Hz passes precisely through all of the data points. Thus, if all we have are these data points, who is to say which is the true frequency? This folding back of frequencies above the Nyquist frequency is known as *aliasing*.

In practice it is preferable to arrange for the Nyquist frequency to be higher than any of the Fourier components that are expected to be present in the signal. In an experiment this can be accomplished by using a low pass filter to remove components with frequencies above the Nyquist frequency, so there is no possibility of aliasing. In numerical work this is generally not a problem, since the sampling interval is usually the time step of a simulation, which should always be small compared to the characteristic time scales of the problem. This is equivalent to saying that all of the Fourier components lie below the Nyquist frequency.

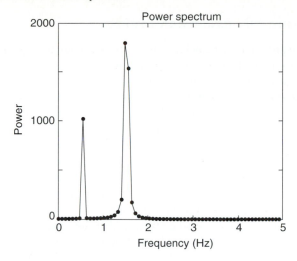

Figure A2.7:   Power spectrum of signal in Figure A2.4. The solid symbols are the calculated values of the power.

A2.3   Estimation of the Power Spectrum

To this point we have always displayed the real (cosine) and imaginary (sine) parts of the FFT separately. Such a presentation has the advantage that it contains *all* of the information in the original signal. This is essential if we want to later use a backward transform to return to the time domain. However, we are often interested only in the frequencies and relative amplitudes of the Fourier components, but don't really care about their phases. In such cases there is another useful way to display the results of an FFT, known as the power spectrum. This name is used for the following reason. Suppose that $y(t)$ is an electrical signal, such as the voltage as a function of time across a resistor. The power dissipated in the resistor at a frequency f_j is proportional to the sum of the squares of the amplitudes of the cosine (real) and sine (imaginary) components at f_j

$$P_j \; = \; Y_j(\text{real})^2 \; + \; Y_j(\text{imaginary})^2 \; . \tag{A2.5}$$

FFT results for $Y_j(\text{real})$ and $Y_j(\text{imaginary})$ can thus be used to compute the power at each frequency, f_j; this is commonly referred to as a power spectrum. As an example, Figure A2.7 shows results for the power spectrum of the signal in Figure A2.4. Here there are just two peaks at the appropriate frequencies, and their relative sizes are proportional to the squares of the corresponding Fourier amplitudes.[6] Note that in computing the power (A2.5) we discard the phase information, since the relative magnitudes of the sine and cosine components cannot be determined solely from P. It is thus not possible to recover the original signal from knowledge of the power spectrum alone.

---

[6]To be precise we should really compare the areas under each peak in the power spectrum.

A2.4   FFT Programs: Discussion and Listings

Listed in Appendix 4 are programs that calculate the individual Fourier components of a signal, as well as the power spectrum, using the FFT. We use several subroutines to do the work. The data points are read in from a file in `readin` and placed in the array `y()`. `readin` also asks the user if a forward or backward transform is desired. The actual FFT algorithm requires that the number of signal values that are passed to it be a power of 2. If the number of data points that are actually available is not precisely a power of 2, `readin` adds zeros to the end of the `y()` array to bring the number up to the next power of 2. The effect of these zeros on the final FFT is usually not significant; we'll leave a discussion of this to the sources in the references. `realft` performs the FFT and returns the Fourier amplitudes in the array `y()`. As noted earlier, the FFT algorithm itself does not involve the value of Δt, so we arrange for `calc_freq` to compute the appropriate frequency values, which are placed in the array `t()`. The results are plotted by `display` and stored in a file by `save`. Note that the real (cosine) and imaginary (sine) Fourier amplitudes are stored in separate files so that they can be graphed, or otherwise dealt with, separately. They are also stored together in a third file, which is convenient if a subsequent back transform is planned.

We also list the main program and a subroutine for use in computing the power spectrum. These routines make use of `readin`, `realft`, and `calc_freq`. The additional routine `power` uses the Fourier components in `y()` to compute the power spectrum.

Exercises

1. Write a program that uses the FFT to filter a signal. Take as input an arbitrary signal (such as the one in Figure A2.1), and begin by using a forward FFT to calculate the individual components. Components whose frequencies are above a given cutoff frequency can be removed by simply setting those Fourier amplitudes to zero in Y_k. Then perform a backward FFT to obtain the original signal with the high frequencies filtered out.

References

PRESS, W. H., B. P. FLANNERY, S. A. TEUKOLSKY, and W. T. VETTERLING. 1986. *Numerical Recipes*. Cambridge: Cambridge University Press. Chapter 12 discusses Fourier transform methods from a practical point of view.

BRACEWELL, R. N. 1978. *The Fourier Transform and Its Applications*. New York: McGraw Hill. Gives a very readable theoretical account of the FFT algorithm.

Appendix 3

The Method of Least Squares

In dealing with data from an experiment or the results of a numerical calculation, we often need to construct a "best fit" curve through "noisy" data. We have encountered this in connection with several problems, including the precession of the perihelion of Mercury (Chapter 4), and the calculation of fractal dimensionalities (Chapter 7). A generic problem of this kind is illustrated in Figure A3.1, which shows some hypothetical "data." The points cluster around a straight line, and the line drawn in the figure seems like a good choice. However, how do we know if this is the best line for this particular set of data, and if it is, how do we go about constructing it? These are the questions we will attempt to answer in this appendix. Actually, the problem need not be restricted to straight lines, but polynomials or more complicated functions can also be considered. We will treat only the case of straight lines in detail here, and leave a few comments about these other cases for the end of this appendix.

A3.1 Linear Least Squares

We imagine that we have some data that consists of a collection of N points $[x(i), y(i)]$, where the index i runs from 1 to N. The points in Figure A3.1 are a typical example. To construct a best-fit line that describes these points we must first have a criteria for what it means to be *best*. An extremely convenient and nearly universally chosen criteria is the following. The fitted line will be of the form $y_{\text{fit}} = mx + b$, where m is the slope and b the intercept. This line will come *close* to passing through all of the points, but in general will not pass exactly through any of them. The difference between the actual and fitted values is just $\Delta y(i) \equiv y(i) - y_{\text{fit}}(i)$, where $y_{\text{fit}}(i) = mx(i) + b$.

The *least-squares criteria* for the best fit is that the sum of the squares of these differences be minimized. That is, we want to choose m and b so as to make

$$\Delta_{LS} \equiv \sum_{i=1}^{N} [\Delta y(i)]^2 \qquad (A3.1)$$

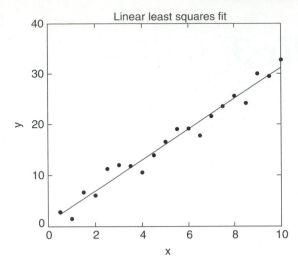

Figure A3.1: Example of a linear least-squares fit. The points are some hypothetical data and the line is the best fit, least-squares line.

as small as possible. Since Δ_{LS} is a function of m and b, this means that the values of m and b that satisfy our best fit criteria are the ones for which[1]

$$\frac{\partial \Delta_{LS}}{\partial b} = 0 \tag{A3.2}$$

$$\frac{\partial \Delta_{LS}}{\partial m} = 0 . \tag{A3.3}$$

If we compute these derivatives using (A3.1) we find

$$b\,N + m \sum x(i) = \sum y(i) \tag{A3.4}$$

$$b \sum x(i) + m \sum x(i)^2 = \sum x(i)\,y(i) ,$$

where all of the sums run from $i = 1$ to N. The problem thus reduces to solving two algebraic equations for the two unknowns, b and m. The solution is just

$$b = \frac{\sum x(i) \, \sum x(i)y(i) \, - \, \sum x(i)^2 \, \sum y(i)}{\left[\sum x(i)\right]^2 \, - \, N \sum x(i)^2} \tag{A3.5}$$

$$m = \frac{\sum x(i) \, \sum y(i) \, - \, N \sum x(i)y(i)}{\left[\sum x(i)\right]^2 \, - \, N \sum x(i)^2} .$$

Now that we have obtained the solution to this least-squares problem, we can appreciate the beauty of the process. This criteria for a "best" fit automatically leads to a set of algebraic equations

---

[1]You might worry that this procedure could actually locate a maximum in Δ_{LS}. However, for a quadratic form such as (A3.1) there is only one extrema, and it is the minimum we are after.

for b and m. The only the way the procedure can fail is if the denominator in (A3.5) vanishes. This will happen *only* if all of the $x(i)$ are the same; that is, if all of the data points have the same x value.[2] So long as at least two of the points have different x values, we are *guaranteed* that (A3.5) is the *unique* solution to the least-squares problem.

A program that performs a least-squares fit of a straight line to a collection of data points is listed in Appendix 4. The program follows our standard pattern. `initialize` reads the data from a file and stores the values in the arrays `x()` and `y()`. Note that we have arranged for the program to stop reading (without an error!) when it reaches the end of the file, so there is no need to enter the number of points separately. The subroutine `calculate` computes the slope and intercept using (A3.5), and returns the results in the variables with the same names. `display` then plots the data along with the fitted line. We should note that *True Basic* actually has library routines to calculate and plot the least-squares line, so if you are using *True Basic* you won't need this program! However, it can easily be translated into other languages, as needed.

A3.2   More General Applications of Least Squares

There is much more to the least-squares story than we have space to cover here. The basic ideas introduced above are adequate for all of the problems covered in this book, and as usual, the references can be used to fill in the gaps. However, we want to give you at least a glimpse of what those gaps contain.

In the problem considered above we treated all of the data points equally. While this is sometimes appropriate, it often happens that some points are more accurate than others. That is, we might have some reason to believe (based, for example, on how the data were acquired) that some points lie closer to the "ideal" line than others. The fit procedure should then give increased influence to the more accurate points and less influence to the points that are less certain. This can readily be accommodated within the least-squares approach. Each value of $y(i)$ is associated with an estimate for its uncertainty $\sigma(i)$, and the importance, or weight, of each point in the fit is by convention taken to be proportional to $1/\sigma(i)^2$. The function to be minimized in this case is

$$\Delta_{LS} = \sum_{i=1}^{N} \frac{[\Delta y(i)]^2}{\sigma(i)^2} . \tag{A3.6}$$

We then proceed as above to obtain two algebraic equations for m and b, and the results are similar to (A3.5). We will leave the details for the references and the curious reader. The important point is that the uncertainty associated with each data point can be included explicitly in the fitting process.

Another useful extension involves fitting to polynomial functions. There are many situations in which a polynominal fitting function is desired, such as

$$y_{\text{fit}} = a_0 + a_1 x + a_2 x^2 + a_3 x^3 + \dots . \tag{A3.7}$$

This is a natural generalization of the linear function considered above, but there are now more parameters to be determined. These can again be chosen according to the criteria that the sum of the squares of the deviations of the actual values of y from y_{fit} be minimized. It turns out that there is,

---

[2] In this case a line with infinite slope would pass exactly through all of the data.

again, a unique set of coefficients, a_i, that satisfies this criteria.[3] The process of solving for the a_i can again be reduced to the problem of solving a system of algebraic equations. There are some numerical complications due to the fact that these equations tend to be ill conditioned (i.e., very sensitive to round-off errors), and interested readers should consult the sources in the references to learn how best to deal with this.

Finally, there is no reason why we should be restricted to polynomial functions. There are many cases in which the appropriate y_{fit} is much more complicated than a polynomial. The problem of fitting to a general function can arise, and there is a well-developed set of algorithms for handling it. This goes under the heading of *nonlinear least squares* and is a problem that is, as they say, beyond the scope of this book. We will leave this, too, for the references.

In this appendix we have treated only one problem, that of constructing a least-squares fit to a straight line. This problem arises quite often in practice, since in many cases things can be transformed so as to make the fitting function linear. For example, in estimating fractal dimensionalities in Chapter 7 we encountered the function $m \sim r^{d_f}$. Taking the logarithm of both sides yields $\log m = A + d_f \log(r)$, so d_f can be determined from a linear least-squares fit involving the variables $\log m$ and $\log r$. The program listed in Appendix 4 will handle all of our needs in this book, and probably also be adequate for the majority of least-squares problems you are likely to encounter.

References

PRESS, W. H., B. P. FLANNERY, S. A. TEUKOLSKY, and W. T. VETTERLING. 1986. *Numerical Recipes*. Cambridge: Cambridge University Press. Chapter 14 discusses many aspects of the method of least squares.

---

[3]This assumes that if there are m coefficients in the polynomial, then at least m of the data points are independent.

Appendix 4

Selected Program Listings

Given in this appendix are listings for representative programs from Chapters 1 through 10 and Appendices 2 and 3. These programs were written in *True Basic* for the Macintosh and are all believed to run correctly. That is, they have all been checked and found to run, and they give what we believe are correct results. These programs are also available through the World Wide Web page associated with this book. The address is `http://www.physics.purdue.edu/~ng/comp_phys.html`. It should be possible, with relatively little effort, to modify these programs to run under *True Basic* on other machines. We have run all of them on a Sun workstation and many of them on an Amiga. It should also be possible to translate them into other languages. Enhanced versions of these programs plus other useful information will be added to the above Web site as they become available.

These programs are all copyrighted by Prentice Hall. You are welcome to use them, modify them, and distribute them freely in any convenient form. The only thing we will not allow is that you sell them for a profit.

A4.1   Chapter 1

Radioactive Decay

```
! Simulation of radioactive decay
! Program to accompany "Computational Physics" by N. Giordano
! Copyright Prentice Hall 1997
program decay
   option nolet                 ! can omit the let keyword
   library "sgfunc*", "sglib*"  ! the graphics routines are found here
   dim n_uranium(100), t(100)   ! declare the arrays we will need
   call initialize(n_uranium,t,tau,dt)   ! use subroutines to do the work
   call calculate(n_uranium,t,tau,dt)
   call display(n_uranium,t,tau,dt)
end
! initialize variables
sub initialize(nuclei(),t(),time_constant,dt)
   input prompt "initial number of nuclei -> ": nuclei(1)
   t(1) = 0
   input prompt "time constant -> ": time_constant
   input prompt "time step -> ": dt
end sub
sub calculate(n_uranium(),t(),tau,dt)
   for i = 1 to size(t)-1            ! now use the Euler method
      n_uranium(i+1) = n_uranium(i) - (n_uranium(i) / tau) * dt
      t(i+1) = t(i) + dt
   next i
end sub
sub display(n_uranium(),t(),tau,dt)
              ! first set up title and label axes for graph
   call settitle("Radioactive Decay    Number of nuclei versus time")
   call sethlabel("Time(s)")
   call setvlabel("Number of Nuclei")
   call datagraph(t,n_uranium,4,0,"black")  ! the graph is produced here
   set cursor 5,30                          ! reposition cursor
   print "time constant = ";tau
   set cursor 6,30
   print "time step = ";dt
end sub
```

A4.2   Chapter 2

Bicycles

```
! Simulation of velocity vs. time for a bicyclist
! assume no air resistance
! Program to accompany "Computational Physics" by N. Giordano
! Copyright Prentice Hall 1997
program bike
   option nolet
   library "sglib*","sgfunc*"
   dim t(5000),velocity(5000)
   call initialize(t,velocity,dt,power,mass,nmax)
   call calculate(t,velocity,dt,power,mass,nmax)
   call display(t,velocity)
end
```

```
! t() = time    v() = velocity
! dt = time step    power = rider power
! mass = mass of rider + bicycle
sub initialize(t(),v(),dt,power,mass,nmax)
   t(1) = 0
   v(1) = 4    ! m/s - all units are mks
   dt = 1      ! second
   power = 400 ! watts
   mass = 70   ! kg
   tmax = 200  ! seconds
   nmax = tmax / dt  ! total number of time steps required
end sub
sub calculate(t(),v(),dt,pmax,mass,nmax)
   for i = 2 to nmax
       t(i) = t(i-1) + dt
       v(i) = v(i-1) + pmax * dt / (mass * v(i-1))    ! Euler method
   next i
   mat redim t(nmax),v(nmax)    ! trim arrays to the size actually used
end sub
sub display(t(),v())
   call settitle("Bicycle velocity vs. time")
   call sethlabel("time (s)")
   call setvlabel("Velocity (m/s)")
   call datagraph(t,v,3,0,"black")
end sub
```

Cannons

```
! simulation of velocity vs. time for a large cannon
! include the effect of air resistance
! Program to accompany "Computational Physics" by N. Giordano
! Copyright Prentice Hall 1997
program cannon
   option nolet
   library "sglib*","sgfunc*"
   dim x(5000), y(5000)
   call initialize(dt,v_init,theta,A_m)
   call calculate(x,y,dt,v_init,theta,A_m)
   call display(x,y)
end
sub initialize(dt,v_init,theta,A_m)
   dt = 0.25      ! seconds - all unit mks
   v_init = 700 ! m/s
   theta = 55   ! firing angle in degrees
   A_m = 4e-5   ! A2/m
end sub
```

```
! x() and y() are the position of the projectile
! dt = time step    v_init = initial speed    theta = launch angle
! A_m = proportional to drag force = A2/m
sub calculate(x(),y(),dt,v_init,theta,A_m)
   option angle degrees    ! use degrees rather than radians
   x(1) = 0
   y(1) = 0
   vx = v_init * cos(theta)
   vy = v_init * sin(theta)
   nmax = size(x)    ! this is the number of elements in the array x()
   for i = 2 to nmax
      x(i) = x(i-1) + vx * dt              ! Euler method equations
      y(i) = y(i-1) + vy * dt
      f = A_m * sqr(vx^2 + vy^2)           ! drag force from air resistance
      vy = vy - 9.8 * dt - f * vy * dt
      vx = vx - f * vx * dt
      if y(i) <= 0 then exit for           ! shell has hit the ground
   next i
   a = -y(i) / y(i-1)                      ! interpolate to find landing point
   x(i) = (x(i) + a*x(i-1)) / (1+a)
   y(i) = 0
   mat redim x(i),y(i)
end sub
sub display(x(),y())      ! display the results with datagraph
   call settitle("Cannon shell y vs. x")
   call sethlabel("x (m)")
   call setvlabel("y (m)")
   call datagraph(x,y,0,1,"black")
end sub
```

A4.3   Chapter 3

Simple Pendulum

```
! motion of a simple pendulum
! theta() = pendulum angle    omega() = pendulum angular velocity t() = time
! length = length of string    dt = time step
! Program to accompany "Computational Physics" by N. Giordano
! Copyright Prentice Hall 1997
program pendulum
   option nolet
   library "sgfunc*","sglib*"
   dim theta(1000), omega(1000), t(1000)
   call initialize(theta,omega,t,length,dt)
   call calculate(theta,omega,t,length,dt)
   call display(theta,omega,t,length,dt)
end
```

```
! initialize variables
! theta() = pendulum angle  omega() = pendulum angular velocity
sub initialize(theta(),omega(),t(),length,dt)
    input prompt "initial pendulum angle (in radians) -> ": theta(1)
    input prompt "initial angular velocity of pendulum (in radians/s) -> ": omega(1)
    t(1) = 0
    input prompt "length of pendulum (in m) -> ": length
    input prompt "time step -> ": dt
end sub
! use the Euler method
sub calculate(theta(),omega(),t(),length,dt)
    i = 0
    g = 9.8
    period = 2 * pi / sqr(g/length)     ! period of pendulum
    do
        i = i + 1
        t(i+1) = t(i) + dt
        omega(i+1) = omega(i) - (g/length) * theta(i) * dt  ! Euler method
        theta(i+1) = theta(i) + omega(i) * dt
    loop until t(i+1) >= 5 * period     ! follow the oscillations for 5 periods
    mat redim omega(i+1),theta(i+1),t(i+1)
end sub
! display theta and omega in separate windows
sub display(theta(),omega(),t(),length,dt)
    set background color "white"
    set color "black"
    call setcanvas("white")
    clear
    open #1: screen 0,.9,0,.48      ! bottom window
    call settitle("Angular velocity vs. time")
    call sethlabel("Time(s)")
    call setvlabel("Omega")
    call datagraph(t,omega,1,1,"black")
    close #1
    open #1: screen 0,.9,.52,1      ! top window
    call settitle("Theta vs. time")
    call sethlabel("Time(s)")
    call setvlabel("Theta")
    call datagraph(t,theta,1,1,"black")
    set cursor 3,10
    print "length = "; length
    set cursor 4,10
    print "time step = "; dt
    close #1
end sub
```

Nonlinear Pendulum

```
! motion of a real pendulum with damping and a driving force
! with the Euler-Cromer method
! Program to accompany "Computational Physics" by N. Giordano
! Copyright Prentice Hall 1997
program nonlinear
    option nolet
    library "sgfunc*", "sglib*"
    dim theta(50000),omega(50000),t(50000)
    call initialize(theta,omega,t,length,dt,damping,force,drive_frequency)
    call calculate(theta,omega,t,length,dt,damping,force,drive_frequency)
    call display(theta,omega,t,length,dt,damping,force,drive_frequency)
end
! initialize variables
! theta() = pendulum angle    omega() = pendulum angular velocity
! damping = damping factor, force = amplitude of drive force
! drive_frequency = angular frequency of drive force
! all angles in radians
sub initialize(theta(),omega(),t(),length,dt,damping,force,drive_frequency)
    input prompt "initial pendulum angle (in radians) -> ": theta(1)
    input prompt "initial angular velocity of pendulum (in radians/s) -> ": omega(1)
    t(1) = 0
    input prompt "length of pendulum (in m) -> ": length
    input prompt "time step -> ": dt
    input prompt "damping constant -> ": damping
    input prompt "amplitude of driving force -> ": force
    input prompt "driving frequency -> ": drive_frequency
end sub
! use the Euler-Cromer method for a damped, nonlinear, driven pendulum
sub calculate(theta(),omega(),t(),length,dt,q,drive_force,drive_frequency)
    i = 0
    g = 9.8
    period = 2 * pi / sqr(g/length)
    do
        i = i + 1
        t(i+1) = t(i) + dt
        omega(i+1) = omega(i) - (g/length) * sin(theta(i)) * dt - q * omega(i)
                        * dt + drive_force * sin(drive_frequency * t(i)) * dt
        theta(i+1) = theta(i) + omega(i+1) * dt
        if theta(i+1) > pi then theta(i+1) = theta(i+1) - 2 * pi ! keep theta in
        if theta(i+1) < -pi then theta(i+1) = theta(i+1) + 2 * pi! range -pi to pi
    loop until t(i+1) >= 60 ! 10 * period
    mat redim omega(i+1),theta(i+1),t(i+1)
end sub
```

```
sub display(theta(),omega(),t(),length,dt,damping,force,drive_frequency)
   set background color "white"
   set color "black"
   call setcanvas("white")
   clear
   open #1: screen 0,.9,0,.48
   call settitle("Angular velocity vs. time")
   call sethlabel("Time(s)")
   call setvlabel("Omega")
   call datagraph(t,omega,1,1,"black")
   close #1
   open #1: screen 0,.9,.52,1
   call settitle("Theta vs. time")
   call sethlabel("Time(s)")
   call setvlabel("Theta")
   call datagraph(t,theta,1,1,"black")
   set cursor 3,10
   print "length = "; length
   set cursor 4,10
   print "time step = "; dt
   close #1
end sub
```

A4.4   Chapter 4

Planetary Motion

```
! Planetary motion with the Euler-Cromer method
! Program to accompany "Computational Physics" by N. Giordano
! Copyright Prentice Hall 1997
program kepler
   option nolet    ! don't need the graphics libraries for this program
   call initialize(x,v_x,y,v_y,dt)   ! set up initial conditions
   call calculate(x,v_x,y,v_y,dt)    ! do the calculation
end
! initialize variables
sub initialize(x,v_x,y,v_y,dt)
   input prompt "initial x position -> ": x
   input prompt "initial y position -> ": y
   input prompt "initial x velocity -> ": v_x
   input prompt "initial y velocity -> ": v_y
   input prompt "time step -> ": dt
                          ! now set up window for plotting
   aspect = 1.33          ! aspect ratio of screen - your's may be different
   r = 1.4 * sqr(x^2+y^2) ! pick a scale a bit larger than the planet's radius
   set window -r,r,-r/aspect,r/aspect  ! set window coordinates
   set color "black"
   clear
   plot -r,0;r,0                      ! plot axes
   plot 0,-r*aspect;0,r*aspect
end sub
```

```
! x,y = position of planet
! v_x,v_y = velocity of planet
! dt = time step
sub calculate(x,v_x,y,v_y,dt)
    do                          ! use Euler-Cromer method
        r = sqr(x^2 + y^2)
        v_x = v_x - (4 * pi^2 * x * dt) / r^3
        v_y = v_y - (4 * pi^2 * y * dt) / r^3
        set color "black"        ! keep trail of the planet black
        plot x,y
        x = x + v_x * dt
        y = y + v_y * dt
        set color "red"          ! current location of the planet is red
        plot x,y
    loop until key input         ! loop until any key is hit
end sub
```

A4.5   Chapter 5

Laplace's Equation

```
! calculate the electric potential and field lines
! between two parallel plates
! use the Jacobi method
! Program to accompany "Computational Physics" by N. Giordano
! Copyright Prentice Hall 1997
program laplace
    option nolet
    library "sgfunc*", "sglib*"
    dim v(0,0)      ! store the potential in this array
    call initialize(v,max)
    call calculate(v,max,n)      ! iterate with relaxation method
    call display(v(,),max)    ! plot final result
end
! initialize variables
! v() = potential    i,j = position    max determines number of grid steps
sub initialize(v(,),max)
    print "number of grid steps per unit distance"
    input prompt "(x and y run from -1 to 1) -> ": max
    mat redim v(-max to max,-max to max)   ! resize array
    for i = -max to max                    ! zero out array
        for j = -max to max
            v(i,j) = 0
        next j
    next i
    for j = -max to max                    ! set up boundary conditions
        v(-max,j) = -1                     ! along edges
        v(max,j) = 1
    next j
    for i = -max to max
        v(i,-max) = i / max
        v(i,max) = i / max
    next i
end sub
```

```
! v() is the potential, max -> determines number of grid steps
! n = number of iterations of relaxation algorithm
sub calculate(v(,),max,n)
   dim v_tmp(0,0)
   mat redim v_tmp(-max to max,-max to max)
   for i = -max to max      ! initialize temporary array
      for j = -max to max      ! not absolutely necessary, but a
         v_tmp(i,j) = v(i,j) ! good general habit
      next j
   next i
   i = 0
   do                          ! main loop - the real work is done here
      i = i + 1
      call update(v,v_tmp,max,diff,n)
      call update(v_tmp,v,max,diff,n)
   loop until i > 10 and diff < 1e-5
end sub
! use Jacobi relaxation algorithm to calculate new values of the potential
! old values are in v1, put new values into v2
! diff is average change in potential during the current iteration
sub update(v1(,),v2(,),max,diff,n)
   diff = 0
   for i = -max+1 to max-1
      for j = -max+1 to max-1
         tmp = v1(i,j)
         v2(i,j) = (v1(i-1,j) + v1(i+1,j) + v1(i,j+1) + v1(i,j-1)) / 4
         diff = diff + abs(tmp - v2(i,j))
      next j
   next i
   diff = diff / (2*max+1)^2
end sub
```

```
! display final results
sub display(v(,),max)
   dim x(0),y(0),ex(0),ey(0)
   set background color "white"
   set color "black"
   clear
   call settitle("Equipotential lines")
   call sethlabel("X")
   call setvlabel("Y")
   call topograph(v,-1,1,-1,1,"black")  ! equipotential lines
   get key z
   max2 = (2*max+1)^2                    ! prepare for vector plot
   mat redim x(max2),y(max2),ex(max2),ey(max2)
   k = 0
   for i = -max+1 to max-1
      for j = -max+1 to max-1
         k = k + 1
         x(k) = i/max
         y(k) = j/max
         ex(k) = -(v(i+1,j) - v(i-1,j)) * max    ! compute electric field
         ey(k) = -(v(i,j+1) - v(i,j-1)) * max    ! components
      next j
   next i
   for i = -max to max step 2*max
      k = k + 1
      x(k) = i/max
      y(k) = i/max
      ex(k) = 0
      ey(k) = 0
   next i
   mat redim x(k),y(k),ex(k),ey(k)
   call settitle("Electric field between two metal plates")
   call sethlabel("x")
   call setvlabel("y")
   call vectorgraph(x,y,ex,ey,.1,3,"black")  ! make vector plot
end sub
```

Magnetic Fields from Currents

```
! magnetic field from a straight wire
! Program to accompany "Computational Physics" by N. Giordano
! Copyright Prentice Hall 1997
program straight_wire
   option nolet
   library "sglib*","sgfunc*"
   dim r(0),field(0)
   lstart = .5
   lfinish = 10
   call initialize(r,field,max)
   length = lstart
   i = 1
   do
      call calculate(r,field,max,length)
      if length = lstart then call display(r,field,max)
      if length > lstart then call adddatagraph(r,field,4,0,"black")
      i = i + 1
      length = 10 * length
   loop until length > lfinish
   call exact(r,field)
end
! initialize variables
sub initialize(r(),field(),max)
   input prompt "number of grid steps -> ": max
   mat redim field(max),r(max)
end sub
sub calculate(r(),field(),max,length)
   for i = 1 to max
      call calculate_field(field(i),i/max,max,length)
      r(i) = i/max
   next i
end sub
sub calculate_field(by,x,max,length)
   dz = 0.1
   by = 0
   for z = -length to length step dz
      r = sqr(x^2 + z^2)
      by = by + dz * x / r^3
   next z
end sub
sub display(r(),field(),max)
   call settitle("Magnetic field from a straight wire")
   call sethlabel("R")
   call setvlabel("B")
   call datagraph(r,field,3,0,"black")
end sub
sub exact(r(),field())
   max = 100
   mat redim r(max),field(max)
   for i = 1 to max
      r(i) = i / max
      field(i) = 2 / r(i)
   next i
   call adddatagraph(r,field,1,1,"black")
end sub
```

```
! compute the magnetic field from a circular current loop
! Program to accompany "Computational Physics" by N. Giordano
! Copyright Prentice Hall 1997
program current_loop
    option nolet
    library "sglib*","sgfunc*"
    dim field(0,0,0)        ! magnetic field at grid location i,j,k
    call initialize(field,max)
    call calculate(field,max)
    call display(field,max)
end
! initialize variables
! True basic initializes all variables to zero, so no need to zero out
! field array       max determines number of grid steps
sub initialize(field(,,),max)
    input prompt "number of grid steps -> ": max
    mat redim field(3,-max to max,-max to max)  ! resize field array
end sub
! sweep through the lattice here
sub calculate(field(,,),max)
    for i = -max to max         ! compute field in x-z plane
        for k = -max to max
            call calculate_field(bx,by,bz,max,i/max,0,k/max)
            field(1,i,k) = bx    ! vector components of the field
            field(2,i,k) = by
            field(3,i,k) = bz
        next k
    next i
end sub
! calculate the field components here
! bx,by,bz are the field components at site x,y,z
sub calculate_field(bx,by,bz,max,x,y,z)
    radius = 0.5    ! radius of circular current loop
    dtheta = 2 * pi / 20     ! step size for integration along theta
    bx = 0
    by = 0
    bz = 0
    for theta = 0 to 2*pi-dtheta step dtheta
        dlx = -radius * dtheta * sin(theta)     ! components of dr
        dly = radius * dtheta * cos(theta)
        rx = x - radius*cos(theta)              ! components of r
        ry = y - radius*sin(theta)
        rz = z
        r = sqr(rx^2 + ry^2 + rz^2)
        if r > 1 / max then                     ! avoid the wire itself
            bx = bx + dly * rz / r^3            ! Biot-Savart law (cross product)
            by = by - dlx * rz / r^3
            bz = bz + (dlx * ry - dly * rx) / r^3
        end if
    next theta
end sub
```

```
! display the results
sub display(field(,,),max)
    dim x(0),z(0),bx(0),by(0),bz(0)   ! arrays used for plotting
    max2 = (2 * max + 1)^2
    mat redim x(max2),z(max2),bx(max2),by(max2),bz(max2)
    m = 0
    if max > 5 then      ! choose a pleasing number of elements to display
        n = 2
    else
        n = 1
    end if
    for i = -max to max step n
        for k = -max to max step n
            m = m + 1
            x(m) = i/max
            z(m) = k /max
            bx(m) = field(1,i,k)
            bz(m) = field(3,i,k)
        next k
    next i
    mat redim x(m),z(m),bx(m),bz(m)
    call settitle("Magnetic field from a current loop")
    call sethlabel("X")
    call setvlabel("Z")
    call vectorgraph(x,z,bx,bz,.010,3,"black")
end sub
```

A4.6   Chapter 6

Waves on a String

```
! simulate waves on a string
! Program to accompany "Computational Physics" by N. Giordano
! Copyright Prentice Hall 1997
program waves
    option NOLET
    dim x(0 to 1000,3)
    call init(x,dt,dx,c,nmax)
    call first_display(x,dx,nmax)
    i = 0
    do
        call propagate(x,dt,dx,c,nmax)
        call display(x,dx,nmax)
        if key input then
            get key z
            if chr$(z) = " " then exit do
        end if
    loop
end
```

```
!   y(,) is a two dimensional array containing the displacement at
!       the current time step y(i,2), the previous time step y(i,1)
!       the next time step corresponds to y(i,3)
!   dt = time step      dx = spatial grid size    c = wave speed
!   nmax = number of spatial units
!   i runs from 0 to nmax, with the fixed ends at i=0 and i=nmax
sub propagate(y(,),dt,dx,c,nmax)
   r2 = (dt * c / dx)^2
   for i = 1 to nmax-1
      y(i,3) = r2 * (y(i+1,2) + y(i-1,2)) + 2*(1.0 - r2)*y(i,2) - y(i,1)
   next i
   for i = 1 to nmax-1
      y(i,1) = y(i,2)
      y(i,2) = y(i,3)
   next i
end sub
! display string profile
sub display(y(,),dx,nmax)
   clear
   set color "red"
   plot 0,0;dx*nmax,0      ! plot axes
   set color "black"
   plot 0,y(0,2);
   for i = 1 to nmax-1     ! plot each interior grid point
      plot i * dx,y(i,2);
   next i
   plot nmax*dx,y(nmax,2)
end sub
! set up for first plot
sub first_display(y(,),dx,nmax)
   set background color "white"
   clear
   set window 0,nmax*dx,-1.5,1.5
   call display(y,dx,nmax)
end sub
! initialize variables   y(i,n) = string position at site i
! n = 3 = new position
! n = 2 = previous position
! n = 3 = position two time steps ago
! dt = time step    dx = spatial step    c = wave speed
! nmax = number of grid steps
sub init(y(,),dt,dx,c,nmax)
   input prompt "number of spatial grid points (try 100) -> ": nmax
   for i = 1 to nmax     ! initial all to zero
      y(i,1) = 0
      y(i,2) = 0
      y(i,3) = 0
   next i
   dx = .01
   c = 300
   dt = dx / c           ! choose so that r = 1 for stability
   for i = 2 to nmax - 1
      y(i,2) = exp(-1000 * (i * dx - 0.3 * nmax * dx)^2)   ! initial profile
      y(i,1) = exp(-1000 * (i * dx - 0.3 * nmax * dx)^2)
   next i
end sub
```

A4.7   Chapter 7

Monte Carlo Integration

```
! Calculate pi using the Monte Carlo method
! estimate the area of circle of radius 1
! Program to accompany "Computational Physics" by N. Giordano
! Copyright Prentice Hall 1997
program pi
   option nolet
   randomize
   n = 100
   do
      call calculate(n,value)
      print n, 4 * value      ! multiply value by 4 to get the area
      n = n * 3               ! of the entire circle
      if key input then exit do
   loop
end
! calculate area of circle with radius = 1
! consider only portion in first quadrant
! n_total = number of points (darts) to generate    value = integral
sub calculate(n_total,value)
   n_sum = 0
   for i = 1 to n_total
      x = rnd       ! generate the coordinates of a random point
      y = rnd
      if y <= sqr(1 - x^2) then n_sum = n_sum + 1     ! check if point is
                                                      ! the circle
   next i
   value = n_sum / n_total
end sub
```

Random Walks

```
! Random walk in 1 dimension
! Program to accompany "Computational Physics" by N. Giordano
! Copyright Prentice Hall 1997
program walk_1d
   option nolet
   library "sgfunc*","sglib*"
   randomize
   dim x2ave(1000)    ! keep x^2 averages here
   call initialize(x2ave,n_walks,n_steps)
   call calculate(x2ave,n_walks,n_steps)
   call display(x2ave)
end
```

```
! initialize variables
! n_walks = number of walkers   n_steps = number of steps taken by each walker
sub initialize(x2ave(),n_walks,n_steps)
   n_steps = 100
   n_walks = 200
   mat redim x2ave(n_steps)
   ymax = sqr(n_steps)  ! set up window for plotting
   clear
   set window 0,n_steps,-2*ymax,2*ymax
   plot 0,0;n_steps,0
end sub
! do the calculation here
! x2ave(n) contains the average of x^2 at step n
! n_walks = total number of walkers
! n_steps = number of steps taken by each walker
sub calculate(x2ave(),n_walks,n_steps)
   plot_flag = 1
   for i = 1 to n_walks
      x = 0                      ! current location of the walker
      for j = 1 to n_steps
         if rnd < 0.5 then
            x = x + 1
         else                  ! just use an else statement
            x = x - 1          ! DO NOT generate a new value using rnd
         end if
         if plot_flag = 1 then plot j,x      ! plot each walk until
                                             ! a keystroke is hit
         if key input then        ! after this just accumulate <x^2>
            plot_flag = 0         ! for later display
            get key z
         end if
         x2ave(j) = x2ave(j) + x^2
      next j
   next i
   for i = 1 to n_steps                   ! normalize x2ave when finished
      x2ave(i) = x2ave(i) / n_walks
   next i
end sub
! display results now
sub display(x2ave())
   dim t(0)  ! dummy array for plotting
   n = size(x2ave)
   mat redim t(n)
   for i = 1 to n
      t(i) = i
   next i
   call datagraph(t,x2ave,1,0,"black")
   call addlsgraph(t,x2ave,1,"black")   ! compute and plot least squares fit
   call fitline(t,x2ave,m,b)
   set cursor 4,12
   print "slope = ";m
end sub
```

Random Fractals

```
! generate simple random fractals recursively
! this one is based on equilateral triangles
! Program to accompany "Computational Physics" by N. Giordano
! Copyright Prentice Hall 1997
program generate
   option nolet
   randomize
   call init
   input prompt "number of recursive levels -> ": level
   open #1: name "random_fractal."&str$(level), organization text, create new
   x_start = 0          ! initialize some variables then call show()
   y_start = 0
   x_end = 300
   y_end = 0
   print #1: x_start,",",y_start
   call show(x_start,y_start,x_end,y_end,level,#1)
   close #1
end
sub show(xi,yi,xf,yf,level,#1)      ! recursive routine for drawing a random fractal
   if level <= 1 then               ! have hit bottom - just draw a line
      plot lines: xi,yi;xf,yf
      print #1: xf,",",yf           ! and save coordinates to a file
   else
      dx = (xf - xi) / 3            ! divide the interval into three parts
      dy = (yf - yi) / 3
      ctheta = 2 * (rnd - 0.5)      ! pick a random angle - get its cosine and sine
      stheta = sqr(1 - ctheta^2)

                                    ! next choose new points based on underlying
                                    ! "structure" of an equilateral triangle
      call show(xi,yi,xi+dx,yi+dy,level-1,#1)
      call show(xi+dx,yi+dy,xi+1.5*dx-stheta*dy,yi+1.5*dy+ctheta*dx,level-1,#1)
      call show(xi+1.5*dx-stheta*dy,yi+1.5*dy+ctheta*dx,xi+2*dx,yi+2*dy,level-1,#1)
      call show(xi+2*dx,yi+2*dy,xf,yf,level-1,#1)
   end if
end sub
sub init    ! set up window for plotting
   set window 0,300,-100,200
   clear
end sub
```

A4.8   Chapter 8

Monte Carlo: Two-Dimensional Ising Model

```
! Ising model in two dimensions on a square lattice
! calculate the magnetization and energy as functions of temperature
! Program to accompany "Computational Physics" by N. Giordano
! Copyright Prentice Hall 1997
program ising_2d
   option nolet
   library "sgfunc*","sglib*"
   dim mag(100),temp(100),energy(100),spin(0,0)
     ! mag() and energy() contain running averages for magnetization and energy
     ! at temperature temp()   spin(i,j) = value of spin at site i,j
   randomize
   call initialize(spin,nmax,t_init,t_final,n_points,n_passes,current_m,current_e)
     ! set up for a temperature sweep
   dt = (t_final - t_init) / (n_points - 1)
   t = t_init
   call init_spin(spin,nmax,current_m,current_e,1)
   for i = 1 to n_points    ! sweep temperature
      call calculate(spin,nmax,t,n_passes,current_m,current_e,mag(i),energy(i))
      temp(i) = t    ! NOT "time"
      print t,mag(i),energy(i)
      t = t + dt
   next i
   mat redim mag(n_points),temp(n_points),energy(n_points)
   call display(temp,mag)     ! display final results
   get key z
   call display(temp,energy)
end
! initialize variables
! nmax = size of lattice  t_init,t_final = starting and ending temperature
! n_points = number of temperatures to consider
! n_passes = number of passes through the lattice at each temperature
sub initialize(spin(,),nmax,t_init,t_final,n_points,n_passes,current_m,current_e)
   nmax = 10    ! lattice size is nmax by nmax
   mat redim spin(nmax,nmax)
   t_init = 1
   t_final = 5
   n_points = 9      ! change this to change the number of temperatures considered
   n_passes = 100    ! make this larger to get more accurate averages
   call init_spin(spin,nmax,current_m,current_e,1)
end sub
```

```
! initialize spin directions
! also initialize magnetization
! and energy
sub init_spin(spin(,),nmax,m,e,flag)
   for i = 1 to nmax
      for j = 1 to nmax
         if flag = 1 then      ! if flag = 1 start with an ordered array of spins
            spin(i,j) = 1
         else                  ! else start with a random array
            if(rnd >= 0.5) then
               spin(i,j) = 1
            else
               spin(i,j) = -1
            end if
         end if
      next j
   next i
   if flag = 1 then            ! initialize mag and energy
      m = nmax^2
      e = -2 * nmax^2
   else
      m = 0
      e = 0
      for i = 1 to nmax
         for j = 1 to nmax
            m = m + spin(i,j)
            call neighbors(spin,nmax,i,j,sum)
            e = - spin(i,j) * sum / 2
         next j
      next i
   end if
end sub
```

```
! do the real work here at temperature t
sub calculate(spin(,),nmax,t,n_passes,current_mag,current_energy,ave_mag,ave_energy)
   dim m(0),e(0),ts(0)
   mat redim m(n_passes+1),e(n_passes+1),ts(n_passes+1)
   m_tmp = 0              ! set up for running averages of mag and energy
   e_tmp = 0
   n = 0
   m(1) = current_mag
   e(1) = current_energy
   ts(1) = 0
   for i = 1 to n_passes    ! make this many sweeps through the lattice
      for j = 1 to nmax     ! sweep along each row and column
         for k = 1 to nmax
            call neighbors(spin,nmax,j,k,sum) !check each spin for possible flip
            call test_for_flip(spin,j,k,t,sum,current_mag,current_energy)
         next k
      next j
      m(i+1) = current_mag
      e(i+1) = current_energy
      ts(i+1) = i
      if i > n_passes / 2 then
         m_tmp = m_tmp + current_mag
         e_tmp = e_tmp + current_energy
         n = n + 1
      end if
   next i
   ave_mag = m_tmp / n
   ave_energy = e_tmp / n
end sub
! find the net alignment of the nearest neighbors of spin j,k
! note periodic boundary conditions
sub neighbors(spin(,),nmax,j,k,sum)
   x1 = j
   y1 = k + 1
   call test_for_edge(y1,nmax)    ! have to deal with edges carefully
   x2 = j
   y2 = k - 1
   call test_for_edge(y2,nmax)
   x3 = j + 1
   y3 = k
   call test_for_edge(x3,nmax)
   x4 = j - 1
   y4 = k
   call test_for_edge(x4,nmax)
   sum = spin(x1,y1) + spin(x2,y2) + spin(x3,y3) + spin(x4,y4)
end sub
```

```
sub test_for_edge(x,nmax)
   if x < 1    then x = nmax
   if x > nmax then x = 1
end sub
! apply the Monte-Carlo flipping rules here
sub test_for_flip(spin(,),j,k,t,sum,current_mag,current_energy)
   denergy = 2 * spin(j,k) * sum
   if denergy < 0 then          ! always flip if it lowers the energy
      spin(j,k) = - spin(j,k)
      current_mag = current_mag + 2 * spin(j,k)
      current_energy = current_energy + denergy
   else                         ! if energy would increase, flip with probability
      if exp(-denergy / t) > rnd then   ! equal to Boltzmann factor
         spin(j,k) = - spin(j,k)
         current_mag = current_mag + 2 * spin(j,k)
         current_energy = current_energy + denergy
      end if
   end if
end sub
! plot final results
sub display(x(),y())
   set background color "white"
   set color "black"
   clear
   call datagraph(x,y,4,1,"black")
end sub
```

A4.9   Chapter 9

Molecular Dynamics

```
! molecular dynamics in two dimensions
! Program to accompany "Computational Physics" by N. Giordano
! Copyright Prentice Hall 1997
program md
   option nolet
   library "sgfunc*","sglib*"
   dim x(0,0), y(0,0), energy(10000), vx(0), vy(0), mytime(10000)
   dim p(0),px(0),py(0),temperature(10000)
   call initialize(x,y,vx,vy,n_particles,len,dt,n_plot)
   t = 0     ! t = time
   i = 0
   j = 0
   n_p = 0
   do                          ! move forward one time step
      call update(x,y,vx,vy,n_particles,len,dt)    ! update system
      t = t + dt
      j = j + 1              ! use to keep track of how often to plot on screen
      if j >= n_plot then    ! and record values for later plotting
         call display(x,y,n_particles)
         j = 0
         i = i + 1
         mytime(i) = t       ! calculate and record time, energy, and temperature
         call calc_energy(x(,),y(,),vx(),vy(),n_particles,len,e,pot_e,temp)
         energy(i) = e
         temperature(i) = temp
         n_p = n_p + 1
      end if
      if key input then
            get key z
            c$ = chr$(z)
            if c$ = "q" then exit do
            if c$ = "c" then clear
            if c$ = "p" then
                  call display_grid(len)
                  call display(x,y,n_particles)
            end if
      end if
   loop
      ! now finished      prepare for plotting final results
   mat redim mytime(i), energy(i), temperature(i)
   call datagraph(mytime,energy,4,0,"red")
   set cursor 1,1
   print "hit any key to proceed -> "
   get key z
   call datagraph(mytime,temperature,4,0,"red")
end
```

```
! move forward one time step
! x(i,n),y(i,n) = position of particle i
! n = 1,2,3 = oldest, current, and new positions
! vx,vy = velocity components   n_particles = number of particles
! len = size of box (use periodic boundary conditions)   dt = time step
sub update(x(,),y(,),vx(),vy(),n_particles,len,dt)
   dim x_new(100),y_new(100)
   for i = 1 to n_particles
       call force(i,x(,),y(,),n_particles,len,fx,fy)  ! compute the forces
       x_new(i) = 2 * x(2,i) - x(1,i) + fx * dt^2     ! use Verlet method
       y_new(i) = 2 * y(2,i) - y(1,i) + fy * dt^2
       vx(i) = (x_new(i) - x(1,i)) / (2 * dt)            ! keep track of velocities
       vy(i) = (y_new(i) - y(1,i)) / (2 * dt)
       if x_new(i) < 0 then    ! periodic boundary conditions
          x_new(i) = x_new(i) + len
          x(2,i) = x(2,i) + len
       else if x_new(i) > len then
          x_new(i) = x_new(i) - len
          x(2,i) = x(2,i) - len
       end if
       if y_new(i) < 0 then
          y_new(i) = y_new(i) + len
          y(2,i) = y(2,i) + len
       else if y_new(i) > len then
          y_new(i) = y_new(i) - len
          y(2,i) = y(2,i) - len
       end if
   next i
   for i = 1 to n_particles                        ! update current and old values
       x(1,i) = x(2,i)
       x(2,i) = x_new(i)
       y(1,i) = y(2,i)
       y(2,i) = y_new(i)
   next i
end sub
```

```
! initialize variables
sub initialize(x(,),y(,),vx(),vy(),n_particles,len,dt,n_plot)
   n_particles = 20
   mat redim x(2,n_particles),y(2,n_particles), vx(n_particles), vy(n_particles)
   len = 10
   dt = 0.02
   n_plot = 3     ! plot and record after every third time step
   vmax = 1
   grid = len / int(sqr(n_particles) + 1)
   n = 0
   i = 1
   do while i < len        ! arrange particles on a roughly square lattice
      j = 1                ! to keep them apart initially
      do while j < len
         n = n + 1
         if n <= n_particles then
            x(2,n) = i + (rnd - 0.5) * grid / 2
            y(2,n) = j + (rnd - 0.5) * grid / 2
            call init_velocity(vx(n),vy(n),vmax)    ! give them all some initial
            x(1,n) = x(2,n) - vx(n) * dt             ! velocity
            y(1,n) = y(2,n) - vy(n) * dt
         end if
         j = j + grid
      loop
      i = i + grid
   loop
   set background color "white"
   set color "black"
   clear
   set window -1,len+1,-1,len+1
   call display_grid(len)
   call display(x,y,n_particles)
end sub
! calculate current energy = potential + kinetic
! also compute temperature via equipartition
sub calc_energy(x(,),y(,),vx(),vy(),n_particles,len,e,pot_e,temp)
   pot_e = 0   ! potential energy
   k_e = 0     ! kinetic energy
   for i = 1 to n_particles
      for j = i+1 to n_particles
         call find_r(i,j,1,x,y,len,r,dx,dy)   ! find spacing of two atoms
         if r < 30 then                       ! using nearest separation rule
            call pair_force(r,f,u)
            pot_e = pot_e + u
         end if
      next j
      k_e = k_e + (vx(i)^2 + vy(i)^2) / 2     ! kinetic energy
   next i
   e = k_e + pot_e
   temp = k_e / n_particles                   ! equipartition in two dimensions
end sub
```

```
! display box edges
sub display_grid(len)
   set color "black"
   clear
   box lines 0,len,0,len
   set color "red"
end sub
! display particles
sub display(x(,),y(,),n_particles)
   for i = 1 to n_particles
      plot x(2,i),y(2,i)
   next i
end sub
! compute forces on all of the particles
sub force(n,x(,),y(,),n_particles,len,fx,fy)
   fx = 0
   fy = 0
   for i = 1 to n_particles
      if i <> n then
         call find_r(i,n,2,x,y,len,r,dx,dy)
         if r < 30 then
            call pair_force(r,f,u)
            fx = fx + f * dx / r
            fy = fy + f * dy / r
         end if
      end if
   next i
end sub
! Lennard-Jones force
sub pair_force(r,f,u)
   u = 4 * (1/r^12 - 1/r^6)
   f = 24 * (2/r^13 - 1/r^7)
end sub
! find spacing taking periodic boundary conditions into account
sub find_r(i,n,flag,x(,),y(,),len,r,dx,dy)
   dx = x(flag,n) - x(flag,i)
   dy = y(flag,n) - y(flag,i)
   if abs(dx) > len / 2 then dx = dx - sgn(dx) * len
   if abs(dy) > len / 2 then dy = dy - sgn(dy) * len
   r = sqr(dx^2 + dy^2)
end sub
! initialize velocities randomly
sub init_velocity(vx,vy,v0)
   vx = v0 * (rnd - 0.5)
   vy = v0 * (rnd - 0.5)
end sub
```

A4.10   Chapter 10

Quantum Mechanics: Shooting Method

```
! Time independent quantum mechanics - square well with shooting method
! Program to accompany "Computational Physics" by N. Giordano
! Copyright Prentice Hall 1997
program square_well
    option nolet
    dim psi(-1 to 2000)    ! wave function (only need to worry about real part)
    call initialize(psi,dx,V,e_guess,de)
    call calculate(psi,dx,V,e_guess,de)
end
! initialize variables
! psi = wave function  dx = spatial step    square well runs from -xmax to xmax
! V = potential outside well    parity = +1 (even) or -1 (odd)
! e = energy and de = energy step
sub initialize(psi(),dx,V,e,de)
    dx = 0.01
    V = 1e5
    e = 3
    de = -.6
    set window -1.5,1.5,-1.5,1.5    ! set up for plotting
    clear
    plot -1.5,0;1.5,0
    plot -1,-1;-1,1
    plot 1,-1;1,1
end sub
! psi() = wave function, dx = spatial grid size, Vmax is potential outside box
! energy is current best guess for E, de is amount E is changed in hunting
! for a solution
sub calculate(psi(),dx,Vmax,energy,de)
    declare def potential      ! potential energy function
    psi(0) = 1                 ! search for an even parity solution
    psi(-1) = 1
    last_diverge = 0           ! use to keep track of direction of last divergence
                               ! loop as we zero in on the proper value of E
    print "Energy (hit any key to go to the next trial energy)"
    do
        print energy
        for i = 0 to size(psi)-1    ! integrate from x=0 to 1
            psi(i+1) = 2*psi(i)-psi(i-1)-2*(energy-potential(i*dx,Vmax))*dx^2*psi(i)
            if abs(psi(i+1)) > 2 then exit for    ! psi is diverging so stop now
        next i
        call display(psi,i,dx)            ! display this estimate for psi
        get key z                         ! wait for a key stroke before continuing
        if chr$(z) = "q" then exit do ! exit if the current solution is close enough
        if psi(i+1) > 0 then
            diverge = +1
        else
            diverge = -1
        end if
        if diverge * last_diverge < 0 then de = -de / 2
        energy = energy + de
        last_diverge = diverge
    loop
end sub
```

```
def potential(x,V)    ! the potential is 0 inside the box and V outside
   if abs(x) <= 1 then    ! walls are at x = +1 and -1
      potential = 0
   else
      potential = V
   end if
end def
! display the wave function
sub display(psi(),max,dx)
   for i = -max to 0       ! assume an even parity solution
      plot i*dx,psi(-i);
   next i
   for i = 1 to max-1
      plot i*dx,psi(i);
   next i
   plot max*dx,psi(i)
end sub
```

Variational–Monte Carlo

```
! Time independent quantum mechanics - Lennard-Jones potential in one dimension
! solve using variational-monte carlo method
! Program to accompany "Computational Physics" by N. Giordano
! Copyright Prentice Hall 1997
program monte
   option nolet
   dim psi(0 to 2000)    ! wave function
   call initialize(psi,dx,d_psi,x_left,x_right,sigma,epsilon,energy)
   n_total = 0
   n_moves = 0
!    call save(psi,x_left,x_right,dx,energy,n_total)
   do
      call calculate(psi,dx,d_psi,x_left,x_right,sigma,epsilon,
                     energy,n_accepted,n_total,n_moves)
      print energy,d_psi,n_accepted;n_total;n_moves
      call display(psi,dx,x_left,x_right)
      if key input then
         get key z
         c$ = chr$(z)
                           ! save the results if desired
         if c$ = "s" then call save(psi,x_left,x_right,dx,energy,n_total)
         if c$ = "c" then  ! clear screen if too cluttered
            clear
            call axes(sigma,epsilon)    ! plot potential for comparison
         end if
      end if
   loop
end
```

```
! initialize variables
! psi(i) = wave function at grid site i
! dx = grid step    d_psi = max size of Monte-Carlo changes in psi
! x_left,x_right = boundaries of region (psi = 0 outside this)
! sigma,epsilon = Lennard-Jones parameters
! energy = energy of initial trial function
sub initialize(psi(),dx,d_psi,x_left,x_right,sigma,epsilon,energy)
   dx = 0.2
   sigma = 1
   epsilon = 10
   x_left = 0.5 * sigma
   x_right = 5 * sigma
   for i = x_left/dx to x_right/dx       ! initialize wave function
      psi(i) = 0
   next i
   delta = 3 * sigma / dx
   i_start = 1.1 * sigma / dx
   for i = i_start to i_start + delta
      psi(i) = 1 / sqr(delta)
   next i
   d_psi = 0.1 / sqr(delta)
   call normalize(psi,dx,x_left,x_right)    ! normalize trial function
   call calc_energy(psi,dx,x_left,x_right,sigma,epsilon,energy)
   set window 0,6,-2,2                 ! calculate energy of trial function
   call axes(sigma,epsilon)
   call display(psi,dx,x_left,x_right)  ! display wave function
end sub
! plot axes and potential
sub axes(sigma,epsilon)
   declare def potential
   set color "black"
   clear
   max = 5
   plot 0,0;max,0
   for x = 0.7 to max step 0.1
      plot x,potential(x,sigma,epsilon) / 6;
   next x
   plot x,potential(x,sigma,epsilon) / 6
end sub
```

```
! do the work here
! n_total = total number of Monte Carlo moves attempted
! n_moves = total number of Monte Carlo moves accepted
sub calculate(psi(),dx,d_psi,x_left,x_right,sigma,epsilon,energy,n_a,n_total,n_moves)
    declare def potential     ! declare my own function for this
    max = x_right/dx
    min = x_left/dx
    n_a = 0
    n_attempts = 1000         ! make this many attempted moves
    for i = 1 to n_attempts
        n = min + int(rnd*(max + 1 - min))  ! choose site to adjust randomly
        psi_old = psi(n)                    ! with uniform probability
        psi(n) = psi(n) + 2*(rnd-0.5)*d_psi ! adjust trial function
        call calc_energy(psi,dx,x_left,x_right,sigma,epsilon,new_energy)
        if new_energy > energy then     ! compare new energy to old energy
           psi(n) = psi_old             ! keep new trial function only if it
        else                            ! lowers the energy
           energy = new_energy
           call normalize(psi,dx,x_left,x_right)
           n_a = n_a + 1
        end if
    next i
    n_total = n_total + n_attempts
    n_moves = n_moves + n_a
end sub
! display wave function
sub display(psi(),dx,x_left,x_right)
    set color "red"
    for n = x_left/dx - 2 to x_right/dx + 2
        plot n*dx,psi(n)
    next n
    plot n*dx,psi(n)
end sub
! Lennard-Jones potential
def potential(x,sigma,epsilon)
    r6 = (x/sigma)^(-6)
    potential = 4 * epsilon * (r6^2 - r6)
end def
! save wave function to a file
sub save(psi(),x_left,x_right,dx,e,n_tot)
    open #1: name "lj_monte." & str$(e) & "." & str$(n_tot), create new,
                   organization text
    m_left = x_left / dx
    m_right = x_right / dx
    for i = m_left to m_right
        print #1: i*dx,psi(i)
    next i
    close #1
end sub
```

```
! calculate energy of trial function
sub calc_energy(psi(),dx,x_left,x_right,sigma,epsilon,energy)
   declare def potential
   energy = 0
   sum = 0
   for i = x_left/dx-1 to x_right/dx+1
      energy = energy + dx * potential(i*dx,sigma,epsilon)*psi(i)^2 - dx * (0.5/(dx^2))
                 *psi(i)*(psi(i+1) + psi(i-1) - 2*psi(i))
      sum = sum + psi(i) * psi(i) * dx
   next i
   energy = energy / sum
end sub
! normalize a trial function
sub normalize(psi(),dx,x_left,x_right)
   sum = 0
   for i = x_left/dx-1 to x_right/dx+1
      sum = sum + dx * psi(i) * psi(i)
   next i
   for i = x_left/dx-1 to x_right/dx+1
      psi(i) = psi(i) / sqr(sum)
   next i
end sub
```

Wave Packet Propagation

```
! wave packet propagation in one dimension
! Program to accompany "Computational Physics" by N. Giordano
! Copyright Prentice Hall 1997
program propagate
   option nolet
   library "sgfunc*", "sglib*"
! use two dimensional arrays to store real and imaginary parts of psi, e, and f
   dim psi_old(0 to 2000,2),psi_new(0 to 2000,2),e(0 to 2000,2),f(0 to 2000,2)
   t = 0
   call initialize(psi_old,max,dx,dt)
   call display(psi_old,max,dx)
   n_display = 30    ! display psi after every 30*dt
   do
      for i = 1 to n_display
         call calculate(psi_old,psi_new,e,f,max,dx,dt,2*dx*dx/dt,dx*dx)
      next i
      call display(psi_old,max,dx)
      t = t + n_display * dt
      if key input then
         get key z
         c$ = chr$(z)
         if c$ = "c" then
            clear
            call axis
         end if
         if c$ = "t" then print t;
         if c$ = "n" then call check_normalization(psi_old,max)
      end if
   loop
end
```

```
! initialize variables
sub initialize(psi(,),max,dx,dt)
   max = 2000
   dx = 1/max
   dt = 2 * dx^2    ! lambda = 1
   call init_psi_packet(psi(,),max,dx)
   clear
   set window 0,1,-0.2,40
   call axis
end sub
sub axis
   plot 0,0;1,0
end sub
! construct a traveling gaussian wave packet
sub init_psi_packet(p(,),m,dx)
   option angle radians
   x_0 = 0.4    ! wave packet is centered here
   k = 500      ! this is the wave vector
   for i = 0 to m
      a = exp(-(i*dx - x_0)^2/.001)    ! a gaussian packet
      p(i,1) = a * cos(k*i*dx)         ! real part of psi
      p(i,2) = a * sin(k*i*dx)         ! imaginary part of psi
   next i
   call normalize(p,m,dx)
end sub
! normalize psi - part of initialization
sub normalize(p(,),m,dx)
   sum = 0
   for i = 0 to m
      sum = sum + p(i,1)*p(i,1) + p(i,2)*p(i,2)
   next i
   sum = sqr(sum*dx)
   for i = 0 to m
      p(i,1) = p(i,1) / sum
      p(i,2) = p(i,2) / sum
   next i
end sub
! first calculate the new e and f factors, the update psi
sub calculate(p_old(,),p_new(,),e(,),f(,),max,dx,dt,lambda,dx2)
   declare def potential
   call calc_ef(p_old,e,f,max,dx,dt,lambda,dx2)
   call calc_psi(p_old,p_new,e,f,max)
   for i = 0 to max
      p_old(i,1) = p_new(i,1)
      p_old(i,2) = p_new(i,2)
   next i
end sub
```

```
! calculate the new wave function
sub calc_psi(p_old(,),p_new(,),e(,),f(,),max)
   declare def potential
   emod = e(max-1,1)^2 + e(max-1,2)^2
   p_new(max-1,1) = -(f(max-1,1)*e(max-1,1) + f(max-1,2)*e(max-1,2)) / emod
   p_new(max-1,2) = -(f(max-1,2)*e(max-1,1) - f(max-1,1)*e(max-1,2)) / emod
   for i = max-1 to 1 step -1
      emod = e(i,1)^2 + e(i,2)^2
      p_new(i,1) = ((p_new(i+1,1) - f(i,1))*e(i,1)
                         + (p_new(i+1,2) - f(i,2))*e(i,2)) / emod
      p_new(i,2) = ((p_new(i+1,2) - f(i,2))*e(i,1)
                         - (p_new(i+1,1) - f(i,1))*e(i,2)) / emod
   next i
end sub
! calculate the new e and f factors
sub calc_ef(p(,),e(,),f(,),max,dx,dt,lambda,dx2)
   declare def potential
   e(1,1) = 2 + 2 * dx2 * potential(dx)
   e(1,2) = - 2 * lambda
   f(1,1) = -p(2,1) + (2*dx2*potential(dx) + 2) * p(1,1) - 2 * lambda * p(1,2) - p(0,1)
   f(1,2) = -p(2,2) + (2*dx2*potential(dx) + 2) * p(1,2) + 2 * lambda * p(1,1) - p(0,2)
   for i = 2 to max-1
      emod = e(i-1,1)^2 + e(i-1,2)^2
      e(i,1) = 2 + 2*dx2*potential(i*dx) - e(i-1,1) / emod
      e(i,2) = - 2 * lambda + e(i-1,2) / emod
      f(i,1) = -p(i+1,1) + (2*dx2*potential(i*dx) + 2) * p(i,1)
                      - 2 * lambda * p(i,2) - p(i-1,1) + (f(i-1,1)*e(i-1,1)
                      + f(i-1,2)*e(i-1,2)) / emod
      f(i,2) = -p(i+1,2) + (2*dx2*potential(i*dx) + 2) * p(i,2)
                      + 2 * lambda * p(i,1) - p(i-1,2) + (f(i-1,2)*e(i-1,1)
                      - f(i-1,1)*e(i-1,2)) / emod
   next i
end sub
sub display(p(,),m,dx)    ! display psi*psi
   for i = 0 to m-1
      plot i*dx,p(i,1)^2+p(i,2)^2;
   next i
   plot m*dx,p(m,1)^2+p(m,2)^2
end sub
def potential(x)           ! just a flat potential
   potential = 0
end def
sub check_normalization(p(,),m)    ! compute the normalization of psi*psi to be sure
   sum = 0                          ! that the algorithm is ok
   for i = 0 to m
      sum = sum + p(i,1)*p(i,1) + p(i,2)*p(i,2)
   next i
   print sum
end sub
```

A4.11   Appendix 2

Fast Fourier Transform

Listed below are two *True Basic* programs that employ the FFT. The first program performs forward and backward transforms and displays and stores the resulting sine and cosine components. It assumes that if a forward transform is requested, that the signal is a real function. If a backward transform is desired, the initial data can be complex, but the program still assumes that the final result will be real. Here when we use the term real we do *not* refer to a cosine component. Rather, we mean that the signal [such as y(t) in (A2.3)] is a real function. The transform of such a function may, of course, have both sine and cosine components, and our program deals with these as discussed in Appendix 4. The second program listed here computes the power spectrum of a real function.

```
! Fourier analysis routines - compute the FFT of a signal
! this program does forward and backward transforms
! for forward transforms: assume that the data is a real function
! for backward transforms: assume that the final result will be a real function,
!     even though the data to be transformed will have both real and imaginary parts
! Program to accompany "Computational Physics" by N. Giordano
! Copyright Prentice Hall 1997
program fourier
    library "sgfunc*","sglib*"
    option nolet
    dim t(1024),y(2048)       ! could make this larger to handle larger data sets
    call readin(t,y,n_points,store$,isign)    ! read in data
    call fft(y,n_points,isign)                ! perform fft
    call calc_freq(t,n_points,isign)          ! calculate corresponding frequencies
    call display(t,y,n_points,isign)          ! display results
    call save(t,y,n_points,store$,isign)      ! save them too
end
! calculate the frequencies that go with the transformed signal
! the time array t() matches the array containing the transform
! so t(i) with i odd is for the cosine transform while i even is for
! the sine transform
sub calc_freq(t(),n,isign)
    if isign = 1 then            ! must be careful to handle forward and backward
        dt = t(3) - t(1)         ! transforms slightly differently
        for i = 1 to n-1 step 2            ! isign = +1 is a forward transform
            t(i) = (i-1) / (2 * n * dt)
            t(i+1) = t(i)
        next i
    else                                   ! isign = -1 is a backward transform
        dt = t(3) - t(1)
        for i = 1 to n
            t(i) = (i-1) / (n * dt)
        next i
    end if
end sub
```

```
! save the transform results
! for forward transforms (isign = +1):
!     the cosine transform goes into the file store$.fft.r
!     the sine transform into store$.fft.i
!     All of the transform data also go into the file store$.fft with real
!     and imaginary parts alternated - this makes it easy to perform the
!     back transform  with the same program
! for backward transforms (isign = -1):
!     store the result in the file store$.bfft
!     note that in this case we assume that the signal is a real function
sub save(t(),y(),n,store$,isign)
    if isign = +1 then                    ! forward transform
       open #1: name store$ & ".fft", organization text, create new
       for i = 1 to n-1 step 2
         print #1: t(i),",",y(i)
         print #1: t(i+1),",",y(i+1)
       next i
       close #1
       open #1: name store$ & ".fft.r", organization text, create new
       open #2: name store$ & ".fft.i", organization text, create new
       for i = 1 to n-1 step 2
          print #1: t(i),",",y(i)
          print #2: t(i+1),",",y(i+1)
       next i
       close #1
       close #2
    else                                  ! backward transform
       open #1: name store$ & ".bfft", organization text, create new
       for i = 1 to n
         print #1: t(i),",",y(i)
       next i
       close #1
    end if
end sub
! read the data from a file and put it into arrays t() (time data)
! and y() (the signal data)
! note that for a forward transform of a real data set,
! the signal should be in the file as follows
! t(1), y(1)
! t(2), y(2)
! t(3), y(3)
! etc.
!
! for a back transform, the data will in general have both real (cosine)
! and imaginary (sine) parts, so the data must be store differently
! in this case the real and imaginary parts are to be placed on
! alternating lines
! t(1), y_real(1)
! t(1), y_imag(1)
! t(2), y_real(2)
! t(2), y_imag(2)
! etc.
```

```
sub readin(t(),y(),n_points,store$,isign)
    input prompt "name of input file -> ": store$
    input prompt "forward (+1) or backward (-1) transform -> ": isign
    open #1: name store$, organization text, create old
    if isign = 1 then
        i = 1
        n_points = 0
        do
            ask #1: pointer place$
            if place$ = "END" then exit do
            input #1: t(i),y(i)
            y(i+1) = 0                  ! fill the imaginary parts with zeros
            t(i+1) = t(i)
            i = i + 2
            n_points = n_points + 1
        loop
        close #1
        k = 1    ! pad with zeros up to the next power of 2 for n_points
        do
            if 2^k >= n_points then exit do
            k = k + 1
        loop
        for j = i to 2^k
            y(j) = 0
        next j
        n_points = 2^k
        mat redim t(2*n_points),y(2*n_points)            ! trim arrays to size used
    else ! for the inverse transform assume that the number of data
            ! points is already 2^n where n is an integer
            ! so no padding will be required
            ! data for the inverse transform is stored differently - see above
        i = 1
        n_points = 0
        do
            ask #1: pointer place$
            if place$ = "END" then exit do
            input #1: t(i),y(i)              ! real part
            input #1: t(i+1),y(i+1)          ! imaginary part
            i = i + 2
            n_points = n_points + 2
        loop
        close #1
        mat redim t(2*n_points),y(2*n_points)
    end if
end sub
```

```
! display the sine and cosine transforms separately if this is a forward
! transform
sub display(t(),d(),n,isign)
   if isign = 1 then
      dim ycos(0),ysin(0),tcos(0)
      mat redim ycos(n/2),ysin(n/2),tcos(n/2)
      for i = 1 to n/2 ! - 1
         ycos(i) = d(2*i-1)
         ysin(i) = d(2*i)
         tcos(i) = t(2*i-1)
      next i
      call datagraph(tcos,ycos,3,1,"black")     ! graph real part
      call adddatagraph(tcos,ysin,4,2,"red")    ! add imaginary part to graph
   else         ! for an inverse transform plot only the real part
      mat redim t(n),d(n)                ! only have to plot the real part
      call datagraph(t,d,3,1,"black")    ! which is already in d()
   end if
   get key z
end sub
! fourier transform of a complex data set
! n_points = number of data points - n_points must be a power of 2
! f_type = +1 -> forward transform
! f_type = -1 -> backward transform
! the data comes in array y()
! real part and imaginary parts are interleaved
! real part in y(0), y
! imaginary part of data comes in yi()
! the result is returned in the arrays yr() and yi()
sub fft(y(),n_points,f_type)
   dim yr(0),yi(0)
   option angle radians
   declare def p_val
   j = 1
   n_p = n_points
   mat redim yr(n_points),yi(n_points)
   for i = 1 to n_points                   ! split the data up into real
      yr(i) = y(j)                         ! and imaginary parts
      yi(i) = y(j+1)
      j = j + 2
   next i
   if f_type = -1 then ! a forward transform
      j = n_points - 1
      for i = n_points + 1 to n_p
         yr(i) = 0
         yi(i) = 0
         j = j - 1
      next i
   end if
```

```
n_power = 1
do     ! first determine n_power where  n_points = 2^n_power
   if n_p / 2 <= 1 then exit do
   n_p = n_p / 2
   n_power = n_power + 1
loop
n1 = n_power - 1
n2 = n_points / 2
for i = 1 to n_power
   k = 0
   do
      for j = 1 to n2
         ex = 2 * pi * p_val(k/(2^n1),n_power) / n_points
         cos_factor = cos(ex)
         sin_factor = sin(-f_type*ex)
         k = k + 1
         tmp_real = cos_factor * yr(k+n2) + sin_factor * yi(k+n2)
         tmp_imag = cos_factor * yi(k+n2) - sin_factor * yr(k+n2)
         yr(k+n2) = yr(k) - tmp_real
         yi(k+n2) = yi(k) - tmp_imag
         yr(k) = yr(k) + tmp_real
         yi(k) = yi(k) + tmp_imag
      next j
      k = k + n2
   loop until k >= n_points
   n1 = n1 - 1
   n2 = n2 / 2
next i
! now do the bit reversal stuff
for i = 1 to n_points
   p = p_val(i-1,n_power) + 1
   if p > i then     ! switch places
      tmp_real = yr(i)
      tmp_imag = yi(i)
      yr(i) = yr(p)
      yi(i) = yi(p)
      yr(p) = tmp_real
      yi(p) = tmp_imag
   end if
next i
! finally have to repack results into the array y()
for i = 1 to n_points
   if f_type > 0 then   ! a forward transform
      y(2*i-1) = yr(i)
      y(2*i) = yi(i)
   else                 ! a backward transform
      y(i) = 2 * yr(i) / n_points
   end if
next i
end sub
```

```
! bit reversal function - does double duty
function p_val(a,b)
   tmp = int(a)
   p = 0
   for i = 1 to b
      p = 2 * p + tmp - 2 * int(tmp / 2)
      tmp = int(tmp / 2)
   next i
   p_val = p
end function
```

Power Spectrum

```
! this program uses the FFT to compute the power spectrum of a signal
! the data should be in a file as
! t1, y1
! t2, y2
! t3, y3
! etc.
! the power spectrum is written to a file
! Program to accompany "Computational Physics" by N. Giordano
! Copyright Prentice Hall 1997
program power
   library "sgfunc*","sglib*"
   option nolet
   dim t(1024),y(2048)      ! could make this larger to handle larger data sets
   call readin(t,y,n_points,store$,isign)   ! read in data
   call fft(y,n_points,isign)               ! perform fft
   call calc_freq(t,n_points)               ! calculate corresponding frequencies
   call power(t,y)                          ! compute power spectrum
   call display(t,y)                        ! display and store results
   call save(t,y,store$)
end
! compute the power spectrum from the Fourier components in y()
sub power(t(),y())
   n = size(t) / 4
   for i = 1 to n
      y(i) = y(2*i-1)^2 + y(2*i)^2
   next i
   mat redim t(n),y(n)
end sub
! calculate the frequencies that go with the transformed signal
! the time array t() matches the array containing the transform
! so t(i) with i odd is for the cosine transform while i even is for
! the sine transform
sub calc_freq(t(),n)
   dt = t(3) - t(1)        ! transforms slightly differently
   for i = 1 to n-1
      t(i) = (i-1) / (n * dt)
   next i
end sub
```

```
! save the power spectrum
sub save(t(),y(),store$)
    open #1: name store$ & ".power", organization text, create new
    for i = 1 to size(t)
        print #1: t(i),",",y(i)
    next i
    close #1
end sub
! read the data from a file and put it into arrays t() (time data)
! and y() (the signal data)
! note that for a forward transform of a real data set,
! the signal should be in the file as follows
! t(1), y(1)
! t(2), y(2)
! t(3), y(3)
! etc.
!
! for a back transform, the data will in general have both real (cosine)
! and imaginary (sine) parts, so the data must be store differently
! in this case the real and imaginary parts are to be placed on
! alternating lines
! t(1), y_real(1)
! t(1), y_imag(1)
! t(2), y_real(2)
! t(2), y_imag(2)
! etc.
sub readin(t(),y(),n_points,store$,isign)
    input prompt "name of input file -> ": store$
    isign = 1
    open #1: name store$, organization text, create old
    if isign = 1 then
        i = 1
        n_points = 0
        do
            ask #1: pointer place$
            if place$ = "END" then exit do
            input #1: t(i),y(i)
            y(i+1) = 0                    ! fill the imaginary parts with zeros
            t(i+1) = t(i)
            i = i + 2
            n_points = n_points + 1
        loop
        close #1
        k = 1    ! pad with zeros up to the next power of 2 for n_points
        do
            if 2^k >= n_points then exit do
            k = k + 1
        loop
        for j = i to 2^k
            y(j) = 0
        next j
        n_points = 2^k
        mat redim t(2*n_points),y(2*n_points)          ! trim arrays to size used
```

```
else  ! for the inverse transform assume that the number of data
         ! points is already 2^n where n is an integer
         ! so no padding will be required
         ! data for the inverse transform is stored differently - see above
      i = 1
      n_points = 0
      do
         ask #1: pointer place$
         if place$ = "END" then exit do
         input #1: t(i),y(i)                   ! real part
         input #1: t(i+1),y(i+1)               ! imaginary part
         i = i + 2
         n_points = n_points + 2
      loop
      close #1
      mat redim t(2*n_points),y(2*n_points)
   end if
end sub
! display the sine and cosine transforms separately if this is a forward
! transform
sub display(t(),d())
   call datagraph(t,d,3,1,"black")     ! graph power spectrum
   get key z
end sub
! fourier transform of a complex data set
! n_points = number of data points - n_points must be a power of 2
! f_type = +1 -> forward transform
! f_type = -1 -> backward transform
! the data comes in array y()
! real part and imaginary parts are interleaved
! real part in y(0), y
! imaginary part of data comes in yi()
! the result is returned in the arrays yr() and yi()
sub fft(y(),n_points,f_type)
   dim yr(0),yi(0)
   option angle radians
   declare def p_val
   j = 1
   n_p = n_points
   mat redim yr(n_points),yi(n_points)
   for i = 1 to n_points                  ! split the data up into real and imaginary
      yr(i) = y(j)                        ! parts
      yi(i) = y(j+1)
      j = j + 2
   next i
   if f_type = -1 then  ! a forward transform
      j = n_points - 1
      for i = n_points + 1 to n_p
         yr(i) = 0
         yi(i) = 0
         j = j - 1
      next i
   end if
```

```
   n_power = 1
   do     ! first determine n_power where  n_points = 2^n_power
      if n_p / 2 <= 1 then exit do
      n_p = n_p / 2
      n_power = n_power + 1
   loop
   n1 = n_power - 1
   n2 = n_points / 2
   for i = 1 to n_power
      k = 0
      do
         for j = 1 to n2
            ex = 2 * pi * p_val(k/(2^n1),n_power) / n_points
            cos_factor = cos(ex)
            sin_factor = sin(-f_type*ex)
            k = k + 1
            tmp_real = cos_factor * yr(k+n2) + sin_factor * yi(k+n2)
            tmp_imag = cos_factor * yi(k+n2) - sin_factor * yr(k+n2)
            yr(k+n2) = yr(k) - tmp_real
            yi(k+n2) = yi(k) - tmp_imag
            yr(k) = yr(k) + tmp_real
            yi(k) = yi(k) + tmp_imag
         next j
         k = k + n2
      loop until k >= n_points
      n1 = n1 - 1
      n2 = n2 / 2
   next i
! now do the bit reversal stuff
   for i = 1 to n_points
      p = p_val(i-1,n_power) + 1
      if p > i then       ! switch places
         tmp_real = yr(i)
         tmp_imag = yi(i)
         yr(i) = yr(p)
         yi(i) = yi(p)
         yr(p) = tmp_real
         yi(p) = tmp_imag
      end if
   next i
! finally have to repack results into the array y()
   for i = 1 to n_points
      if f_type > 0 then   ! a forward transform
         y(2*i-1) = yr(i)
         y(2*i) = yi(i)
      else                 ! a backward transform
         y(i) = 2 * yr(i) / n_points
      end if
   next i
end sub
```

```
! bit reversal function - does double duty
function p_val(a,b)
    tmp = int(a)
    p = 0
    for i = 1 to b
        p = 2 * p + tmp - 2 * int(tmp / 2)
        tmp = int(tmp / 2)
    next i
    p_val = p
end function
```

A4.12   Appendix 3

Method of Least Squares

```
! Perform a linear least squares fit
! Program to accompany "Computational Physics" by N. Giordano
! Copyright Prentice Hall 1997
program fit
    option nolet
    library "sgfunc*", "sglib*"
    dim x(1000),y(1000)
    call initialize(x,y)
    call calculate(x,y,slope,intercept)
    call display(x,y,slope,intercept)
end
! read in the data from the file "fit.dat"
! put the points in arrays x() and y()
! the values of the dependent variable go into y()
sub initialize(x(),y())
    open #1: name "fit.dat", access input, create old, organization text
    i = 1
    do
        input #1: x(i),y(i)
        ask #1: pointer place$
        if place$ = "END" then exit do  ! read up to the end of the file
        i = i + 1
    loop
    close #1
    mat redim x(i),y(i)  ! redimension the arrays to make them just the
end sub                  ! right length
```

```
! perform linear least squares fit - return results in the
! variables "slope" and "intercept"
sub calculate(x(),y(),slope,intercept)
    sum_x = 0       ! sum of all the x values
    sum_y = 0       ! sum of all the y values
    sum_xy = 0      ! sum of xy
    sum_x2 = 0      ! sum of x^2
    n = size(x)     ! total number of points
    for i = 1 to n
        sum_x = sum_x + x(i)
        sum_y = sum_y + y(i)
        sum_xy = sum_xy + x(i)*y(i)
        sum_x2 = sum_x2 + x(i)^2
    next i
    slope = (n * sum_xy - sum_x * sum_y) / (n * sum_x2 - sum_x * sum_x)
    intercept = (sum_y * sum_x2 - sum_x * sum_xy) / (n * sum_x2 - sum_x * sum_x)
end sub
! display the results - the data plus the fitted line
sub display(x(),y(),slope,intercept)
    call settitle("Linear least squares fit")
    call sethlabel("x")
    call setvlabel("y")
    call datagraph(x,y,4,0,"black")   ! plot the data first
    y(1) = intercept + slope * x(1)   ! calculate the end points of the fitted
    x(2) = x(size(x))                 ! line - assume the data are in order
    y(2) = intercept + slope * x(2)
    mat redim x(2),y(2)
    call adddatagraph(x,y,0,1,"red") ! add the least squares line to the graph
    set cursor 5,12                   ! also print the fitting parameters on the graph
    print "slope = ";slope;"    intercept = ";intercept
end sub
```

Index